APPLIED MATHEMATICS
FOR ENGINEERS AND PHYSICISTS

Applied Mathematics for Engineers and Physicists

LOUIS A. PIPES, Ph.D.

Professor of Engineering
University of California
at Los Angeles

Second Edition

1958

McGRAW-HILL BOOK COMPANY, INC.

New York   Toronto   London

THE MAPLE PRESS COMPANY, YORK, PA.

PREFACE

The first edition of this book was written in order to acquaint a group of students of diversified interests at the Graduate School of Engineering of Harvard University with the more common mathematical techniques used in solving technical problems that arise in electrical, mechanical, aeronautical, thermal, and other branches of engineering.

In the 12 years that have elapsed since the publication of the first edition of this book, there has been a tremendous development of high-speed computing devices. These modern calculating machines have made possible the solution of problems in engineering and the physical sciences that had been considered too formidable for analytical solutions. As a consequence of this development, there has been considerably more interest and emphasis on the analytical formulation of problems in the engineering and physical sciences.

The problems that arise in mathematical technology may usually be divided into four main categories and their combinations. These broad classifications are, first, the analysis of linear lumped systems; second, the analysis of linear distributed systems; third, the analysis of non-linear lumped and distributed systems; and, fourth, problems involving statistical methods and the theory of probability.

In the present edition, considerable new material for the analysis of problems in the first three classifications has been added. The chapters on matrix algebra, Fourier methods, variational methods, Laplace transforms, and nonlinear differential equations have been considerably expanded. A new section on Cartesian tensors has been added to the chapter on vector analysis. Unfortunately, because of space limitations, it was not possible to include material on the theory of probability and statistical methods. The references at the ends of the chapters have been extended and brought up to date, and numerous new problems have been added.

It is of course impossible and futile to attempt to acknowledge the indebtedness to the many individuals, both students and faculty members, from whom the author has learned and with whom he has had stimulating contacts and who in this manner assisted in the preparation of the manuscript. However, the author wishes to express particular

v

thanks to Professor Kurt Forster and to Mr. John Staudhammer at the University of California for helpful suggestions.   The author also wishes to thank Mr. L. M. K. Boelter, Dean of the Department of Engineering, for providing an environment in which research and pedagogical experiments are stimulated.

LOUIS A. PIPES

CONTENTS

Application to Hydrodynamics—The Equation of Heat Flow in Solids—The Gravitational Potential—Maxwell's Equations—The Wave Equation—The Skin-effect, or Diffusion, Equation—Tensors (Qualitative Introduction)—Coordinate Transformations—Scalars, Contravariant Vectors, Covariant Vectors—Addition, Multiplication, and Contraction of Tensors—Associated Tensors—Differentiation of an Invariant—Differentiation of Tensors: The Christoffel Symbols—Intrinsic and Covariant Derivatives of Tensors of Higher Order—Application of Tensor Analysis to the Dynamics of a Particle.

CHAPTER 1

INFINITE SERIES

1. Introduction. This chapter will be devoted to the exposition of some of the properties of infinite series. Particular attention will be given to power series. The subject of infinite series is of extreme importance in applied mathematics. Infinite series make possible the numerical solution of many important physical problems. The solutions of certain differential equations that occur frequently in the mathematical solution of many physical problems are expressed in terms of infinite series, and a study of the properties of these solutions requires a knowledge of the manner in which infinite series may be manipulated. Hence it is essential that students of applied science acquire an intelligent understanding of the subject.

In this chapter some of the fundamental notions and concepts of infinite series will be discussed. The algebra and calculus of series will be developed, and some of the practical uses of series will be used as illustrations of the general principles.

2. Definitions. In this section we shall consider some fundamental definitions of the subject of infinite series.

Sequence. A sequence is a succession of terms formed according to some fixed rule or law. For example,

$$(2.1) \qquad\qquad 1, 4, 9, 16, 25$$

and

$$(2.2) \qquad\qquad x, x^2, \frac{x^3}{1 \times 2}, \frac{x^4}{1 \times 2 \times 3}$$

are sequences.

Series. A series is the indicated sum of the terms of a sequence. That is, from the foregoing sequences we obtain the series

$$(2.3) \qquad\qquad 1 + 4 + 9 + 16 + 25$$

and

$$(2.4) \qquad\qquad x + x^2 + \frac{x^3}{1 \times 2} + \frac{x^4}{1 \times 2 \times 3}$$

1

If the number of terms is limited, the sequence or series is said to be finite. If the number of terms is unlimited, the sequence or series is said to be an infinite sequence or series.

The general term, or nth term, is the expression that indicates the law of formation of the terms of the series. For example, in the preceding illustrations suitable general terms are

$$n^2 \quad \text{and} \quad \frac{nx^n}{n!}$$

where $n!$ is the factorial number given by

(2.5) $$n! = 1 \times 2 \times 3 \times \cdots \times (n - 1) \times n$$

3. The Geometric Series. Consider the series of n terms

(3.1) $$S_n = a + ar + ar^2 + \cdots + ar^{n-1}$$

This series is called the geometric series. A simple expression for S_n may be obtained for the sum S_n of the geometric series in the following manner:

Multiply (3.1) by r. We thus obtain

(3.2) $$rS_n = ar + ar^2 + ar^3 + \cdots + ar^n$$

Let us now subtract (3.1) from (3.2). This gives

(3.3) $$rS_n - S_n = ar^n - a \qquad .$$

Hence

(3.4) $$S_n = \frac{a(1 - r^n)}{1 - r} = \frac{a}{1 - r} - \frac{ar^n}{1 - r}$$

Now if $|r| < 1$, then r^n decreases in absolute value as n increases so that we have

(3.5) $$\lim_{n \to \infty} r^n = 0$$

From (3.4) we then have

(3.6) $$\lim_{n \to \infty} S_n = \frac{a}{1 - r} = S$$

Hence, if $|r| < 1$, the sum S_n of a geometric series approaches a limit as the number of terms is increased indefinitely. In this case the infinite series $a + ar + ar^2 + \cdots$ is said to be *convergent*.

If $|r| > 1$, then r^n will become infinite as n increases indefinitely. Hence, from (3.4), $|S_n|$ will increase without limit. In this case the series is said to be *divergent*.

If $r = -1$, we encounter an interesting situation. In this case the geometric series becomes

(3.7) $$a - a + a - a + \cdots$$

In this case, if n is even, S_n is zero. If n is odd, S_n is a. As n increases indefinitely, the absolute value of S_n does not increase indefinitely but still S_n does not approach a limit. A series of this sort is called an *oscillating series*. It also is a divergent series.

If we place $a = 1$ and $r = \frac{1}{2}$ in the general geometric series, we obtain

(3.8) $$S_n = 1 + \frac{1}{2} + \frac{1}{4} + \cdots + \frac{1}{2^{n-1}}$$

and we have

(3.9) $$\lim_{n \to \infty} S_n = \frac{1}{1 - \frac{1}{2}} = 2$$

4. Convergent and Divergent Series. Let us consider the series

(4.1) $$S_n = u_1 + u_2 + u_3 + \cdots + u_n$$

The variable S_n denoting the sum of the series is a function of n. If we now allow the number of terms, n, to increase without limit, one of two things may happen.

Case I. S_n *approaches a limit* S indicated by

(4.2) $$\lim_{n \to \infty} S_n = S$$

In this case the infinite series is said to be *convergent* and to converge to the value S or to have the sum S.

Case II. In this case S_n *approaches no limit*. The infinite series is then said to be *divergent*.

For example, the series

$$1 + 2 + 3 + 4 + 5 + \cdots$$
$$2 - 2 + 2 - 2 + \cdots$$

are said to be divergent.

In applied mathematics, convergent series are of the utmost importance; it is thus necessary to have a means of testing a series for convergence or divergence.

5. General Theorems. The following theorems, whose proofs are omitted, are of importance in the study of the convergence of series:

THEOREM I. If S_n is a variable which always increases as n increases but which never exceeds some definite fixed number A, then, as n increases without limit, S_n will approach a limit S which is not greater than A.

Fig. 5.1

This statement may be illustrated by Fig. 5.1.

The points determined by the values S_1, S_2, S_3, etc., approach the point S where

(5.1)
$$\lim_{n \to \infty} S_n = S$$

and S is less than or equal to A.

This theorem enables us to establish the convergence of certain series. For example, let us consider the series

(5.2)
$$1 + 1 + \frac{1}{1 \times 2} + \frac{1}{1 \times 2 \times 3} + \cdots + \frac{1}{n!} + \cdots$$

If we temporarily neglect the first term, we may write

(5.3)
$$S_n = 1 + \frac{1}{1 \times 2} + \frac{1}{1 \times 2 \times 3} + \cdots + \frac{1}{n!}$$

Now let us consider the series defined by

(5.4)
$$U_n = 1 + \frac{1}{2} + \frac{1}{2 \times 2} + \cdots + \frac{1}{2^{n-1}}$$

Since the corresponding terms of the series S_n are less than the corresponding terms of the series U_n with the exception of the first two terms, it is obvious that

(5.5)
$$S_n < U_n$$

Now the series U_n is a geometric series with $a = 1$ and $r = \frac{1}{2}$. Hence, $U_n < 2$ no matter how large n may be.

It follows therefore that S_n is a variable that always increases as n increases but remains less than 2. Hence S_n approaches a limit as n becomes infinite, and this limit is less than 2. It is thus apparent that the series (5.2) is convergent and that its value is less than 3. It will be shown later that the sum of the infinite series (5.2) is the constant $e = 2.71828 \cdots$, the base of the natural-logarithm system.

Another fundamental theorem of great importance in testing for convergence will now be stated.

THEOREM II. If S_n is a variable which always decreases as n increases but which is never less than a certain number B, then, as n increases without limit, S_n will approach a limit which is not less than B.

Let us consider the convergent series

(5.6)
$$S = u_1 + u_2 + u_3 + \cdots + u_n + \cdots$$

for which

(5.7)
$$\lim_{n \to \infty} S_n = S$$

Now consider that the points determined by the values S_1, S_2, S_3, etc., are plotted on a directed line. Then these points as n increases will approach the point determined by S. It is thus evident that

$$(5.8) \qquad\qquad \lim_{n \to \infty} u_n = 0$$

That is, in a convergent series, the terms must approach zero as a limit. If, however, the nth term of a series does *not* approach zero as n becomes infinite, we know at once that the series is divergent.

Although (5.8) is a necessary condition for convergence, it is not *sufficient*. That is, even if the nth term does approach zero, we cannot state that the series is convergent. Consider the series for which

$$(5.9) \qquad\qquad S_n = 1 + \frac{1}{2} + \frac{1}{3} + \cdots + \frac{1}{n}$$

Here we have

$$(5.10) \qquad\qquad \lim_{n \to \infty} u_n = \lim_{n \to \infty} \frac{1}{n} = 0$$

Therefore (5.8) is fulfilled. However, we shall prove later that this series is divergent.

Although the use of the preceding theorems in determining the convergence or divergence of series is fundamental, we shall now turn to the development of special tests that are, as a rule, easier to apply than these theorems.

6. The Comparison Test. In many cases the question of the convergence or divergence of a given series may be answered by comparing the given series with one whose character is known.

Let it be required to test the series

$$(6.1) \qquad\qquad U = u_1 + u_2 + u_3 + \cdots + u_n + \cdots$$

where all the terms of (6.1) are positive.

Now if a convergent series of positive terms

$$(6.2) \qquad\qquad V = v_1 + v_2 + v_3 + \cdots + v_n + \cdots$$

can be found whose terms are never less than the corresponding terms in the series (6.1), then (6.1) is a convergent series and its sum does not exceed that of (6.2).

To prove this statement, let

$$(6.3) \qquad\qquad U_n = u_1 + u_2 + u_3 + \cdots + u_n$$

and

$$(6.4) \qquad\qquad V_n = v_1 + v_2 + v_3 + \cdots + v_n$$

Since by hypothesis (6.2) is convergent, we have

(6.5)
$$\lim_{n \to \infty} V_n = V$$

Now since

(6.6) $V_n < V$ and $U_n < V_n$

it follows that

(6.7) $U_n < V$

Therefore by Theorem I of Sec. 5, U_n approaches a limit, and the series (6.1) is convergent.

As an example of this test, consider the series

(6.8) $$U = 1 + \frac{1}{2^2} + \frac{1}{3^3} + \frac{1}{4^4} + \cdots$$

This series can be compared with the series

(6.9) $$V = 1 + \frac{1}{2} + \frac{1}{2^2} + \frac{1}{2^3} + \frac{1}{2^4} + \cdots$$

The latter series is a geometric series that is known to be convergent. Now the terms of (6.9) are never less than the corresponding terms of (6.8). Hence it follows that the series (6.8) is convergent.

Test for Divergence. By the use of the comparison principle, it is also possible to test a series for divergence. Let

(6.10) $$U = u_1 + u_2 + u_3 + \cdots$$

be a series of positive terms to be tested which are never less than the corresponding terms of a series of positive terms

(6.11) $$W = w_1 + w_2 + w_3 + \cdots$$

which is known to be divergent. Then (6.10) is a divergent series.

By the use of this principle, we may prove that the harmonic series

(6.12) $$U = 1 + \frac{1}{2} + \frac{1}{3} + \frac{1}{4} + \cdots + \frac{1}{n} + \cdots$$

is divergent. This may be done by rewriting (6.12) in the form

(6.13) $U = 1 + \frac{1}{2} + (\frac{1}{3} + \frac{1}{4}) + (\frac{1}{5} + \frac{1}{6} + \frac{1}{7} + \frac{1}{8})$
$$+ (\frac{1}{9} + \cdots + \frac{1}{16}) + \cdots$$

Let us now compare this series with the series

(6.14) $W = \frac{1}{2} + \frac{1}{2} + (\frac{1}{4} + \frac{1}{4}) + (\frac{1}{8} + \frac{1}{8} + \frac{1}{8} + \frac{1}{8})$
$$+ (\frac{1}{16} + \cdots + \frac{1}{16}) + \cdots$$

Now the terms of (6.13) are never less than the terms of (6.14). But the series (6.14) is divergent since the sum of the terms in each pair of parentheses is $\frac{1}{2}$; hence the sum of these terms increases without limit as the number of terms becomes infinite. Hence the series (6.13) is divergent.

7. Cauchy's Integral Test. The comparison test requires that at least a few types of convergent series be known. For the establishment of such types and for the test of many series of positive terms, Cauchy's integral test is useful. This test may be stated in the following manner. Let

$$(7.1) \qquad u_1 + u_2 + u_3 + \cdots = \sum_{n=1}^{\infty} u_n$$

be a series of positive terms such that

$$(7.2) \qquad u_{n+1} < u_n$$

Now if there exists a positive function $f(n)$, decreasing for $n > 1$ and such that $f(n) = u_n$, then the given series converges if the integral

$$(7.3) \qquad I = \int_1^{\infty} f(n) \, dn$$

exists; the series diverges if the integral does not exist.

Fig. 7.1

The proof of this test is deduced simply from Fig. 7.1. We may think of each term u_n of the series as representing the area of a rectangle of base unity and height $f(n)$. The sum of the areas of the first n inscribed rectangles is less than the integral

$$(7.4) \qquad \int_1^{n+1} f(n) \, dn$$

Hence

$$(7.5) \qquad u_2 + u_3 + u_4 + \cdots + u_{n+1} < \int_1^{n+1} f(n) \, dn$$

Now, since $f(x)$ is positive, we have

$$(7.6) \qquad \int_1^{n+1} f(n) \, dn < \int_1^{\infty} f(n) \, dn = I$$

Hence we have

$$(7.7) \qquad \sum_{n=2}^{n=\infty} u_n < \int_1^{\infty} f(n) \, dn = I$$

and if the integral I exists, the series converges. We also have, from the figure, the relation

$$(7.8) \qquad \sum_1^\infty u_n > \int_1^\infty f(n)\, dn$$

and hence, if the integral does not exist, the series diverges. As an example of the application of this test, consider the series

$$(7.9) \qquad \frac{1}{1^p} + \frac{1}{2^p} + \frac{1}{3^p} + \cdots + \frac{1}{n^p} + \cdots = \sum_{n=1}^{n=\infty} \frac{1}{n^p}$$

To apply Cauchy's integral test, we let

$$(7.10) \qquad f(n) = \frac{1}{n^p}$$

Now we have

$$(7.11) \qquad I = \int_1^\infty \frac{dn}{n^p} = \begin{cases} \left. \dfrac{1}{1-p}\, n^{1-p} \right|_1^\infty & \text{if } p \neq 1 \\[2ex] \left. \log n \right|_1^\infty & \text{if } p = 1 \end{cases}$$

It is thus seen that I exists if $p > 1$ and does not exist if $p \leq 1$. Hence the series converges if $p > 1$ and diverges if $p \leq 1$. This series is a very useful one to use in comparison with others.

8. Cauchy's Ratio Test. In the infinite geometric series

$$(8.1) \qquad a + ar + ar^2 + \cdots + ar^n + \cdots$$

the ratio of the consecutive general terms ar^n and ar^{n+1} is the common ratio r. We have seen that this series is convergent when $|r| < 1$ and divergent for other values. We shall now consider a ratio test that may be applied to any series. Let

$$(8.2) \qquad u_1 + u_2 + u_3 + \cdots + u_n + u_{n+1} + \cdots$$

be an infinite series of positive terms.

Consider consecutive general terms u_n and u_{n+1}, and form the test ratio.

$$(8.3) \qquad \frac{u_{n+1}}{u_n} = \text{test ratio}$$

Now find the limit of this test ratio when n becomes infinite. Let this be

$$(8.4) \qquad \rho = \lim_{n \to \infty} \frac{u_{n+1}}{u_n}$$

We then have:

1. When $\rho < 1$, the series is convergent.
2. When $\rho > 1$, the series is divergent.
3. When $\rho = 1$, the test gives no information.

Proof. 1. When $\rho < 1$. By the definition of a limit we can choose n so large, say, $n \geq m$, that the ratio u_{n+1}/u_n will differ from ρ by as little as we please and will therefore be less than a proper fraction $r < 1$. Hence

(8.5)
$$u_{m+1} < u_m r$$
$$u_{m+2} < u_m r^2$$
$$u_{m+3} < u_m r^3$$
$$\cdot \ \cdot \ \cdot \ \cdot \ \cdot \ \cdot$$

It therefore follows that after the term u_m each term of the series (8.2) is less than the corresponding term of the geometric series

(8.6)
$$u_m(1 + r + r^2 + \cdots)$$

But since $r < 1$, the series (8.6), and therefore also the series (8.2), is convergent.

2. If $\rho > 1$, the same line of reasoning as in (1) shows that the series is divergent.

3. If $\rho = 1$, the test fails. For example, consider the p series given by (7.9) above. In this case, we have

(8.7)
$$\text{Test ratio} = \frac{u_{n+1}}{u_n} = \left(\frac{n}{n+1}\right)^p = \left(1 - \frac{1}{n+1}\right)^p$$

and we have

(8.8)
$$\rho = \lim_{n \to \infty} \left(1 - \frac{1}{n+1}\right)^p = (1)^p = 1$$

Hence we have $\rho = 1$ no matter what value p may have. But in Sec. 7 it was demonstrated that when $p > 1$ the series converges and when $p \leq 1$ the series diverges. It is thus evident that ρ can equal unity for both convergent and divergent series.

We note that for convergence it is not enough that the test ratio is less than unity for all values of n. The test requires that the limit of the test ratio shall be less than unity. For example, in the series

(8.9)
$$1 + \frac{1}{2} + \frac{1}{3} + \frac{1}{4} + \cdots = \sum_{n=1}^{\infty} \frac{1}{n}$$

the test ratio is always less than unity. The *limit*, however, equals unity.

9. Alternating Series. A series whose terms are alternately positive and negative is called an *alternating series.* Consider the alternating series

(9.1)
$$S = u_1 - u_2 + u_3 - u_4 + \cdots$$

If each term of the series is numerically less than the one preceding it and if

(9.2)
$$\lim_{n \to \infty} u_n = 0$$

then the series is convergent.

Proof. When n is even, S_n may be written in the form

(9.3) $S_n = (u_1 - u_2) + (u_3 - u_4) + \cdots + (u_{n-1} - u_n)$
(9.4) $S_n = u_1 - (u_2 - u_3) - \cdots - (u_{n-2} - u_{n-1}) - u_n$

Each expression in parentheses is positive. Therefore, when n increases through even values, (9.3) shows that S_n increases and (9.4) shows that S_n is always less than u_1. Therefore S_n approaches a limit L. But S_{n+1} also approaches this limit L, since

(9.5)
$$S_{n+1} = S_n + u_{n+1}$$

and

(9.6)
$$\lim_{n \to \infty} u_{n+1} = 0$$

Hence, when n increases through all integral values, $S_n \to L$ and the series is convergent. An important consequence of this proof is given in the following statement:

The error made by terminating a convergent alternating series at any term does not exceed numerically the value of the first of the terms discarded.

For example, it will be shown in a later section that the sum of the series

(9.7) $S = 1 - \frac{1}{2} + \frac{1}{3} - \frac{1}{4} + \frac{1}{5} - \cdots = \ln 2 = 0.693$

to three decimal places. Now the sum of the first 10 terms of the series (9.7) is 0.646, and the value of the series differs from this by less than one-eleventh.

10. Absolute Convergence. A series is said to be *absolutely*, or unconditionally, convergent when the series formed from it by making all its terms positive is convergent. Other convergent series are said to be conditionally convergent. For example, the series

(10.1) $1 - \dfrac{1}{2^2} + \dfrac{1}{3^3} - \dfrac{1}{4^4} + \dfrac{1}{5^5} - \cdots + (-1)^{n-1}\dfrac{1}{n^n} + \cdots$

is absolutely convergent since the series

(10.2) $1 + \dfrac{1}{2^2} + \dfrac{1}{3^3} + \dfrac{1}{4^4} + \dfrac{1}{5^5} + \cdots + \dfrac{1}{n^n} + \cdots$

is convergent.   The alternating series

$$(10.3) \qquad 1 - \tfrac{1}{2} + \tfrac{1}{3} - \tfrac{1}{4} + \tfrac{1}{5} - \cdots = \ln 2$$

is conditionally convergent since the harmonic series is divergent.

In a conditionally convergent series, it is *not* always allowable to change the order of the terms or to group the terms together in parentheses in an arbitrary manner.   These operations may alter the sum of such a series, or may change a convergent series into a divergent series, or vice versa. As an example, let us again consider the convergent series

$$(10.4) \qquad 1 - \frac{1}{2} + \frac{1}{3} - \frac{1}{4} + \cdots + \frac{1}{2n + 1} - \frac{1}{2n + 2} + \cdots$$

The sum of this series is equal to the limit of the expression

$$(10.5) \qquad S = \sum_{n=0}^{n=\infty} \left(\frac{1}{2n + 1} - \frac{1}{2n + 2} \right)$$

Let us write the terms of this series in another way, putting two negative terms after each positive term in the following manner:

$$(10.6) \quad S_1 = 1 - \frac{1}{2} - \frac{1}{4} + \frac{1}{3} - \frac{1}{6} - \frac{1}{8} + \cdots + \frac{1}{2n + 1}$$
$$- \frac{1}{4n + 2} - \frac{1}{4n + 4} + \cdots$$

This series converges, and its sum is given by

$$(10.7) \qquad S = \sum_{n=0}^{n=\infty} \left(\frac{1}{2n + 1} - \frac{1}{4n + 2} - \frac{1}{4n + 4} \right)$$

Now from the identity

$$(10.8) \qquad \frac{1}{2n + 1} - \frac{1}{4n + 2} - \frac{1}{4n + 4} = \frac{1}{2} \left(\frac{1}{2n + 1} - \frac{1}{2n + 2} \right)$$

it is evident that the sum of the series (10.6) is half the sum of the series (10.4).

In general, given a series that is convergent but not absolutely convergent, it is possible to arrange the terms in such a way that the new series converges toward any preassigned number A whatsoever.

A series with some positive and some negative terms is convergent if the series deduced from it by making all the signs positive is convergent. The proof of this statement is omitted.

11. Power Series.   A series of the form

$$(11.1) \qquad S = a_0 + a_1 x + a_2 x^2 + \cdots + a_n x^n + \cdots$$

where the coefficients a_0, a_1, a_2, . . . are independent of x, is called a power series in x.   A power series in x may converge for all values of x or for no value of x except $x = 0$; or it may converge for some values of x different from 0 and be divergent for other values.

Interval of Convergence.   Let us take the ratio of the $(n + 1)$st to the nth term of the power series (11.1).   We thus obtain

$$(11.2) \qquad \frac{a_{n+1} x^{n+1}}{a_n x^n} = \frac{a_{n+1}}{a_n} x$$

Let us consider the case where the coefficients of the series are such that

$$(11.3) \qquad \lim_{n \to \infty} \frac{a_{n+1}}{a_n} = L$$

where L is a definite number.   We thus see that the test ratio of Sec. 8 is given by

$$(11.4) \qquad \rho = xL$$

By Cauchy's ratio test we have two cases:

1. If $L = 0$, the series (11.1) converges for all values of x since in this case $\rho = 0$.

2. If L is not zero, the series will converge when xL is numerically less than 1, that is, when x lies in the interval

$$(11.5) \qquad -\frac{1}{|L|} < x < \frac{1}{|L|}$$

and will diverge for values of x outside this interval.   This interval is called the interval of convergence.   The end points of this interval must be examined separately.

As an example, consider the power series

$$(11.6) \qquad x - \frac{x^2}{2^2} + \frac{x^3}{3^2} - \frac{x^4}{4^2} + \cdots + (-1)^{n-1} \frac{x^n}{n^2} + \cdots$$

Here we have

$$(11.7) \qquad L = \lim_{n \to \infty} \frac{a_{n+1}}{a_n} = \lim_{n \to \infty} -\frac{n^2}{(n+1)^2} = -1$$

Hence this series converges when x is numerically less than 1 and diverges when x is numerically greater than 1.   We must now examine the end points.   If we place $x = 1$ in (11.6), we get

$$(11.8) \qquad\qquad 1 - \frac{1}{2^2} + \frac{1}{3^2} - \frac{1}{4^2} + \cdots$$

This is an alternating series that converges.   If we now place $x = -1$ in (11.6), we obtain

$$(11.9) \qquad\qquad -1 - \frac{1}{2^2} - \frac{1}{3^2} - \frac{1}{4^2} - \cdots$$

This is a convergent series, as can be seen by comparison with the p series of (7.9) when $p > 1$.

We thus see that the series (11.6) has the interval of convergence

$$(11.10) \qquad\qquad -1 \leq x \leq 1$$

12. Theorems Regarding Power Series.   In this section we shall state some fundamental theorems that are of importance in the use of power series in applied mathematics.   The proofs of these theorems belong in a book on analysis rather than one devoted to applied mathematics.   Accordingly the proofs will be omitted, and the interested reader is advised to refer to the works listed at the end of this chapter.

THEOREM I. *Sum of Two Convergent Power Series.*   Let

$$(12.1) \qquad S_1(x) = a_0 + a_1 x + a_2 x^2 + \cdots + a_n x^n + \cdots$$

be a power series convergent for $|x| < r_1$ and

$$(12.2) \qquad S_2(x) = b_0 + b_1 x + b_2 x^2 + \cdots + b_n x^n + \cdots$$

be a second power series convergent for $|x| < r_2$.   Now if we let r be the smaller of the two numbers r_1 and r_2 so that both series converge for $|x| < r$, then the sum of $S_1(x)$ and $S_2(x)$ is represented by the power series

$$(12.3) \quad S_1(x) + S_2(x) = (a_0 + b_0) + (a_1 + b_1)x + \cdots$$
$$+ (a_n + b_n)x^2 + \cdots$$

The series (12.3) is convergent at least for $|x| < r$.   That is, two power series may be added term by term and the resulting series converges to $S_1(x) + S_2(x)$ for those values of x for which both of the given series converge.   For example, let

$$(12.4) \qquad S_1(x) = e^x = 1 + x + \frac{x^2}{2!} + \cdots + \frac{x^n}{n!} + \cdots$$

and

$$(12.5) \quad S_2(x) = e^{-x} = 1 - x + \frac{x^2}{2!} + \cdots + (-1)^n \frac{x^n}{n!} + \cdots$$

Then

(12.6) $\quad S_1(x) + S_2(x) = e^x + e^{-x}$

$$= 2\left[1 + \frac{x^2}{2!} + \cdots + \frac{1 + (-1)^n}{2}\frac{x^n}{n!} + \cdots\right]$$

$$= 2\cosh x$$

In this case both series $S_1(x)$ and $S_2(x)$ converge for all values of x, and hence their sum converges for all values of x.

THEOREM II. *The Product of Two Convergent Power Series.* If

(12.7) $$S_1(x) = \sum_{n=0}^{n=\infty} a_n x^n$$

and

(12.8) $$S_2(x) = \sum_{n=0}^{n=\infty} b_n x^n$$

both converge for $|x| < r$ and the product $S_1(x)S_2(x)$ is given by the power series

(12.9) $\quad S_1(x)S_2(x) = a_0b_0 + (a_0b_1 + a_1b_0)x$
$$+ (a_0b_2 + a_1b_1 + a_2b_0)x^2 + \cdots$$

which also converges at least for $|x| < r$.

That is, one power series may be multiplied by another to obtain the expansion of the product of two functions. The coefficients are formed just as in the multiplication of two polynomials. The product series converges whenever the two given series are convergent.

As an illustration of this theorem, let us consider the two series

(12.10) $\quad S_1(x) = \sinh x = x + \frac{x^3}{3!} + \frac{x^5}{5!} + \cdots + \frac{x^{2n-1}}{(2n-1)!} + \cdots$

(12.11) $\quad S_2(x) = \cosh x = 1 + \frac{x^2}{2!} + \frac{x^4}{4!} + \cdots + \frac{x^{2n-2}}{(2n-2)!} + \cdots$

We then have

(12.12) $\quad S_1(x)S_2(x) = \sinh x \cosh x$

$$= x + \left(\frac{1}{2!} + \frac{1}{3!}\right)x^3 + \left(\frac{1}{4!} + \frac{1}{3!2!} + \frac{1}{5!}\right)x^5 + \cdots$$

$$= x + \tfrac{2}{3}x^3 + \tfrac{2}{15}x^5 + \cdots$$

$$= \frac{1}{2}\left[2x + \frac{(2x)^3}{3!} + \frac{(2x)^5}{5!} + \cdots\right]$$

$$= \tfrac{1}{2}\sinh 2x$$

Since the original series converge for all values of x, so does the product series.

THEOREM III. *The Quotient of Two Convergent Series.* If

$$(12.13) \qquad S_1(x) = \sum_{n=0}^{n=\infty} a_n x^n$$

and

$$(12.14) \qquad S_2(x) = \sum_{n=0}^{n=\infty} b_n x^n$$

both converge for $|x| < r$, and if $b_0 \neq 0$, then the quotient is represented by the series

$$(12.15) \quad \frac{S_1(x)}{S_2(x)} = \frac{a_0}{b_0} + \frac{a_1 b_0 - a_0 b_1}{b_0^2} x$$
$$+ \frac{a_2 b_0^2 - a_1 b_0 b_1 + a_0 b_1^2 - a_0 b_0 b_2}{b_0^3} x^2 + \cdots$$

obtained by dividing the series for $S_1(x)$ by that for $S_2(x)$. In this case no conclusion can be drawn concerning the region of convergence of the quotient series from a knowledge of the regions of convergence of the series $S_1(x)$ and $S_2(x)$.

This may be illustrated by considering the two series

$$(12.16) \quad S_1(x) = \sin x = x - \frac{x^3}{3!} + \frac{x^5}{5!} - \cdots + \frac{(-1)^{n-1} x^{2n-1}}{(2n-1)!} + \cdots$$

$$(12.17) \quad S_2(x) = \cos x = 1 - \frac{x^2}{2!} + \frac{x^4}{4!} - \cdots + \frac{(-1)^{n-1} x^{2n-2}}{(2n-2)!} + \cdots$$

If we now divide $S_1(x)$ by $S_2(x)$, we have

$$(12.18) \qquad \frac{S_1(x)}{S_2(x)} = \frac{\sin x}{\cos x} = x + \frac{x^3}{3} + \frac{2x^5}{15} + \cdots = \tan x$$

Now although the series for $\sin x$ and $\cos x$ converge for all values of x, the series for $\tan x$ is convergent only for $|x| < \pi/2$.

THEOREM IV. *Substitution of One Series into Another.* Let the series

$$(12.19) \qquad z = a_0 + a_1 y + a_2 y^2 + \cdots + a_n y^n + \cdots$$

converge for $|y| < r_1$, and let the series

$$(12.20) \qquad y = b_0 + b_1 x + b_2 x^2 + \cdots + b_n x^n + \cdots$$

converge for $|x| < r_2$.

Now if $|b_0| < r_1$, then we may substitute for y in the first series its value in terms of x from the second series and thus obtain z as a power series in x. This will converge if x is sufficiently small.

In the special case that the given series for z converges for *all* values of y, the series for z in terms of x may then always be found, and this series will converge for all values of $|x| < r_2$.

As an example, let us consider the expansion of $e^{\cos x}$ as a power series in x. In this case we have

$$(12.21) \qquad z = e^y = 1 + \frac{y}{1!} + \frac{y^2}{2!} + \cdots + \frac{y^n}{n!} + \cdots$$

and

$$(12.22) \qquad y = \cos x = 1 - \frac{x^2}{2!} + \frac{x^4}{4!} - \frac{x^6}{6!} + \cdots$$

In this case the series (12.21) and (12.22) converge for all values of x. We now form the various powers of y and substitute into (12.21).

$$(12.23) \qquad \begin{aligned} y^2 &= 1 - x^2 + \tfrac{1}{3}x^4 - \cdots \\ y^3 &= 1 - \tfrac{3}{2}x^2 + \tfrac{7}{8}x^4 - \cdots \\ y^4 &= 1 - 2x^2 + \tfrac{5}{3}x^4 - \cdots \end{aligned}$$

Hence

$$(12.24) \qquad \begin{aligned} e^3 &= 1 + \left(1 - \frac{x^2}{2} + \frac{x^4}{24} - \cdots\right) \\ &\quad + \frac{1}{2}\left(1 - x^2 + \frac{x^4}{3} - \cdots\right) \\ &\quad + \frac{1}{6}\left(1 - \frac{3x^2}{2} + \frac{7}{8}x^4 - \cdots\right) \\ &\quad + \tfrac{1}{24}(1 - 2x^2 + \tfrac{5}{3}x^4 - \cdots) \\ &= (1 + 1 + \tfrac{1}{2} + \tfrac{1}{6} + \tfrac{1}{24} + \cdots) \\ &\quad - (\tfrac{1}{2} + \tfrac{1}{2} + \tfrac{1}{4} + \tfrac{1}{12} + \cdots)x^2 \\ &\quad + (\tfrac{1}{24} + \tfrac{1}{6} + \tfrac{7}{48} + \tfrac{5}{72} + \cdots)x^4 + \cdots \end{aligned}$$

Hence

$$(12.25) \qquad e^y = e^{\cos x} = 2\tfrac{17}{24} - 1\tfrac{1}{3}x^2 + \tfrac{61}{144}x^4 - \cdots$$

It should be noted that the coefficients in this series are really infinite series and that the final values here given are only the approximate values found by taking the first few terms of each series. This situation arises whenever $b_0 \neq 0$ in (12.20). However, it is sometimes possible to make a preliminary change that simplifies the final result. In the above case we could write

$$(12.26) \qquad e^{\cos x} = e^{\cos x - 1 + 1} = e^{\cos x - 1}e$$

$$= e^u e = e\left(1 + u + \frac{u^2}{2!} + \frac{u^3}{3!} + \cdots\right)$$

where

$$(12.27) \qquad u = \cos x - 1 = -\frac{x^2}{2!} + \frac{x^4}{4!} - \frac{x^6}{6!} + \cdots$$

Raising u to the various required powers and substituting the result into (12.26), we have

$$(12.28) \qquad e^{\cos x} = e\left(1 - \frac{x^2}{2} + \frac{x^4}{6} - \frac{31}{720}x^6 + \cdots\right)$$

The coefficients are now exact, and the computation of the successive terms is much simpler than by the previous method.

THEOREM V. *Differentiation of a Power Series.* If

$$(12.29) \qquad S_1(x) = a_0 + a_1x + a_2x^2 + \cdots + a_nx^n + \cdots$$

converges for $|x| < r$, the derivatives of $S_1(x)$ may be obtained by term-by-term differentiation of the series (12.29) in the form

$$(12.30) \qquad \frac{d}{dx}S_1(x) = a_1 + 2a_2x + \cdots + na_nx^{n-1} + \cdots$$

and the series (12.30) is also convergent for $|x| < r$.

As an example, consider

$$(12.31) \quad \sin x = x - \frac{x^3}{3!} + \frac{x^5}{5!} - \cdots + (-1)^{n-1}\frac{x^{2n-1}}{(2n-1)!} + \cdots$$

We have

$$(12.32) \quad \frac{d}{dx}\sin x = 1 - \frac{x^2}{2!} + \frac{x^4}{4!} - \cdots + (-1)^{n-1}\frac{x^{2n-2}}{(2n-2)!} + \cdots$$

$$= \cos x$$

In this case both series converge for all values of x.

THEOREM VI. *Integration of a Power Series.* If

$$(12.33) \qquad S_1(x) = \sum_{n=0}^{n=\infty} a_nx^n$$

converges for $|x| < r$, the integral of $S_1(x)$ may be found by integrating the series (12.33) term by term and we have

$$(12.34) \qquad \int_0^x S_1(x)\,dx = \sum_{n=0}^{n=\infty} \frac{a_n}{n+1}x^{n+1}$$

The new series converges for $|x| < r$.

For example, we have

$$(12.35) \quad \frac{1}{1+x^2} = 1 - x^2 + x^4 - \cdots + (-1)^{n-1}x^{2n-2} + \cdots$$

and therefore,

$$(12.36) \quad \int_0^x \frac{dx}{1 + x^2} = x - \frac{x^3}{3} + \frac{x^5}{5} - \cdots + (-1)^{n-1} \frac{x^{2n-1}}{2n - 1} + \cdots$$
$$= \tan^{-1} x$$

Since the series (12.35) is convergent for $|x| < 1$, the series for $\tan^{-1} x$ is also convergent in this interval.

THEOREM VII.   *Equality of Power Series.*   If we have

$$(12.37) \qquad \sum_{n=0}^{n=\infty} a_n x^n = \sum_{n=0}^{n=\infty} b_n x^n$$

for $|x| < r$, then the coefficients of like powers of the two series must be equal.   That is, we must have

$$(12.38) \qquad a_s = b_s \qquad s = 0, 1, 2, 3, \ldots$$

It then follows that if a function is expanded in a certain interval by different methods the series obtained must be identical.

THEOREM VIII.   *Reversion of a Power Series.*   In certain applications of mathematical analysis to physical problems it is necessary to *reverse* a power series.   Let the given series be

$$(12.39) \quad y = ax + bx^2 + cx^3 + dx^4 + ex^5 + fx^6 + gx^7 + \cdots$$

where it is stipulated that the coefficient a is not equal to zero.

It is required to find the coefficients of the series

$$(12.40) \quad x = Ay + By^2 + Cy^3 + Dy^4 + Ey^5 + Fy^6 + Gy^7 + \cdots$$

In order to determine the coefficients A, B, C, etc., the series (12.40) is substituted into the series (12.39), and the coefficients of like powers of y are equated to each other.   Following this procedure, the following equations are obtained:

$$(12.41) \quad \begin{aligned} A &= \frac{1}{a} \qquad B = -\frac{b}{a^3} \qquad C = \frac{2b^2 - ac}{a^5} \\ D &= \frac{5abc - a^2d - 5b^3}{a^7} \\ E &= \frac{6a^2bd + 3a^2c^2 + 14b^4 - a^3e - 21ab^2c}{a^9} \\ F &= \frac{7a^3be + 7a^3cd + 84ab^3c - a^4f - 28a^2b^2d - 28a^2bc^2 - 42b^5}{a^{11}} \\ G &= \frac{\begin{aligned}&8a^4bf + 8a^4ce + 4a^4d^2 + 120a^2b^3d + 180a^2b^2c^2 + 132b^6 \\ &\quad - a^5g - 36a^3b^2e - 72a^3bcd - 12a^3c^3 - 330ab^4c\end{aligned}}{a^{13}} \end{aligned}$$

Additional coefficients are given in the publication "Smithsonian Mathematical Formulae and Tables of Elliptic Functions."[*]

13. Series of Functions and Uniform Convergence. Consider a series of the form

$$(13.1) \qquad S(x) = u_0(x) + u_1(x) + \cdots + u_n(x) + \cdots$$

whose terms are continuous functions of a variable x in an interval (a,b) and which converges for every value of x inside that interval. This series does not necessarily represent a continuous function, as one might be tempted to believe. For example, let us consider the series

$$(13.2) \qquad S(x) = x^2 + \frac{x^2}{1 + x^2} + \cdots + \frac{x^2}{(1 + x^2)^n} + \cdots$$

Now if $x \neq 0$, this series is a geometric progression whose ratio is $1/(1 + x^2)$, and hence the sum of the series is

$$(13.3) \qquad S(x) = \frac{x^2}{1 - \dfrac{1}{1 + x^2}} = \frac{x^2(1 + x^2)}{x^2} = 1 + x^2 \qquad x \neq 0$$

If we call $S_n(x)$ the sum of the first n terms of the series, then we have

$$(13.4) \qquad S(0) = \lim_{n \to \infty} S_n(0) = 0$$

since every term of the series is zero when $x = 0$. However, we also have

$$(13.5) \qquad \lim_{x \to 0} S(x) = \lim_{x \to 0} (1 + x^2) = 1$$

In this example the function $S(x)$ approaches a definite limit as x approaches zero, but that limit is different from the value of the function for $x = 0$. Thus $S(x)$ is not continuous at $x = 0$.

Since a large number of the functions that occur in mathematics are defined by series, it has been found necessary to study the properties of the functions given in the form of a series. The first question which arises is that of determining whether or not the sum of a given series is a continuous function of the variable. This has led to the development of the very important notion of *uniform convergence*.

A series of the type (13.1) each of whose terms is a function of x which is defined in an interval (a,b) is said to be *uniformly convergent* in that interval if it converges for every value of x between a and b, and if, corresponding to any arbitrary preassigned positive number δ, a positive integer N, independent of x, can be found such that the absolute value of the remainder R_n of the given series

$$(13.6) \qquad R_n = u_{n+1}(x) + u_{n+2}(x) + \cdots$$

---

[*] P. 116, Smithsonian Institution, Washington, D.C., 1922.

is less than δ for every value of $n \geq N$ and for every value of x that lies in the interval (a,b).

The Weierstrass M Test for Uniform Convergence. It would seem at first thought very difficult to determine whether or not a given series is uniformly convergent in a given interval. The following theorem, due to the German mathematician Weierstrass, enables us to show in many cases that a given series converges uniformly. Let

$$(13.7) \qquad u_0(x) + u_1(x) + \cdots + u_n(x) + \cdots$$

be a series each of whose terms is a continuous function of x in an interval (a,b), and let

$$(13.8) \qquad M_0 + M_1 + M_2 + \cdots + M_n + \cdots$$

be a convergent series whose terms are positive constants. Then if

$$(13.9) \qquad |u_n| \leq M_n$$

for all values of x in the interval (a,b) and for all values of n, the series (13.7) converges uniformly in the interval (a,b).

Proof. It is evident from (13.9) that

$$(13.10) \qquad |u_{n+1} + u_{n+2} + \cdots| \leq M_{n+1} + M_{n+2} + \cdots$$

for all values of x between a and b. If n is chosen so large that the remainder R_n of the series (13.8) is less than δ for all values of n greater than N, we shall also have

$$(13.11) \qquad |u_{n+1} + u_{n+2} + \cdots| < \delta$$

whenever n is greater than N for all values of x in the interval (a,b).

As an example, let it be required to examine the series

$$(13.12) \qquad \frac{\sin x}{1} + \frac{\sin 2x}{2^2} + \cdots + \frac{\sin nx}{n^2} + \cdots$$

for uniform convergence.

In this case since

$$(13.13) \qquad |\sin nx| \leq 1 \qquad \text{for all values of } x$$

we may take

$$(13.14) \qquad 1 + \frac{1}{2^2} + \frac{1}{3^2} + \cdots + \frac{1}{n^2} + \cdots$$

for the M series. Since the series (13.14) converges, it follows that the series (13.12) converges uniformly in any interval.

14. Integration and Differentiation of Series. Two theorems concerning the integration and differentiation of uniformly convergent series will now be stated without proof.

I. Any series of continuous functions that converges uniformly in an interval (a,b) may be integrated term by term, provided the limits of integration are finite and lie in the interval (a,b).

II. Any convergent series may be differentiated term by term if the resulting series converges uniformly.

For example, the series

$$(14.1) \quad S(x) = \frac{\sin x}{1} + \frac{\sin 2x}{2^2} + \frac{\sin 3x}{3^2} + \cdots + \frac{\sin nx}{n^2} + \cdots$$

has been shown to be uniformly convergent in any interval and hence defines a continuous function of x, $S(x)$, in that interval.

The term-by-term derivative of (14.1) gives

$$(14.2) \qquad \cos x + \frac{\cos 2x}{2} + \frac{\cos 3x}{3} + \cdots + \frac{\cos nx}{n} + \cdots$$

In this case we cannot find the proper M series to test (14.2) for uniform convergence since the series

$$1 + \frac{1}{2} + \frac{1}{3} + \cdots + \frac{1}{n} + \cdots$$

is divergent. The series (14.2) converges in the interval $(0,\pi)$. However, we have no assurance that it converges to the derivative of $S(x)$.

15. Taylor's Series. We now consider a method by which we may expand a given function $f(x)$ into a

Fig. 15.1

power series. This section will be devoted to a derivation of Taylor's formula and a discussion of Taylor's series.

Let us consider

$$(15.1) \qquad \int_{x_0}^{x_0+h} f'(x) \, dx = f(x_0 + h) - f(x_0)$$

Let us now change the variable of integration from x to t by means of the equation

$$(15.2) \qquad x = (x_0 + h) - t$$

The relation between h and t is made clear by Fig. 15.1.

Introducing this new variable of integration into (15.1), we have

$$(15.3) \quad \int_{x_0}^{x_0+h} f'(x) \, dx = - \int_{h}^{0} f'(x_0 + h - t) \, dt = \int_{0}^{h} f'(x_0 + h - t) \, dt$$

We now apply the formula of integration by parts,

$$(15.4) \qquad \int u \, dv = uv - \int v \, du$$

to (15.3).

We have here

$$(15.5) \qquad u = f'(x_0 + h - t) \qquad\qquad dv = dt$$
$$du = -f''(x_0 + h - t)\, dt \qquad v = t$$

Hence

$$(15.6) \qquad \int_0^h f''(x_0 + h - t)\, dt = tf'(x_0 + h - t)\Big|_0^h$$
$$+ \int_0^h tf''(x_0 + h - t)\, dt = hf'(x_0) + \int_0^h tf''(x_0 + h - t)\, dt$$

Integrating by parts again, we obtain

$$(15.7) \qquad \int_0^h tf''(x_0 + h - t)\, dt = \frac{h^2}{2!}f''(x_0) + \int_0^h \frac{t^2}{2!}f'''(x_0 + h - t)\, dt$$

After n integrations by parts, we have

$$(15.8) \qquad \int_{x_0}^{x_0+h} f'(x)\, dx = hf'(x_0) + \frac{h^2}{2!}f''(x_0) + \frac{h_3}{3!}f'''(x_0) + \cdots$$
$$+ \frac{h^n}{n!}f^{(n)}(x_0) + \int_0^h \frac{t^n}{n!}f^{(n+1)}(x_0 + h - t)\, dt$$
$$= f(x_0 + h) - f(x_0)$$

We may write the last integral of (15.8) in the form

$$(15.9) \qquad \int_0^h \frac{t^n}{n!}\,\phi(t)\, dt = \frac{1}{n!}\int_0^h t^n\phi(t)\, dt = I$$

Now the integral I may be regarded as representing the area under the curve $y = t^n\phi(t)$ from the point $t = 0$ to $t = h$. If $\phi(t)$ is a continuous function of t, there will be some point t_0 such that $0 < t_0 < h$ for which we shall have

$$(15.10) \qquad I = \frac{1}{n!}\int_0^h t^n\phi(t)\, dt = \frac{\phi(t_0)}{n!}\int_0^h t^n\, dt$$
$$= \frac{h^{n+1}}{(n+1)!}\,\phi(t_0)$$
$$= \frac{h^{n+1}}{(n+1)!}f^{(n+1)}(x_0 + \theta h) \qquad 0 < \theta < 1$$

where $\theta h = h - t_0$.

Hence we may write (15.8) in the form

$$(15.11) \quad f(x_0 + h) = f(x_0) + \frac{h}{1!}f'(x_0) + \frac{h^2}{1!}f''(x_0) + \cdots$$
$$+ \frac{h^n f^{(n)}}{n!}(x_0) + \frac{h^{n+1}}{(n+1)!}f^{(n+1)}(x_0 + \theta h) \qquad 0 < \theta < 1$$

This is known as Taylor's formula with the Lagrangian form of the remainder.

In this derivation of Taylor's formula, it was assumed that $f(x)$ possesses a continuous nth derivative.   The term

$$(15.12) \qquad R_{n+1} = \frac{h^{n+1}}{(n+1)!} f^{(n+1)}(x_0 + \theta h)$$

is called the remainder after $n + 1$ terms.   It may happen that $f(x)$ possesses derivatives of all orders and that

$$(15.13) \qquad \lim_{n \to \infty} R_{n+1} = 0$$

In that case, we have the *convergent* infinite series

$$(15.14) \quad f(x_0 + h) = f(x_0) + \frac{hf'(x_0)}{1!} + \cdots + \frac{h^n f^{(n)}(x_0)}{n!} + \cdots$$

If we place $x_0 = 0$ and $h = x$ in (15.14), we obtain

$$(15.15) \quad f(x) = f(0) + \frac{xf'(0)}{1!} + \frac{x^2 f''(0)}{2!} + \cdots + \frac{x^n f^n(0)}{n!} + \cdots$$

This series is called Maclaurin's series.

As an example, let us obtain the Maclaurin-series expansion of the function $f(x) = e^x$.

In this case, we have

$$(15.16) \qquad f(0) = 1 \qquad f'(0) = 1 \qquad \cdots \qquad f^{(n)}(0) = 1$$

Hence

$$(15.17) \qquad e^x = 1 + \frac{x}{1!} + \frac{x^2}{2!} + \frac{x^3}{3!} + \cdots + \frac{x^n}{n!} + \cdots$$

This series is seen to converge for all values of x.

As another example, let it be required to expand the function $f(x) = \cos x$ into a Maclaurin series.   In this case we have

$$(15.18) \quad f(x) = \cos x \qquad f'(x) = -\sin x \qquad f''(x) = -\cos x$$

$$f^{(n)}(x) = \cos\left(x + \frac{n\pi}{2}\right)$$

Substituting this into (15.15), we have

$$(15.19) \quad \cos x = 1 - \frac{x^2}{2!} + \frac{x^4}{4!} - \frac{x^6}{6!} + \cdots + (-1)^{n-1} \frac{x^{2n-2}}{(2n-2)!} + \cdots$$

This series is seen to converge for all values of x.

The Binomial Series.   If we consider the function

$$(15.20) \qquad f(x) = (1 + x)^n$$

and expand it in a Maclaurin series in powers of x, we have

$$f'(x) = n(1 + x)^{n-1} \qquad f''(x) = n(n - 1)(1 + x)^{n-2}$$
$$f'''(x) = n(n - 1)(n - 2)(1 + x)^{n-3}$$

(15.21) $\cdots \cdots \cdots \cdots \cdots \cdots \cdots \cdots \cdots$

$$f^{(r)}(x) = n(n - 1)(n - 2) \cdots (n - r + 1)(1 + x)^{n-r}$$

$\cdots \cdots \cdots \cdots \cdots \cdots \cdots \cdots \cdots \cdots \cdots \cdots \cdots \cdots$

On substituting this into (15.15), we have

$$(15.22) \quad (1 + x)^n = 1 + nx + \frac{n(n - 1)x^2}{2!} + \frac{n(n - 1)(n - 2)x^3}{3!}$$
$$+ \cdots + \frac{n(n - 1)(n - 2) \cdots (n - r + 1)x^r}{r!} + \cdots$$

This series is convergent if $|x| < 1$ and divergent when $|x| > 1$, as may be seen by applying the ratio test. Equation (15.22) expresses the binomial theorem. If n is a positive integer, the series is finite. We may also write

$$(15.23) \quad (a + b)^n = a^n(1 + x)^n \qquad \text{if } x = \frac{b}{a}$$
$$= a^n + na^{n-1}b + \frac{n(n - 1)}{2!} a^{n-2}b^2 + \cdots$$
$$+ \frac{n!a^{n-r}b^r}{(n - r)!r!} + \cdots \qquad \text{valid for } |b| < |a|$$

16. Symbolic Form of Taylor's Series. *Taylor's-series Expansion of Functions of Two or More Variables.* A very useful and convenient form of Taylor's expansion may be obtained by the use of the symbolic operator D defined by

$$(16.1) \qquad D_x = \frac{d}{dx} \qquad D_x^2 = \frac{d^2}{dx^2} \qquad \cdots \qquad D_x^n = \frac{d^n}{dx^n}$$

By the use of the derivative operator D_x, defined by (16.1), we may write Taylor's expansion in the form

$$(16.2) \quad f(x_0 + h) = f(x_0) + \frac{h}{1!} D_x f(x_0) + \frac{h^2}{2!} D_x^2 f(x_0) + \cdots$$
$$+ \frac{h^n}{n!} D_x^n f(x_0) + \cdots$$

where

$$(16.3) \qquad D_x^r f(x_0) = \frac{d^r}{dx^r} f(x) \qquad \text{at } x = x_0$$

We may write (16.2) in the form

$$(16.4) \quad f(x_0 + h) = \left(1 + \frac{hD_x}{1!} + \frac{h^2 D_x^2}{2!} + \cdots + \frac{h^n D_x^n}{n!} + \cdots\right) f(x_0)$$

However, if we place $x = hD_x$ in (15.17), we obtain

(16.5) $\qquad e^{hD_x} = 1 + \dfrac{hD_x}{1!} + \dfrac{h^2 D_x^2}{2!} + \cdots + \dfrac{h^n D_x^n}{n!} + \cdots$

Hence we may write (16.4) in the symbolic form

(16.6) $\qquad\qquad\qquad f(x_0 + h) = e^{hD_x}f(x_0)$

This form of Taylor's expansion is compact and easy to remember. By the use of (16.6) we may deduce the form of Taylor's expansion for a function of two or more variables.

Let $F(x,y)$ be a function of the two independent variables x and y, and let it have continuous partial derivatives of all orders. Now if we hold y constant, we have by (16.6)

(16.7) $\qquad\qquad\qquad F(x + h, y) = e^{hD_x}F(x,y)$

where in this case D_x^r has the significance

(16.8) $\qquad\qquad\qquad D_x^r = \dfrac{\partial^r}{\partial x^r}$

since we are holding y constant.

In the same way, if we hold x constant, we have

(16.9) $\qquad\qquad\qquad F(x, y + k) = e^{kD_y}F(x,y)$

where

(16.10) $\qquad\qquad\qquad D_y^r = \dfrac{\partial^r}{\partial y^r}$

If we operate on (16.7) with e^{kD_y}, we obtain

(16.11) $\qquad e^{kD_y}F(x + h, y) = F(x + h, y + k)$
$$= e^{kD_y}e^{hD_x}F(x,y)$$
$$= e^{hD_x + kD_y}F(x,y)$$

We thus have the important result that

(16.12) $\quad F(x + h, y + k) = e^{hD_x + kD_y}F(x,y)$
$$= \left[1 + \dfrac{hD_x + kD_y}{1!} + \dfrac{(hD_x + kD_y)^2}{2!} + \cdots \right.$$
$$\left. + \dfrac{(hD_x + kD_y)^n}{n!} + \cdots \right] F(x,y)$$
$$= F(x,y) + h\dfrac{\partial F}{\partial x} + k\dfrac{\partial F}{\partial y} + \dfrac{1}{2!}\left(h^2\dfrac{\partial^2 F}{\partial x^2} + 2hk\dfrac{\partial^2 F}{\partial x\,\partial y} + k^2\dfrac{\partial^2 F}{\partial y^2} \right) + \cdots$$

Equation (16.12) is Taylor's expansion of a function of two variables. The symbolic derivation given above is based on the fact that the operators D_x and D_y commute with constants and satisfy many of the basic laws of algebra and hence may be treated in many ways as if they were algebraic quantities. This matter will be discussed in greater detail in Chaps. 6 and 10.

By the same reasoning, if we have a function $F(x_1, x_2, x_3, \ldots, x_n)$ of the n variables $(x_1, x_2, \ldots, x_n)$ that has continuous partial derivatives of all orders, we have

$$(16.13) \quad F(x_1 + h_1, x_2 + h_2, \ldots, x_n + h_n)$$
$$= e^{h_1 D_1 + h_2 D_2 + \cdots + h_n D_n} F(x_1, x_2, \ldots, x_n)$$

where

$$(16.14) \qquad D_m^r = \frac{\partial^r}{\partial x_m^r} \qquad D_m^r D_n^s = \frac{\partial^{r+s}}{\partial x_m^r \, \partial x_n} \qquad \text{etc.}$$

This is Taylor's expansion of a function of n variables.

17. Evaluation of Integrals by Means of Power Series. In applied mathematics we frequently encounter definite integrals in which the indefinite integral cannot be found in closed form. Such integrals as, for example,

$$\int_0^1 \sin x^2 \, dx \qquad \int_0^1 e^{-x^2} \, dx$$

and many others are frequently encountered in the investigation of physical problems. By the use of the power-series expansions of the integrand, we may find the value of these integrals to any desired accuracy. For example, let us consider the integral

$$(17.1) \qquad\qquad \int_0^1 \sin x^2 \, dx = I$$

If we let $x^2 = u$, we have the Maclaurin expansion for $\sin u$,

$$(17.2) \qquad\qquad \sin u = u - \frac{u^3}{3!} + \frac{u^5}{5!} - \cdots$$

Hence we have

$$(17.3) \qquad\qquad \sin x^2 = x^2 - \frac{x^6}{3!} + \frac{x^{10}}{5!} - \cdots$$

Hence we have

$$(17.4) \quad I = \int_0^1 \sin x^2 \, dx = \int_0^1 \left(x^2 - \frac{x^6}{3!} + \frac{x^{10}}{5!} \right) dx \text{ approx.}$$
$$= \left(\frac{x^3}{3} - \frac{x^7}{42} + \frac{x^{11}}{1,320} \right) \Big|_0^1 = 0.3333 - 0.0238 + 0.0008$$
$$= 0.3103$$

Using the fact that the error is less than the first term neglected, we may show that this result is correct to four decimal places.

In certain investigations, we encounter the integral

$$(17.5) \qquad F(k,\phi) = \int_0^\phi \frac{du}{\sqrt{1 - k^2 \sin^2 u}} \qquad k^2 < 1$$

This integral is called an *elliptic integral of the first kind.*

The integrand of this integral may be expanded by the binomial theorem in the form

$$(17.6) \qquad (1 - k^2 \sin^2 u)^{-\frac{1}{2}} = 1 + \frac{k^2}{2} \sin^2 u + \frac{3k^4}{8} \sin^4 u + \cdots$$

This series is convergent for $|k| < 1$ and for any value of u. If we place $u = \pi/2$, we get the convergent series

$$(17.7) \qquad 1 + \frac{k^2}{2} + \frac{3k^4}{8} + \frac{5k^6}{16} + \cdots$$

Since $|\sin u| \leq 1$, the terms of the series (17.6) are less than the corresponding terms of the series (17.7). It follows, therefore, by Weierstrass's M test that the series (17.6) is uniformly convergent in any interval of u. We may therefore integrate term by term. The integration is facilitated by the recursion formula

$$(17.8) \qquad \int \sin^n u \, du = -\frac{\sin^{n-1} u \cos u}{n} + \frac{n-1}{n} \int \sin^{n-2} u \, du$$

given by No. 263 of Peirce's tables of integrals. If, in particular, $\phi = \pi/2$, we have

$$(17.9) \qquad K(k) = \int_0^{\pi/2} \frac{du}{\sqrt{1 - k^2 \sin^2 u}} \qquad k^2 < 1$$

This is the complete elliptic integral of the first kind. The integration may then be facilitated by Wallis's formula

$$(17.10) \qquad \int_0^{\pi/2} \sin^n u \, du = \frac{1 \times 3 \times 5 \times \cdots \times (n-1)}{2 \times 4 \times 6 \times \cdots \times n} \frac{\pi}{2}$$

if n is an even integer (Peirce No. 483).
We then have

$$(17.11) \quad K = \frac{\pi}{2}\left[1 + \left(\frac{1}{2}\right)^2 k^2 + \left(\frac{1 \times 3}{2 \times 4}\right)^2 k^4 + \left(\frac{1 \times 3 \times 5}{2 \times 4 \times 6}\right)^2 k^6 + \cdots \right]$$

This series may be used to compute K for various values of k. If, for example, $k = \sin 10°$, we have

$$(17.12) \qquad K = \frac{\pi}{2}(1 + 0.00754 + 0.00012 + \cdots) = 1.5828$$

We may sometimes obtain the power-series expansion of a function most readily by the evaluation of an integral.

For example, we have

(17.13) $$\frac{d}{dx}\sin^{-1}x = \frac{1}{\sqrt{1-x^2}}$$

Hence

(17.14) $$\sin^{-1}x = \int_0^x \frac{du}{\sqrt{1-u^2}}$$

Now, by the binomial theorem, we have

(17.15) $$(1-u^2)^{-\frac{1}{2}} = 1 + \frac{u^2}{2} + \frac{1\times 3}{2\times 4}u^4 + \frac{1\times 3\times 5}{2\times 4\times 6}u^6 + \cdots$$

This series converges when $|u| < 1$.

If we now substitute this into (17.14) and integrate term by term, we have

(17.16) $$\sin^{-1}x = x + \frac{1}{2}\frac{x^3}{3} + \frac{1\times 3}{2\times 4}\frac{x^5}{5} + \frac{1\times 3\times 5}{2\times 4\times 6}\frac{x^7}{7} + \cdots$$

This series converges when $|x| < 1$.

If we let $x = \frac{1}{2}$, we have

(17.17) $$\sin^{-1}\frac{1}{2} = \frac{\pi}{6} = \frac{1}{2} + \frac{1\times 1}{2\times 3}\left(\frac{1}{2}\right)^3 + \frac{1\times 3\times 1}{2\times 4\times 5}\left(\frac{1}{2}\right)^5 + \cdots$$

or

(17.18) $$\pi = 3.1415 \cdots$$

18. Approximate Formulas Derived from Maclaurin's Series. It frequently happens in applied mathematics that by using a few terms of the power series by which a function is represented we obtain an approximate formula that has some degree of accuracy. Such approximate formulas are of great utility.

For example, by the use of the binomial series we may write down at once the following approximate formulas valid for small values of x:

(18.1) $$(1+x)^n \doteq \underset{\text{First approx.}}{1+nx} \doteq \underset{\text{Second approx.}}{1+nx+\tfrac{1}{2}n(n-1)x^2}$$

where the symbol $\doteq$ means "approximately equal to." Also, we have

(18.2) $$(1+x)^{-n} \doteq 1-nx \doteq 1-nx+\tfrac{1}{2}n(n+1)x^2$$

From the Maclaurin series for the sine we have

(18.3) $$\sin x \doteq x - \frac{x^3}{6}$$

We might inquire for what value of x we may use the approximation

(18.4) $$\sin x \doteq x$$

such that the result is accurate to three decimal places. Since the Maclaurin series for the sine is an alternating series, we know that if only the first term is retained the value of the remaining series is numerically less than the term $x^3/6$. Hence we *must* have

(18.5) $$\left| \frac{x^3}{6} \right| < 0.0005$$

so that the result of the approximation shall be valid to three decimal places. Hence

(18.6) $$|x| < \sqrt[3]{0.003}$$
or $$|x| < 0.1442 \text{ radian}$$

This corresponds to

(18.7) $$|x| < 8.2°$$

19. Use of Series for the Computation of Functions. In many cases the series expansion of a function gives a direct means for the computation of the numerical value of a function for a certain given value of the argument. In this way, tables of functions may be computed.

For example, let it be required to compute the value of sin 10°. This may be done by the use of the Maclaurin-series expansion of the sine.

(19.1) $$\sin x = x - \frac{x^3}{3!} + \frac{x^5}{5!} - \frac{x^7}{7!} + \cdots$$

In this case $x = 10° = \pi/18$ radians. Hence we have

(19.2) $$\sin \left(\frac{\pi}{18} \right) = \frac{\pi}{18} - \left(\frac{\pi}{18} \right)^3 \frac{1}{3!} + \left(\frac{\pi}{18} \right)^5 \frac{1}{5!} - \left(\frac{\pi}{18} \right)^7 \frac{1}{7!} + \cdots$$
$$= 0.1736$$

Since this is an alternating series, we know that the error introduced by stopping at this term is less than

$$\left(\frac{\pi}{18} \right)^9 \frac{1}{9!}$$

As another example, let us consider a series useful in the computation of logarithms.

The Maclaurin-series expansion of the function $\ln (1 + x)$ is easily shown to be

(19.3) $$\ln (1 + x) = x - \frac{x^2}{2} + \frac{x^3}{3} - \frac{x^4}{4} + \cdots$$

If we let $x = -x$ in (19.3), we have

$$(19.4) \qquad \ln (1 - x) = -x - \frac{x^2}{2} - \frac{x^3}{3} - \frac{x^4}{4} - \cdots$$

Now we have

$$(19.5) \quad \ln \frac{1 + x}{1 - x} = \ln (1 + x) - \ln (1 - x)$$

$$= 2 \left(x + \frac{1}{3} x^3 + \frac{1}{5} x^5 + \frac{x^7}{7} + \cdots \right)$$

This series converges when $|x| < 1$.

Now if we let

$$(19.6) \qquad\qquad x = \frac{1}{2n + 1} \qquad n > 0$$

we have

$$(19.7) \qquad\qquad \frac{1 + x}{1 - x} = \frac{n + 1}{n}$$

Then $|x| < 1$ for all values of $n > 0$. If we substitute this into (19.5), we have

$$(19.8) \quad \ln (n + 1) = \ln n$$

$$+ 2 \left[\frac{1}{2n + 1} + \frac{1}{3} \frac{1}{(2n + 1)^3} + \frac{1}{5} \frac{1}{(2n + 1)^5} + \cdots \right]$$

This series converges for all positive values of n and is well adapted to computation. For example, if we let $n = 1$, we have

$$(19.9) \qquad \ln 2 = 2 \left(\frac{1}{3} + \frac{1 \times 1}{3 \times 3^3} + \frac{1 \times 1}{5 \times 3^5} + \cdots \right)$$

$$= 0.69315$$

If we let $n = 2$, we have

$$(19.10) \qquad \ln 3 = \ln 2 + 2 \left(\frac{1}{5} + \frac{1 \times 1}{3 \times 5^3} + \frac{1 \times 1}{5 \times 5^5} + \cdots \right)$$

$$= 1.09861$$

In this way we may compute the natural logarithms of any number. If we wish the Briggs or common logarithms of numbers, written $\log n$, we have

$$(19.11) \qquad\qquad \log n = \frac{\ln n}{\ln 10} = \frac{\ln n}{2.30259}$$

For example,

$$(19.12) \qquad\qquad \log 2 = \frac{\ln 2}{\ln 10} = \frac{0.69315}{2.30259} = 0.3010 \cdots$$

20. Evaluation of a Function Taking On an Indeterminate Form.
a. The Form $0/0$. It sometimes happens that we encounter functions of the form $(\sin x)/x$, $(1 - \cos x)/x^2$, etc., and we wish to investigate the limiting value of these functions as the variable approaches a critical value. That is, we are given a function of the form $f(x)/\phi(x)$ such that $f(a) = 0$ and $\phi(a) = 0$. The function is indeterminate when $x = a$. It is then required to find

$$(20.1) \qquad \lim_{x \to a} \frac{f(x)}{\phi(x)}$$

Now we have

$$(20.2) \qquad \frac{f(a + b)}{\phi(a + b)} = \frac{f(a) + f'(a)b + f''(a)(b^2/2!) + \cdots}{\phi(a) + \phi'(a)b + \phi''(a)(b^2/2!) + \cdots}$$

by Taylor's-series expansion for $f(a + b)$ and $\phi(a + b)$. Now

$$(20.3) \qquad \lim_{x \to a} \frac{f(x)}{\phi(x)} = \lim_{b \to 0} \frac{f(a + b)}{\phi(a + b)}$$

But since by hypothesis $f(a) = 0$ and $\phi(a) = 0$, we have from (20.2) and (20.3)

$$(20.4) \qquad \lim_{x \to a} \frac{f(x)}{\phi(x)} = \frac{f'(a)}{\phi'(a)}$$

This is known as *L'Hospital's rule*. If $f'(a)/\phi'(a)$ is again indeterminate, we apply the rule again. For example,

$$(20.5) \qquad \lim_{x \to 0} \frac{1 - \cos x}{x^2} = \lim_{x \to 0} \frac{\sin x}{2x} = \lim_{x \to 0} \frac{\cos x}{2} = \frac{1}{2}$$

This form could have also been evaluated by the use of the first few terms of the Maclaurin expansion for the cosine; that is, if x is small, we have

$$(20.6) \qquad \cos x \doteq 1 - \frac{x^2}{2}$$

hence

$$(20.7) \qquad 1 - \cos x \doteq \frac{x^2}{2}$$

and we therefore have

$$(20.8) \qquad \lim_{x \to 0} \frac{1 - \cos x}{x^2} = \lim_{x \to 0} \frac{x^2/2}{x^2} = \frac{1}{2}$$

b. The Form ∞/∞. The indeterminate form ∞/∞ may be brought under the form $0/0$ by the device of writing the quotient in the form

$$(20.9) \qquad \lim_{x \to a} \frac{f(x)}{\phi(x)} = \lim_{x \to a} \frac{1/\phi(x)}{1/f(x)}$$

Now since by hypothesis $\phi(a) = \infty$ and $f(a) = \infty$, we again have the form $0/0$ and we may then apply L'Hospital's rule.

For example, consider

$$(20.10) \qquad \lim_{x \to \pi/2} \frac{\sec 3x}{\sec 5x} = \lim_{x \to \pi/2} \frac{1/\sec 5x}{1/\sec 3x}$$

$$= \lim_{x \to \pi/2} \frac{\cos 5x}{\cos 3x} = \lim_{x \to \pi/2} \frac{-5 \sin 5x}{-3 \sin 3x}$$

$$= -\tfrac{5}{3}$$

It may be shown that indeterminate forms of the form ∞ / ∞ may be brought under the same rule as L'Hospital's rule for the form $0/0$. The proof of this statement is rather lengthy, but it may be made plausible by the following heuristic process: Consider

$$(20.11) \qquad \lim_{x \to a} \frac{f(x)}{\phi(x)}$$

where $f(a) = \infty$ and $\phi(a) = \infty$. Then we may write the quotient in the form

$$(20.12) \qquad \lim_{x \to a} \frac{f(x)}{\phi(x)} = \lim_{x \to a} \frac{1/\phi(x)}{1/f(x)}$$

where this is now of the form $0/0$, and hence we may apply L'Hospital's rule to it. On carrying out the differentiation, we have

$$(20.13) \qquad \lim_{x \to a} \frac{f(x)}{\phi(x)} = \lim_{x \to a} \frac{-\phi'(x)/\phi^2(x)}{-f'(x)/f^2(x)}$$

$$= \lim_{x \to a} \left\{ \left[\frac{f(x)}{\phi(x)} \right]^2 \frac{\phi'(x)}{f'(x)} \right\}$$

Now since the limit of a product is equal to the product of the limits, we have

$$(20.14) \qquad \lim_{x \to a} \frac{f(x)}{\phi(x)} = \lim_{x \to a} \frac{f^2(x)}{\phi^2(x)} \lim_{x \to a} \frac{\phi'(x)}{f'(x)}$$

and hence

$$(20.15) \qquad \lim_{x \to a} \frac{f(x)}{\phi(x)} = \lim_{x \to a} \frac{f'(x)}{\phi'(x)}$$

This is the same rule as that for the evaluation of indeterminate forms of the form $0/0$.

As an example of this rule, consider

$$(20.16) \qquad \lim_{x \to 0} \frac{\ln x}{\csc x} = \lim_{x \to 0} \frac{1/x}{-\csc x \cot x}$$

$$= \lim_{x \to 0} \frac{-\sin^2 x}{x \cos x} = \lim_{x \to 0} \frac{-x^2}{x} = 0$$

c. Form $0 \times \infty$. If a function $f(x) \times \phi(x)$ takes on the indeterminate form $0 \times \infty$ for $x = a$, we may write the given function in the form

$$(20.17) \qquad f(x) \times \phi(x) = \frac{f(x)}{1/\phi(x)} = \frac{\phi(x)}{1/f(x)}$$

This causes it to take on one of the forms $0/0$ or ∞/∞ which we may evaluate by the methods of part *a* or *b* above.

For example, consider

$$(20.18) \qquad \lim_{x \to 0} x \ln x = \lim_{x \to 0} \frac{\ln x}{1/x} = \lim_{x \to 0} \frac{1/x}{-1/x^2}$$
$$= 0$$

d. Form $\infty - \infty$. It is possible in general to transform the expression into a fraction that will assume the form $0/0$ or ∞/∞ for the critical value of the argument.

$$(20.19) \qquad \lim_{x \to \pi/2} (\sec x - \tan x) = \lim_{x \to \pi/2} \frac{1 - \sin x}{\cos x}$$
$$= \lim_{x \to \pi/2} \frac{-\cos x}{-\sin x} = 0$$

e. Forms 1^∞, 0^0, ∞^0. In general it is possible to transform these forms into the cases discussed in parts *a* and *b*.

Example 1

$$(20.20) \qquad \lim_{x \to 0} (\cos x)^{1/x^2} = 1^\infty$$

Let

$$(20.21) \qquad y = (\cos x)^{1/x^2}$$

$$(20.22) \qquad \lim_{x \to 0} \ln u = \lim_{x \to 0} \frac{\ln (\cos x)}{x^2} = \lim_{x \to 0} \frac{-\sin x/\cos x}{2x}$$
$$= \lim_{x \to 0} \frac{-\sec^2 x}{2} = -\frac{1}{2}$$

Hence

$$(20.23) \qquad \lim_{x \to 0} u = e^{-\frac{1}{2}}$$

Example 2

$$(20.24) \qquad \lim_{x \to 0} x^{\sin x} = 0^0$$

$$(20.25) \qquad \lim_{x \to 0} x^{\sin x} = \lim_{x \to 0} x^x$$

Let

$$(20.26) \qquad u = x^x$$

$$(20.27) \qquad \lim_{x \to 0} \ln u = \lim_{x \to 0} x \ln x = \lim_{x \to 0} \frac{\ln x}{1/x}$$
$$= \lim_{x \to 0} \frac{1/x}{-1/x^2} = 0$$

Hence

(20.28)
$$\lim_{x \to 0} u = e^0 = 1$$

Example 3

(20.29)
$$\lim_{x \to 0} \left(\frac{1}{x}\right)^{\sin x} = \infty^0$$

Let

(20.30)
$$u = \left(\frac{1}{x}\right)^{\sin x}$$

Hence

(20.31)
$$\lim_{x \to 0} \ln u = \lim \sin x \ln \frac{1}{x} = \lim_{x \to 0} \frac{\cos x}{-1/x} = 0$$

Hence

(20.32)
$$\lim_{x \to 0} u = e^0 = 1$$

Example 4

(20.33)
$$\lim_{n \to \infty} \left(1 + \frac{1}{n}\right)^n = 1^\infty$$

Let

(20.34)
$$u = \left(1 + \frac{1}{n}\right)^x \qquad \frac{1}{n} = x$$

(20.35)
$$\lim_{n \to \infty} \ln u = \lim_{x \to 0} \frac{\ln(1 + x)}{x}$$
$$= \lim_{x \to 0} \frac{1/(1 + x)}{1} = 1$$

Hence

(20.36)
$$\lim_{n \to \infty} u = \lim_{x \to 0} u = e^1 = e$$

The above examples are typical of indeterminate forms that may be brought under cases a and b by the use of logarithmic transformations.

PROBLEMS

Test the following series for convergence or divergence:

1. $\dfrac{1}{1} + \dfrac{1}{\sqrt{2^3}} + \dfrac{1}{\sqrt{3^3}} + \cdots + \dfrac{1}{\sqrt{n^3}} + \cdots$ convergent.

2. $\dfrac{1}{1} + \dfrac{1}{\sqrt[3]{2}} + \dfrac{1}{\sqrt[3]{3}} + \cdots + \dfrac{1}{\sqrt[3]{n}} + \cdots$ divergent.

3. $\dfrac{1}{3} + \dfrac{1}{\sqrt{3}} + \dfrac{1}{\sqrt[3]{3}} + \cdots + \dfrac{1}{\sqrt[n]{3}} + \cdots$ divergent.

4. $\dfrac{1}{2 \ln 2} + \dfrac{1}{3 \ln 3} + \dfrac{1}{4 \ln 4} + \cdots + \dfrac{1}{(n + 1) \ln (n + 1)} + \cdots$ divergent.

5. $\dfrac{1}{2} + \dfrac{1}{5} + \dfrac{1}{10} + \cdots + \dfrac{1}{1 + n^2} + \cdots$ convergent.

For what values of the variable x are the following series convergent?

6. $1 + x + x^2 + x^3 + \cdots$.   *Ans.* $-1 < x < 1$.

7. $x - \dfrac{x^2}{2} + \dfrac{x^3}{3} - \dfrac{x^4}{4} + \cdots$.   *Ans.* $-1 < x \leq 1$.

8. $x + \dfrac{x^2}{\sqrt{2}} + \dfrac{x^3}{\sqrt{3}} + \cdots$.   *Ans.* $-1 \leq x < 1$.

9. $1 + x + \dfrac{x^2}{2!} + \dfrac{x^3}{3!} + \cdots$.   *Ans.* All values of x.

10. $1 - x + \dfrac{x^2}{2^2} - \dfrac{x^3}{3^2} + \cdots$.   *Ans.* $-1 \leq x \leq 1$.

11. $\dfrac{ax}{2} + \dfrac{a^2x^3}{5} + \dfrac{a^3x^3}{10} + \cdots + \dfrac{a^n x^n}{n^2 + 1} + \cdots \ a > 0$.   *Ans.* $-\dfrac{1}{a} \leq x \leq \dfrac{1}{a}$.

Using the binomial series, find approximately the values of the following numbers:

12. $\sqrt{98}$.   **13.** $\sqrt[5]{35}$.   **14.** $\dfrac{1}{\sqrt[5]{30}}$.   **15.** $\sqrt[4]{630}$.

Verify the following expansions of functions by Maclaurin's series, and determine for what values of the variable they are convergent:

16. $e^x = 1 + x + \dfrac{x^2}{2!} + \cdots + \dfrac{x^{n-1}}{(n-1)!} + \cdots$ all values.

17. $\ln(1 + x) = x - \dfrac{x^2}{2} + \dfrac{x^3}{3} - \dfrac{x^4}{4} + \cdots$ $-1 < x \leq 1$.

18. $\sin^{-1} x = x + \dfrac{1 \times x^3}{2 \times 3} + \dfrac{1 \times 3 \times x^5}{2 \times 4 \times 5} + \cdots$.

Verify the following expansions:

19. $\tan x = x + \dfrac{x^3}{3} + \dfrac{2x^5}{15} + \dfrac{17x^7}{315} + \cdots$.

20. $\cosh x \dfrac{1}{2}(e^x + e^{-x}) = 1 + \dfrac{x^2}{2!} + \dfrac{x^4}{4!} + \dfrac{x^6}{6!} + \cdots$.

21. $\ln \cos x = -\dfrac{x^2}{2} - \dfrac{x^4}{12} - \dfrac{x^6}{45} \cdots$.

Compute the values of the following functions by substituting directly in their power-series expansion:

22. $e = 2.7183$.   **23.** $\tan^{-1} \frac{1}{5} = 0.1973$.

24. $\cos 10° = 0.9848$.   **25.** $\sqrt{e} = 1.6487$.

Obtain the following expansions:

26. $e^{-x} \cos x = 1 - x + \frac{1}{3}x^3 - \frac{1}{6}x^4 + \cdots$.

27. $\dfrac{\cos x}{\sqrt{1+x}} = 1 - \frac{1}{2} - \frac{1}{8}x^2 - \dfrac{x^3}{16} + \dfrac{49x^4}{384} + \cdots$.

28. $\dfrac{\ln(1+x)}{1 + \sin x} = x - \frac{3}{2}x^2 + \frac{11}{6}x^3 - \frac{23}{12}x^4 + \cdots$.

Using series, find approximately the values of the following integrals:

29. $\int_0^{\frac{1}{2}} \dfrac{\cos x \, dx}{1 + x} \doteq 0.3914.$

30. $\int_0^{\frac{1}{3}} e^x \ln (1 + x) \, dx \doteq 0.0628.$

31. $\int_0^{\frac{1}{2}} \dfrac{e^{-x^2} \, dx}{\sqrt{1 - x^2}} \doteq 0.4815.$

32. $\int_0^1 e^{-x^2} \, dx.$

33. $\int_0^1 e^{-x} \cos \sqrt{x} \, dx.$

34. How many terms of the Maclaurin's series for $\sin x$ must be taken to give $\sin 45°$ correct to five decimal places?

35. How many terms of the series $\ln (1 + x)$ must be taken to give $\ln 1.2$ correct to five decimals?

36. Verify the approximate formula $\ln (10 + x) \doteq 2.303 + x/10.$

Evaluate each of the following indeterminate forms:

37. $\displaystyle\lim_{x \to \infty} \dfrac{\ln x}{x^n}.$ *Ans.* 0.

38. $\displaystyle\lim_{\theta \to \pi/2} \dfrac{\tan 3\theta}{\tan \theta}.$ *Ans.* $\frac{1}{3}$.

39. $\displaystyle\lim_{x \to 0} \left(\dfrac{1}{\sin^2 x} - \dfrac{1}{x^2} \right).$ *Ans.* $\frac{1}{3}$.

40. $\displaystyle\lim_{x \to \infty} \dfrac{x + \ln x}{x \ln x}.$

41. $\displaystyle\lim_{x \to 1} \left(\dfrac{2}{x^2 - 1} - \dfrac{1}{x - 1} \right).$ *Ans.* $-\frac{1}{2}$.

42. $\displaystyle\lim_{x \to 2} \dfrac{x^2 - 4}{x^2} \tan \dfrac{\pi x}{4}.$ **43.** $\displaystyle\lim_{x \to 0} \left(\dfrac{1}{\sin^3 x} - \dfrac{1}{x^3} \right).$

Test the following series for uniform convergence:

44. $\dfrac{\cos x}{1^2} + \dfrac{\cos 3x}{3^2} + \dfrac{\cos 5x}{5^2} + \cdots + \dfrac{\cos (2n - 1)x}{(2n - 1)^2} + \cdots.$

45. $\dfrac{\sin x}{1} + \dfrac{\sin 3x}{3} + \dfrac{\sin 5x}{5} + \cdots + \dfrac{\sin (2n - 1)x}{2n - 1} + \cdots.$

REFERENCES

1. Goursat, E.: "A Course in Mathematical Analysis," Ginn & Company, Boston, 1904.
2. Wilson, E. B.: "Advanced Calculus," Ginn & Company, Boston, 1911.
3. Bromwich, T. J.: "Theory of Infinite Series," The Macmillan Company, New York, 1908.
4. Whittaker, E. T., and G. N. Watson: "A Course in Modern Analysis," Cambridge University Press, New York, 1927.

CHAPTER 2

COMPLEX NUMBERS

1. Introduction. In this chapter some of the fundamental definitions and operations involving complex numbers will be discussed. The study of the complex variable will be taken up in Chap. 19 in detail. Complex numbers are of great importance in applied mathematics. The calculation of the distribution of alternating currents in electrical circuits, the study of the forced vibrations of a dynamical system, the study of the variation of temperature in solids, and a host of other problems of applied mathematics are most easily solved by the use of complex numbers. Accordingly the basic definitions and operations involving complex quantities must be clearly understood.

2. Complex Numbers. A complex number is a quantity of the form

$$(2.1) \qquad z = x + jy$$

Here x and y are real numbers and j is a unit defined by the equations

$$(2.2) \qquad j = \sqrt{-1} \qquad j^2 = -1$$

The number x is called the *real* part of the complex number, and the number y is the *imaginary* part. It is seen that, when $y = 0$, the complex number becomes a real number, so that the real numbers form a subclass of the complex numbers. If $x = 0$, the complex number becomes a pure imaginary number.

3. Rules for the Manipulation of Complex Numbers. Having defined complex numbers, it is necessary to state rules for their manipulation. These two fundamental rules are:

1. A complex number $z = x + jy$ is zero when, and only when, $x = 0$ and $y = 0$.

2. Complex numbers obey the ordinary laws of algebra, with the addition that $j^2 = -1$.

From these two rules follow the formulas for addition, subtraction, and multiplication. That is, we have

$$(3.1) \qquad z_1 \pm z_2 = (x_1 + jy_1) \pm (x_2 + jy_2) = (x_1 \pm x_2) \pm j(y_1 \pm y_2)$$
$$(3.2) \qquad z_1 z_2 = (x_1 + jy_1)(x_2 + jy_2) = (x_1 x_2 - y_1 y_2) + j(x_1 y_2 + x_2 y_1)$$

The quotient of two numbers, such as

$$(3.3) \qquad \frac{z_1}{z_2} = \frac{x_1 + jy_1}{x_2 + jy_2}$$

provided that $x_2 + jy_2 \neq 0$, may be most conveniently found by multiplying the dividend and divisor by $x_2 - jy_2$. We thus have

$$(3.4) \qquad \frac{z_1}{z_2} = \frac{(x_1 + jy_1)(x_2 - jy_2)}{(x_2 + jy_2)(x_2 - jy_2)} = \frac{x_1 x_2 + y_1 y_2}{x_2^2 + y_2^2} + j \frac{x_2 y_1 - x_1 y_2}{x_2^2 + y_2^2}$$

It thus appears that the sum, difference, and quotient of two complex numbers are themselves complex numbers. If two complex numbers are equal, we have

$$(3.5) \qquad x_1 + jy_1 = x_2 + jy_2$$

Then, from (3.1), we have

$$(3.6) \qquad (x_1 - x_2) + j(y_1 - y_2) = 0$$

Now by fundamental rule 1

$$(3.7) \qquad \begin{matrix} x_1 - x_2 = 0 & \quad x_1 = x_2 \\ y_1 - y_2 = 0 & \quad y_1 = y_2 \end{matrix}$$

We therefore see that two complex numbers are equal when, and only when, the real part of one is equal to the real part of the other and the imaginary part of one is equal to the imaginary part of the other.

Two complex numbers that differ only in the sign of their imaginary parts are called conjugate imaginary. That is,

$$(3.8) \qquad z_1 = x + jy$$

and

$$(3.9) \qquad z_2 = x - jy$$

are conjugate imaginary. This relation is expressed symbolically by the notation

$$(3.10) \qquad z_1 = \bar{z}_2 \quad \text{or} \quad z_2 = \bar{z}_1$$

4. Graphical Representation and Trigonometric Form.

Although complex numbers are essentially algebraic quantities, they may be given a convenient geometric interpretation. Let us consider the point P of the xy plane given by Fig. 4.1.

FIG. 4.1

To the point P corresponds a definite pair of values of x and y, the coordinates of the point. Therefore to P there may be made to correspond the complex number z where

$$(4.1) \qquad z = x + jy$$

In this diagram, the x axis is called the *axis of reals* since real numbers are represented by points on it.   The y axis is called the *axis of imaginaries*.   If we introduce polar coordinates, we have

(4.2) $$x = r \cos \theta \qquad y = r \sin \theta$$

Then, from (4.1), we have

(4.3) $$z = r(\cos \theta + j \sin \theta)$$

This is called the *polar* form of the complex number.   The number r, which is always taken positive, is called the *modulus*, or the absolute value, of the complex number z, and is equal to the length of the line OP. Then

(4.4) $$|z| = r = \sqrt{x^2 + y^2}$$

The angle θ is called the *angle*, or argument, of z.   Then

(4.5) $$\cos \theta = \frac{x}{\sqrt{x^2 + y^2}} \qquad \sin \theta = \frac{y}{\sqrt{x^2 + y^2}}$$

In Chap. 1 it was demonstrated that $\cos \theta$, $\sin \theta$, and e^u have the following Maclaurin expansions:

(4.6) $$\cos \theta = 1 - \frac{\theta^2}{2!} + \frac{\theta^4}{4!} - \frac{\theta^6}{6!} + \cdots$$

$$\sin \theta = \theta - \frac{\theta^3}{3!} + \frac{\theta^5}{5!} - \frac{\theta^7}{7!} + \cdots$$

$$e^u = 1 + \frac{u}{1!} + \frac{u^2}{2!} + \frac{u^3}{3!} + \cdots$$

Hence we have

$$\cos \theta + j \sin \theta = \left(1 - \frac{\theta^2}{2!} + \frac{\theta^4}{4!} + \cdots\right) + j\left(\theta - \frac{\theta^3}{3!} + \frac{\theta^5}{5!} + \cdots\right)$$

$$= 1 + j\theta - \frac{\theta^2}{2!} - \frac{j\theta^3}{3!} + \frac{\theta^4}{4!} + \frac{j\theta^5}{5!} + \cdots$$

$$= 1 + j\theta + \frac{(j\theta)^2}{2!} + \frac{(j\theta)^3}{3!} + \frac{(j\theta)^4}{4!} + \cdots$$

so that

(4.7) $$\cos \theta + j \sin \theta = e^{j\theta}$$

where we have made use of the fact that $j^2 = -1$, $j^3 = -j$, $j^4 = 1$, etc. In the same manner we obtain

(4.8) $$e^{-j\theta} = \cos \theta - j \sin \theta$$

From (4.7) and (4.8) it follows immediately that

(4.9) $$\cos \theta = \frac{e^{j\theta} + e^{-j\theta}}{2} \qquad \sin \theta = \frac{e^{j\theta} - e^{-j\theta}}{2j}$$

These formulas show a remarkable relation between the exponential and trigonometric functions. By the law of multiplication of series it is easy to show that even for complex exponents

$$(4.10) \qquad e^{x_1} e^{x_2} = e^{x_1 + x_2}$$

Hence we have

$$(4.11) \qquad e^{x+jy} = e^x e^{jy} = e^x(\cos y + j \sin y)$$

From (4.10), we also have for integral values of n

$$(4.12) \qquad (e^{j\theta})^n = e^{jn\theta}$$

Hence by (4.7), we obtain

$$(4.13) \qquad (\cos \theta + j \sin \theta)^n = \cos n\theta + j \sin n\theta$$

Equations (4.3) and (4.7) make it possible to write a complex number in the convenient form

$$(4.14) \qquad z = x + jy = r(\cos \theta + j \sin \theta) = re^{j\theta}$$

This form of writing complex numbers is very convenient when complex numbers are to be multiplied or divided. For example,

$$(4.15) \qquad \begin{aligned} z_1 z_2 &= (r_1 e^{j\theta_1})(r_2 e^{j\theta_2}) \\ &= r_1 r_2 e^{j(\theta_1 + \theta_2)} \end{aligned}$$

That is, to multiply two complex numbers, we multiply their moduli to get the modulus of the product and add their angles to get the angle of the product. Division is performed as follows:

$$(4.16) \qquad \frac{z_1}{z_2} = \frac{r_1 e^{j\theta_1}}{r_2 e^{j\theta_2}} = \frac{r_1}{r_2} e^{j(\theta_1 - \theta_1)}$$

In this case the moduli are divided and the angles subtracted.

Let us take two complex numbers z_1 and z_2 represented by the points P_1 and P_2, respectively, as shown in Fig. 4.2.

FIG. 4.2

It is easy to see from the principle of addition of two complex numbers that their sum $z_1 + z_2$ is represented by the point P_3 found by constructing a parallelogram on the sides OP_1 and OP_2.

From the figure it follows that

$$(4.17) \qquad |z_1 + z_2| \leq |z_1| + |z_2|$$

The equality sign holds when OP_1 and OP_2 are in the same straight line and have equal angles.

5. Powers and Roots. The value of z^n, where n is a positive integer, may be found by successive multiplication of z by itself. Since

$$(5.1) \qquad\qquad z = x + jy$$

we can find $(x + jy)^n$ by applying the binomial theorem. That is, we have

$$(5.2) \qquad \begin{aligned} z^2 &= (x + jy)^2 = x^2 - y^2 + 2jxy \\ z^3 &= (x + jy)^3 = x^3 - 3xy^2 + j(3x^2y - y^3) \end{aligned}$$

A simpler method of raising a complex number to a power is to use the polar form of z. We then have

$$(5.3) \qquad\qquad z^n = (re^{j\theta})^n = r^n e^{jn\theta}$$

If $r = 1$, we have De Moivre's theorem,

$$(5.4) \qquad (e^{j\theta})^n = (\cos\theta + j\sin\theta)^n = \cos n\theta + j\sin n\theta$$

It must be noted that any integral multiple of 2π may be added to the angle θ without altering z since

$$(5.5) \qquad \begin{aligned} z &= r(\cos\theta + j\sin\theta) \\ &= r[\cos(\theta + 2k\pi) + j\sin(\theta + 2k\pi)] \\ &= re^{j(\theta + 2k\pi)} \end{aligned}$$

where k is any integer. This is the general form of the complex number z.

The root $z^{1/n}$, where n is a positive integer, is a number which raised to the nth power gives z. From the general form of z given by (5.5), we have

$$(5.6) \qquad z^{1/n} = r^{1/n} e^{j\frac{\theta + 2k\pi}{n}} = r^{1/n}\left(\cos\frac{\theta + 2k\pi}{n} + j\sin\frac{\theta + 2k\pi}{n}\right)$$

We obtain n *distinct* values of $z^{1/n}$ by giving k the values $0, 1, 2, \ldots,$ $n - 1$ successively. Here $r^{1/n}$ is to be taken as the positive root of the real positive number r. This enables us to solve the equation

$$(5.7) \qquad\qquad \omega^n = 1$$

Here we have

$$(5.8) \qquad\qquad \omega = 1^{1/n}$$

If we write 1 in the general polar form, we have

$$(5.9) \qquad\qquad 1 = e^{j(0 + 2k\pi)}$$

Hence

$$(5.10) \qquad 1^{1/n} = e^{j(2k\pi/n)} = \cos\frac{2k\pi}{n} + j\sin\frac{2k\pi}{n}$$

where $k = 0, 1, 2, \ldots, n - 1$.

It is thus seen that the n roots of unity are spaced around a unit circle in the complex plane in a symmetric fashion.

6. Exponential and Trigonometric Functions. We define the trigonometric and exponential function for complex values of the argument z by the Maclaurin-series expansions

$$(6.1) \qquad e^z = 1 + \frac{z}{1!} + \frac{z^2}{2!} + \frac{z^3}{3!} + \cdots + \frac{z^n}{n!} + \cdots$$

$$(6.2) \quad \sin z = z - \frac{z^3}{3!} + \frac{z^5}{5!} - \cdots + (-1)^{n-1} \frac{z^{2n-1}}{(2n-1)!} + \cdots$$

$$(6.3) \quad \cos z = 1 - \frac{z^2}{2!} + \frac{z^4}{4!} - \cdots + (-1)^{n-1} \frac{z^{2n-2}}{(2n-2)!} + \cdots$$

When z is real, these become the elementary functions. From (6.1) we have

$$(6.4) \qquad\qquad e^0 = 1$$
$$(6.5) \qquad\qquad e^{z_1} e^{z_2} = e^{z_1+z_2}$$

These are the fundamental properties of the exponential function. From (6.1) to (6.3) we also get

$$(6.6) \qquad\qquad e^{jz} = \cos z + j \sin z$$
$$(6.7) \qquad\qquad e^{-jz} = \cos z - j \sin z$$

From (6.6) and (6.7) we have

$$(6.8) \qquad \sin z = \frac{e^{jz} - e^{-jz}}{2j} \qquad \cos z = \frac{e^{jz} + e^{-jz}}{2}$$

With the aid of (6.5) we have

$$(6.9) \qquad \begin{aligned} \sin (z_1 + z_2) &= \sin z_1 \cos z_2 + \cos z_1 \sin z_2 \\ \cos (z_1 + z_2) &= \cos z_1 \cos z_2 - \sin z_1 \sin z_2 \end{aligned}$$

If we place $z_1 = x$, $z_2 = jy$ in the equations, we obtain

$$(6.10) \qquad \begin{aligned} \sin (x + jy) &= \sin x \cos jy + \cos x \sin jy \\ &= \sin x \frac{e^y + e^{-y}}{2} + \cos x j \frac{e^y - e^{-y}}{2} \\ &= \sin x \cosh y + j \cos x \sinh y \end{aligned}$$

In the same way

$$(6.11) \qquad \begin{aligned} \cos (x + jy) &= \cos x \frac{e^y + e^{-y}}{2} - \sin x j \frac{e^y - e^{-y}}{2} \\ &= \cos x \cosh y - j \sin x \sinh y \end{aligned}$$

We know from elementary trigonometry that

$$(6.12) \qquad \begin{aligned} \sin (x + 2k\pi) &= \sin x \\ \cos (x + 2k\pi) &= \cos x \end{aligned}$$

where x is a real number and k is an integer. Hence

(6.13) $e^{z+2k\pi j} = e^z e^{2k\pi j} = e^z(\cos 2k\pi + j \sin 2k\pi) = e^z$

From (6.10) and (6.11) we have

(6.14) $\sin (z + 2k\pi) = \sin z$ $\cos (z + 2k\pi) = \cos z$

It is thus evident that the exponential function is a periodic function with the imaginary period $2\pi j$. The sine and cosine are periodic functions with the real period 2π.

7. The Hyperbolic Functions. The hyperbolic sine and the hyperbolic cosine are defined for complex values of their argument by the equation

(7.1) $\sinh z = \dfrac{e^z - e^{-z}}{2}$ $\cosh z = \dfrac{e^z + e^{-z}}{\cdot 2}$

From these definitions, we have

(7.2) $\sinh jz = \dfrac{e^{jz} - e^{-jz}}{2} = j \sin z$

(7.3) $\cosh jz = \dfrac{e^{jz} + e^{-jz}}{2} = \cos z$

Also

(7.4) $\sinh z = \dfrac{e^{-j(jz)} - e^{j(jz)}}{2} = -j \sin jz$

(7.5) $\cosh z = \dfrac{e^{-j(jz)} + e^{j(jz)}}{2} = \cos jz$

It is thus apparent that hyperbolic functions are essentially trigonometric functions of complex variables. Relations between trigonometric functions therefore give rise to relations between hyperbolic functions with certain differences arising from the presence of the factor j.

For example, since we have from (6.2) and (6.3)

(7.6) $\sin^2 jz + \cos^2 jz = 1$

we have from (7.4) and (7.5)

(7.7) $\cosh^2 z - \sinh^2 z = 1$

From the above definitions it is easy to show that

(7.8) $\begin{aligned}\sinh (z_1 + z_2) &= \sinh z_1 \cosh z_2 + \cosh z_1 \sinh z_2 \\ \cosh (z_1 + z_2) &= \cosh z_1 \cosh z_2 + \sinh z_1 \sinh z_2\end{aligned}$

As a special case of these equations we have

(7.9) $\begin{aligned}\sinh (x + jy) &= \sinh x \cos y + j \cosh x \sin y \\ \cosh (x + jy) &= \cosh x \cos y + j \sinh x \sin y\end{aligned}$

These equations enable one to separate the hyperbolic functions into their real and imaginary parts.

It may be seen from (7.8) that

(7.10)
$$\sinh (z + 2k\pi j) = \sinh z$$
$$\cosh (z + 2k\pi j) = \cosh z$$

That is, the hyperbolic sine and the hyperbolic cosine are periodic functions with the imaginary period $2\pi j$.

8. The Logarithmic Function. By definition, if

(8.1)
$$z = e^\omega$$

then

(8.2)
$$\omega = \ln z$$

From this definition we deduce the following fundamental properties of the logarithmic function:

(8.3)
$$\ln (z_1 \times z_2) = \ln z_1 + \ln z_2$$

(8.4)
$$\ln \frac{z_1}{z_2} = \ln z_1 - \ln z_2$$

(8.5)
$$\ln z^n = n \ln z$$

(8.6)
$$\ln 1 = 0$$

The logarithm of a complex number may be separated into its real and imaginary parts in the following manner:

(8.7)
$$z = x + jy = r(\cos \theta + j \sin \theta) = re^{j\theta}$$

Then

(8.8)
$$\ln z = \ln re^{j\theta} = \ln r + \ln e^{j\theta} = \ln r + j\theta$$
$$= \tfrac{1}{2} \ln (x^2 + y^2) + j \tan^{-1} \frac{y}{x}$$

In Eq. (8.8) $\ln r$ is the real logarithm of the positive number r, which is found in the usual tables.   The logarithm of a real negative number may now be found.   For example, we may find the logarithm of -5 as follows:

(8.9)
$$-5 = 5e^{j\pi}$$

Hence

(8.10)
$$\ln (-5) = \ln 5 + j\pi = 1.6094 + j\pi$$

In particular

(8.11)
$$\ln (-1) = j\pi$$

It must be noted that the logarithm of a number has an infinite number of values differing by multiples of $2\pi j$. This may easily be seen since

$$(8.12) \qquad z = re^{j(\theta + 2k\pi)} \qquad k = 0, \pm 1, \pm 2, \ldots$$

Hence

$$(8.13) \quad \ln z = \ln r + j(\theta + 2k\pi) \qquad k = 0, \pm 1, \pm 2, \pm 3, \ldots$$

9. The Inverse Hyperbolic and Trigonometric Functions.   The inverse hyperbolic and trigonometric functions are closely connected with the logarithmic function.

By definition, if

$$(9.1) \qquad z = \sinh \omega = \frac{e^\omega - e^{-\omega}}{2}$$

$$(9.2) \qquad \omega = \sinh^{-1} z$$

From (9.1) we have

$$(9.3) \qquad 2z = e^\omega - e^{-\omega}$$

or

$$(9.4) \qquad e^{2\omega} - 2ze^\omega - 1 = 0$$

If we let

$$(9.5) \qquad y = e^\omega$$

Eq. (9.4) becomes

$$(9.6) \qquad y^2 - 2zy - 1 = 0$$

and therefore

$$(9.7) \qquad y = z \pm \sqrt{z^2 + 1} = e^\omega$$

Hence

$$(9.8) \qquad \omega = \sinh^{-1} z = \ln (z \pm \sqrt{z^2 + 1})$$

By definition we have, if

$$(9.9) \qquad z = \cosh \omega = \frac{e^\omega + e^{-\omega}}{2}$$

then

$$(9.10) \qquad \omega = \cosh^{-1} z = \ln (z \pm \sqrt{z^2 - 1})$$

The hyperbolic tangent is defined by

$$(9.11) \qquad z = \tanh \omega = \frac{\sinh \omega}{\cosh \omega} = \frac{e^\omega - e^{-\omega}}{e^\omega + e^{-\omega}}$$

and by definition

(9.12) $$\omega = \tanh^{-1} z = \tfrac{1}{2} \ln \frac{1+z}{1-z}$$

The foregoing equations are true for any complex quantity z.

The inverse trigonometric functions $\sin^{-1} z$, $\cos^{-1} z$, and $\tan^{-1} z$ may also be expressed in terms of logarithms. This may be done in the same manner as that used above for the hyperbolic functions. We have, if

(9.13) $$z = \sin \omega = \frac{e^{j\omega} - e^{-j\omega}}{2j}$$

then

(9.14) $$\omega = \sin^{-1} z = \frac{1}{j} \ln (jz \pm \sqrt{1 - z^2})$$

If

(9.15) $$z = \cos \omega = \frac{e^{j\omega} + e^{-j\omega}}{2}$$

then

(9.16) $$\omega = \cos^{-1} z = \frac{1}{j} \ln (z \pm \sqrt{z^2 - 1})$$

If

(9.17) $$z = \tan \omega = \frac{\sin \omega}{\cos \omega} = \frac{e^{j\omega} - e^{-j\omega}}{j(e^{j\omega} + e^{-j\omega})}$$

then

(9.18) $$\omega = \tan^{-1} z = \frac{1}{2j} \ln \frac{1+jz}{1-jz}$$

These equations are true for any complex quantity z. The detailed study of functions of a complex variable in general will be postponed until Chap. 19.

PROBLEMS

1. Show that the sum of two conjugate imaginary quantities is real and that their difference is a pure imaginary. Prove that their product is real. When will their quotient be real?

2. Determine all the roots of the equation $z^5 = 2 + 4j$, and plot them.

3. Find the cube roots of -1, and plot them.

4. Write the polynomial $x^4 + a^4$ as the product of its linear factors and as the product of its quadratic factors.

5. Show that $e^{\pi i} = -1$ and $e^{\pi i/2} = j$.

6. Compute e^{1+i} in the form $a + jb$, and determine a and b to four places of decimals.

7. Show that $|e^z| = e^x$ and that $|e^{j\theta}| = 1$, where $z = x + jy$ and θ is real.

8. Find all the possible values of j^i.

9. Determine all the values of π^π.

10. Find all the values of $\ln (2 - j3)$.

11. Express e^z in terms of $\tan z$.

12. Find the sum of the geometric progression

$$\sum_{r=1}^{r=n} e^{jrz}$$

From this sum and the result obtained when z is replaced by $-z$, deduce that

$$\sum_{r=1}^{r=n} \sin rz = \frac{\cos (z/2) - \cos (n + \tfrac{1}{2})z}{2 \sin (z/2)}$$

and

$$\sum_{r=1}^{r=n} \cos rz = \frac{\sin (n + \tfrac{1}{2})z - \sin (z/2)}{2 \sin (z/2)}$$

REFERENCES

1. Osgood, W. F.: "Advanced Calculus," chap. 20, The Macmillan Company, New York, 1933.
2. MacRobert, T. M.: "Functions of a Complex Variable," The Macmillan Company, New York, 1933.
3. Rothe, R., F. Ollendorf, and K. Pohlhausen: "Theory of Functions as Applied to Engineering Problems," Massachusetts Institute of Technology Press, Cambridge, Mass., 1933.
4. Whittaker, E. T., and G. N. Watson: "A Course in Modern Analysis," Cambridge University Press, New York, 1927.

CHAPTER 3

MATHEMATICAL REPRESENTATION OF PERIODIC PHENOMENA, FOURIER SERIES, AND THE FOURIER INTEGRAL

1. Introduction. In this chapter the mathematical representation of periodic phenomena will be considered. The use of complex numbers for this purpose will be developed. This leads naturally to a consideration of the complex form of the Fourier representation of periodic functions. This form of Fourier series is extensively used by physicists but is not generally used by engineers. From the standpoint of utility the complex form of Fourier series has marked advantages over the more cumbersome form involving sines and cosines. It is widely used in the modern literature in studying the response of electrical circuits and mechanical vibrating systems to the action of periodic potentials and forces. A brief discussion of the Fourier integral is given. The treatment of the Fourier series and the Fourier integral is heuristic; an account of the rigorous investigations of Dirichlet on the subject belongs in a book on analysis.

2. Simple Harmonic Vibrations. The simplest periodic process that occurs in nature is described mathematically by the sine or the cosine function. Such processes as the oscillations of a pendulum through small amplitudes, the vibrations of a tuning fork, and other similar physical phenomena are of this type. If the process repeats itself f times a second, the function representing the simple oscillation may be either

$$(2.1) \qquad u = A \sin 2\pi f t \qquad \text{or} \qquad u = A \cos 2\pi f t$$

where t is time measured in seconds from a suitable starting point, A is called the amplitude, and f the frequency of the vibration. Besides the frequency f, it is customary to speak of the angular frequency of the vibration ω defined by

$$(2.2) \qquad \omega = 2\pi f$$

A phenomenon described by a simple sine or cosine function is called a *simple harmonic vibration*.

We may simplify the computations involving these functions considerably by using imaginary exponentials instead of trigonometric functions. We have from the Euler formula [Chap. 2, Eq. (4.7)]

$$(2.3) \qquad e^{j\omega t} = \cos \omega t + j \sin \omega t \qquad j = \sqrt{-1}$$

If we let

$$(2.4) \qquad Z = A e^{j\omega t}$$

then Z represents a complex number whose representative point in the complex plane describes a circle of radius A with angular velocity ω. The projections on the real and imaginary axes are, respectively,

$$(2.5) \qquad \begin{aligned} x &= \operatorname{Re} Z = A \cos \omega t \\ y &= \operatorname{Im} Z = A \sin \omega t \end{aligned}$$

where Re means "the real part of" and Im means "the imaginary part of." Since physical calculations deal with real quantities, the final results of a computation using complex numbers must be translated into real magnitudes. This may be done simply, since an equation involving complex numbers means that the real as well as the imaginary parts satisfy the equation.

It sometimes happens that the square of the amplitude of the oscillation is of importance. This may be readily obtained from its complex representation by multiplying it by its conjugate. That is, since

$$(2.6) \qquad \bar{Z} = A e^{-j\omega t}$$

then

$$(2.7) \qquad Z\bar{Z} = A e^{j\omega t} A e^{-j\omega t} = A^2$$

Consider two vibrations of the same frequency but of different phase δ of the form

$$(2.8) \qquad \begin{aligned} u_1 &= A_1 \cos \omega t = \operatorname{Re} A_1 e^{j\omega t} \\ u_2 &= A_2 \cos (\omega t + \delta) = \operatorname{Re} A_2 e^{j(\omega t + \delta)} \end{aligned}$$

Hence

$$(2.9) \qquad u_1 + u_2 = \operatorname{Re} (A_1 e^{j\omega t} + A_2 e^{j(\omega t + \delta)})$$

We also have

$$(2.10) \qquad A_1 e^{j\omega t} + A_2 e^{j(\omega t + \delta)} = e^{j\omega t}(A_1 + A_2 e^{j\delta})$$

and

$$(2.11) \qquad \begin{aligned} A_1 + A_2 e^{j\delta} &= A_1 + A_2 \cos \delta + j A_2 \sin \delta \\ &= M e^{j\phi} \end{aligned}$$

where

(2.12) $$M = \sqrt{(A_1 + A_2 \cos \delta)^2 + A_2^2 \sin^2 \delta}$$

and

(2.13) $$\phi = \tan^{-1} \frac{A_2 \sin \delta}{A_1 + A_2 \cos \delta}$$

Hence we have from (2.9)

(2.14) $$u_1 + u_2 = \operatorname{Re} M e^{j(\omega t + \phi)}$$
$$= M \cos (\omega t + \phi)$$

The amplitude M of the resulting vibration is given as a third side of the triangle having the amplitudes A_1 and A_2 as adjacent sides and δ as

FIG. 2.1

exterior angle, as shown in Fig. 2.1. The difference in phase ϕ between the resultant vibration and u_1 is the angle between the sides M and A_1 of this triangle. It is noted that the construction in Fig. 2.1 corresponds exactly with the addition of two complex numbers in the complex plane. From this consideration we obtain the following rule:

To obtain the resultant of two vibrations having equal frequencies but differing in phase, add the corresponding complex numbers. The amplitude and phase of the resultant are given by the length and direction, respectively, of the complex number representing this sum.

This method is most frequently used in electrical engineering and is sometimes referred to as the "vector diagram" because of the manner in which the quantities are combined. This diagram may be drawn for any instant of time, but since the phase difference is constant, the entire triangle rotates as a rigid figure with the angular speed ω as time advances. It is therefore possible to choose any position such as the real axis, for example, for the line of the first vibration.

If more than two vibrations of the same frequency but of different phases are to be compounded, we obtain the magnitude and phase resultant by plotting the individual complex numbers representing the several vibrations and adding them.

3. Representation of More Complicated Periodic Phenomena, Fourier Series. Let us consider an arbitrary process that is repeated every T sec. Let this process be represented by

(3.1) $$u = F(t)$$

Since, by hypothesis, the process repeats itself every T sec, we have

(3.2) $$F(t + T) = F(t)$$

Let us make the proviso that $F(t)$ is single-valued and finite and has a finite number of discontinuities and a finite number of maxima and minima in the interval of one oscillation, T. Under these conditions, which in the mathematical literature are known as Dirichlet conditions, the function $F(t)$ may be represented over a complete period and hence from $t = -\infty$ to $t = +\infty$, except at the discontinuities, by a series of simple harmonic functions, the frequencies of which are integral multiples of the fundamental frequency. Such series are called *Fourier series* after their discoverer. For a proof of the possibility of developing $F(t)$ in a Fourier series under these very general conditions, the reader may consult the literature cited in the references at the end of this chapter. Dirichlet's treatment of the subject is long and difficult and has no place in a book on applied mathematics. In his treatment the sum of n terms of the series is taken, and it is shown that when n becomes infinitely great the sum approaches $F(t)$ provided the above conditions are satisfied. At a discontinuity in $F(t)$ the value of the series is the mean of the values of $F(t)$ on both sides of the discontinuity.

The method of determining the coefficients will now be given. It is most convenient to start from the complex representation and write

$$(3.3) \quad F(t) = a_0 + a_1 e^{j\omega t} + a_2 e^{2j\omega t} + \cdots + a_n e^{jn\omega t} + \cdots$$
$$+ a_{-1} e^{-j\omega t} + a_{-2} e^{-2j\omega t} + \cdots + a_{-n} e^{-jn\omega t} + \cdots$$
$$= \sum_{n=-\infty}^{n=+\infty} a_n e^{jn\omega t}$$

where

$$(3.4) \qquad \omega = \frac{2\pi}{T}$$

Since the left member of (3.3) is real, the coefficients of the series on the right must be such that no imaginary terms occur. To determine a_0, we integrate both sides over one complete period, that is, from 0 to $T = 2\pi/\omega$. We thus obtain

$$(3.5) \qquad \int_0^{2\pi/\omega} F(t)\, dt = \int_0^{2\pi/\omega} \left(\sum_{n=-\infty}^{n=+\infty} a_n e^{jn\omega t} \right) dt$$
$$= \sum_{n=-\infty}^{n=+\infty} a_n \int_0^{2\pi/\omega} e^{jn\omega t}\, dt$$

where we have assumed term-by-term integration permissible.

The integral of the general term is

$$(3.6) \qquad \int_0^{2\pi/\omega} e^{jn\omega t}\, dt = \frac{1}{jn\omega} e^{jn\omega t} \Big|_0^{2\pi/\omega} = \frac{1}{jn\omega} (e^{j2n\pi} - 1) = 0$$

if $n \neq 0$.

If $n = 0$, we have

(3.7)
$$\int_0^{2\pi/\omega} dt = \frac{2\pi}{\omega} = T$$

Hence (3.5) reduces to

(3.8)
$$\int_0^T F(t)\, dt = a_0 T$$

or

(3.9)
$$a_0 = \frac{1}{T} \int_0^T F(t)\, dt = \overline{F(t)}$$

where $\overline{F(t)}$ denotes the mean value of $F(t)$.

To determine the other coefficients, we multiply both sides of (3.3) by $e^{-in\omega t}$ and integrate as before from $t = 0$ to $t = T = 2\pi/\omega$. Again all terms on the right are equal to zero because of the periodicity of the imaginary exponentials, except the a_n term, which contains no exponential factor. This gives the value T on integration. We then have

(3.10)
$$\int_0^T F(t)e^{-in\omega t}\, dt = a_n T$$

or

(3.11)
$$a_n = \frac{1}{T} \int_0^T F(t)e^{-in\omega t}\, dt$$

Equation (3.11) gives the coefficient of the general term in the expression (3.3). The coefficient a_0 is a special case of (3.11). We have also from (3.11) the relation

(3.12)
$$a_{-n} = \frac{1}{T} \int_0^T F(t)e^{in\omega t}\, dt$$

We thus see that a_n and a_{-n} are conjugate imaginaries, and we have

(3.13)
$$a_{-n} = \bar{a}_n$$

The usual real form of the Fourier series may be obtained in the following manner. Equation (3.3) may be written in the following form:

(3.14)
$$F(t) = \sum_{n=-\infty}^{n=-1} a_n e^{in\omega t} + a_0 + \sum_{n=1}^{n=\infty} a_n e^{in\omega t}$$
$$= \sum_{n=\infty}^{n=1} a_{-n} e^{-in\omega t} + a_0 + \sum_{n=1}^{n=\infty} a_n e^{in\omega t}$$
$$= a_0 + \sum_{n=1}^{n=\infty} (a_n e^{in\omega t} + a_{-n} e^{-in\omega t})$$

By using Euler's relation, this may be written in the form

$$(3.15) \quad F(t) = a_0 + \sum_{n=1}^{n=\infty} (a_n + a_{-n}) \cos n\omega t + \sum_{n=1}^{n=\infty} j(a_n - a_{-n}) \sin n\omega t$$

If we now let

$$(3.16) \quad A_n = a_n + a_{-n} \qquad B_n = j(a_n - a_{-n}) \qquad \frac{A_0}{2} = a_0$$

we obtain

$$(3.17) \quad F(t) = \frac{A_0}{2} + \sum_{n=1}^{n=\infty} A_n \cos n\omega t + \sum_{n=1}^{n=\infty} B_n \sin n\omega t$$

This is the usual real form of the Fourier series. By using (3.16) and (3.11), we obtain the coefficients A_n and B_n directly in terms of $F(t)$. We thus obtain

$$(3.18) \quad A_n = a_n + a_{-n} = \frac{1}{T} \int_0^T F(t)(e^{-jn\omega t} + e^{jn\omega t}) \, dt$$

$$= \frac{2}{T} \int_0^T F(t) \cos n\omega t \, dt$$

We also have

$$(3.19) \quad B_n = j(a_n - a_{-n}) = \frac{1}{T} \int_0^T F(t)j(e^{-jn\omega t} - e^{jn\omega t}) \, dt$$

$$= \frac{2}{T} \int_0^T F(t) \sin n\omega t \, dt$$

The $A_0/2$ term is introduced in the series (3.17) so that Eq. (3.18) giving the general term A_n will be applicable for A_0 as well. In either the complex or the real form of Fourier series the constant term is always equal to the mean value of the function.

A third form of the Fourier series involving phase angles may be obtained from (3.17) by letting

$$(3.20) \quad A_n \cos n\omega t + B_n \sin n\omega t = C_n \cos (n\omega t - \phi_n)$$
$$= C_n \cos n\omega t \cos \phi_n + C_n \sin n\omega t \sin \phi_n$$

Equating the coefficients of like cosine and sine terms, we have

$$(3.21) \quad A_n = C_n \cos \phi_n \qquad B_n = C_n \sin \phi_n$$

and hence

$$(3.22) \quad C_n = \sqrt{A_n^2 + B_n^2} \qquad \phi_n = \tan^{-1} \frac{B_n}{A_n}$$

In this case the series takes the form

$$(3.23) \qquad F(t) = \frac{A_0}{2} + \sum_{n=1}^{n=\infty} C_n \cos (n\omega t - \phi_n)$$

or

$$(3.24) \qquad F(t) = \frac{A_0}{2} + \sum_{n=1}^{n=\infty} C_n \sin \left(n\omega t + \frac{\pi}{2} - \phi_n\right)$$

The complex form of the Fourier series has many advantages over the real form involving sines and cosines. It is much simpler to perform processes of differentiation and integration with the form (3.3) than with the real forms, and also no harmonic phase angles appear explicitly in the complex form but are contained in the complex character of the coefficients.

4. Examples of Fourier Expansions of Functions. Let it be required to obtain the Fourier expansion of the function of Fig. 4.1.

FIG. 4.1

This function is assumed to continue in the same fashion in both directions. The origin of the time is arbitrarily chosen as indicated.

The coefficients of the complex Fourier series are given by Eq. (3.11). We thus have

$$(4.1) \quad a_n = \frac{1}{T} \int_0^T F(t)e^{-jn\omega t} \, dt = \frac{A}{T} \int_0^{T/2} e^{-jn\omega t} \, dt - \frac{A}{T} \int_{T/2}^T e^{-jn\omega t} \, dt$$

$$= \frac{A}{T} \left(\int_0^{\pi/\omega} e^{-jn\omega t} \, dt - \int_{\pi/\omega}^{2\pi/\omega} e^{-jn\omega t} \, dt \right)$$

$$= \frac{A}{Tjn\omega} \left(e^{-jn\omega t} \Big|_{\pi/\omega}^0 + e^{-jn\omega t} \Big|_{\pi/\omega}^{2\pi/\omega} \right)$$

$$= \begin{cases} 0 & \text{if } n = 0, \text{ or } n \text{ is even} \\ \dfrac{2A}{jn\pi} & \text{if } n \text{ is odd} \end{cases}$$

The complex Fourier-series expansion of this function is therefore

$$(4.2) \qquad F(t) = \frac{2A}{j\pi} \sum_{n=-\infty}^{n=+\infty} \frac{e^{jn\omega t}}{n} \qquad n \text{ odd}$$

The coefficients of the real Fourier series are given by (3.18). We thus have

(4.3)
$$A_n = a_n + a_{-n} = \frac{2A}{\pi j}\left(\frac{1}{n} - \frac{1}{n}\right) = 0$$

$$B_n = j(a_n - a_{-n}) = \frac{2A}{\pi}\left(\frac{1}{n} + \frac{1}{n}\right) = \frac{4A}{n\pi}$$

Hence the real Fourier-series expansion of this function is

(4.4)
$$F(t) = \frac{4A}{\pi} \sum_{n=1}^{n=\infty} \frac{\sin n\omega t}{n} \qquad n \text{ odd}$$

It is interesting to determine the character of the Fourier-series expansion of the function of Fig. 4.1 if we had taken the origin of time at a point t_0 to the right of the origin in Fig. 4.1, where

(4.5)
$$t_0 = \frac{\theta}{\omega}$$

We may obtain the required result from (4.2) if we introduce the change of variable

(4.6)
$$t = t' + \frac{\theta}{\omega}$$

where t' is the time measured from the new origin. Substituting this into (4.2), we obtain

(4.7)
$$F\left(t' + \frac{\theta}{\omega}\right) = \frac{2A}{\pi j} \sum_{n=-\infty}^{n=+\infty} \frac{e^{jn\theta}e^{jn\omega t'}}{n} \qquad n \text{ odd}$$

The coefficient of the general term is now

(4.8)
$$a_n = \frac{2A}{\pi j n} e^{jn\theta} \qquad n \text{ odd}$$

If $\theta = \pi/2$, the origin of time is chosen at the center of the positive half cycle. In this case we have

(4.9)
$$a_n = \frac{2A}{\pi j n} e^{jn(\pi/2)} \qquad n \text{ odd}$$

Hence in this case we have

(4.10)
$$A_n = a_n + a_{-n} = \frac{2A}{\pi j n}\left(e^{jn(\pi/2)} - e^{-jn(\pi/2)}\right)$$

$$= \frac{2A}{\pi j n}\left(2j \sin \frac{n\pi}{2}\right) = \frac{4A}{n\pi} \sin \frac{n\pi}{2}$$

(4.11) $B_n = j(a_n - a_{-n}) = \frac{2A}{\pi n}\left(e^{jn(\pi/2)} + e^{-jn(\pi/2)}\right) = \frac{4A}{n\pi} \cos \frac{n\pi}{2} = 0$

Hence in this we have

$$(4.12) \qquad F\left(t' + \frac{T}{4}\right) = \frac{4A}{\pi} \sum_{n=1}^{n=\infty} \frac{\sin(n\pi/2)}{n} \cos n\omega t \qquad n \text{ odd}$$

for the real form of the Fourier expansion of the function of Fig. 4.1.

As a more complicated example of the Fourier-series expansion of a function, let us consider the function defined by Fig. 4.2. This function consists essentially of a series of positive and negative pulses that have a fundamental period of τ sec. The time origin has been chosen so that

Fig. 4.2

each pulse comes in the center of a half period. This choice of origin makes the Fourier series simpler. The duration of each pulse is denoted by a.

To obtain the general coefficient of the complex Fourier series of this function, we use the general equation (3.11). We then have

$$(4.13) \qquad a_n = \frac{A}{\tau} \left(\int_{\tau/4-a/2}^{\tau/4+a/2} e^{-jn\omega t} \, dt - \int_{3\tau/4-a/2}^{3\tau/4+a/2} e^{-jn\omega t} \, dt \right)$$

where

$$(4.14) \qquad \tau = \frac{2\pi}{\omega}$$

We notice that the second integral is identical with the first except for the limits of integration, which are advanced by $\tau/2 = \pi/\omega$. We may therefore combine the above integral into a single integral and obtain

$$(4.15) \qquad a_n = \frac{\omega A}{2\pi} (1 - e^{-jn\pi}) \int_{\pi/2\omega-a/2}^{\pi/2\omega+a/2} e^{-jn\pi i} \, dt$$

Evaluating the integral, we obtain

$$(4.16) \qquad a_n = \frac{A(1 - e^{-jn\pi})e^{-jn(\pi/2)}}{2\pi jn} \left(e^{jn(\omega a/2)} - e^{-jn(\omega a/2)} \right)$$

The factor $1 - e^{-jn\pi}$ vanishes for $n = 0$ and for even values of n. For odd integral values of n it is equal to 2. For these values we also have

$$(4.17) \qquad e^{-jn(\pi/2)} = j(-1)^{(n+1/2)} \qquad n \text{ odd}$$

If we let

$$(4.18) \qquad \delta = \frac{2a}{\tau} = \frac{\omega a}{\pi}$$

the parameter δ is the ratio of the duration of the pulse a to the fundamental half period. δ is a real number that varies from zero to unity depending on the relative width of the pulse as compared with the fundamental half period. If $\delta = 1$, we have the function of Fig. 4.1.

With this notation, (4.16) becomes

$$(4.19) \qquad a_n = j(-1)^{(n+1)/2} \frac{2A \sin (n\delta\pi/2)}{n\pi} \qquad n \text{ odd}$$

It is easy to show that if $\delta = 1$ this reduces to

$$(4.20) \qquad a_n = \frac{2A}{jn\pi}$$

as it should.

5. Some Remarks about Convergence of Fourier Series. It remains to say something about the convergence of Fourier series. To do this, it is convenient to examine the coefficients of the real form of the Fourier series. These are given by (3.18) and (3.19) in the form

$$(5.1) \qquad A_n = \frac{2}{T} \int_0^T F(t) \cos n\omega t \, dt$$

and

$$(5.2) \qquad B_n = \frac{2}{T} \int_0^T F(t) \sin n\omega t \, dt$$

From these equations it is plausible that the coefficients A_n and B_n must diminish indefinitely as n increases because of the more and more rapid fluctuation in sign of $\cos n\omega t$ and $\sin n\omega t$ and the consequent more complete canceling of the various elements of the definite integrals (5.1) and (5.2). This result is known as the *Riemann-Lebesgue theorem.*[4]

Stokes has formulated more definite results. The following statement must be understood to refer to a function that satisfies the Dirichlet conditions, but care is necessary in particular cases to determine whether discontinuities of $F(t)$ or its derivatives are introduced at the terminal points of the various segments.

1. If $F(t)$ has a finite number of isolated discontinuities in a period, the coefficients converge ultimately toward zero like the members of the sequence

$$(5.3) \qquad 1, \tfrac{1}{2}, \tfrac{1}{3}, \tfrac{1}{4}, \ldots$$

2. If $F(t)$ is everywhere continuous while its first derivative $F'(t)$ has a finite number of isolated discontinuities, the convergence is ultimately like that of the sequence

$$(5.4) \qquad\qquad 1, \frac{1}{2^2}, \frac{1}{3^2}, \frac{1}{4^2}, \cdots$$

3. If $F(t)$ and $F'(t)$ are continuous while $F''(t)$ is discontinuous at isolated points, the sequence of comparison is

$$(5.5) \qquad\qquad 1, \frac{1}{2^3}, \frac{1}{3^3}, \frac{1}{4^3}, \cdots$$

4. In general, if $F(t)$ and its derivatives up to the order $n - 1$ are continuous while the nth derivative (in a period) has a finite number of isolated discontinuities, the convergence is ultimately as

$$(5.6) \qquad\qquad 1, \frac{1}{2^{n+1}}, \frac{1}{3^{n+1}}, \frac{1}{4^{n+1}}, \cdots$$

The nature of the proof of these statements, which is simple, may be briefly indicated for the sine series.

If we integrate by parts, we have

$$(5.7) \quad B_n = \frac{2}{T} \int_0^T F(t) \sin n\omega t \, dt$$

$$= -\frac{1}{n} \left[\frac{F(t) \cos n\omega t}{\pi} \right]_0^T + \frac{1}{\pi n} \int_0^T F'(t) \cos n\omega t \, dt$$

The integrated term is to be calculated separately for each of the segments lying between the points of discontinuity of $F(t)$, if there are any that lie in the range extending from $t = 0$ to $t = T$. If there is no discontinuity of $F(t)$ even at the points $t = 0$ and $t = T$, the first term vanishes. If there is a discontinuity, then there is for all values of n an upper limit to the coefficient of $1/n$ in the first part of (5.7). Let us denote this limit by M. The definite integral in the second term tends ultimately to zero as n increases because of the fluctuations in the sign of $\cos n\omega t$. Hence B_n is comparable with M/n.

If there is no discontinuity in $F(t)$, we have

$$(5.8) \qquad\qquad B_n = \frac{1}{\pi n} \int_0^T F'(t) \cos n\omega t \, dt$$

If we again integrate by parts, we obtain

$$(5.9) \quad B_n = \frac{1}{n^2} \left[\frac{F'(t) \sin n\omega t}{\pi \omega} \right]_0^T - \frac{1}{\pi \omega n^2} \int_0^T F''(t) \sin n\omega t \, dt$$

In the integrated term of (5.9) we must take into account the discontinuities of $F'(t)$ in the interval, if there are any. If $F'(t)$ has discontinuities, denote by M the upper limit of the coefficient of $1/n^2$; we then see that B_n is ultimately comparable with M/n^2 since the second term of (5.9) vanishes because of the fluctuation of sin $n\omega t$. This outlines the method of proof, and the course of the argument is apparent.

The preceding statements concerning the convergence of Fourier series are very useful. We thus know beforehand how well or how poorly the series will converge. We also have a partial check on the numerical work in some problems.

Differentiating a Fourier series makes the convergence poorer, while integrating the series increases its rate of convergence. When a Fourier series has been differentiated until it converges as $1/n$, it cannot be further differentiated.

6. Effective Values and the Average of a Product. The determination of the root-mean-square, or effective, value of a periodic function is a common problem in electrical-circuit theory and in the theory of mechanical vibrations. The manner in which this may be done by the use of the complex Fourier-series expansion of the function will be demonstrated.

Suppose that we have a periodic function $F(t)$ whose Fourier-series expansion is given by

$$(6.1) \qquad F(t) = \sum_{n=-\infty}^{n=+\infty} a_n e^{jn\omega t}$$

By definition the root-mean-square, or effective, value of the function F_E over a period T is given by

$$(6.2) \qquad F_E^2 = \frac{1}{T} \int_0^T F^2(t)\, dt \qquad T = \frac{2\pi}{\omega}$$

To obtain $F^2(t)$, we use the series expansion (6.1) and obtain

$$(6.3) \qquad F^2(t) = \left(\sum_{n=-\infty}^{n=+\infty} a_n e^{jn\omega t} \right) \left(\sum_{r=-\infty}^{r=+\infty} a_r e^{jr\omega t} \right)$$

$$= \sum_{n=-\infty}^{n=+\infty} \sum_{r=-\infty}^{r=+\infty} a_n a_r e^{j(n+r)\omega t}$$

It is necessary to use two different indices in the multiplication to avoid confusion. Substituting (6.3) into (6.2), we obtain

$$(6.4) \qquad F_E^2 = \frac{1}{T} \int_0^T \sum_{n=-\infty}^{n=+\infty} \sum_{r=-\infty}^{r=+\infty} a_n a_r e^{j(n+r)\omega t}\, dt$$

Carrying out term-by-term integration, we obtain

$$(6.5) \qquad F_E^2 = \frac{1}{T} \sum_{n=-\infty}^{n=+\infty} \sum_{r=-\infty}^{r=+\infty} a_n a_r \int_0^{2\pi/\omega} e^{j(n+r)\omega t} \, dt$$

However, we have

$$(6.6) \qquad \int_0^{2\pi/\omega} e^{jm\omega t} \, dt = \frac{e^{jm\omega t}}{jm\omega} \Big|_0^{2\pi/\omega} = 0 \qquad \text{if } m \text{ is any integer} \neq 0$$

$$= \frac{2\pi}{\omega} = T \qquad \text{if } m = 0$$

It follows, therefore, that all the integrals in (6.5) vanish except those for which

$$(6.7) \qquad\qquad\qquad r = -n$$

and we have

$$(6.8) \qquad F_E^2 = \frac{1}{T} \sum_{n=-\infty}^{n=+\infty} a_n a_{-n} T = \sum_{n=-\infty}^{n=+\infty} a_n a_{-n}$$

This result may be put into a different form by recognizing that a_{-n} is the conjugate of a_n; hence the quantity in the summation sign is the square of the magnitude of a_n. Since summation over negative values of n gives the same result as summation over positive values of n, we have

$$(6.9) \qquad\qquad F_E^2 = 2 \sum_{n=1}^{\infty} |a_n|^2 + a_0^2$$

Another problem that occurs frequently in electrical-circuit theory and the theory of mechanical vibrations is the problem of determining the average value over a period of the product of two periodic functions having the same period. Suppose we have the two periodic functions, having the period T,

$$(6.10) \qquad \begin{aligned} F_1(t) &= \sum_{n=-\infty}^{n=+\infty} a_n e^{jn\omega t} \\ F_2(t) &= \sum_{r=-\infty}^{r=+\infty} b_r e^{jr\omega t} \end{aligned} \qquad T = \frac{2\pi}{\omega}$$

We wish to compute

$$(6.11) \qquad\qquad P = \frac{1}{T} \int_0^T F_1(t) F_2(t) \, dt$$

Substituting (6.10) into (6.11) and interchanging the order of summation and integration, we have

$$(6.12) \qquad P = \frac{1}{T} \sum_{n=-\infty}^{n=+\infty} \sum_{r=-\infty}^{r=+\infty} a_n b_r \int_0^T e^{j(n+r)\omega t}\, dt$$

This is the same integral that we evaluated in (6.5). The result is

$$(6.13) \qquad P = \sum_{n=-\infty}^{n=+\infty} a_n b_{-n}$$

This is a very concise form for the average of the product.

7. Modulated Vibrations and Beats. A very interesting type of oscillation occurs in radiotelephony. There we encounter *modulated vibrations*. These are oscillations in which the maximum amplitude itself is a periodic function of the time. The amplitude changes slowly compared with the frequency of the actual vibration. The latter vibration is called the *carrier wave* and has a frequency of the order of 10^6 cycles per sec, while the frequency of modulation is the frequency of the radiated tone and is of the order of 1,000 cycles per sec. This type of oscillation may be represented by the equation

$$(7.1) \qquad u = A(1 + K \sin \omega_1 t) \sin \omega_2 t \qquad \omega_2 \gg \omega_1$$

By a familiar trigonometric formula this may be written in the form

$$(7.2) \qquad u = A \sin \omega_2 t - \frac{AK}{2} \cos (\omega_2 + \omega_1)t + \frac{AK}{2} \cos (\omega_2 - \omega_1)t$$

This signifies the combination of two vibrations of equal amplitude and having angular frequencies $\omega_2 + \omega_1$ and $\omega_2 - \omega_1$ which are very close together. In practice this type of vibration may be produced in either of two ways. One method is to modulate a carrier frequency, and another is to combine two oscillations that differ very little in frequency. This latter case is known in the theory of sound as *beats*. The angular frequency of the beats is $\omega_2 - \omega_1$.

Equation (7.1) represents the simplest case of a class of functions called *almost-periodic*. If, for example, ω_1 and ω_2 are not commensurable, then the function u has no definite period; that is, no fixed interval T exists such that the value of u is repeated at a time $T + t$.

8. The Propagation of Periodic Disturbances in the Form of Waves. Let us consider a process that varies as either the real or imaginary part of the function

$$(8.1) \qquad u(x,t) = A e^{j\omega(t - x/v)}$$

In this case, as t (the time) increases, the argument of the function changes. If, however, the coordinate x increases in such a way that the argument of the exponential function remains constant, that is, if

$$(8.2) \qquad t - \frac{x}{v} = \text{const}$$

then the phase of the function $u(x,t)$ is unaltered. We thus see that (8.1) represents a disturbance that travels along the x axis with a phase velocity of

$$(8.3) \qquad \frac{dx}{dt} = v$$

Now let us consider a given instant of time t_0. For this value of t we have

$$(8.4) \qquad u(x,t_0) = A e^{j\omega(t_0 - x/v)}$$

The value of the function at a given point x_1 is given at this instant by

$$(8.5) \qquad u(x_1,t_0) = A e^{j\omega(t_0 - x_1/v)}$$

If we now move along the x axis to the first new point x_2 such that the function at x_2 resumes its value at x_1, we have

$$(8.6) \qquad e^{j\omega(t_0 - x_1/v)} = e^{j\omega(t_0 - x_2/v)}$$

or

$$(8.7) \qquad e^{-j(\omega x_1/v)} = e^{-j(\omega x_2/v)}$$

and hence

$$(8.8) \qquad e^{j\frac{\omega}{v}(x_2 - x_1)} = 1$$

or

$$(8.9) \qquad \frac{\omega}{v}(x_2 - x_1) = 2\pi$$

and hence

$$(8.10) \qquad x_2 - x_1 = \lambda = \frac{2\pi v}{\omega} = vT$$

The distance λ that gives the separation of the successive points of equal phase is called the *wavelength*. If f is the frequency of the oscillation, we have from (8.10)

$$(8.11) \qquad \frac{\lambda}{T} = \lambda f = v$$

that is,

$$(8.12) \qquad \text{Wavelength} \times \text{frequency} = \text{velocity of propagation of phase}$$

A process that varies in the form (8.1) is called a *plane wave* since u is constant in any plane perpendicular to the direction of propagation x. The simple plane wave (8.1) is a particular integral of a partial differential equation that is easily deduced. If u is differentiated twice with respect to t and twice with respect to x, we obtain

(8.13)
$$\frac{\partial^2 u}{\partial t^2} = -\omega^2 A e^{j\omega(t-x/v)}$$
$$\frac{\partial^2 u}{\partial x^2} = -\frac{\omega^2}{v^2} A e^{j\omega(t-x/v)}$$

and hence

(8.14)
$$\frac{\partial^2 u}{\partial x^2} = \frac{1}{v^2} \frac{\partial^2 u}{\partial t^2}$$

This is called the *wave equation in one dimension*. It is fundamental in the study of many important physical phenomena. A detailed discussion of the wave equation is given in Chap. 16.

9. The Fourier Integral. In this section we shall consider the limiting form of the Fourier series as the fundamental period T is made infinite. We shall see that when this is done the series passes into an integral. A rigorous derivation of the Fourier integral is beyond the scope of this discussion and will be found in the works quoted in the references at the end of this chapter. However, the heuristic derivation given here shows the general trend of the argument. We start with the complex Fourier-series expansion of the periodic function $F(t)$.

(9.1)
$$F(t) = \sum_{n=-\infty}^{n=+\infty} a_n e^{jn\omega t} \qquad T = \frac{2\pi}{\omega}$$

where the coefficients a_n are given by

(9.2)
$$a_n = \frac{1}{T} \int_0^T F(u) e^{-jn\omega u} \, du$$

Now, because of the like periodicity of $F(t)$ and $e^{-jn\omega u}$, we can take the range of integration in (9.2) from $-T/2$ to $+T/2$ instead of from 0 to T. We thus have

(9.3)
$$a_n = \frac{1}{T} \int_{-T/2}^{T/2} F(u) e^{-jn\omega u} \, du \qquad \omega = \frac{2\pi}{T}$$

Substituting this into (9.1), we obtain

(9.4)
$$F(t) = \sum_{n=-\infty}^{n=+\infty} \frac{1}{T} \int_{-T/2}^{+T/2} F(u) e^{(2\pi nj/T)(t-u)} \, du$$

Let us now place

(9.5)
$$\frac{1}{T} = \Delta s$$

This gives

(9.6)
$$F(t) = \sum_{n=+\infty}^{n=-\infty} \Delta s \int_{-T/2}^{+T/2} F(u) e^{2\pi nj(t-u) \, \Delta s} \, du$$

Now the definite integral $\int_0^\infty \phi(s)\, ds$ may be defined as the limit, as Δs approaches zero, of the sum

$$(9.7) \qquad \sum_{n=0}^{n=\infty} \phi(n\, \Delta s)\, \Delta s$$

Also, we have

$$(9.8) \quad \int_{-\infty}^{+\infty} \phi(s)\, ds = \int_{-\infty}^{0} \phi(s)\, ds + \int_{0}^{\infty} \phi(s)\, ds = \lim_{\Delta S \to 0} \sum_{n=-\infty}^{n=+\infty} \phi(n\, \Delta s)\, \Delta s$$

From this it follows that as T grows beyond all bounds the expression (9.6) passes over into the Fourier integral

$$(9.9) \qquad \begin{aligned} F(t) &= \int_{-\infty}^{+\infty} ds \int_{-\infty}^{+\infty} F(u) e^{2\pi js(t-u)}\, du \\ &= \int_{-\infty}^{+\infty} e^{2\pi jst}\, ds \int_{-\infty}^{+\infty} F(u) e^{-2\pi jsu}\, du \end{aligned}$$

The second form of the identity (9.9) shows that the function $F(t)$ may be expressed by a continuous series of harmonics, one for each value of s.

The possibility of such a representation is of great importance in the analytical treatment of functions that are otherwise not expressible by a unified mathematical expression.

The limitations on $F(t)$ that allow the above formal procedure to be valid will now be given:

1. $F(t)$ must be a single-valued function of the real variable t throughout the range $-\infty < t < \infty$. It may, however, have a finite number of finite discontinuities.

2. At a point of discontinuity t_0 the function will be given the mean value

$$F(t_0) = \tfrac{1}{2}[F(t_0 + 0) + F(t_0 - 0)]$$

3. The integral $\int_{-\infty}^{+\infty} |F(t)|\, dt$ must exist.

We noted that when we expand a function into a Fourier series in a certain range then the function is defined by the series outside this range in a periodic manner. However, by the Fourier integral, we obtain analytical expressions for discontinuous functions that represent the function throughout the infinite range $-\infty < t < +\infty$. The following example will make this clear. Let us suppose that $F(t)$ is the single pulse given by Fig. 9.1 (page 66).

The pulse has a height equal to A and begins at $t = -a$ and ends at $t = a$. Hence we have

$$(9.10) \qquad F(t) = \begin{cases} 0 & t < -a \\ 0 & t > a \\ A & -a < t < a \end{cases}$$

Substituting this value of $F(t)$ into (9.9), we obtain

$$(9.11) \qquad F(t) = \int_{-\infty}^{+\infty} e^{2\pi jst}\, ds \int_{-a}^{+a} A e^{-2\pi jsu}\, du$$

If we let

$$(9.12) \qquad\qquad 2\pi s = v$$

we have

$$(9.13) \qquad F(t) = \frac{A}{2\pi j} \int_{-\infty}^{+\infty} \frac{\left(e^{jv(t+a)} - e^{jv(t-a)}\right)\, dv}{v}$$

This is the Fourier-integral representation of the function (9.10).

Another form of the Fourier integral may be obtained from (9.9) by using Euler's relation on the complex exponentials and the fact that the cosine is an even function and the sine is an odd function of its argument. We thus obtain the real form of the Fourier integral,

$$(9.14) \qquad F(t) = 2 \int_{0}^{\infty} ds \int_{-\infty}^{+\infty} F(u) \cos 2\pi s(t - u)\, du$$

The Fourier integral is of great importance in the field of electrical communication and forms the basis of a powerful method for the solution of partial differential equations due to Cauchy.

Fourier Transforms. In the modern literature of the mathematical theory of communication engineering, wave propagation, and other branches of applied mathematics the expression (9.9) is written in a slightly different form.

Let us introduce the new variable

$$(9.15) \qquad\qquad \omega = 2\pi s$$

In terms of the variable ω (9.9) is transformed to

$$(9.16) \qquad F(t) = \frac{1}{2\pi} \int_{-\infty}^{+\infty} e^{j\omega t}\, d\omega \int_{-\infty}^{+\infty} F(u) e^{-j\omega u}\, du$$

It is convenient to write

$$(9.17) \qquad g(\omega) = \frac{1}{2\pi} \int_{-\infty}^{+\infty} F(u) e^{-j\omega u}\, du$$

Then, as a consequence of (9.16), we have

$$(9.18) \qquad F(t) = \int_{-\infty}^{+\infty} g(\omega) e^{j\omega t}\, d\omega$$

Since the letter chosen as a variable of integration in a definite integral is of no importance, the letter t may be used instead of the letter u and we write (9.17) in the form

$$(9.19) \qquad g(\omega) = \frac{1}{2\pi} \int_{-\infty}^{+\infty} F(t) e^{-j\omega t}\, dt$$

The relations (9.18) and (9.19) are known in the literature as *Fourier transforms*. The relations are symmetrical. Many writers enhance the symmetry by writing the factor $1/\sqrt{2\pi}$ before each integral rather than having no factor for the integral (9.18) and a factor of $1/2\pi$ for the integral (9.19). This notation introduces a change in the scale factor and is of small importance. In the literature the expression (9.19) is usually called the *Fourier transform of the function $F(t)$*.

$F(t)$

A

$-a$ $+a$ t

FIG. 9.1

The Fourier transform of the pulse function of Fig. 9.1 is given by

$$(9.20) \qquad g(\omega) = \frac{A}{2\pi} \int_{-a}^{+a} e^{-i\omega t}\, dt = \frac{A \sin \omega a}{\pi \omega}$$

The Fourier-integral representation of the pulse function as given by (9.18) is therefore

$$(9.21) \quad F(t) = \frac{A}{\pi} \int_{-\infty}^{+\infty} \frac{\sin \omega a}{\omega} e^{j\omega t}\, d\omega$$

$$= \frac{A}{\pi} \int_{-\infty}^{+\infty} \frac{\sin \omega a \cos \omega t}{\omega}\, d\omega + \frac{jA}{\pi} \int_{-\infty}^{+\infty} \frac{\sin \omega a \sin \omega t}{\omega}\, d\omega$$

Since the integrand of the second integral of (9.21) is an odd function of ω, we have

$$(9.22) \qquad \int_{-\infty}^{+\infty} \frac{\sin \omega a \sin \omega t}{\omega}\, d\omega = 0$$

Hence the pulse function is represented analytically by

$$(9.23) \qquad F(t) = \frac{A}{\pi} \int_{-\infty}^{+\infty} \frac{\sin \omega a \cos \omega t}{\omega}\, d\omega$$

The fact that (9.23) actually represents the pulse function of Fig. 9.1 may be seen by using the trigonometric identity

$$(9.24) \qquad \sin \omega a \cos \omega t = \tfrac{1}{2}[\sin \omega(a + t) + \sin \omega(a - t)]$$

and the following result (see Chap. 11, Sec. 11):

$$(9.25) \qquad \int_{0}^{\infty} \frac{\sin k\omega}{\omega}\, d\omega = \begin{cases} -\dfrac{\pi}{2} & k < 0 \\[2mm] 0 & k = 0 \\[2mm] \dfrac{\pi}{2} & k > 0 \end{cases}$$

An interesting discussion of physical applications of the Fourier integral is given by Guillemin.*

An extensive table of Fourier transforms is given in a paper by Campbell and Foster.†

PROBLEMS

1. Show that if $F(t)$ is an even function, that is, $F(t) = F(-t)$, then its real Fourier-series expansion contains no sine terms.

2. Show that if $F(t)$ is an odd function so that $F(-t) = -F(t)$ then its real Fourier-series expansion contains no cosine terms and no constant term.

3. Expand the function $F(t) = kt$ in the interval $-T/2 < t < T/2$ in a complex Fourier series. Plot the function defined by the series outside this range.

4. Expand t^2 in the interval $0 < t < T$ in a complex and a real Fourier series.

5. Expand the function e^{at} in a complex and a real Fourier series in the interval $0 < t < T$.

6. Show that, if A is a constant, then in the range $0 < t < \pi$

$$A = \frac{4A}{\pi} \left(\sin t + \frac{\sin 3t}{3} + \frac{\sin 5t}{5} + \cdots \right)$$

7. Show that if $F(t) = \phi(-t)$ for $-T/2 < t < 0$ and $F(t) = \phi(t)$ for $0 < t < T/2$ then the real Fourier series for $F(t)$ contains no sine terms.

8. Show that if $F(t) = -\phi(-t)$ for $-T/2 < t < 0$ and $F(t) = \phi(t)$ for $0 < t < T/2$ then the real Fourier series for $F(t)$ contains no cosine terms.

9. Show by using the results of Probs. 7 and 8 that a function $F(t)$ may be expanded in the range $0 < t < T/2$ either in terms of sines alone or in terms of cosines alone.

10. Expand the function of period 12 defined by the following equations in the interval $-6 < t < 6$:

$$\begin{aligned}
F(t) &= 0 && \text{for } -6 \leq t \leq -3 \\
F(t) &= t + 3 && \text{for } -3 < t \leq 0 \\
F(t) &= 3 - t && \text{for } 0 < t \leq 3 \\
F(t) &= 0 && \text{for } 3 < t \leq 6
\end{aligned}$$

Plot the function.

11. Prove that the numerical value of $\sin t$, $|\sin t|$, is an even function of period π, and find the Fourier series that represents it.

12. Find the Fourier series that represents $|\cos t|$.

13. Show that if a is not an integer

$$\sin ax = \frac{2 \sin a\pi}{\pi} \left(\frac{\sin x}{1^2 - a^2} - \frac{2 \sin 2x}{2^2 - a^2} + \frac{3 \sin 3x}{3^2 - a^2} - \cdots \right)$$

14. Show that

$$\cosh ax = \frac{2a \sinh a\pi}{\pi} \left(\frac{1}{2a^2} - \frac{\cos x}{1^2 + a^2} + \frac{\cos 2x}{2^2 + a^2} - \frac{\cos 3x}{3^2 + a^2} + \cdots \right)$$

15. The quantity $g(\omega)$ given by $g(\omega) = \int_{-\infty}^{+\infty} F(t)e^{-j\omega t}\, dt$ is the complex Fourier transform of $F(t)$. Use the results of Sec. 9 to show that the inverse transform of

* E. A. Guillemin, "Communication Networks," vol. II, chap. XI, John Wiley & Sons, Inc., New York, 1935.

† G. A. Campbell and R. M. Foster, Fourier Integrals for Practical Applications, *Bell Telephone System Technical Publications,* *Monograph* B-584, September, 1931.

$g(\omega)$ is given by

$$F(t) = \frac{1}{2\pi} \int_{-\infty}^{+\infty} g(\omega)e^{i\omega t} \, d\omega$$

16. Compute the complex Fourier transform of the function $F(t) = e^{-|t|}$.

17. Use the results of Sec. 9 to deduce that, if $g(p) = \int_0^\infty f(x) \sin px \, dx$, then

$$f(x) = \frac{2}{\pi} \int_0^\infty g(p) \sin xp \, dp$$

under suitable restrictions. The quantity $g(p)$ is said to be the Fourier sine transform of $f(x)$, and $f(x)$ is said to be the inverse Fourier sine transform of $g(p)$.

18. Deduce that, under suitable restrictions, if $g(p) = \int_0^\infty f(x) \cos px \, dx$, then

$$f(x) = \frac{2}{\pi} \int_0^\infty g(p) \cos xp \, dp$$

$g(p)$ is the Fourier cosine transform of $f(x)$, and $f(x)$ is the inverse Fourier cosine transform of $g(p)$.

19. Show that if

$$F(\theta) = \frac{a_0}{2} + \sum_{n=1}^\infty (a_n \cos n\theta + b_n \sin n\theta)$$

then

$$\frac{1}{\pi} \int_{-\pi}^{+\pi} [F(\theta)]^2 \, d\theta = \frac{a_0^2}{2} + \sum_{n=1}^\infty (a_n^2 + b_n^2)$$

20. By the use of the Fourier cosine integral, show that, for $x > 0$,

$$e^{-bx} = \frac{2b}{\pi} \int_0^\infty \frac{\cos ux \, du}{u^2 + b^2}$$

REFERENCES

1. Byerly, W. E.: "Fourier's Series and Spherical Harmonics," Ginn & Company, Boston, 1893.
2. Churchill, R. V.: "Fourier Series and Boundary Value Problems," McGraw-Hill Book Company, Inc., New York, 1941.
3. Whittaker, E. T., and G. N. Watson: "A Course in Modern Analysis," chap. 9, Cambridge University Press, New York, 1927.
4. Titchmarsh, E. C.: "Introduction to the Theory of Fourier Integrals," Oxford University Press, New York, 1937.
5. Sneddon, I. N.: "Fourier Transforms," McGraw-Hill Book Company, Inc., New York, 1951.
6. Tranter, C. J.: "Integral Transforms in Mathematical Physics," John Wiley & Sons, Inc., New York, 1951.
7. Erdélyi, A.: "Tables of Integral Transforms," vol. I, McGraw-Hill Book Company, Inc., New York, 1954.

CHAPTER 4

LINEAR ALGEBRAIC EQUATIONS, DETERMINANTS, AND MATRICES

1. Introduction. This chapter will be devoted to the discussion of the solution of linear algebraic equations and the related topics determinants and matrices. These subjects are of extreme importance in applied mathematics, since a great many physical phenomena are expressed in terms of linear differential equations. By appropriate transformations the solution of a set of linear differential equations with constant coefficients may be reduced to the solution of a set of algebraic equations. Such problems as the determination of the transient behavior of an electrical circuit or the determination of the amplitudes and modes of oscillation of a dynamical system lead to the solution of a set of algebraic equations.

It is therefore important that the algebraic processes useful in the solution and manipulation of these equations should be known and clearly understood by the student.

2. Simple Determinants. Before considering the properties of determinants in general, let us consider the solution of the following two linear equations:

$$(2.1) \qquad \begin{aligned} a_{11}x_1 + a_{12}x_2 &= k_1 \\ a_{21}x_1 + a_{22}x_2 &= k_2 \end{aligned}$$

If we multiply the first equation by a_{22} and the second by $-a_{12}$ and add, we obtain

$$(2.2) \qquad (a_{11}a_{22} - a_{21}a_{12})x_1 = k_1a_{22} - k_2a_{12}$$

The expression $(a_{11}a_{22} - a_{21}a_{12})$ may be represented by the symbol

$$(2.3) \qquad \begin{vmatrix} a_{11} & a_{12} \\ a_{21} & a_{22} \end{vmatrix} = a_{11}a_{22} - a_{21}a_{12}$$

This symbol is called a *determinant of the second order*. The solution of (2.2) is

$$(2.4) \qquad x_1 = \frac{k_1a_{22} - k_2a_{12}}{a_{11}a_{22} - a_{21}a_{12}} = \frac{\begin{vmatrix} k_1 & a_{12} \\ k_2 & a_{22} \end{vmatrix}}{\begin{vmatrix} a_{11} & a_{12} \\ a_{21} & a_{22} \end{vmatrix}}$$

Similarly, if we multiply the first equation of (2.1) by $-a_{21}$ and the second one by a_{11} and add, we obtain

$$(2.5) \qquad x_2 = \frac{\begin{vmatrix} a_{11} & k_1 \\ a_{21} & k_2 \end{vmatrix}}{\begin{vmatrix} a_{11} & a_{12} \\ a_{21} & a_{22} \end{vmatrix}}$$

The expression for the solution of Eqs. (2.1) in terms of the determinants is very convenient and may be generalized to a set of n linear equations in n unknowns. We must first consider the fundamental definitions and rules of operation of determinants and matrices.

3. Fundamental Definitions. Consider the square array of n^2 quantities a_{ij}, where the subscripts i and j run from 1 to n, and written in the form

$$(3.1) \qquad |a| = \begin{vmatrix} a_{11} & a_{12} & a_{13} & \cdots & a_{1n} \\ a_{21} & a_{22} & a_{23} & \cdots & a_{2n} \\ a_{31} & a_{32} & a_{33} & \cdots & a_{3n} \\ \cdots & \cdots & \cdots & \cdots & \cdots \\ a_{n1} & a_{n2} & a_{n3} & \cdots & a_{nn} \end{vmatrix}$$

This square array of quantities, bordered by vertical bars, is a symbolical representation of a certain homogeneous polynomial of the nth order in the quantities a_{ij} to be defined later and constructed from the rows and columns of $|a|$ in a certain manner. This symbolical representation is called a *determinant*. The n^2 quantities a_{ij} are called the *elements* of the determinant.

In this brief treatment we cannot go into a detailed exposition of the fundamental theorems concerning the homogeneous polynomial that the determinant represents; only the essential theorems that are important to the solution of sets of linear equations will be considered. Before giving explicit rules concerning the construction of the homogeneous polynomial from the symbolic array of rows and columns, it will be necessary to define some terms that are of paramount importance in the theory of determinants.

a. Minors. If in the determinant $|a|$ of (3.1) we delete the ith row and the jth column and form a determinant from all the elements remaining, we shall have a new determinant of $n - 1$ rows and columns. This new determinant is defined to be the *minor* of the element a_{ij}. For example, if $|a|$ is a determinant of the fourth order,

$$(3.2) \qquad |a| = \begin{vmatrix} a_{11} & a_{12} & a_{13} & a_{14} \\ a_{21} & a_{22} & a_{23} & a_{24} \\ a_{31} & a_{32} & a_{33} & a_{34} \\ a_{41} & a_{42} & a_{43} & a_{44} \end{vmatrix}$$

the minor of the element a_{32} is denoted by M_{32} and is given by

$$(3.3) \qquad M_{32} = \begin{vmatrix} a_{11} & a_{13} & a_{14} \\ a_{21} & a_{23} & a_{24} \\ a_{41} & a_{43} & a_{44} \end{vmatrix}$$

b. *Cofactors.* The cofactor of an element of a determinant a_{ij} is the minor of that element with a sign attached to it determined by the numbers i and j which fix the position of a_{ij} in the determinant $|a|$. The sign is chosen by the equation

$$(3.4) \qquad A_{ij} = (-1)^{i+j} M_{ij}$$

where A_{ij} is the cofactor of the element a_{ij} and M_{ij} is the minor of the element a_{ij}.

4. The Laplace Expansion. We come now to a consideration of what may be regarded as the definition of the homogeneous polynomial of the nth order that the symbolical array of elements of the determinant represents. Let us, for simplicity, first consider the second-order determinant

$$(4.1) \qquad |a| = \begin{vmatrix} a_{11} & a_{12} \\ a_{21} & a_{22} \end{vmatrix}$$

By definition this symbolical array represents the second-order homogeneous polynomial

$$(4.2) \qquad |a| = a_{11}a_{22} - a_{21}a_{12}$$

The third-order determinant

$$(4.3) \qquad |a| = \begin{vmatrix} a_{11} & a_{12} & a_{13} \\ a_{21} & a_{22} & a_{23} \\ a_{31} & a_{32} & a_{33} \end{vmatrix}$$

represents the unique third-order homogeneous polynomial defined by any one of the six equivalent expressions

$$(4.4) \qquad |a| = \sum_{j=1}^{3} a_{ij}A_{ij} \quad \text{or} \quad \sum_{i=1}^{3} a_{ij}A_{ij}$$

where the elements a_{ij} in (4.4) must be taken from a *single* row or a *single* column of a. The A_{ij}'s are the cofactors of the corresponding elements a_{ij} as defined in Sec. 3. As an example of this definition, we see that the third-order determinant may be expanded into the proper third-order homogeneous polynomial that it represents, in the following manner:

$$(4.5) \qquad |a| = a_{11} \begin{vmatrix} a_{22} & a_{23} \\ a_{32} & a_{33} \end{vmatrix} - a_{12} \begin{vmatrix} a_{21} & a_{23} \\ a_{31} & a_{33} \end{vmatrix} + a_{13} \begin{vmatrix} a_{21} & a_{22} \\ a_{31} & a_{32} \end{vmatrix}$$

$$(4.6) \qquad |a| = a_{11}(a_{22}a_{33} - a_{32}a_{23}) - a_{12}(a_{21}a_{33} - a_{31}a_{23}) \\ + a_{13}(a_{21}a_{32} - a_{31}a_{22})$$

This expansion was obtained by applying the fundamental rule (4.4) and expanding in terms of the first row. Since one has the alternative of using any row or any column, it may be seen that (4.3) could be expanded in six different ways by the fundamental rule (4.4). It is easy to show that all six ways lead to the same third-order homogeneous polynomial (4.6).

The definition (4.4) may be generalized to the nth-order determinant (3.1), and this symbol is defined to represent the nth-order homogeneous polynomial given by

$$(4.7) \qquad |a| = \sum_{j=1}^{n} a_{ij} A_{ij} \quad \text{or} \quad \sum_{i=1}^{n} a_{ij} A_{ij}$$

where the a_{ij} quantities must be taken from a *single* row or a *single* column. In this case the cofactors A_{ij} are determinants of the $(n-1)$st order, but they may in turn be expanded by the rule (4.7), and so on, until the result is a homogeneous polynomial of the nth order.

It is easy to demonstrate that, in general,

$$(4.8) \qquad \sum_{j=1}^{n} a_{ji} A_{jk} = \sum_{j=1}^{n} a_{ij} A_{kj} = \begin{cases} |a| & \text{if } i = k \\ 0 & \text{if } i \neq k \end{cases}$$

5. Fundamental Properties of Determinants. From the basic definition (4.7), the following properties of determinants may be deduced:

a. If *all* the elements in a row or in a column are zero, the determinant is equal to zero. This may be seen by expanding in terms of that row or column, in which case each term of the expansion contains a factor of zero.

b. If all elements but one in a row or column are zero, the determinant is equal to the product of that element and its cofactor.

c. The value of a determinant is not altered when the rows are changed to columns and the columns to rows. This may be proved by developing the determinant by (4.7).

d. The interchange of any two columns or two rows of a determinant changes the sign of the determinant.

e. If two columns or two rows of a determinant are identical, the determinant is equal to zero.

f. If all the elements in any row or column are multiplied by any factor, the determinant is multiplied by that factor.

g. If each element in any column or any row of a determinant is expressed as the sum of two quantities, the determinant can be expressed as the sum of two determinants of the same order.

h. It is possible, without changing the value of a determinant, to multiply the elements of any row (or any column) by the same constant and add the products to any other row (or column). For example, consider the third-order determinant

$$(5.1) \qquad |a| = \begin{vmatrix} a_{11} & a_{12} & a_{13} \\ a_{21} & a_{22} & a_{23} \\ a_{31} & a_{32} & a_{33} \end{vmatrix}$$

With the aid of property g we have

$$(5.2) \quad \Delta = \begin{vmatrix} a_{11} + ma_{13} & a_{12} & a_{13} \\ a_{21} + ma_{23} & a_{22} & a_{23} \\ a_{31} + ma_{33} & a_{32} & a_{33} \end{vmatrix} = \begin{vmatrix} a_{11} & a_{12} & a_{13} \\ a_{21} & a_{22} & a_{23} \\ a_{31} & a_{32} & a_{33} \end{vmatrix}$$
$$+ m \begin{vmatrix} a_{13} & a_{12} & a_{13} \\ a_{23} & a_{22} & a_{23} \\ a_{33} & a_{32} & a_{33} \end{vmatrix}$$

Since the second determinant is zero because the first and third columns are identical, we have

$$(5.3) \qquad\qquad |a| = \Delta$$

6. The Evaluation of Numerical Determinants. The evaluation of determinants whose elements are numbers is a task of frequent occurrence in applied mathematics. This evaluation may be carried out by a direct application of the fundamental Laplacian expansion (4.7). This process, however, is most laborious for high-order determinants, and the expansion may be more easily effected by the application of the fundamental properties outlined in Sec. 5 and by the use of two theorems that will be mentioned in this section.

As an example, let it be required to evaluate the numerical determinant

$$(6.1) \qquad |a| = \begin{vmatrix} 2 & -1 & 5 & 1 \\ 1 & 4 & 6 & 3 \\ 4 & 2 & 7 & 4 \\ 3 & 1 & 2 & 5 \end{vmatrix}$$

This determinant may be transformed by the use of principle 2 of Sec. 5. The procedure is to make all elements but one in some row or column equal to zero. The presence of the factor -1 in the second column suggests that we add four times the first row to the second, then add two times the first row to the third row, and finally add the first row to the fourth row. By Sec. 5h these operations do not change the value of the determinant. Hence we have

$$(6.2) \qquad |a| = \begin{vmatrix} 2 & -1 & 5 & 1 \\ 9 & 0 & 26 & 7 \\ 8 & 0 & 17 & 6 \\ 5 & 0 & 7 & 6 \end{vmatrix} = \begin{vmatrix} 9 & 26 & 7 \\ 8 & 17 & 6 \\ 5 & 7 & 6 \end{vmatrix}$$

If we now subtract the elements of the last column from the first column, we have

$$(6.3) \qquad |a| = \begin{vmatrix} 2 & 26 & 7 \\ 2 & 17 & 6 \\ -1 & 7 & 6 \end{vmatrix}$$

We now add two times the third row to the first row and two times the third row to the second row and obtain

$$(6.4) \qquad |a| = \begin{vmatrix} 0 & 40 & 19 \\ 0 & 31 & 18 \\ -1 & 7 & 6 \end{vmatrix} = - \begin{vmatrix} 40 & 19 \\ 31 & 18 \end{vmatrix}$$

Now we may subtract the second row from the first row and obtain

$$(6.5) \qquad |a| = -1 \begin{vmatrix} 9 & 1 \\ 31 & 18 \end{vmatrix} = -(162 - 31) = -131$$

This procedure is much shorter than a direct application of the Laplacian expansion rule.

A Useful Theorem. We now turn to a consideration of a theorem of great power for evaluating numerical determinants. The method of evaluation, based on the theorem to be considered, was found most successful at the Mathematical Laboratory of the University of Edinburgh and was due originally to F. Chiò.

To deduce the theorem in question, consider the fourth-order determinant

$$(6.6) \qquad |b| = \begin{vmatrix} b_{11} & b_{12} & b_{13} & b_{14} \\ b_{21} & b_{22} & b_{23} & b_{24} \\ b_{31} & b_{32} & b_{33} & b_{34} \\ b_{41} & b_{42} & b_{43} & b_{44} \end{vmatrix}$$

We now notice whether any element is equal to unity. If not, we prepare the determinant in such a manner that one of the elements is unity. This may be done by dividing some row or column by a suitable number, say m, that will make one of the elements equal to unity and then placing the number m as a factor outside the determinant. The same result may also be effected in many cases with the aid of Sec. 5h. For simplicity we shall suppose that this has been done and that, in this case, the element b_{23} is equal to unity.

Now let us divide the various columns of the determinant b by b_{21}, b_{22}, b_{23}, and b_{24}, respectively; then in view of the fact that the element b_{23} has been made unity, we have

$$(6.7) \qquad |b| = b_{21}b_{22}b_{23}b_{24} \begin{vmatrix} \dfrac{b_{11}}{b_{21}} & \dfrac{b_{12}}{b_{22}} & b_{13} & \dfrac{b_{14}}{b_{24}} \\ 1 & 1 & 1 & 1 \\ \dfrac{b_{31}}{b_{21}} & \dfrac{b_{32}}{b_{22}} & b_{33} & \dfrac{b_{34}}{b_{24}} \\ \dfrac{b_{41}}{b_{21}} & \dfrac{b_{42}}{b_{22}} & b_{43} & \dfrac{b_{44}}{b_{24}} \end{vmatrix}$$

Now, if we subtract the elements of the third column from those of the other columns, we obtain

$$(6.8) \qquad |b| = b_{21}b_{22}b_{23}b_{24}|a|$$

where

$$|a| = \begin{vmatrix} \dfrac{b_{11}}{b_{21}} - b_{13} & \dfrac{b_{12}}{b_{22}} - b_{13} & b_{13} & \dfrac{b_{14}}{b_{24}} - b_{13} \\ 0 & 0 & 1 & 0 \\ \dfrac{b_{31}}{b_{21}} - b_{33} & \dfrac{b_{32}}{b_{22}} - b_{33} & b_{33} & \dfrac{b_{34}}{b_{24}} - b_{33} \\ \dfrac{b_{41}}{b_{21}} - b_{43} & \dfrac{b_{42}}{b_{22}} - b_{43} & b_{43} & \dfrac{b_{44}}{b_{24}} - b_{43} \end{vmatrix}$$

Expanding in terms of the second row, we obtain

$$(6.9) \qquad |a| = (-1)^{2+3} \begin{vmatrix} \dfrac{b_{11}}{b_{21}} - b_{13} & \dfrac{b_{12}}{b_{22}} - b_{13} & \dfrac{b_{14}}{b_{24}} - b_{13} \\ \dfrac{b_{31}}{b_{21}} - b_{33} & \dfrac{b_{32}}{b_{22}} - b_{33} & \dfrac{b_{34}}{b_{24}} - b_{33} \\ \dfrac{b_{41}}{b_{21}} - b_{43} & \dfrac{b_{42}}{b_{22}} - b_{43} & \dfrac{b_{44}}{b_{24}} - b_{43} \end{vmatrix}$$

Substituting this value of $|a|$ into (6.8) and multiplying the various columns by the factors outside, we finally obtain

$$(6.10) \qquad |b| = (-1)^{2+3} \begin{vmatrix} b_{11} - b_{21}b_{13} & b_{12} - b_{22}b_{13} & b_{14} - b_{24}b_{13} \\ b_{31} - b_{21}b_{33} & b_{32} - b_{22}b_{33} & b_{34} - b_{24}b_{33} \\ b_{41} - b_{21}b_{43} & b_{42} - b_{22}b_{43} & b_{44} - b_{24}b_{43} \end{vmatrix}$$

The theorem may be formulated by means of the following rule. The element that has been made unity at the start of the process is called the *pivotal element.* In this case it is the element b_{23}. The rule says:

The row and column intersecting in the pivotal element of the original determinant, say the rth row and the sth column, are deleted; then every element u is diminished by the product of the elements which stand where the eliminated row and column are met by perpendiculars from u, and the whole determinant is multiplied by $(-1)^{r+s}$.

By the application of this theorem we reduce the order of the determinant by one unit. Repeated application of this theorem reduces the determinant to one of the second order, and then its value is immediately written down.

Before turning to a consideration of linear algebraic equations and to the application of the theory of determinants to their solution, a brief discussion of matrix algebra and the fundamental operations involving matrices is necessary. In this chapter the fundamental definitions and the most important properties of matrices will be outlined.

7. Definition of a Matrix. By a square matrix a of order n is meant a system of elements that may be real or complex numbers arranged in a square formation of n rows and columns. That is, the symbol $[a]$ stands for the array

$$(7.1) \qquad [a] = \begin{bmatrix} a_{11} & a_{12} & \cdots & a_{1n} \\ a_{21} & a_{22} & \cdots & a_{2n} \\ \cdots & \cdots & \cdots & \cdots \\ a_{n1} & a_{n2} & \cdots & a_{nn} \end{bmatrix}$$

where a_{ij} denotes the element standing in the ith row and jth column. The determinant having the same elements as the matrix $[a]$ is denoted by $|a|$ and is called the *determinant* of the matrix.

Besides square arrays like (7.1) we shall have occasion to use rectangular arrays or matrices of m rows and n columns. Such arrays will be called *matrices of order* $(m \times n)$. Where there is only one row so that $m = 1$, the matrix will be termed a *vector of the first kind*, or a *prime*. As an example, we have

$$(7.2) \qquad [a] = [a_{11} \quad a_{12} \quad \cdots \quad a_{1n}]$$

On the other hand, a matrix of a single column of n elements will be termed a *vector of the second kind*, or a *point*. To save space, it will be printed horizontally and not vertically and will be denoted by parentheses thus:

$$(7.3) \qquad \{b\} = (b_{11} \quad b_{21} \quad \cdots \quad b_{n1})$$

Transposition of Matrices. The accented matrix $[a]' = [a_{ji}]$ obtained by a complete interchange of rows and columns in $[a]$ is called the *transposed matrix of* $[a]$. The ith row of $[a]$ is identical with the ith column of $[a]'$. For vectors we have

$$(7.4) \qquad [u]' = \{u\} \qquad \{v\}' = [v], \text{ a row}$$

8. Special Matrices. *a. Square Matrix.* If the numbers of rows and of columns of a matrix are equal to n, then such a matrix is said to be a *square matrix of order* n, or simply a *matrix of order* n.

b. Diagonal Matrix. If all the elements other than those in the principal diagonal are zero, then the matrix is called a *diagonal matrix.*

c. The Unit Matrix. The unit matrix of order n is defined to be the diagonal matrix of order n which has 1's for all its diagonal elements. It is denoted by U_n or simply by U when its order is apparent.

d. Symmetrical Matrices. If $a_{ij} = a_{ij}$ for all i and j, the matrix $[a]$ is said to be symmetrical and it is identical to its transposed matrix. That is, if $[a]$ is symmetrical, then $[a]' = [a]$, and conversely.

e. Skew-symmetric Matrix. If $a_{ij} = -a_{ji}$ for all unequal i and j, but the elements a_{ii} are not all zero, then the matrix is called a *skew* matrix. If $a_{ij} = -a_{ji}$ for all i and j so that all $a_{ii} = 0$, the matrix is called a *skew-symmetric* matrix. It may be noted that both symmetrical and skew matrices are necessarily square.

f. Null Matrices. If a matrix has all its elements equal to zero, it is called a *null* matrix and is represented by $[0]$.

9. Equality of Matrices, Addition and Subtraction. It is apparent from what has been said concerning matrices that a matrix is entirely different from a determinant. A determinant is a symbolic representation of a certain homogeneous polynomial formed from the elements of the determinant as described in Sec. 4. A matrix, on the other hand, is merely a square or rectangular array of quantities. By defining certain rules of operation that prescribe the manner in which these arrays are to be manipulated, a certain algebra may be developed that has a formal similarity to ordinary algebra but involves certain operations that are performed on the elements of the matrices. It is to a consideration of these fundamental definitions and rules of operation that we now turn.

a. Equality of Matrices. The concept of equality is fundamental in algebra and is likewise of fundamental importance in matrix algebra. In matrix algebra two matrices $[a]$ and $[b]$ of the same order are defined to be equal if and only if their corresponding elements are identical; that is, we have

(9.1) $$[a] = [b]$$

provided that

(9.2) $$a_{ij} = b_{ij} \qquad \text{all } i \text{ and } j$$

b. Addition and Subtraction. If $[a]$ and $[b]$ are matrices of the same order, then the sum of $[a]$ and $[b]$ is defined to be a matrix $[c]$, the typical element of which is $c_{ij} = a_{ij} + b_{ij}$. In other words, by definition

(9.3) $$[c] = [a] + [b]$$

provided

(9.4) $$c_{ij} = a_{ij} + b_{ij}$$

In a similar manner we have

(9.5) $$[d] = [a] - [b]$$

provided that

(9.6) $$d_{ij} = a_{ij} - b_{ij}$$

10. Multiplication of Matrices. *a. Scalar Multiplication.* By definition, multiplication of a matrix [a] by an ordinary number or scalar k results in a new matrix b defined by

(10.1) $$k[a] = [b]$$

where

(10.2) $$b_{ij} = ka_{ij}$$

That is, by definition, the multiplication of a matrix by a scalar quantity yields a new matrix whose elements are obtained by multiplying the elements of the original matrix by the scalar multiplier.

b. Matrix Multiplication. The definition of the operation of multiplication of matrices by matrices differs in important respects from ordinary scalar multiplication. The rule of multiplication is such that two matrices can be multiplied only when the number of columns of the first is equal to the number of rows of the second. Matrices that satisfy this condition are termed *conformable matrices*.

Definition. The product of a matrix [a] by a matrix [b] is defined by the equation

(10.3) $$[a][b] = [c]$$

where

(10.4) $$c_{ij} = \sum_{k=1}^{k=p} a_{ik}b_{kj}$$

and the orders of the matrices [a], [b], and [c] are $(m \times p)$, $(p \times n)$, and $(m \times n)$, respectively. As an example of this definition, let us consider the multiplication of the matrix

(10.5) $$[a] = \begin{bmatrix} a_{11} & a_{12} & a_{13} \\ a_{21} & a_{22} & a_{23} \\ a_{31} & a_{32} & a_{33} \end{bmatrix}$$

by

(10.6) $$[b] = \begin{bmatrix} b_{11} & b_{12} \\ b_{21} & b_{22} \\ b_{31} & b_{32} \end{bmatrix}$$

By applying the definition we obtain

$$(10.7) \quad [a][b] = \begin{bmatrix} a_{11}b_{11} + a_{12}b_{21} + a_{13}b_{31} & a_{11}b_{12} + a_{12}b_{22} + a_{13}b_{32} \\ a_{21}b_{11} + a_{22}b_{21} + a_{23}b_{31} & a_{21}b_{12} + a_{22}b_{22} + a_{23}b_{32} \\ a_{31}b_{11} + a_{32}b_{21} + a_{33}b_{31} & a_{31}b_{12} + a_{32}b_{22} + a_{33}b_{32} \end{bmatrix}$$

If the matrices are square and each of order n, then the corresponding relation $|a| \, |b| = |c|$ is true for the determinants of the matrices $[a]$, $[b]$, and $[c]$. The proof of this frequently useful result will be omitted.

Since matrices are regarded as equal only when they are element for element identical, it follows that, since a row-by-column rule will, in general, give different elements than a column-by-row rule, the product $[b][a]$, when it exists, is usually different from $[a][b]$. Therefore it is necessary to distinguish between *premultiplication*, as when $[b]$ is premultiplied by $[a]$ to yield the product $[a][b]$, and *postmultiplication*, as when $[b]$ is postmultiplied by $[a]$ to yield the product $[b][a]$. If we have the equality

$$(10.8) \qquad [a][b] = [b][a]$$

the matrices a and b are said to *commute* or to be *permutable*. The unit matrix U, it may be noted, commutes with any square matrix of the same order. That is, we have for all such $[a]$

$$(10.9) \qquad [a]U = U[a] = [a]$$

c. *Continued Products of Matrices.* Except for the noncommutative law of multiplication (and therefore of division, which is defined as the inverse operation), all the ordinary laws of algebra apply to matrices. Of particular importance is the associative law of continued products,

$$(10.10) \qquad ([a][b][c]) = [a]([b][c])$$

which allows one to dispense with parentheses and to write $[a][b][c]$ without ambiguity, since the double summation

$$\sum_k \sum_l a_{ik}b_{kl}c_{lj}$$

can be carried out in either of the orders indicated.

It must be noted, however, that the product of a chain of matrices will have meaning only if the adjacent matrices of the chain are conformable.

d. *Positive Powers of a Square Matrix.* If a square matrix is multiplied by itself n times, the resultant matrix is defined as $[a]^n$. That is,

$$(10.11) \qquad [a]^n = [a][a] \cdots [a] \text{ to } n \text{ factors}$$

11. Matrix Division, the Inverse Matrix. If the determinant $|a|$ of a square matrix $[a]$ does not vanish, $[a]$ is said to be *nonsingular* and possesses a *reciprocal*, or inverse, matrix $[R]$ such that

$$(11.1) \qquad [a][R] = U = [R][a]$$

where U is the unit matrix of the same order as $[a]$.

 a. The Adjoint Matrix of a Matrix.   Let A_{ij} denote the cofactor of the element a_{ij} in the determinant $|a|$ of the matrix $[a]$.   Then the matrix $[A_{ji}]$ is called the *adjoint* of the matrix $[a]$.   This matrix exists whether $[a]$ is singular or not.   Now by (4.8) we have

$$(11.2) \qquad [a][A_{ji}] = |a|U = [A_{ji}][a]$$

It is thus seen that the product of $[a]$ and its adjoint is a special type of diagonal matrix called a *scalar matrix*.   Each diagonal element $i = j$ is equal to the determinant $|a|$, and the other elements are zero.

If $|a| \neq 0$, we may divide through by the scalar $|a|$ and hence obtain at once the required form of $[R]$, the inverse of $[a]$.   From (11.2) we thus have

$$(11.3) \qquad \frac{[a][A_{ji}]}{|a|} = U$$

Therefore, comparing this with (11.1) we see that

$$(11.4) \qquad [R] = \frac{[A_{ji}]}{|a|} = [a]^{-1}$$

The notation $[a]^{-1}$ is introduced to denote the inverse of $[a]$.   By actual multiplication it may be proved that

$$(11.5) \qquad [a][a]^{-1} = [a]^{-1}[a] = U$$

so that the name *reciprocal* and the notation $[a]^{-1}$ are justified.

If a square matrix is nonsingular, it possesses a reciprocal and multiplication by the reciprocal is in many ways analogous to division in ordinary algebra.   As an illustration, let it be required to obtain the inverse of the matrix

$$(11.6) \qquad [a] = \begin{bmatrix} a_{11} & a_{12} & a_{13} \\ a_{21} & a_{22} & a_{23} \\ a_{31} & a_{32} & a_{33} \end{bmatrix}$$

Let $|a|$ denote the determinant of $[a]$.   The next step in the process is to form the transpose of a.

$$(11.7) \qquad [a]' = \begin{bmatrix} a_{11} & a_{21} & a_{31} \\ a_{12} & a_{22} & a_{32} \\ a_{13} & a_{23} & a_{33} \end{bmatrix}$$

We now replace the elements of $[a]'$ by their corresponding cofactors and obtain

$$(11.8) \quad [A_{ji}] = \begin{bmatrix} a_{22}a_{33} - a_{23}a_{32} & a_{13}a_{32} - a_{12}a_{33} & a_{12}a_{23} - a_{13}a_{22} \\ a_{23}a_{31} - a_{21}a_{33} & a_{11}a_{33} - a_{13}a_{31} & a_{13}a_{21} - a_{11}a_{23} \\ a_{21}a_{32} - a_{22}a_{31} & a_{12}a_{31} - a_{11}a_{32} & a_{11}a_{22} - a_{12}a_{21} \end{bmatrix}$$

This inverse $[a]^{-1}$ is therefore

$$(11.9) \qquad \frac{[A_{ji}]}{|a|}$$

As has been mentioned, multiplication by an inverse matrix plays the same role in matrix algebra that division plays in ordinary algebra. That is, if we have

$$(11.10) \qquad [a][b] = [c][d]$$

where $[a]$ is a nonsingular matrix, then, on premultiplying by $[a]^{-1}$, the inverse of $[a]$, we obtain

$$(11.11) \qquad [a]^{-1}[a][b] = [a]^{-1}[c][d]$$

or

$$(11.12) \qquad [b] = [a]^{-1}[c][d]$$

b. Negative Powers of a Square Matrix. If $[a]$ is a nonsingular matrix, then negative powers of $[a]$ are defined by raising the inverse matrix of $[a]$, $[a]^{-1}$, to positive powers. That is,

$$(11.13) \qquad [a]^{-n} = ([a]^{-1})^n$$

12. The Reversal Law in Transposed and Reciprocated Products. One of the fundamental consequences of the noncommutative law of matrix multiplication is the *reversal law* exemplified in transposing and reciprocating a continued product of matrices.

a. Transposition. Let $[a]$ be a $(p \times n)$ matrix, that is, one having p rows and n columns, and let $[b]$ be an $(m \times p)$ matrix. Then the product $[c] = [b][a]$ is an $(m \times n)$ matrix of which the typical element is

$$(12.1) \qquad c_{ij} = \sum_{r=1}^{p} b_{ir}a_{rj}$$

When transposed, $[a]'$ and $[b]'$ become $(n \times p)$ and $(p \times m)$ matrices; they are now conformable when multiplied in the order $[a]'[b]'$. This product is an $(n \times m)$ matrix, which may be readily seen to be the transpose of $[c]$ since its typical element is

$$(12.2) \qquad c_{ji} = \sum_{r=1}^{p} a_{ri}b_{jr}$$

It thus follows that when a matrix product is transposed the order of the matrices forming the product must be reversed. That is,

(12.3) $$([a][b])' = [b]'[a]'$$

and similarly

(12.4) $$([a][b][c])' = [c]'[b]'[a]', \text{ etc.}$$

b. Reciprocation. Let us suppose that in the equation $[c] = [b][a]$ the matrices are square and nonsingular. If we premultiply both sides of the equation by $[a]^{-1}[b]^{-1}$ and postmultiply by $[c]^{-1}$, then we obtain $[a]^{-1}[b]^{-1} = [c]^{-1}$. We thus get the rule that

(12.5) $$[a]^{-1}[b]^{-1} = ([b][a])^{-1}$$

Similarly

(12.6) $$([a][b][c])^{-1} = [c]^{-1}[b]^{-1}[a]^{-1}$$

13. Properties of Diagonal and Unit Matrices. Suppose that $[a]$ is a square matrix of order n and $[b]$ is a diagonal matrix, that is, a matrix that has all its elements zero with the exception of the elements in the main diagonal, and is of the same order as $[a]$. Then, if $[c] = [b][a]$, we have

(13.1) $$c_{ij} = \sum_{r=1}^{n} b_{ir}a_{rj} = b_{ii}a_{ij}$$

since $b_{ir} = 0$ unless $r = i$.

It is thus seen that premultiplication by a diagonal matrix has the effect of multiplying every element in any row of a matrix by a constant. It can be similarly shown that postmultiplication by a diagonal matrix results in the multiplication of every element in any column of a matrix by a constant. The unit matrix plays the same role in matrix algebra that the number 1 does in ordinary scalar algebra.

14. Matrices Partitioned into Submatrices. It is sometimes convenient to extend the use of the fundamental laws of combinations of matrices to the case where a matrix is regarded as constructed from elements that are submatrices or minor matrices of elements. As an example, consider

(14.1) $$[a] = \begin{bmatrix} 1 & 9 & \cdot & 3 \\ 2 & 8 & \cdot & 4 \\ \cdots & \cdots & \cdots & \cdots \\ 6 & 2 & \cdot & 7 \end{bmatrix}$$

This can be written in the form

$$(14.2) \qquad [a] = \begin{bmatrix} P & Q \\ R & S \end{bmatrix}$$

where

$$[P] = \begin{bmatrix} 1 & 9 \\ 2 & 8 \end{bmatrix} \qquad \{Q\} = \begin{bmatrix} 3 \\ 4 \end{bmatrix} \qquad [R] = [6 \quad 2] \qquad [S] = [7]$$

In this case the diagonal submatrices $[P]$ and $[S]$ are square, and the partitioning is diagonally symmetrical. Let $[b]$ be a square matrix of the third order that is similarly partitioned.

$$(14.3) \qquad [b] = \begin{bmatrix} 2 & 9 & \cdot & 4 \\ & & \cdot & \\ 3 & 6 & \cdot & 8 \\ & & \cdot & \\ \cdots & \cdots & \cdots \\ 1 & 5 & \cdot & 7 \end{bmatrix} = \begin{bmatrix} P_1 & Q_1 \\ R_1 & S_1 \end{bmatrix}$$

Then, by addition and multiplication, we have

$$(14.4) \qquad [a] + [b] = \begin{bmatrix} P + P_1 & Q + Q_1 \\ R + R_1 & S + S_1 \end{bmatrix}$$

$$(14.5) \qquad [a][b] = \begin{bmatrix} PP_1 + QR_1 & PQ_1 + QS_1 \\ RP_1 + SR_1 & RQ_1 + SS_1 \end{bmatrix}$$

as may be easily verified.

In each case the resulting matrix is of the same order and is partitioned in the same way as the original matrix factors. As has been stated in Sec. 10, a rectangular matrix $[b]$ may be premultiplied by another rectangular matrix $[a]$ provided the two matrices are *conformable*, that is, the number of rows of $[b]$ is equal to the number of columns of $[a]$. Now, if $[a]$ and $[b]$ are both partitioned into submatrices such that the grouping of columns in $[a]$ agrees with the grouping of rows in $[b]$, it can be shown that the product $[a][b]$ may be obtained by treating the submatrices as elements and proceeding according to the multiplication rule.

15. Matrices of Special Types. *a. Conjugate Matrices.* To the operations $[a]'$ and $[a]^{-1}$, defined by transposition and inversion, may be added another one. This operation is denoted by $[\bar{a}]$ and implies that if the elements of $[a]$ are complex numbers the corresponding elements of $[\bar{a}]$ are their respective complex conjugates. The matrix $[\bar{a}]$ is called the conjugate of $[a]$.

b. The Associate of $[a]$. The transposed conjugate of $[a]$, $[\bar{a}]'$, is called the *associate* of $[a]$.

c. *Symmetric Matrix.* If $[a] = [a]'$, the matrix $[a]$ is symmetric.

d. *Involutory Matrix.* If $[a] = [a]^{-1}$, the matrix $[a]$ is involutory.

e. If $[a] = [\bar{a}]$, $[a]$ is a *real matrix.*

f. *Orthogonal Matrix.* If $[a] = ([a]')^{-1}$, $[a]$ is an orthogonal matrix.

g. *Hermitian Matrix.* If $[a] = [\bar{a}]'$, $[a]$ is a Hermitian matrix.

h. *Unitary Matrix.* If $[a] = ([\bar{a}]')^{-1}$, $[a]$ is unitary.

i. *Skew-symmetric Matrix.* If $[a] = -[a]'$, $[a]$ is skew symmetric.

j. *Pure Imaginary.* If $[a] = -[\bar{a}]$, $[a]$ is pure imaginary.

k. *Skew Hermitian.* If $[a] = -[\bar{a}]'$, $[a]$ is skew Hermitian.

16. The Solution of n Linear Equations in n Unknowns. In later chapters the methods of the operational calculus and matrix algebra will be applied to the solution of sets of linear algebraic and operational equations. The operations involved in the solution of these equations may be expressed most concisely and elegantly by means of matrix algebra.

Suppose we have the set of n linear algebraic equations in n unknowns,

$$
\begin{aligned}
e_1 &= Z_{11}i_1 + Z_{12}i_2 + \cdots + Z_{1n}i_n \\
e_2 &= Z_{21}i_1 + Z_{22}i_2 + \cdots + Z_{2n}i_n \\
&\ \cdots\cdots\cdots\cdots\cdots\cdots\cdots\cdots\cdots \\
e_n &= Z_{n1}i_1 + Z_{n2}i_2 + \cdots + Z_{nn}i_n
\end{aligned}
$$

(16.1)

The quantities e_j, Z_{ij}, and i_j may be real or complex numbers. If the relation (16.1) exists between the variables e_j and i_j, then the set of variables e_j is said to be derived from the set i_j by a *linear transformation.* The whole set of Eqs. (16.1) may be represented by the single matrix equation

(16.2)
$$ \{e\} = [Z]\{i\} $$

where $\{e\}$ and $\{i\}$ are column matrices whose elements are the variables e_j and i_j. The square matrix $[Z]$ is called the *matrix of the transformation.* When $[Z]$ is nonsingular, Eq. (16.2) may be premultiplied by $[Z]^{-1}$ and we obtain

(16.3)
$$ [Z]^{-1}\{e\} = [Z]^{-1}[Z]\{i\} = \{i\} $$

We thus have a very convenient explicit solution for the unknowns $(i_1, i_2, \ldots, i_n)$. The elements of the matrix $[Z]^{-1}$ may be calculated by Eq. (11.4). As a simple example, let us solve the system of Eqs. (2.1) by using matrix notation. If we introduce the matrices

(16.4)
$$ [a] = \begin{bmatrix} a_{11} & a_{12} \\ a_{21} & a_{22} \end{bmatrix} \quad \{x\} = \begin{Bmatrix} x_1 \\ x_2 \end{Bmatrix} \quad \{x\} = \begin{Bmatrix} x_1 \\ x_2 \end{Bmatrix} $$

then Eqs. (2.1) may be written in the form

(16.5)
$$ [a]\{x\} = \{k\} $$

and if $[a]$ is nonsingular, the solution is

(16.6)
$$\begin{Bmatrix} x_1 \\ x_2 \end{Bmatrix} = \begin{bmatrix} a_{11} & a_{12} \\ a_{21} & a_{22} \end{bmatrix}^{-1} \begin{Bmatrix} k_1 \\ k_2 \end{Bmatrix}$$

But by (11.4) we have

(16.7)
$$\begin{bmatrix} a_{11} & a_{12} \\ a_{21} & a_{22} \end{bmatrix}^{-1} = \frac{1}{a_{11}a_{22} - a_{21}a_{12}} \begin{bmatrix} a_{22} & -a_{12} \\ -a_{21} & a_{11} \end{bmatrix}$$

Hence, carrying out the matrix multiplication expressed in (16.6), we obtain

(16.8)
$$x_1 = \frac{k_1 a_{22} - k_2 a_{12}}{a_{11}a_{22} - a_{21}a_{12}}$$
$$x_2 = \frac{k_2 a_{11} - k_1 a_{21}}{a_{11}a_{22} - a_{21}a_{12}}$$

Although the solution of a set of linear equations is very elegantly and concisely expressed in terms of the inverse matrix of the coefficients, it frequently happens in practice that it is necessary to solve for only one or two of the unknowns.

In this case it is frequently more convenient to use Cramer's rule to obtain the solution. The proof of Cramer's rule follows from the properties of the determinant expressed by Eq. (4.8) and will not be given. Let us consider the set of n equations in the unknowns $(x_1, x_2, \ldots , x_n)$,

(16.9)
$$\begin{aligned} a_{11}x_1 + a_{12}x_2 + \cdots + a_{1n}x_n &= k_1 \\ a_{21}x_1 + a_{22}x_2 + \cdots + a_{2n}x_n &= k_2 \\ \cdots \cdots \cdots \cdots \cdots \cdots \cdots \cdots \cdots \\ a_{n1}x_1 + a_{n2}x_2 + \cdots + a_{nn}x_n &= k_n \end{aligned}$$

Then if the determinant of the system

(16.10)
$$|a| = \begin{vmatrix} a_{11} & a_{12} & \cdots & a_{1n} \\ \cdots & \cdots \cdots \cdots & \cdots \\ a_{n1} & a_{n2} & \cdots & a_{nn} \end{vmatrix} \neq 0$$

the system of Eqs. (16.9) has a unique solution given by

(16.11)
$$x_1 = \frac{D_1}{|a|} \qquad x_2 = \frac{D_2}{|a|} \qquad \cdots \qquad x_n = \frac{D_n}{|a|}$$

where D_r is the determinant formed by replacing the elements

$$a_{1r}, a_{2r}, \ldots , a_{nr}$$

of the rth column of $|a|$ by $(k_1, k_2, \ldots , k_n)$, respectively.

For example, let us solve the system

$$(16.12) \qquad \begin{aligned} x_1 - 2x_2 + 3x_3 &= 2 \\ 2x_1 \qquad - 3x_3 &= 3 \\ x_1 + x_2 + x_3 &= 6 \end{aligned}$$

We have

$$(16.13) \qquad |a| = \begin{vmatrix} 1 & -2 & 3 \\ 2 & 0 & -3 \\ 1 & 1 & 1 \end{vmatrix} = 19$$

Hence

$$(16.14) \qquad \begin{aligned} x_1 &= \frac{\begin{vmatrix} 2 & -2 & 3 \\ 3 & 0 & -3 \\ 6 & 1 & 1 \end{vmatrix}}{19} = 3 \\[2em] x_2 &= \frac{\begin{vmatrix} 1 & 2 & 3 \\ 2 & 3 & -3 \\ 1 & 6 & 1 \end{vmatrix}}{19} = 2 \\[2em] x_3 &= \frac{\begin{vmatrix} 1 & -2 & 2 \\ 2 & 0 & 3 \\ 1 & 1 & 6 \end{vmatrix}}{19} = 1 \end{aligned}$$

If it happens that the determinant of the coefficients $|a|$ is zero, then the investigation of the solutions is more complicated. In such a case it is of great value to use the notion of *rank* of a determinant.

If $|a|$ is a determinant of the nth order and it is not zero, then it is said to be of *rank* n.

If $|a|$ is zero and also every $(r + 1)$-rowed minor formed from $|a|$ is zero but there exists at least one r-rowed minor that is not zero, then the determinant $|a|$ is said to be of *rank* r.

The idea of rank is important in stating the properties of the solution of n nonhomogeneous linear equations in n unknowns. The following various possibilities may arise:

1. If the determinant $|a| \neq 0$, there exists a unique solution that is given by Cramer's rule, that is, Eq. (16.11).

2. If $|a|$ is of rank $r < n$ and any of the determinants $D_1, D_2, \ldots,$ D_n of Eq. (16.11) are of rank greater than r, there is no solution of the system (16.9).

3. If $|a|$ is of rank $r < n$ and the rank of none of $D_1 D_2 \cdots D_n$ *exceeds* r, then there exist infinitely many sets of solutions of the system.

Homogeneous Linear Equations. Let us consider the following system of n linear equations in n unknowns:

$$a_{11}x_1 + a_{12}x_2 + a_{13}x_3 + \cdots + a_{1n}x_n = 0$$

(16.15) $\cdots\cdots\cdots\cdots\cdots$

$$a_{n1}x_1 + a_{n2}x_2 + a_{n3}x_3 + \cdots + a_{nn}x_n = 0$$

This set of equations has the trivial solution

(16.16) $$x_1 = x_2 = x_3 = \cdots = x_n = 0$$

A necessary and sufficient condition that the system (16.15) have a solution other than the trivial solution (16.16) is that the determinant $|a|$ of the coefficients must vanish. That is, we must have

(16.17) $$|a| = 0$$

This condition is of extreme importance in obtaining the frequency equation of oscillating systems.

17. Differentiation of a Matrix. If the elements of a matrix, $[a(t)] = [a_{rs}(t)]$, are functions of a scalar variable t, the matrix $[a(t)]$ is called a *matrix function* of t. The derivative of this matrix, when it exists, is defined by the equation

(17.1) $$\frac{d}{dt}[a(t)] = \left[\frac{d}{dt}a_{rs}(t)\right]$$

where $a_{rs}(t)$ is the matrix element in the rth row and sth column. Hence the elements of the derivative matrix $(d/dt)[a]$ are the derivatives of the corresponding elements of $[a]$.

18. Integration of Matrices. The integral of the matrix $[a(t)]$ is defined by the following equation:

(18.1) $$\int[a(t)]\,dt = \left[\int a_{rs}(t)\,dt\right]$$

The integral exists provided that the integral of each element of the matrix $[a(t)]$ exists. It is thus seen that the integral of a matrix whose elements are functions of a variable is obtained by integrating each of its corresponding elements.

19. The Characteristic Matrix and the Characteristic Equation of a Matrix. If μ is a scalar parameter and $[M]$ is a square matrix of order n, the following matrix,

(19.1) $$[K] = [\mu U - M]$$

$U = $ the nth-order unit matrix, is called the *characteristic matrix* of the matrix $[M]$. The determinant of the characteristic matrix, det $[K]$, is called the *characteristic function* of $[M]$. That is,

(19.2) $$\Delta(\mu) = \det[K]$$

is the characteristic function of the matrix $[M]$.

The equation

(19.3) $$\Delta(\mu) = \det [K] = 0$$

is the *characteristic equation* of the matrix $[M]$. In general, if $[M]$ is a square matrix of the nth order, its characteristic equation is an equation of the nth degree in μ. The n roots of this equation are called the characteristic roots, or *eigenvalues*, of the matrix $[M]$.

20. Reduction of a Matrix to Diagonal Form. In matrix algebra, when a matrix contains only one column, it is called a *column vector*. If $\{x\}$ is a column vector of the nth order and $[M]$ is an nth-order square matrix, the product

(20.1) $$\{y\} = [M]\{x\}$$

expresses the fact that the vector $\{y\}$ is derived from the vector $\{x\}$ by a linear transformation. The square matrix $[M]$ is called the *transformation matrix*. If it is required that

(20.2) $$\{y\} = \mu\{x\}$$

then (20.1) reduces to

(20.3) $$\mu\{x\} = [M]\{x\}$$

and the only effect of the transformation matrix $[M]$ on the vector $\{x\}$ is to multiply it by the scalar factor μ. Equation (20.3) may be written in the form

(20.4) $$[\mu U - M]\{x\} = [K]\{x\} = 0$$

This equation represents a set of homogeneous linear equations in the unknowns $x_1, x_2, \ldots, x_n$. Except in the trivial case where all the elements of $\{x\}$ are zero, the determinant of $[K]$ must vanish. Conversely, if $|K| = 0$, there exist nontrivial solutions. In order for this to be the case, the scalar μ can take only the values $\mu_1, \mu_2, \ldots, \mu_n$ which are the roots of the characteristic equation (19.3). The possible values of μ which satisfy (20.3) are thus the eigenvalues of $[M]$. The nontrivial solutions of (20.4) associated with these eigenvalues are called *eigenvectors* of $[M]$.

To each eigenvalue μ_i there corresponds an equation of the form (20.4) which can be written as follows:

(20.5) $$\mu_i\{x\}_i = [M]\{x\}_i \qquad i = 1, 2, 3, \ldots, n$$

where $\{x\}_i$ is any eigenvector associated with μ_i.

If (20.5) is premultiplied by $[M]$, it becomes

(20.6) $$\mu_i[M]\{x\}_i = \mu_i^2\{x\}_i = [M]^2\{x\}_i$$

By repeated multiplications by $[M]$ it can be shown that

(20.7) $$[M]^r\{x\}_i = \mu_i^r\{x\}_i$$

Let the ith eigenvector be denoted by the following notation:

(20.8) $$\{x\}_i = \begin{bmatrix} x_{1i} \\ x_{2i} \\ x_{3i} \\ . \\ . \\ . \\ x_{ni} \end{bmatrix}$$

and let the square matrix $[x]$ be the matrix formed by grouping the column eigenvectors into a square matrix so that

(20.9) $$[x] = \begin{bmatrix} x_{11} & x_{12} & x_{13} & \cdots & x_{1n} \\ x_{21} & x_{22} & x_{23} & \cdots & x_{2n} \\ \cdot & \cdot & \cdot & \cdots & \cdot \\ x_{n1} & x_{n2} & x_{n3} & & x_{nn} \end{bmatrix}$$

If $[d]$ denotes the following square diagonal matrix:

(20.10) $$[d] = \begin{bmatrix} \mu_1 & 0 & \cdots & 0 \\ 0 & \mu_2 & \cdots & 0 \\ \cdot & \cdot & \cdots & \cdot \\ 0 & 0 & & \mu_n \end{bmatrix}$$

it can be seen that the set of n equations (20.5) may be written in the form

(20.11) $$[x][d] = [M][x]$$

If the n eigenvalues of $[M]$ are distinct, it can be shown that the matrix $[x]$ is nonsingular and possesses an inverse $[x]^{-1}$. Hence (20.11) may be written in the form

(20.12) $$[d] = [x]^{-1}[M][x]$$

or

(20.13) $$[M] = [x][d][x]^{-1}$$

It is thus seen that a matrix $[x]$ which diagonalizes $[M]$ may be found by grouping the eigenvectors of $[M]$ into a square matrix. This may be done when the eigenvalues of $[M]$ are all different. When two or more of the eigenvalues of $[M]$ are equal to each other, reduction to the diagonal form is not always possible.

21. The Trace of a Matrix. The sum of all the diagonal elements of a square matrix is called the *trace* of the matrix and is denoted by the following expression:

$$(21.1) \qquad \mathrm{Tr}\,[M] = \sum_{i=1}^{i=n} M_{ii}$$

There exist some interesting relations between the trace of a matrix and the characteristic equation of the matrix.* The characteristic equation of $[M]$ has the form

$$(21.2) \quad \Delta(\mu) = \det\,[\mu U - M] = 0$$
$$= \mu^n + c_1\mu^{n-1} + c_2\mu^{n-2} + \cdots + c_{n-1}\mu + c_n = 0$$

It can be shown that

$$(21.3) \quad c_1 = -(M_{11} + M_{22} + M_{33} + \cdots + M_{nn}) = -\,\mathrm{Tr}\,[M]$$

If $\mu_1, \mu_2, \ldots, \mu_n$ are the *eigenvalues* of $[M]$, then as a result of (21.3) we have

$$(21.4) \qquad \mu_1 + \mu_2 + \mu_3 + \cdots + \mu_n = \mathrm{Tr}\,[M]$$

It can be shown that the product of the eigenvalues is given by the equation

$$(21.5) \qquad \mu_1 \times \mu_2 \times \mu_3 \times \cdots \times \mu_n = \det\,[M]$$

Maxime Bôcher has shown that there is an intimate connection between the traces of powers of a matrix and the coefficients of its characteristic equation (21.2). These results are of importance in obtaining the characteristic equations of matrices and in the computation of the inverses of matrices. The results of Bôcher are deduced in his book on higher algebra and are given here without proof.

The characteristic equation of a square matrix $[M]$ of the nth order is, in general, an equation of the nth degree as given by (21.2). Bôcher's results relate the coefficients c_i of the characteristic equation of $[M]$ to the traces of powers of $[M]$. Let

$$(21.6) \quad S_1 = \mathrm{Tr}\,[M] \qquad S_2 = \mathrm{Tr}\,[M]^2 \qquad \cdots \qquad S_n = \mathrm{Tr}\,[M]^n$$

Then the coefficients $c_1, c_2, \ldots, c_n$ of the characteristic equations are

$$(21.7) \qquad \begin{aligned} c_1 &= -S_1 \\ c_2 &= -\tfrac{1}{2}(c_1 S_1 + S_2) \\ c_3 &= -\tfrac{1}{3}(c_2 S_1 + c_1 S_2 + S_3) \\ &\cdots\cdots\cdots\cdots\cdots\cdots \\ c_n &= -\frac{1}{n}(c_{n-1}S_1 + c_{n-2}S_2 + \cdots + c_1 S_{n-1} + S_n) \end{aligned}$$

These equations enable one to obtain the characteristic equation of a matrix in a more efficient manner than by the direct expansion of

* M. Bôcher, "Introduction to Higher Algebra," The Macmillan Company, New York, 1931.

det $[\mu U - M]$. If the determinant of $[M]$ itself is desired, it can be calculated by the use of the following equation,

$$(21.8) \qquad\qquad \det [M] = (-1)^n c_n$$

where c_n is as given above.

22. The Cayley-Hamilton Theorem. One of the most important theorems of the theory of matrices is the Cayley-Hamilton theorem. By the use of this theorem many properties of matrices may be deduced, and functions of matrices can be simplified. The Cayley-Hamilton theorem is frequently stated in the following terse manner: Every square matrix satisfies its own characteristic equation in a matrix sense. This statement means that if the characteristic equation of the nth-order matrix $[M]$ is given by

$$(22.1) \quad \Delta(\mu) = \mu^n + c_1\mu^{n-1} + c_2\mu^{n-2} + \cdots + c_{n-1}\mu + c_n = 0$$

the Cayley-Hamilton theorem states that

$$(22.2) \quad \Delta([M]) = [M]^n + c_1[M]^{n-1} + c_2[M]^{n-2} + \cdots$$
$$+ c_{n-1}[M] + c_n U = [0]$$

where U is the nth-order unit matrix.

A heuristic proof of this theorem may be given by the use of the following result of Sec. 20,

$$(22.3) \quad [M]^r\{x\}_i = \mu_i^r\{x\}_i \qquad r = 1, 2, 3, \ldots \qquad i = 1, 2, 3, \ldots, n$$

where μ_i is the ith eigenvalue of $[M]$ and $\{x\}_i$ is the corresponding eigenvector. *The characteristic function* of $[M]$ is given by

$$(22.4) \qquad \Delta(\mu) = \mu^n + c_1\mu^{n-1} + c_2\mu^{n-2} + \cdots + c_{n-1}\mu + c_n$$

If in (22.4) the scalar μ is replaced by the square matrix $[M]$ and the coefficient of c_n is multiplied by the nth-order unit matrix U, the result may be written in the following form:

$$(22.5) \qquad \Delta([M]) = [M]^n + c_1[M]^{n-1} + c_2[M]^{n-2} + \cdots + c_n U$$

If (22.5) is postmultiplied by the eigenvector $\{x\}_i$, the result is

$$(22.6) \quad \Delta(M)\{x\}_i = ([M]^n + c_1[M]^{n-1} + c_2[M]^{n-2} + \cdots + c_n)\{x\}_i$$

As a consequence of (22.3), this may be written in the following form:

$$(22.7) \quad \Delta([M])\{x\}_i = (\mu_i^n + c_1\mu_i^{n-1} + c_2\mu_i^{n-2} + \cdots + c_n)\{x\}_i$$

However, since μ_i is one of the eigenvalues of $[M]$, we have

$$(22.8) \qquad \mu_i^n + c_1\mu_i^{n-1} + c_2\mu_i^{n-2} + \cdots + c_n = 0$$

Hence (22.7) reduces to

$$(22.9) \qquad \Delta([M])\{x\}_i = \{0\} \qquad i = 1, 2, 3, \ldots, n$$

The set of equations (22.9) may be written as the single equation

$$(22.10) \qquad \Delta([M])[x] = [0]$$

where $[x]$ is the square matrix (20.9) and $[0]$ is an nth-order square matrix of zeros. If $[M]$ has n distinct eigenvalues, the matrix $[x]$ is nonsingular and has an inverse. If (22.10) is postmultiplied by $[x]^{-1}$, the result is

$$(22.11) \qquad \Delta([M]) = [0]$$

This important result is the Cayley-Hamilton theorem. It may be shown that the Cayley-Hamilton theorem holds for singular matrices and for matrices that have repeated eigenvalues.[*]

If the matrix $[M]$ is nonsingular, its inverse may be computed by the use of the Cayley-Hamilton theorem in the following manner: Expand (22.11) in the form

$$(22.12) \quad \Delta([M]) = [M]^n + c_1[M]^{n-1} + c_2[M]^{n-2} + \cdots + c_n U = [0]$$

If this equation is premultiplied by $[M]^{-1}$, the result is

$$(22.13) \qquad [M]^{n-1} + c_1[M]^{n-2} + \cdots + c_n[M]^{-1} = [0]$$

Hence, if this equation is solved for $[M]^{-1}$, the result is

$$(22.14) \quad [M]^{-1} = -\frac{1}{c_n}([M]^{n-1} + c_1[M]^{n-2} + \cdots + c_{n-1}U)$$

This result expresses the inverse of $[M]$ in terms of the $n - 1$ powers of $[M]$ and has been suggested as a practical method for the computation of the inverses of large matrices.[†] Hotelling gives the following application of (22.14) to the computation of the inverse of a numerical matrix: Let the matrix to be inverted be

$$(22.15) \qquad [M] = \begin{bmatrix} 15 & 11 & 6 & -9 & -15 \\ 1 & 3 & 9 & -3 & -8 \\ 7 & 6 & 6 & -3 & -11 \\ 7 & 7 & 5 & -3 & -11 \\ 17 & 12 & 5 & -10 & -16 \end{bmatrix}$$

Then

$$(22.16) \qquad [M]^2 = \begin{bmatrix} -40 & -9 & 105 & -9 & -40 \\ -76 & -43 & 32 & 44 & 23 \\ -55 & -22 & 62 & 20 & -10 \\ -61 & -25 & 65 & 20 & -7 \\ -40 & -9 & 110 & -14 & -40 \end{bmatrix}$$

[*] M. Bôcher, "Introduction to Higher Algebra," p. 296, The Macmillan Company, New York, 1931.

[†] H. Hotelling, New Methods in Matrix Calculation, *The Annals of Mathematical Statistics*, vol. 14, no. 1, pp. 1–34, March, 1943.

$$(22.17) \quad [M]^3 = \begin{bmatrix} -617 & -380 & 64 & 499 & 256 \\ -260 & -189 & -316 & 355 & 280 \\ -443 & -279 & -106 & 415 & 259 \\ -464 & -300 & -136 & 439 & 292 \\ -617 & -385 & 69 & 499 & 256 \end{bmatrix}$$

$$(22.18) \quad [M]^4 = \begin{bmatrix} -1,342 & -978 & -2,963 & 2,444 & 2,006 \\ 944 & 522 & -1,982 & -10 & 503 \\ -358 & -333 & -2,435 & 1,307 & 1,334 \\ -175 & -243 & -2,645 & 1,247 & 1,355 \\ -1,312 & -963 & -2,978 & 2,444 & 1,991 \end{bmatrix}$$

From the diagonals of the above matrices, the following traces may be calculated:

$$(22.19) \quad \begin{aligned} S_1 &= \operatorname{Tr}[M] = 5 \\ S_2 &= \operatorname{Tr}[M]^2 = -41 \\ S_3 &= \operatorname{Tr}[M]^3 = -217 \\ S_4 &= \operatorname{Tr}[M]^4 = -17 \end{aligned}$$

By means of (21.7) the following coefficients of the characteristic equation of $[M]$ can be computed:

$$(22.20) \quad c_1 = -5 \qquad c_2 = 33 \qquad c_3 = -51 \qquad c_4 = 135 \qquad c_5 = 225$$

The characteristic equation of $[M]$ is therefore

$$(22.21) \qquad \mu^5 - 5\mu^4 + 33\mu^3 - 51\mu^2 + 135\mu + 225 = 0$$

The inverse of $[M]$ is now computed by the use of (22.14) and is given by

$$(22.22) \quad [M]^{-1} = \frac{-1}{225} \begin{bmatrix} -207 & 64 & -124 & 111 & 171 \\ -315 & 30 & 195 & -180 & 270 \\ -315 & 30 & -30 & 45 & 270 \\ -225 & 75 & -75 & 0 & 225 \\ -414 & 53 & 52 & -3 & 342 \end{bmatrix}$$

If the determinant of $[M]$ is desired, it may be obtained from the equation

$$(22.23) \qquad \det[M] = (-1)^n c_n = -225$$

This method for the computation of the inverse of a matrix is straightforward and easily checked and is ideally adapted to matrix multiplication by means of punched cards. As a by-product of the computation the characteristic equation and the determinant of the matrix are obtained.

23. The Inversion of Large Matrices. With the development of many powerful modern instruments of calculation such as punched-card machines, electronic digital-computing machines, analogue computers, etc., the field of application of mathematical analysis has vastly increased. Many diversified problems in various fields may be reduced to one mathematical operation: that of the solution of systems of linear algebraic equations. A few of the problems that may be reduced to this mathematical common denominator are the following:

1. The distribution of electrical currents in multimesh electrical circuits
2. The distribution of the rate of flow of water in complex hydraulic systems
3. The approximate solution of potential problems
4. The solution of the normal equations in the application of the method of least squares to various physical investigations
5. The applications of statistical studies to psychology, sociology, and economics
6. The determination of the amplitudes of motion in the forced vibrations of mechanical systems
7. The approximate solution of certain problems of electromagnetic radiation

The above list is far from complete, but it gives an indication of the diversified classes of problems that may be reduced to the solution of a system of linear equations.

It may be thought that the problem of solving systems of linear equations is an old one and that it can be effected by means of well-known techniques such as Cramer's rule (Sec. 16). However, in studying problems of the type enumerated above, it is frequently necessary to solve 150 or 200 simultaneous equations. This task presents practically insurmountable difficulties if undertaken by well-known elementary methods. In the past few years many powerful and apparently unrelated methods have been devised to perform this task. A very complete survey of these methods, with a bibliography containing 131 references, will be found in the paper by Forsythe.*

The magnitude of the task of solving a large system of linear equations by conventional elementary methods and the spectacular reduction of effort that may be effected by the use of modern techniques are vividly presented by Forsythe. He points out that the conventional Cramer's-rule procedure for solving n simultaneous equations requires the evaluation of $n + 1$ determinants. If these determinants are evaluated by the Laplace expansion (Sec. 4), this requires $n!$ multiplications per determinant. It is thus apparent that the conventional determinantal method of solution requires $(n + 1)!$ multiplications. Therefore, if it is required

---

* G. E. Forsythe, Solving Linear Equations Can Be Interesting, *Bulletin of the American Mathematical Society*, vol. 59, no. 4, pp. 299–329, July, 1953.

to solve 26 equations, it would, in general, require $(n + 1)! = 27! \approx 10^{28}$ multiplications. A typical high-speed digital machine such as the National Bureau of Standards Western automatic computer can perform 2,600 multiplications per second. Hence, it would take this machine approximately 10^{17} years to effect the solution of this problem by the use of the conventional Cramer's-rule technique. By more efficient techniques the computational procedure may be arranged so that only about $n^3/3$ multiplications are required to solve the system of n equations. If this efficient method is used, 6,000 multiplications would be required, and the Bureau of Standards machine can solve the problem in about 3 sec.

The detailed theory of the various methods that have been developed in recent years will be found in the above survey article by Forsythe and should be consulted by those interested in the solution of large numbers of simultaneous linear equations. A simple method that has been found valuable and that makes use of partitioned matrices will now be described.

Let the matrix whose inverse is desired be the matrix $[M]$, of order n. Then, by the methods of Sec. 14, the matrix $[M]$ can be partitioned into four submatrices in the following manner:

$$(23.1) \qquad [M] = \begin{bmatrix} M_{11}(r,r) & M_{12}(r,s) \\ M_{21}(s,r) & M_{22}(s,s) \end{bmatrix}$$

The orders of the various matrices are indicated by the letters in parentheses. The first letter denotes the number of rows and the second letter the number of columns. Since the original matrix is of order n, we have the relation

$$(23.2) \qquad r + s = n$$

Now let the reciprocal of $[M]$ be the matrix $[B]$, and let it be correspondingly partitioned so that we have

$$(23.3) \qquad [B] = [M]^{-1} = \begin{bmatrix} B_{11}(r,r) & B_{12}(r,s) \\ B_{21}(s,r) & B_{22}(s,s) \end{bmatrix}$$

Since $[B]$ is the inverse of $[M]$, we have

$$(23.4) \qquad [B][M] = U_n$$

where U_n is the unit matrix of order n. If the multiplication indicated by (23.4) is carried out, we have

$$(23.5) \qquad \begin{aligned} B_{11}M_{11} + B_{12}M_{21} &= U_r \\ B_{11}M_{12} + B_{12}M_{22} &= [0] \\ B_{21}M_{11} + B_{22}M_{21} &= [0] \\ B_{21}M_{12} + B_{22}M_{22} &= U_s \end{aligned}$$

These equations may, in general, be solved to give the submatrices of the required matrix $[B]$ explicitly. The results may be expressed as follows: Let

$$(23.6) \qquad X = M_{11}^{-1} M_{12} \qquad Y = M_{21} M_{11}^{-1}$$
$$\theta = M_{22} - Y M_{12} = M_{22} - M_{21} X$$

We then have explicitly

$$(23.7) \qquad B_{11} = M_{11}^{-1} + X \theta^{-1} Y \qquad B_{21} = -\theta^{-1} Y$$
$$B_{12} = -X \theta^{-1} \qquad B_{22} = \theta^{-1}$$

These equations determine $[B] = [M]^{-1}$ provided that the reciprocals M_{11}^{-1} and θ^{-1} exist. If M_{11}^{-1} is known, then the matrices X, Y, and θ can be calculated by matrix multiplication and $[B]$ can be determined by the use of (23.7). The choice of the manner in which the original matrix $[M]$ is partitioned depends on the particular matrix to be inverted. From the above description of the method it is obvious that it yields to various modifications. The method of Sec. 22 may advantageously be applied to find M_{11}^{-1} and θ^{-1}. By this procedure the inversion of a large matrix may be reduced to the inversion of several smaller matrices.

Choleski's Method. Another very effective method for the inversion of matrices is Choleski's method. In its simplest form it applies to the inversion of symmetric matrices and is simple in theory and straightforward in practice. This method is sometimes called the *square-root method*, and an excellent exposition of this method is given in the paper by Fox, Huskey, and Wilkinson.* Choleski's method consists simply in expressing the symmetric matrix $[M]$ whose inverse is desired in the form

$$(23.8) \qquad\qquad [M] = [L][L]_t$$

where $[L]$ is a lower triangular matrix and $[L]_t$, its transpose, an upper triangular matrix. Then the desired inverse is given by

$$(23.9) \qquad\qquad [M]^{-1} = [L]_t^{-1}[L]^{-1}$$

and the problem is solved. To fix the fundamental ideas involved, consider the case of a third-order symmetric matrix $[M]$. We then have to find the third-order matrices $[L]$ and $[L]_t$ by means of the equation

$$(23.10) \quad [L][L]_t = \begin{bmatrix} a & 0 & 0 \\ b & d & 0 \\ c & e & f \end{bmatrix} \begin{bmatrix} a & b & c \\ 0 & d & e \\ 0 & 0 & f \end{bmatrix} = \begin{bmatrix} 1 & 2 & 3 \\ 2 & 3 & 4 \\ 3 & 4 & 4 \end{bmatrix} = [M]$$

---

* L. Fox, H. D. Huskey, and J. H. Wilkinson, Notes on the Solution of Algebraic Linear Simultaneous Equations, *Quarterly Journal of Mechanics and Applied Mathematics*, vol. 1, pp. 149–173, 1948.

By matrix multiplication of $[L][L]_t$ the following result is obtained:

$$(23.11) \qquad \begin{bmatrix} a^2 & ab & ac \\ ab & b^2 + d^2 & bc + de \\ ac & bc + de & c^2 + e^2 + f^2 \end{bmatrix} = \begin{bmatrix} 1 & 2 & 3 \\ 2 & 3 & 4 \\ 3 & 4 & 4 \end{bmatrix}$$

By equating the elements of $[L][L]_t$ to those of $[M]$ and solving the resulting equations one finds $a = 1$, $b = 2$, $c = 3$, $d = j$, $e = 2j$, $f = j$. In order to determine $[M]^{-1}$ by (23.9), it is necessary to invert $[L]_t$. This is easily done because $[L]_t^{-1}$ is also an upper triangular matrix of the form

$$(23.12) \qquad [L]_t^{-1} = \begin{bmatrix} P & Q & R \\ 0 & S & T \\ 0 & 0 & U \end{bmatrix}$$

The elements of $[L]_t^{-1}$ may be determined by the equation

$$(23.13) \quad [L]_t [L]_t^{-1} = \begin{bmatrix} 1 & 2 & 3 \\ 0 & j & 2j \\ 0 & 0 & j \end{bmatrix} \begin{bmatrix} P & Q & R \\ 0 & S & T \\ 0 & 0 & U \end{bmatrix} = \begin{bmatrix} 1 & 0 & 0 \\ 0 & 1 & 0 \\ 0 & 0 & 1 \end{bmatrix} = U$$

From (23.13) we find that $P = 1$, $Q = 2j$, $R = -j$, $S = -j$, $T = 2j$, $U = -j$. The required inverse of $[M]$ is given by

$$(23.14)$$

$$[M]^{-1}[L]_t^{-1}[L]^{-1} = \begin{bmatrix} 1 & 2j & -j \\ 0 & -j & 2j \\ 0 & 0 & -j \end{bmatrix} \begin{bmatrix} 1 & 0 & 0 \\ 2j & -j & 0 \\ -j & 2j & -j \end{bmatrix} = \begin{bmatrix} -4 & 4 & -1 \\ 4 & -5 & 2 \\ -1 & 2 & -1 \end{bmatrix}$$

The work involved in the Choleski method appears formidable in the above example but in practice can be greatly reduced. The method can be extended to the computations of inverses of unsymmetric matrices.

24. Sylvester's Theorem. A very important and useful theorem of matrix algebra is known as *Sylvester's theorem*. This theorem states that, if the n eigenvalues μ_1, μ_2, . . . , μ_n of the square matrix $[M]$ are all distinct and $P([M])$ is a polynomial in $[M]$ of the following form,

$$(24.1) \qquad P([M]) = c_0[M]^k + c_1[M]^{k-1} + \cdots + c_{k-1}[M] + c_k U$$

where U is the nth-order unit matrix and the c_k's are constants, then the polynomial $P([M])$ may be expressed in the following form,

$$(24.2) \qquad P([M]) = \sum_{r=1}^{n} P(\mu_r) Z_0(\mu_r)$$

where

$$(24.3) \qquad Z_0(\mu_r) = \frac{[A(\mu_r)]}{\Delta'(\mu_r)}$$

In (24.3) $\Delta(\mu)$ is the characteristic function of $[M]$ as defined by (19.2); $[A(\mu)]$ is the adjoint matrix of the characteristic matrix of $[M]$ defined by

(24.4) $$[A(\mu)] = \Delta(\mu)[\mu U - M]^{-1}$$

and

(24.5) $$\Delta'(\mu_r) = \left(\frac{d\Delta}{d\mu}\right)_{\mu=\mu_r}$$

A proof of Sylvester's theorem as well as the confluent form of the theorem in the case that the matrix $[M]$ does not have distinct eigenvalues will be found in the book by Frazer, Duncan, and Collar.*

Sylvester's theorem is very useful for simplifying the calculations of powers and functions of matrices. For example, let it be required to find the value of $[M]^{256}$, where

(24.6) $$[M] = \begin{bmatrix} 1 & 0 \\ 0 & 3 \end{bmatrix}$$

To do this, consider the special polynomial

(24.7) $$P([M]) = [M]^{256}$$

and apply the results of Sylvester's theorem. In this special case we have

(24.8) $$[\mu U - M] = \begin{bmatrix} \mu - 1 & 0 \\ 0 & \mu - 3 \end{bmatrix}$$

and

(24.9) $$\Delta(\mu) = (\mu - 1)(\mu - 3) = \mu^2 - 4\mu + 3$$

The eigenvalues of $[M]$ are $\mu_1 = 1$ and $\mu_2 = 3$. $[A(\mu)]$ is now given by

(24.10) $$[A(\mu)] = \begin{bmatrix} \mu - 3 & 0 \\ 0 & \mu - 1 \end{bmatrix}$$

and

(24.11) $$\Delta'(\mu) = 2\mu - 4$$

Hence we have

(24.12) $$Z_0(1) = \begin{bmatrix} 1 & 0 \\ 0 & 0 \end{bmatrix} \qquad Z_0(3) = \begin{bmatrix} 0 & 0 \\ 0 & 1 \end{bmatrix}$$

Therefore, by Sylvester's theorem, we have

(24.13) $$\begin{vmatrix} 1 & 0 \\ 0 & 3 \end{vmatrix}^{256} = 1^{256}\begin{bmatrix} 1 & 0 \\ 0 & 0 \end{bmatrix} + 3^{256}\begin{bmatrix} 0 & 0 \\ 0 & 1 \end{bmatrix} = \begin{bmatrix} 1 & 0 \\ 0 & 3^{256} \end{bmatrix}$$

$$\approx 3^{256}\begin{bmatrix} 0 & 0 \\ 0 & 1 \end{bmatrix} \qquad \text{approx.}$$

* R. A. Frazer, W. J. Duncan, and A. R. Collar, "Elementary Matrices," pp. 78–79, Cambridge University Press, New York, 1938.

As the last step above suggests, Sylvester's theorem is very useful in obtaining the approximate value of a matrix raised to a high power. Thus, if μ_m is the *largest* eigenvalue of the square matrix $[M]$, then, if k is very large, the term $P(\mu_m)Z_0(\mu_m)$ will dominate the right-hand member of (24.2) and we have the following *approximate* value of $[M]^k$:

$$(24.14) \qquad [M]^k = \frac{\mu_m^k[A(\mu_m)]}{\Delta'(\mu_m)} \qquad \text{for } k \text{ very large}$$

This expression is useful in certain applications of matrix algebra to physical problems.

25. Power Series of Matrices; Functions of Matrices. A series of the following type,

$$(25.1) \quad S([M]) = c_0 U + c_1[M] + c_2[M]^2 + c_3[M]^3 + \cdots = \sum_{i=0}^{\infty} c_i[M]^i$$

where $[M]$ is a square matrix of order n, the coefficients c_i are ordinary numbers, and $[M]^0 = U$, the nth-order unit matrix, is called a *power series of matrices*. The general question of the convergence of such series will not be discussed here; however, if $[M]$ is a square matrix of order n, it is clear that by the use of the Cayley-Hamilton theorem (Sec. 22) it is possible to reduce any matrix polynomial of $[M]$ to a polynomial of maximum degree $n - 1$ regardless of the degree of the original polynomial. Hence, if the series (25.1) converges, it may be expressed in the following form,

$$(25.2) \qquad S([M]) = \sum_{r=1}^{r=n} S(\mu_r)Z_0(\mu_r)$$

where

$$(25.3) \qquad Z_0(\mu_r) = \frac{[A(\mu_r)]}{\Delta'(\mu_r)}$$

as a consequence of Sylvester's theorem (Sec. 24). For example, it can be shown that the series

$$(25.4) \qquad \exp[M] = \sum_{k=0}^{\infty} \frac{[M]^k}{k!} \qquad [M]^0 = U$$

converges for *any* square matrix $[M]$. In particular, suppose that the matrix $[M]$ is the following second-order matrix:

$$(25.5) \qquad [M] = \begin{bmatrix} 1 & 0 \\ 0 & 2 \end{bmatrix}$$

The characteristic equation of this matrix is

$$(25.6) \quad \Delta(\mu) = \begin{vmatrix} \mu - 1 & 0 \\ 0 & \mu - 2 \end{vmatrix} = (\mu - 1)(\mu - 2) = \mu^2 - 3\mu + 2 = 0$$

so that the latent roots of $[M]$ are $\mu_1 = 1$, $\mu_2 = 2$. The matrix $[A(\mu)]$ is now

$$(25.7) \qquad [A(\mu)] = \begin{bmatrix} \mu - 2 & 0 \\ 0 & \mu - 1 \end{bmatrix}$$

Since $\Delta'(1) = -1$ and $\Delta'(2) = +1$, we have as a consequence of (25.2)

$$(25.8) \qquad \exp[M] = e^2 \begin{bmatrix} 0 & 0 \\ 0 & 1 \end{bmatrix} - e \begin{bmatrix} -1 & 0 \\ 0 & 0 \end{bmatrix} = \begin{bmatrix} e & 0 \\ 0 & e^2 \end{bmatrix}$$

Other functions of matrices such as trigonometric, hyperbolic, and logarithmic functions are defined by the same power series that define these functions for scalar values of their arguments and by replacing these scalar arguments by square matrices. For example, we have

$$(25.9) \qquad \sin[M] = [M] - \frac{[M]^3}{3!} + \frac{[M]^5}{5!} - \cdots$$

$$(25.10) \qquad \cos[M] = U - \frac{[M]^2}{2!} + \frac{[M]^4}{4!} - \cdots$$

$$(25.11) \qquad \sinh[M] = [M] + \frac{[M]^3}{3!} + \frac{[M]^5}{5!} + \cdots$$

$$(25.12) \qquad \cosh[M] = U + \frac{[M]^2}{2!} + \frac{[M]^4}{4!} + \cdots$$

Although every scalar power series has its matrix analogue, the matrix power series have, in general, more complex properties. The properties of the matrix functions may be deduced from their series expansions. For example, if it is a scalar variable and $[u]$ is a square matrix of constants, we have

$$(25.13) \qquad \exp[u]t = U + \frac{[u]}{1!} t + [u]^2 \frac{t^2}{2!} + [u]^3 \frac{t^3}{3!} + \cdots$$

The series obtained by the term-by-term differentiation of (25.13) is

$$(25.14) \qquad \frac{d}{dt} \exp[u]t = [u] + [u]^2 t + [u]^3 \frac{t^2}{2!} + \cdots$$
$$= [u] \exp[u]t$$

In the same way, it may be shown that, if

$$(25.15) \qquad \sin[u]t = [u]t - [u]^3 \frac{t^3}{3!} + [u]^5 \frac{t^5}{5!} - \cdots$$

then

$$(25.16) \qquad \frac{d}{dt} \sin[u]t = [u] - [u]^3 \frac{t^2}{2!} + [u]^5 \frac{t^4}{4!} - \cdots$$
$$= [u] \cos[u]t$$

26. Association of Matrices with Linear Differential Equations. A very important field of application of the theory of matrices is the solution of systems of linear differential equations. Matrix notation and operations with matrices lead to concise formulations of otherwise cumbersome procedures. This conciseness is very important in many practical problems that involve several dependent variables. Such problems arise in dynamics, the theory of vibrations of structures and machinery, the oscillations of electrical circuits, electric filters, and many other branches of physics and engineering.

In order to apply matrix notation to a set of differential equations, it is advisable to express the equations in forms that involve only the first-order differential coefficients. Any set of differential equations can be easily changed into another set that involves only first-order differential coefficients by writing the highest-order coefficient as the differential coefficient of a new dependent variable. All the other differential coefficients are regarded as separate dependent variables, and, for each new variable introduced, another equation must be added to the set. As a very simple example, consider the following equation:

$$(26.1) \qquad \frac{d^2x}{dt^2} + x = 0$$

In order to express this as a set of first-order equations, let $x = x_1$ and

$$(26.2) \qquad \frac{dx_1}{dt} = x_2$$

With this notation (26.1) becomes

$$(26.3) \qquad \frac{dx_2}{dt} = -x_1$$

Therefore the original second-order differential equation (26.1) may be written in the following matrix form:

$$(26.4) \qquad \frac{d}{dt}\begin{bmatrix} x_1 \\ x_2 \end{bmatrix} = \begin{bmatrix} 0 & 1 \\ -1 & 0 \end{bmatrix}\begin{bmatrix} x_1 \\ x_2 \end{bmatrix}$$

This is a special case of the first-order matrix differential equation

$$(26.5) \qquad \frac{d}{dt}(x) = [u](x)$$

where (x) is in general a column vector of the n elements $x_1, x_2, \ldots, x_n n$ and $[u]$ is a square matrix of the nth order. A general set of homogeneous linear differential equations may be expressed in the form (26.5). In general the elements u_{ij} of the matrix $[u]$ are functions of the independent variable t; however, in many special cases of practical importance the elements of $[u]$ are constants.

The set of differential equations (26.5) may be integrated by means of the Peano-Baker method.* The principle of this method of integration is quite simple. Let the initial conditions of the system be such that

$$(26.6) \qquad\qquad (x) = (x)_0 \qquad \text{at } t = 0$$

where $(x)_0$ is a column vector of initial values of the elements of (x). Direct integration of (26.5) gives the following integral equation,

$$(26.7) \qquad\qquad (x) = (x)_0 + \int_0^t [u(\phi)](x) \, d\phi$$

where ϕ is a subsidiary variable of integration. This integral equation may be solved by repeated substitutions of (x) from the left-hand member of (26.7) into the integral. If the following integral operator is introduced,

$$(26.8) \qquad\qquad Q = \int_0^t (\quad) \, d\phi$$

then (26.7) may be written in the following form:

$$(26.9) \qquad\qquad (x) = (x)_0 + Q[u](x)$$

By repeated substitution, the following equation is obtained:

$$(26.10) \qquad (x) = (U + Q[u] + Q[u]Q[u] + Q[u]Q[u]Q[u] + \cdots)(x)_0$$

Let

$$(26.11) \quad G(u) = U + Q[u] + Q[u]Q[u] + Q[u]Q[u]Q[u] + \cdots$$

This expression has been called the *matrizant* of $[u]$. In the series (26.9) U is the unit matrix of order n, and the second term is the integral of $[u]$ taken between the limits 0 and t. To obtain $Q[u]Q[u]$, $[u]$ and $Q[u]$ are multiplied in the order $uQ[u]$, and the product is integrated between 0 and t. The remaining terms are formed in the same manner. If the elements of the matrix $[u(t)]$ remain bounded in the range 0 to t, it may be shown that the series (26.11) is absolutely and uniformly convergent and that it defines a square matrix $G(u)$ in a unique manner.

The solution of the set of differential equations (26.5) is given by

$$(26.12) \qquad\qquad (x) = G(u)(x)_0$$

If the elements of the matrix $[u]$ are constants, we have, by direct integration of the series (26.9),

$$(26.13) \qquad G(u) = U + [u]\frac{t}{1!} + [u]^2\frac{t^2}{2!} + [u]^3\frac{t^3}{3!} + \cdots$$

$$= \exp [u]t$$

* See E. L. Ince, "Ordinary Differential Equations," pp. 408–415, Longmans, Green & Co., Inc., New York, 1927.

Therefore, if $[u]$ is a matrix of *constants*, the solution of (26.5) is

(26.14) $(x) = \exp [u]t(x)_0$

The interpretation of $e^{[u]t}$, for purposes of calculation, may be made by the use of Sylvester's theorem (24.2). To illustrate the general procedure, consider the second-order case in which the matrix $[u]$ has the form

(26.15) $[u] = \begin{bmatrix} u_{11} & u_{12} \\ u_{21} & u_{22} \end{bmatrix}$

In this case the characteristic equation of $[u]$ is given by

(26.16) $\mu^2 - (u_{11} + u_{22})\mu + (u_{11}u_{22} - u_{12}u_{21}) = 0$

Let the two roots of (26.15) or the eigenvalues of $[u]$ be given by

(26.17) $\mu_1 = a + b \qquad \mu_2 = a - b$

By the use of Sylvester's theorem (24.2) the function $e^{[u]t}$ may be expressed in the following form,

(26.18) $\exp [u]t = \begin{bmatrix} G_{11} & G_{12} \\ G_{21} & G_{22} \end{bmatrix}$

where

$$G_{11} = \left[(u_{11} - a) \sinh \frac{bt}{b} + \cosh bt \right] e^{at}$$

$$G_{12} = u_{12}e^{at} \sinh \frac{bt}{b}$$

(26.19)

$$G_{21} = u_{21}e^{at} \sinh \frac{bt}{b}$$

$$G_{22} = \left[(u_{22} - a) \sinh \frac{bt}{b} + \cosh bt \right] e^{at}$$

To illustrate this method of solution by an example of technical importance, consider the differential equations

(26.20) $L\dfrac{di}{dt} + Ri + \dfrac{q}{C} = 0 \qquad \dfrac{dq}{dt} = i$

These differential equations govern the oscillation of a series electrical circuit having a resistance R, an inductance L, and a capacitance C, all in series (see Chap. 7). The variable q is the charge on the capacitance, and i is the current that flows in the circuit. The free oscillations of such a circuit are completely determined when the initial charge q_0 and the initial current i_0 of the circuit at $t = 0$ are specified. If we let $x_1 = q$

and $x_2 = i$, Eqs. (26.20) may be written in the standard matrix form,

$$(26.21) \qquad \frac{d}{dt}\begin{bmatrix} x_1 \\ x_2 \end{bmatrix} = \begin{bmatrix} 0 & 1 \\ -\dfrac{1}{CL} & -\dfrac{R}{L} \end{bmatrix}\begin{bmatrix} x_1 \\ x_2 \end{bmatrix} = [u](x)$$

The characteristic equation of $[u]$ is, in this case,

$$(26.22) \qquad \mu^2 + \frac{R}{L}\mu + \frac{1}{CL} = 0$$

In this case

$$(26.23) \qquad a = \frac{-R}{2L} \qquad b = \sqrt{a^2 - \frac{1}{LC}}$$

The oscillations of the circuit are given by the following matrix equation,

$$(26.24) \qquad \begin{bmatrix} q \\ i \end{bmatrix} = \begin{bmatrix} G_{11} & G_{12} \\ G_{21} & G_{22} \end{bmatrix}\begin{bmatrix} q_0 \\ i_0 \end{bmatrix}$$

where the elements G_{ij} are given by (26.19). If b is imaginary so that $b = j\omega$, then we have

$$(26.25) \qquad \frac{\sinh bt}{b} = \frac{\sinh j\omega t}{j\omega} = \frac{\sin \omega t}{\omega}$$
$$\cosh bt = \cosh j\omega t = \cos \omega t$$

so that the hyperbolic functions are replaced by trigonometric functions and the circuit oscillates. If $b = 0$, the circuit is critically damped and $(\sinh bt)/b$ becomes indeterminate. When this is evaluated by L'Hospital's rule for indeterminate forms, it is seen that it must be replaced by t. The result (26.24) is thus seen to be a convenient expression that gives the current and charge of the circuit in terms of the initial conditions in concise form.

Differential Equations with Variable Coefficients. The Peano-Baker method is a convenient method for the integration of homogeneous linear differential equations with variable coefficients. As an example of the general procedure, consider the differential equation

$$(26.26) \qquad \frac{d^2y}{dt^2} + ty = 0$$

This equation is known as *Stokes's equation* in the mathematical literature of the diffraction and reflection of electromagnetic waves and in quantum mechanics.*

In order to reduce this equation to the form (26.5), let

$$(26.27) \qquad x_1 = \frac{-dy}{dt} \qquad x_2 = y$$

---

* See "Tables of the Modified Hankel Functions of Order One-third," Harvard University Press, Cambridge, Mass., 1945.

The system

(26.28)
$$\frac{d}{dt}\begin{bmatrix} x_1 \\ x_2 \end{bmatrix} = \begin{bmatrix} 0 & t \\ -1 & 0 \end{bmatrix}\begin{bmatrix} x_1 \\ x_2 \end{bmatrix}$$

replaces the original equation (26.26). Let the initial-condition vector at $t = 0$ be

(26.29)
$$(x)_0 = \begin{bmatrix} x_{10} \\ x_{20} \end{bmatrix} = \begin{bmatrix} x_1 \\ x_2 \end{bmatrix}_{t=0}$$

The matrizant $G(u)$ is now computed by means of the series (26.10). We have

(26.30)
$$Q[u] = Q\begin{bmatrix} 0 & t \\ -1 & 0 \end{bmatrix} = \begin{bmatrix} 0 & \dfrac{t^2}{2} \\ -t & 0 \end{bmatrix}$$

(26.31)
$$Q[u]Q[u] = \begin{bmatrix} \dfrac{-t^3}{3} & 0 \\ 0 & \dfrac{-t^3}{2 \times 3} \end{bmatrix}$$

(26.32)
$$Q[u]Q[u]Q[u] = \begin{bmatrix} 0 & \dfrac{-t^5}{2 \times 3 \times 5} \\ \dfrac{t^4}{3 \times 4} & 0 \end{bmatrix}$$

The first few terms of the matrizant are, by (26.11),

(26.33)
$$G(u) = \begin{bmatrix} 1 - \dfrac{t^3}{3} + \dfrac{t^6}{3 \times 4 \times 6} - \cdots & \dfrac{t^2}{2} - \dfrac{t^5}{2 \times 3 \times 5} + \dfrac{t^8}{2 \times 3 \times 5 \times 6 \times 8} - \cdots \\ -t + \dfrac{t^4}{3 \times 4} - \dfrac{t^7}{3 \times 4 \times 6 \times 7} + \cdots & 1 - \dfrac{t^3}{2 \times 3} + \dfrac{t^6}{2 \times 3 \times 5 \times 6} - \cdots \end{bmatrix}$$

The elements of the matrizant $G(u)$ are series expansions of the Bessel functions of order $\frac{1}{3}$ and $-\frac{2}{3}$. The solution of Stokes's equation may be expressed in terms of the initial conditions in the form

(26.34)
$$\begin{bmatrix} x_1 \\ x_2 \end{bmatrix} = \begin{bmatrix} G_{11} & G_{12} \\ G_{21} & G_{22} \end{bmatrix}\begin{bmatrix} x_{10} \\ x_{20} \end{bmatrix}$$

27. Linear Equations with Periodic Coefficients.

The mathematical analysis of a considerable variety of physical problems leads to a formulation involving a differential equation that may be reduced to the following form,

$$(27.1) \qquad \frac{d^2y}{dt^2} + F(t)y = 0$$

where $F(t)$ is a single-valued periodic function of fundamental period T. An equation of this type is known as *Hill's equation* in the mathematical literature. If a change of variable of the form

$$(27.2) \qquad t = nT + \tau \qquad 0 \leq \tau \leq T \qquad n = 0, 1, 2, 3, \ldots$$

is introduced into the Hill equation (27.1), the equation is transformed into

$$(27.3) \qquad \frac{d^2y}{d\tau^2} + F(\tau)y = 0$$

as a consequence of the periodicity of $F(t)$. Hence Hill's equation is *invariant* under the change of variable (27.2), and it is thus apparent that it is necessary only to obtain a solution of (27.1) in a fundamental interval $0 \leq t \leq T$. The final values of y and $\dot{y}$ at the end of one interval of the variation of $F(t)$ are the *initial* values of y and $\dot{y}$ in the following interval.

Let $u_1(t)$ and $u_2(t)$ be two linearly independent solutions of Hill's equation (27.1) in the fundamental interval $0 \leq t \leq T$. Let $y = x_1$ and $\dot{y} = x_2$. Then we have

$$(27.4) \qquad \begin{matrix} x_1(t) = K_1u_1(t) + K_2u_2(t) \\ x_2(t) = K_1\dot{u}_1(t) + K_2\dot{u}_2(t) \end{matrix} \right\} \quad \text{for } 0 \leq t \leq T$$

where K_1 and K_2 are arbitrary constants. Equations (27.4) may be written in the following convenient matrix form:

$$(27.5) \qquad \begin{bmatrix} x_1(t) \\ x_2(t) \end{bmatrix} = \begin{bmatrix} u_1(t) & u_2(t) \\ \dot{u}_1(t) & \dot{u}_2(t) \end{bmatrix} \begin{bmatrix} K_1 \\ K_2 \end{bmatrix}$$

The following notation will be introduced in order to simplify the writing:

$$(27.6) \qquad \begin{aligned} [x(t)] &= \begin{bmatrix} x_1(t) \\ x_2(t) \end{bmatrix} \qquad [K] = \begin{bmatrix} K_1 \\ K_2 \end{bmatrix} \\ [u(t)] &= \begin{bmatrix} u_1(t) & u_2(t) \\ \dot{u}_1(t) & \dot{u}_2(t) \end{bmatrix} = \begin{bmatrix} u_{11}(t) & u_{12}(t) \\ u_{21}(t) & u_{22}(t) \end{bmatrix} \end{aligned}$$

In this notation (27.5) may be expressed in the following concise form:

$$(27.7) \qquad [x(t)] = [u(t)][K]$$

The determinant

$$(27.8) \qquad \det [u(t)] = u_1\dot{u}_2 - \dot{u}_1u_2 = W_0$$

is called the *Wronskian* of the two solutions $u_1(t)$ and $u_2(t)$. It is a constant in the fundamental interval $0 \leq t \leq T$. Since the two solutions $u_1(t)$ and $u_2(t)$ are linearly independent, $W_0 \neq 0$. The matrix $[u(t)]$ is therefore nonsingular and has the following inverse:

$$(27.9) \qquad [u(t)]^{-1} = \frac{1}{W_0} \begin{bmatrix} u_{22}(t) & -u_{12}(t) \\ -u_{21}(t) & u_{11}(t) \end{bmatrix}$$

At $t = 0$, (27.7) reduces to

$$(27.10) \qquad [x(0)] = [u(0)][K]$$

If this is premultiplied by $u(0)^{-1}$, the result may be written in the following form:

$$(27.11) \qquad K = u(0)^{-1}x(0)$$

This equation determines the column of arbitrary constants in terms of the *initial* conditions. If (27.11) is now substituted into (27.7), the result is

$$(27.12) \qquad [x(t)] = [u(t)][u(0)]^{-1}[x(0)]$$

At the end of the fundamental interval, $t = T$, and the solution is given in terms of the initial conditions by the equation

$$(27.13) \qquad [x(T)] = [u(T)][u(0)]^{-1}[x(0)]$$

Cascading the Solution. Since, during the second fundamental interval, Hill's equation has the same form as it has during the first interval, the relation expressing the initial and final values of $[x(t)]$ in this interval has the same form as that given in (27.13). Therefore, at the end of the second cycle of the variation of $F(t)$ we have

$$(27.14) \qquad [x(2T)] = [u(T)][u(0)]^{-1}[x(T)]$$

Introduce the following notation:

$$(27.15) \qquad [M] = [u(T)][u(0)]^{-1} = \begin{bmatrix} A & B \\ C & D \end{bmatrix}$$

It is easy to see that, at the end of n periods of the variation of $F(t)$, the solution of Hill's equation is given by

$$(27.16) \qquad [x(nT)] = [M]^n[x(0)] \qquad n = 0, 1, 2, 3, \ldots$$

and the solution within the $(n + 1)$st interval is given by

$$(27.17) \qquad [x(nT + \tau)] = [u(\tau)][u(0)]^{-1}[x(nT)] \qquad 0 \leq \tau \leq T$$

This gives the solution of Hill's equation at any time $t > 0$ in terms of the *initial* conditions and two linearly independent solutions in the fundamental interval $0 \leq t \leq T$. The solution involves the computation of positive integral powers of the matrix $[M]$.

Computation of Integral Powers of $[M]$. As a consequence of the constancy of the Wronskian determinant W_0 given by (27.8), the determinant of the matrix $[M]$ is equal to unity. We thus have

(27.18) $\det [M] = 1$

The characteristic equation of $[M]$ is

(27.19) $\mu^2 - (A + D)\mu + 1 = 0$

If $A + D \neq \pm 2$, the eigenvalues of $[M]$ are given by

(27.20) $\mu_1 = e^a$ $\mu_2 = e^{-a}$ $\cosh a = \dfrac{A + D}{2}$

and in this case $[M]$ has distinct eigenvalues. By Sylvester's theorem (24.2) the nth power of $[M]$ may easily be computed. The result is

(27.21) $[M]^n = \dfrac{1}{S_1} \begin{bmatrix} S_{n+1} - DS_n & BS_n \\ CS_n & S_{n+1} - AS_n \end{bmatrix}$ $n = 0, 1, 2, 3, \ldots$

where

(27.22) $S_n = \sinh an$ $n = 0, 1, 2, 3, \ldots$

Equation (27.21) gives the proper form for $[M]^n$ only when $A + D \neq \pm 2$. When $A + D = \pm 2$, the two eigenvalues of $[M]$ are not distinct and a confluent form of Sylvester's theorem must be used to compute $[M]^n$.*

28. Matrix Solution of the Hill-Meissner Equation. If the function $F(t)$ has the form of the rectangular ripple of Fig. 28.1, Eq. (27.1) is

FIG. 28.1

known as the *Hill-Meissner*. The Hill-Meissner equation is of importance in the study of the oscillations of the driving rods of electric locomotives, and its solution is easily effected by the use of matrix algebra. In this case Eq. (27.1) reduces to two equations of the form

(28.1)
$$\dfrac{d^2y}{dt^2} + F_1 y = 0 \qquad 0 \leq t \leq \dfrac{T}{2}$$
$$\dfrac{d^2y}{dt^2} + F_2 y = 0 \qquad \dfrac{T}{2} \leq t \leq T$$

---

* See L. A. Pipes, Matrix Solutions of Equations of the Mathieu-Hill Type, *Journal of Applied Physics*, vol. 24, no. 7, pp. 902–910, July, 1953.

The solution of Eqs. (28.1) at $t = T$ may be expressed in terms of the *initial* values of y and $\dot{y}$ at $t = 0$ by the equation

$$(28.2) \quad \begin{bmatrix} x_1(T) \\ x_2(T) \end{bmatrix} = \begin{bmatrix} \cos\theta_2 & \dfrac{\sin}{w_2}\theta_2 \\ -w_2\sin\theta_2 & \cos\theta_2 \end{bmatrix} \begin{bmatrix} \cos\theta_1 & \dfrac{\sin}{w_1}\theta_1 \\ -w_1\sin\theta_1 & \cos\theta_1 \end{bmatrix} \begin{bmatrix} x_1(0) \\ x_2(0) \end{bmatrix}$$

where $x_1 = y$, $x_2 = \dot{y}$, and

$$(28.3) \quad \begin{aligned} \theta_1 &= \frac{T}{2}\sqrt{F_1} & w_1 &= \sqrt{F_1} \\ \theta_2 &= \frac{T}{2}\sqrt{F_2} & w_2 &= \sqrt{F_2} \end{aligned}$$

If the indicated matrix multiplication in (28.2) is performed, the result may be written in the following form:

$$(28.4) \quad \begin{bmatrix} x_1(T) \\ x_2(T) \end{bmatrix} = \begin{bmatrix} A & B \\ C & D \end{bmatrix} \begin{bmatrix} x_1(0) \\ x_2(0) \end{bmatrix} = [M][x(0)]$$

In this case the matrix $[M]$ has the form

$$(28.5) \quad [M] = \begin{bmatrix} A & B \\ C & D \end{bmatrix}$$

where

$$(28.6) \quad \begin{aligned} A &= \cos\theta_1\cos\theta_2 - \sin\theta_1\sin\theta_2\frac{w_1}{w_2} \\ B &= \frac{\cos\theta_2\sin\theta_1}{w_1} - \frac{\cos\theta_1\sin\theta_2}{w_2} \\ C &= -(w_2\cos\theta_1\sin\theta_2 + w_1\cos\theta_2\sin\theta_1) \\ D &= \cos\theta_1\cos\theta_2 - \sin\theta_1\sin\theta_2\frac{w_2}{w_1} \cdot \end{aligned}$$

The eigenvalues of $[M]$ are given by

$$(28.7) \quad \mu_1 = e^a \qquad \mu_2 = e^{-a}$$

where

$$(28.8) \quad \cosh a = \frac{A + D}{2} = \cos\theta_1\cos\theta_2 - \left(\frac{w_1}{w_2} + \frac{w_2}{w_1}\right)\sin\theta_1\sin\theta_2$$

The values of y and $\dot{y}$ after the end of n complete periods of the square-wave variation are given by

$$(28.9) \quad [x(nT)] = [M]^n[x(0)] \qquad n = 0, 1, 2, 3, \ldots$$

The Stability of the Solution. The nature of the solution of the Hill-Meissner equation depends on the form taken by the powers of the matrix $[M]$, as given by (27.22). There are two separate cases to be considered. If $A + D > 2$, a must have a positive real part and the elements of $[M]^n$ increase exponentially with the number of periods, n. This leads to an *unstable* solution in physical applications. If, on the other hand, $A + D < 2$, a must be a pure imaginary number and the elements of $[M]^n$ oscillate with n. This leads to *stable* solutions in physical applications. The dividing line leads to the case $A + D = 2$. In this case the eigenvalues of $[M]$ are repeated and both have the value $\mu_1 = \mu_2 = 1$. The form (27.22) is no longer applicable and must be replaced by one obtained from a confluent form of Sylvester's theorem. In general the condition $A + D = 2$ leads to *instability* in physical problems. The question of stability may be summarized by the following expressions:

$$
\begin{array}{lll}
& A + D > 2 & \textit{unstable} \\
(28.10) & A + D < 2 & \textit{stable} \\
& A + D = 2 & \textit{unstable}
\end{array}
$$

In any special cases the conditions for stability or instability may be deduced from (28.8).

29. The Use of Matrices to Determine the Roots of Algebraic Equations. The properties of matrices may be used to determine the roots of algebraic equations. As a simple example, consider the equation

$$(29.1) \qquad z^3 + a_1 z^2 + a_2 z + a_3 = 0$$

Let the following third-order matrix be constructed:

$$(29.2) \qquad [C] = \begin{bmatrix} 0 & 1 & 0 \\ 0 & 0 & 1 \\ -a_3 & -a_2 & -a_1 \end{bmatrix}$$

This matrix is called the *companion matrix* of the cubic equation (29.1). It is easy to show that the characteristic equation of the companion matrix $[C]$ is the cubic equation. Therefore the eigenvalues of $[C]$ are the roots of (29.1). The general algebraic equation of the nth degree,

$$(29.3) \qquad z^n + a_1 z^{n-1} + a_2 z^{n-2} + \cdots + a_n = 0$$

has a companion matrix of the nth order,

$$(29.4) \qquad C = \begin{bmatrix} 0 & 1 & 0 & \cdots & 0 \\ 0 & 0 & 1 & \cdots & 0 \\ 0 & 0 & 0 & \cdots & 0 \\ \cdots & \cdots & \cdots & \cdots & \cdots \\ 0 & 0 & 0 & \cdots & 1 \\ -a_n & -a_{n-1} & -a_{n-2} & \cdots & -a_1 \end{bmatrix}$$

The eigenvalues of $[C]$, μ_1, μ_2, μ_3, . . . , μ_n, are the roots of the equation (29.3). If the various roots of the nth-degree equation (29.3) are real and distinct and if μ_1 is the root having the largest absolute value, then it can be shown by Sylvester's theorem (24.2) that for a *sufficiently large m* we have

(29.5) $$[C]^{m+1} \approx \mu_1[C]^m$$

That is, for a sufficiently large-power m, a further multiplication of $[C]^m$ by $[C]$ yields a new matrix whose elements are μ_1 times the elements of $[C]^m$. This multiple, μ_1, is the dominant root of (29.3). A practical procedure for extracting the dominant root of an equation is to choose an arbitrary column vector of the nth order, (x), and set up the following sequence:

(29.6) $$[C](x) = (x)_1 \qquad [C](x)_1 = (x)_2 = [C]^2(x)$$
$$[C]^m(x) = (x)_m$$

Then, for a sufficiently large m, we have

(29.7) $$[C](x)_m = \mu_1(x)_m$$

so that after a sufficient number of multiplications one more multiplication merely multiplies all the elements of the vector $(x)_m$ by a common factor. This common factor μ_1 is the largest root of the equation and the largest eigenvalue of the companion matrix. As a simple numerical example, consider the following cubic equation:

(29.8) $$z^3 - 16z^2 + 68z - 80 = 0$$

The companion matrix of this equation is

(29.9) $$[C] = \begin{bmatrix} 0 & 1 & 0 \\ 0 & 0 & 1 \\ 80 & -68 & 16 \end{bmatrix}$$

We now choose the *arbitrary* column vector

$$(x) = \begin{bmatrix} 1 \\ 1 \\ 1 \end{bmatrix}$$

By direct multiplication we obtain

(29.10)
$$[C](x) = \begin{bmatrix} 1 \\ 1 \\ 28 \end{bmatrix} = (x)_1 \qquad [C](x)_1 = \begin{bmatrix} 1 \\ 28 \\ 460 \end{bmatrix} = (x)_2$$

$$[C](x)_2 = \begin{bmatrix} 28 \\ 460 \\ 5{,}540 \end{bmatrix} = 28\begin{bmatrix} 1 \\ 16.4 \\ 198 \end{bmatrix} = (x)_3$$

The factor 28 may be discarded since we are interested only in the ratios of similar elements after successive multiplication. Let $\doteqdot$ denote the fact that a factor has been discarded, and proceed.

$$[C](x)_3 \doteqdot \begin{bmatrix} 16.4 \\ 198 \\ 2{,}125 \end{bmatrix} \doteqdot \begin{bmatrix} 1 \\ 12.1 \\ 130 \end{bmatrix} \doteqdot (x)_4$$

(29.11) $\quad [C](x)_4 \doteqdot \begin{bmatrix} 1 \\ 10.3 \\ 104 \end{bmatrix} \doteqdot (x)_5 \qquad [C](x)_5 \doteqdot \begin{bmatrix} 1 \\ 10.3 \\ 104 \end{bmatrix} = (x)_6$

$$[C](x)_6 \doteqdot \begin{bmatrix} 1 \\ 10.1 \\ 101 \end{bmatrix} = (x)_7 \qquad [C](x)_7 \doteqdot \begin{bmatrix} 1 \\ 10 \\ 100 \end{bmatrix}$$

Further multiplications only multiply the elements of the vectors by a factor of 10. Hence the *dominant* root is $\mu_1 = 10$. After having determined the dominant root, it may be divided out by dividing the polynomial $f(z) = z^3 - 16z^2 + 68z - 80$ by $z - 10$. This procedure may be performed by the synthetic division

$$\begin{array}{r} 1 - 16 + 68 - 80 \ \underline{|10} \\ + 10 - 60 \\ \hline 1 - 6 + 8 \qquad |0 \end{array}$$

Since the remainder is zero, the dominant root is exactly $\mu_1 = 10$. The polynomial $f(z)$ is seen to have the factors $f(z) = (z - 10)(z^2 - 6z + 8)$. The roots of the quadratic $z^2 - 6z + 8 = 0$ are $\mu_2 = 4$ and $\mu_3 = 2$. The eigenvalues of the companion matrix (29.9) are therefore $\mu_1 = 10$, $\mu_2 = 4$, $\mu_3 = 2$. If only the *smallest* root of the equation is desired, the substitution $z = 1/y$ may be made in Eq. (29.3) and the companion matrix of the resulting equation in y may be constructed. The iteration scheme (29.7) then yields the *largest* root in y and therefore the *smallest* root of the original equation.

The method of matrix iteration may be used to determine repeated and complex roots of algebraic equations.*

PROBLEMS

1. Solve the following system of equations by the use of determinants:

$$\begin{aligned} x - 2y + 3z &= 2 \\ 2x - 3z &= 3 \\ x + y + z &= 6 \end{aligned}$$

$\qquad$ *Ans.* $x = 3$, $y = 2$, $z = 1$.

---

* See L. A. Pipes, Matrix Solution of Polynomial Equations, *Journal of the Franklin Institute*, vol. 225, no. 4, pp. 437–454, April, 1938.

2. Evaluate the determinant

$$D = \begin{vmatrix} 3 & 1 & -1 & 2 & 1 \\ -2 & 3 & 1 & 4 & 3 \\ 1 & 4 & 2 & 3 & 1 \\ 5 & -2 & -3 & 5 & -1 \\ -1 & 1 & 2 & 3 & 2 \end{vmatrix}$$

Ans. $D = 446$.

3. Solve the following system of equations:

$$\begin{aligned} 9x + 3y + 4z + 2w &= 28 \\ 3x + 5z - 4w &= 12 \\ y + z + w &= 5 \\ 6x - y + 3w &= 19 \end{aligned}$$

Ans. $x = \frac{4}{3}$, $y = -2$, $z = 4$, $w = 3$.

4. Prove Cramer's rule for the general case of n equations.   HINT: Use Eq. (4.8).

5. Given

$$[a] = \begin{bmatrix} 1 & 2 \\ 3 & 4 \end{bmatrix}$$

compute $[a]^{10}$.

6. Given

$$[a] = \begin{bmatrix} 8 & 4 & 3 \\ 2 & 1 & 1 \\ 1 & 2 & 1 \end{bmatrix}$$

compute $[a]^{-2}$.

7. Find the characteristic equation and the eigenvalues of the following matrix:

$$[a] = \begin{bmatrix} 1 & 1 & 1 \\ 1 & 2 & 2 \\ 1 & 2 & 3 \end{bmatrix}$$

8. Show that the matrix

$$[A] = \begin{bmatrix} a & h \\ h & b \end{bmatrix}$$

is transformed to the diagonal form

$$B = T_\theta [A] T_\theta'$$

where T_θ is the following matrix:

$$T_\theta = \begin{bmatrix} \cos\theta & \sin\theta \\ -\sin\theta & \cos\theta \end{bmatrix}$$

and $\tan 2\theta = 2h/(a - b)$ (Jacobi's transformation).

9. Show that

$$\begin{bmatrix} \cos\theta & -\sin\theta \\ \sin\theta & \cos\theta \end{bmatrix} = \begin{bmatrix} 1 & -\tan\dfrac{\theta}{2} \\ \tan\dfrac{\theta}{2} & 1 \end{bmatrix} \begin{bmatrix} 1 & -\tan\dfrac{\theta}{2} \\ -\tan\dfrac{\theta}{2} & 1 \end{bmatrix}^{-1}$$

10. Show that the matrix

$$[J] = \begin{bmatrix} 0 & -1 \\ 1 & 0 \end{bmatrix}$$

has properties similar to those of the imaginary number $j = (-1)^{\frac{1}{2}}$. Show that $[J]^2 = -U$, where U is the second-order unit matrix, and that $[J]^3 = -[J]$, $[J]^4 = u$, $[J]^5 = [J]$, etc.

11. Determine the eigenvalues and eigenvectors of the matrix

$$[M] = \begin{bmatrix} 2 & -2 & 2 \\ 1 & 1 & 1 \\ 1 & 3 & -1 \end{bmatrix}$$

$$Ans. \; \mu_1 = 1, \; \mu_2 = -2, \; \mu_3 = 3.$$

12. Determine the roots of the equation $z^3 - 16z^2 + 65z - 50 = 0$ by the matrix iteration method.

13. Solve the differential equation $d^2y/dt^2 + w^2y = 0$, subject to the conditions $y(0) = y_0$ and $\dot{y}(0) = v_0$, by the Peano-Baker method.

REFERENCES

1. Bôcher, M.: "Introduction to Higher Algebra," The Macmillan Company, New York, 1931. (An exposition of the classical mathematical theory of matrices.)
2. Frazer, R. A., W. J. Duncan, and A. R. Collar: "Elementary Matrices," Cambridge University Press, New York, 1938. (An excellent exposition of the theory of matrices and applications to dynamics and oscillation problems of aeronautical engineering.)
3. Kaufmann, A., and M. Denis-Papin: "Course de calcul matriciel," Albin Michel, Paris, 1951. (An excellent expository account of the theory, with numerous applications to technical problems in the fields of electricity, vibrations, wave propagation, and elastic structures.)
4. MacDuffee, C. C.: "The Theory of Matrices," Chelsea Publishing Company, New York, 1946. (An excellent concise exposition of the fundamental mathematical theory.)
5. Pipes, L. A.: Matrices in Engineering, *Electrical Engineering*, vol. 56, pp. 1177–1190, 1937. (A concise exposition of the elementary theory, with applications to electrical-circuit theory.)
6. Simultaneous Linear Equations and the Determination of Eigenvalues, edited by L. J. Paige and Olga Taussky, *National Bureau of Standards, Applied Mathematics Series* 29, August, 1953. (Contains a bibliography of over 450 titles on the solution of linear equations and a description of useful methods for the determination of the eigenvalues and eigenvectors of numerical matrices.)
7. Turnbull, H. W., and A. C. Aitken: "An Introduction to the Theory of Canonical Matrices," Blackie & Son, Ltd., Glasgow, 1932. (An exposition of the classical mathematical theory.)
8. Wedderburn, J. H. M.: "Lectures on Matrices," J. W. Edwards, Publisher, Inc., Ann Arbor, Mich., 1949. (Contains a bibliography of 661 entries covering the mathematical literature through 1936.)
9. Zurmuhl, R.: "Matrizen," Springer-Verlag OHG, Berlin, 1950. (An excellent exposition of the elementary theory, with numerous applications to electrical circuits, differential equations, numerical methods, and vibration theory.)

CHAPTER 5

THE SOLUTION OF TRANSCENDENTAL
AND POLYNOMIAL EQUATIONS

1. Introduction. In applied mathematics the need frequently arises for solving numerically transcendental or higher-degree algebraic equations; for example, in determining the natural frequencies of oscillation of a uniform prismatic bar built in at one end and with the other end supported, it is necessary to solve the transcendental equation

$$(1.1) \qquad \tan \theta = \tanh \theta$$

Transcendental equations occur very frequently in determining the natural frequencies and modes of oscillation of electrical and mechanical systems. Higher-degree polynomial equations also arise frequently in practice. Algebraic formulas exist for the solution of the general quadratic, cubic, and quartic equations with literal coefficients. However, no formulas exist for the solution of a general algebraic equation with literal coefficients if it is of higher degree than the fourth. The formulas for the cubic and quartic equations are sometimes laborious to apply to given cases. The importance of being able to solve numerically equations of this type is very great, and this chapter will be devoted to a brief discussion of possible methods of solution.

2. Graphical Solution of Transcendental Equations. As an example, let us solve the transcendental equation

$$(2.1) \qquad \cos x \cosh x + 1 = 0$$

This equation occurs in determining the natural frequencies of oscillation of a clamped cantilever beam.

Equation (2.1) is satisfied by an infinite number of values of x. Let us write the equation (2.1) in the form

$$(2.2) \qquad \cos x = -\frac{1}{\cosh x}$$

If we plot the curves

$$(2.3) \qquad y_1 = -\frac{1}{\cosh x}$$

and

(2.4) $$y_2 = \cos x$$

the roots of (2.1) are given by the abscissas of the points of intersection of these two curves as shown in Fig. 2.1.

From the figure, we find the first three roots to be approximately

(2.5) $$x_1 = 1.87 \qquad x_2 = \frac{3\pi}{2} \qquad x_3 = \frac{5\pi}{2}$$

Since

(2.6) $$\lim_{x \to \infty} \frac{1}{\cosh x} = 0$$

the higher roots are given with satisfactory accuracy by the equation

(2.7) $$x_r = (r - \tfrac{1}{2})\pi \qquad r = 2, 3, 4, \ldots$$

This example illustrates the general principle involved in the graphical solution of transcendental equations. That is, if we wish to solve the equation

(2.8) $$F(x) = 0$$

we write it in the form

(2.9) $$F_1(x) = F_2(x)$$

This may usually be done in many ways. We then draw the curves

(2.10) $$\begin{aligned} y_1 &= F_1(x) \\ y_2 &= F_2(x) \end{aligned}$$

The real roots of $F(x) = 0$ are evidently the abscissas of the points of intersection of these curves. The larger the scale of the graph and the more carefully the drawing is performed, the greater the accuracy of the roots. Having once found

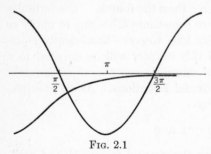

FIG. 2.1

the approximate location of the roots, the accuracy may be improved by an iterative process called the *Newton-Raphson method*.

3. The Newton-Raphson Method. Let us consider the function

(3.1) $$y = F(x)$$

Let us draw this curve as in Fig. 3.1.

The point $x = A$ is a root of the equation

(3.2) $$F(x) = 0$$

Let us draw the tangent to the curve at the point P. This tangent will intersect the x axis at a point x_1.

From the figure we have

(3.3) $$\tan \phi = \frac{F(x_0)}{x_0 - x_1} = F'(x_0)$$

Hence

(3.4) $$x_1 = x_0 - \frac{F(x_0)}{F'(x_0)}$$

If we now set up the sequence

(3.5) $$x_{r+1} = x_r - \frac{F(x_r)}{F'(x_r)}$$

it is apparent from the figure that this sequence tends to the root A. If we start on the other side of A where the arc of the curve is convex to the x axis, the first step carries us to the opposite side of A where the arc is concave to the x axis; after this the sequence tends to the root as before.

FIG. 3.1

This discussion is based on the following two assumptions:

1. That the slope of the curve does not become zero along the arc Q_1, P.

2. That the curve has no inflection point along Q_1, P.

More precisely, we can say that, if $F(x)$ has only one root between two points Q_1 and P while $F'(x)$ and $F''(x)$ are never zero between these two points, then the Newton-Raphson process will succeed if we begin it at one of the points for which $F(x)$ and $F''(x)$ have the same sign.

It is sometimes more convenient to use the formula

(3.6) $$x_{r+1} = x_r - \frac{F(x_r)}{F'(x_0)}$$

instead of (3.5).

This means that in the successive steps of the process we replace the tangents calculated at x_1, x_2, etc., by lines parallel to the tangent at P. This saves the trouble of calculating $F'(x_r)$ at each stage.

As an example of the method, let it be required to determine the solution of the equation

(3.7) $$x = \sin x + \frac{\pi}{2}$$

To obtain a rough estimate of the root, we draw the curves

(3.8) $$y_1 = x - \frac{\pi}{2} \quad \text{and} \quad y_2 = \sin x$$

as in Fig. 3.2.

From the graph, we obtain

(3.9) $x_0 = 2.3$ radians

as a rough estimate of the root. With this value for x_0, we begin the iterative process. Here we have

(3.10) $F(x) = x - \sin x - \dfrac{\pi}{2}$

(3.11) $F'(x) = 1 - \cos x$

The first approximation is

(3.12) $x_1 = x_0 - \dfrac{F(x_0)}{F'(x_0)} = x_0 - \dfrac{x_0 - \sin x_0 - \pi/2}{1 - \cos x_0}$

Now

(3.13) $x_0 = 2.3$ radians $= 132°$
(3.14) $\sin x_0 = 0.7431 \qquad \cos x_0 = -0.669$

Hence

(3.15) $x_1 = 2.3 - \dfrac{2.3 - 0.743 - 1.57}{1 + 0.669} = 2.308$

This is a very good approximation to the root. If more significant figures are desired, the iterative process of (3.6) may be repeated.

FIG. 3.2

4. Solution of Cubic Equations. In the study of the natural frequencies of undamped electrical and mechanical systems with three degrees of freedom, we have to determine the solution of the equation

(4.1) $Z^3 + A_2 Z^2 + A_1 Z + A_0 = 0$

We may eliminate the Z^2 term by the substitution

(4.2) $Z = x - \dfrac{A_2}{3}$

We then obtain

(4.3) $x^3 + \left(A_1 - \dfrac{A_2^2}{3}\right) x + \left(A_0 - \dfrac{A_1 A_2}{3} + \tfrac{2}{27}A_2^3\right) = 0$

This may be written in the form

(4.4) $x^3 - qx - r = 0$

There are two principal cases to consider.

a. *The Case where* $27r^2 > 4q^3$. In this case the cubic has one real root and two complex roots. Then, if q and r are *both* positive, we find ϕ

such that

$$(4.5) \qquad \cosh \phi = \left(\frac{3}{q}\right)^{\frac{3}{2}} \frac{r}{2}$$

Then the real root is given by the equation

$$(4.6) \qquad x_0 = \frac{2}{\sqrt{3}} q^{\frac{1}{2}} \cosh \frac{\phi}{3}$$

Dividing (4.4) by $x - x_0$, we reduce the equation to a quadratic and obtain the pair of complex roots by solving the resulting quadratic.

If q is *negative* and r is *positive*, we find ϕ such that

$$(4.7) \qquad \sinh \phi = \left(\frac{3}{-q}\right)^{\frac{3}{2}} \frac{r}{2}$$

Then the real root is given by the equation

$$(4.8) \qquad x = \frac{2}{\sqrt{3}} (-q)^{\frac{1}{2}} \sinh \frac{\phi}{3}$$

It may be noted that we may always suppose that r is positive since if we change the sign of r we merely change the sign of the roots.

b. The Case where $27r^2 < 4q^3$. In this case the cubic equation has three real roots. We now find the smallest positive angle ϕ such that

$$(4.9) \qquad \cos \phi = \left(\frac{3}{q}\right)^{\frac{3}{2}} \frac{r}{2}$$

Then the real roots are given by

$$(4.10) \qquad \begin{aligned} x_1 &= \frac{2}{\sqrt{3}} q^{\frac{1}{2}} \cos \frac{\phi}{3} \\ x_2 &= - \frac{2}{\sqrt{3}} q^{\frac{1}{2}} \cos \frac{\pi - \phi}{3} \\ x_3 &= - \frac{2}{\sqrt{3}} q^{\frac{1}{2}} \cos \frac{\pi + \phi}{3} \end{aligned}$$

For example, let it be required to solve

$$(4.11) \qquad Z^3 + 9Z^2 + 23Z + 14 = 0$$

In this case we remove the Z^2 term by writing

$$(4.12) \qquad Z = x - 3$$

and the equation becomes

$$(4.13) \qquad x^3 - 4x - 1 = 0$$

We now have

$$(4.14) \qquad 27 \times 1^2 < 4 \times 4^3$$

Hence this equation comes under case b, and the roots are all real. We now compute

$$(4.15) \qquad \frac{\phi}{3} = 23°41'$$

and, substituting into (4.10), we obtain

$$(4.16) \qquad \begin{aligned} x_1 &= 2.11 \\ x_2 &= -1.86 \\ x_3 &= -0.254 \end{aligned}$$

Hence the roots of (4.11) are

$$(4.17) \qquad \begin{aligned} Z_1 &= -0.89 \\ Z_2 &= -4.86 \\ Z_3 &= -3.254 \end{aligned}$$

5. Graeffe's Root-squaring Method. In the last section we considered some algebraic formulas for the solution of the cubic equation. There also exists a formula solution for the quartic equation.* These formulas are, in general, laborious to use in numerical computations. No formulas exist for the solution of a general algebraic equation with literal coefficients if it is of higher degree than the fourth.

In this section we shall discuss a method for the numerical solution of an algebraic equation of any degree. Before considering this method, it is well to recall the following properties concerning the nature of algebraic equations:

1. The equation

$$(5.1) \qquad x^n + a_1 x^{n-1} + a_2 x^{n-2} + \cdots + a_n = 0$$

where the coefficients a_r are real numbers, has exactly n roots. Some of the roots may be repeated roots.

2. If n is a positive odd integer, the equation always has one real root.

3. The number of positive roots either is equal to the number of variations of signs of the a's or is less than this number of variations by an even integer (Descartes' rule of signs).

4. The complex roots occur in conjugate complex pairs.

The method we shall consider was suggested by Dandelin in 1826 and independently by Graeffe in 1837. It is of great use, especially in the case of equations possessing complex roots. The fundamental principle of the method is to form a new equation whose roots are some high power of the roots of the given equation. That is, if the roots of the original equation are $x_1, x_2, \ldots, x_n$, the roots of the new equation are

---

* See, for example, E. R. Dickson, "Elementary Theory of Equations," p. 31, John Wiley & Sons, Inc., New York, 1922.

$x_1^s, x_2^s, \ldots, x_n^s$. If s is large, then the high powers of the roots will be *widely separated*. If the roots are very widely separated, they may be obtained by a simple process.

Let the roots of the Eq. (5.1) be $-r_1, -r_2, \ldots, -r_n$. These values are the roots of the equation with the signs reversed and are called the *Encke roots*. (We shall assume at present that they are real and unequal.) Since the r quantities are the roots of the equation with the signs reversed, it may be factored in the form

$$(5.2) \qquad (x + r_1)(x + r_2)(x + r_3) \cdots (x + r_n) = 0$$

If we use the convenient notation

$$(5.3) \qquad \begin{aligned} [r_i] &= r_1 + r_2 + \cdots + r_n = \text{sum of Encke roots} \\ [r_i r_j] &= r_1 r_2 + r_1 r_3 + \cdots = \text{sum of products of Encke} \\ &\qquad\qquad\qquad\qquad\quad\; \text{roots taken two at a time} \\ [r_i r_j r_k] &= r_1 r_2 r_3 + r_1 r_2 r_4 + \cdots = \text{sum of products of Encke} \\ &\qquad\qquad\qquad\qquad\qquad\quad \text{roots taken three at a} \\ &\qquad\qquad\qquad\qquad\qquad\quad \text{time} \end{aligned}$$

$$[a_1 r_2 \cdots r_n] = \text{product of all the roots}$$

then on multiplying the various factors of (5.2) we obtain

$$(5.4) \qquad x^n + [r_i]x^{n-1} + [r_i r_j]x^{n-2} + \cdots + [r_1 r_2 \cdots r_n] = 0$$

Squaring the Roots. A simple device by which one may obtain a new equation whose Encke roots are the squares of the Encke roots of the original equation will now be explained. Let us write

$$(5.5) \qquad F(x) = (x + r_1)(x + r_2) \cdots (x + r_n) = 0$$

Then

$$(5.6) \qquad F(-x) = (-x + r_1)(-x + r_2) \cdots (-x + r_n) = 0$$

and

$$(5.7) \quad F(x)F(-x) = (r_1^2 - x^2)(r_2^2 - x^2)(r_3^2 - x^2) \cdots (r_n^2 - x^2) = 0$$

If in (5.7) we let

$$(5.8) \qquad\qquad\qquad y = -x^2$$

we obtain

$$(5.9) \qquad F(x)F(-x) = (y + r_1^2)(y + r_2^2) \cdots (y + r_n^2) = 0$$

Now the roots of (5.9) are $-r_1^2, -r_2^2, \ldots, -r_n^2$, and hence the *Encke* roots are $r_1^2, r_2^2, \ldots, r_n^2$, and hence they are the squares of the Encke roots of (5.5). If we now write $F(x)$ in the form

$$(5.6a) \qquad F(x) = x^n + a_1 x^{n-1} + a_2 x^{n-2} + \cdots + a_n = 0$$

then

$$(5.7a) \quad F(x)F(-x) = (x^n + a_1 x^{n-1} + \cdots + a_n)$$
$$[(-x)^n + a_1(-x)^{n-1} + \cdots + a_n] = 0$$

Carrying out the multiplication and writing

$$(5.8a) \qquad\qquad -x^2 = y$$

we obtain

$$(5.9a) \quad y^n + (a_1^2 - 2a_2)y^{n-1} + (a_2^2 - 2a_1a_3 + 2a_4)y^{n-2} + \cdots = 0$$

This may be written in the form

(5.10)

$$y^n + \left\{ \begin{array}{c} a_1^2 \\ -2a_2 \end{array} \right\} y^{n-1} + \left\{ \begin{array}{c} a_2^2 \\ -2a_1a_3 \\ +2a_4 \end{array} \right\} y^{n-2} + \left\{ \begin{array}{c} a_3^2 \\ -2a_2a_4 \\ +2a_1a_5 \\ -2a_6 \end{array} \right\} y^{n-3} + \cdots = 0$$

We notice that the coefficients of (5.9a) are found from the coefficients of the original equation (5.6) by the following simple rule:

The coefficient of any power of y is formed by adding to the square of the corresponding coefficient in the original equation the doubled product of every pair of coefficients which stand equally far from it on either side. These products are taken with signs alternately negative and positive.

If a power of x is absent, then it is taken with a coefficient equal to zero. To facilitate the process, a table is constructed in the following manner:

$$F(x) = x^n + a_1 x^{n-1} + a_2 x^{n-2} + \cdots + a_n = 0$$

1	a_1	a_2	a_3	a_4	a_5
	a_1^2	a_2^2	a_3^2	a_4^2	
	$-2a_2$	$-2a_1a_3$	$-2a_2a_4$	$-2a_3a_5$	etc.
		$+2a_4$	$+2a_1a_5$	$+2a_2a_6$	
			$-2a_6$	$-2a_1a_7$	
				$+2a_8$	
1	b_1	b_2	b_3	b_4	b_5

The b's are the coefficients of the equation whose Encke roots are the squares of the Encke roots of the original equation.

If we now repeat this process several times, we finally arrive at an equation whose Encke roots are the mth powers of the Encke roots of the original equation. This equation has the form

$$(5.11) \qquad x^n + [r_i^m]x^{n-1} + [r_i^m r_j^m]x^{n-2} + \cdots = 0$$

If now

$$(5.12) \qquad r_1 > r_2 > r_3 > \cdots > r_n$$

then

$$(5.13) \qquad r_1^m \gg r_2^m \gg r_3^m \cdots \gg r_n^m$$

That is, if the roots differ in magnitude in the manner (5.12), then the mth powers of the roots, where m is a large number, are widely separated. Hence

$$(5.14) \qquad [r_i^m] = r_1^m + r_2^m + \cdots + r_n^m \doteq r_1^m$$

for a sufficiently large m.   We also have

$$(5.15) \qquad [r_i^m r_j^m] = r_1^m r_2^m + r_1^m r_2^m + \cdots \doteq r_1^m r_2^m$$

Hence from (5.14) we obtain

$$(5.16) \qquad \log |r_1| \doteq \frac{1}{m} \log [r_i^m]$$

and from (5.15) we have

$$(5.17) \qquad \log |r_2| \doteq \frac{1}{m} \log [r_i^m r_j^m] - \frac{1}{m} \log [r_i^m]$$

Equation (5.16) determines the absolute value of the largest root r_1, and Eq. (5.17) determines the absolute value of the second largest root r_2, and so on.

In the solution of equations by this method it is very necessary to know when to stop the root-squaring process.   The time to stop is when another doubling of m produces new coefficients $[r_i^{2m}]$, $[r_i^{2m} r_j^{2m}]$ that are practically the squares of the corresponding coefficients $[r_i^m]$, $[r_i^m r_j^m]$ in the equation already obtained.   To illustrate the general theory, let us consider the solution of the equation

$$(5.18) \qquad F(x) = x^3 + 9x^2 + 23x + 14 = 0$$

which has three real roots.

We construct the following table:

	x^3	x^2	x	c
p	1	9	23	14
p^2	i	35	277	196
p^4	1	671	63,009	38,416
p^8	1	324,223	3.9185×10^9	1.4757×10^9
p^{16}	1	9.728×10^{10}	1.535×10^{21}	2.177×10^{18}
p^{32}	1	9.433×10^{21}	2.357×10^{38}	$(2.177 \times 10^{18})^2$
p^{64}	1	8.898×10^{43}	$(2.357 \times 10^{38})^2$	$(2.177 \times 10^{18})^4$

In this table p^2 denotes the equation whose Encke roots are the squares of the Encke roots of p, etc.

If we stop at this stage, we have

(5.19) $$\log r_1^{64} = \log (8.898 \times 10^{43}) = 43.9493$$
(5.20) $$\log |r_1| = 0.68670$$

and hence

(5.21) $$r_1 = \pm 4.860$$

This is the magnitude of the numerically greatest root.   We also have

(5.22) $$\log (r_1 r_2)^{64} = 2 \log (2.357 \times 10^{38})$$
$$= 76.74492$$

Hence

(5.23) $$\log r_2 = \tfrac{1}{64}(76.7449 - 43.9493)$$
$$= 0.51243$$

Therefore

(5.24) $$r_2 = \pm 3.254$$

Finally, we have

(5.25) $$\log (r_1 r_2 r_3)^{64} = 4 \log (2.177 \times 10^{18})$$
$$= 73.352$$

and

(5.26) $$\log |r_3| = \tfrac{1}{64}(73.352 - 76.7449)$$
$$= 0.94698$$

and therefore

(5.27) $$r_3 = \pm 0.885$$

It is not possible to determine the signs of the roots by this process. Descartes' rule of signs shows that all the roots are negative, and they are therefore

(5.28) $$\begin{aligned} x_1 &= -4.860 \\ x_2 &= -3.254 \\ x_3 &= -0.885 \end{aligned}$$

Complex Roots.   We shall now discuss briefly the modifications which must be introduced in the above procedure in case the equation under consideration has complex roots.   To illustrate the general procedure, let the equation under consideration be of the fifth degree, and let it have the following Encke roots:

$$r_1, \; Z_1, \; \bar{Z}_1, \; r_2, \; r_3$$

where

(5.29)
$$|r_1| > |Z| > |r_2| > |r_3|$$

We carry out the root-squaring process as before and obtain an equation whose Encke roots are the mth powers of the Encke roots of the original equation.   For a sufficiently large m we have

(5.30)
$$[r_i^m] \doteq r_1^m$$

as before, since by hypothesis r_1 is the dominant root numerically.   Hence this root may be determined as before.   We now have

(5.31)
$$[r_i^m r_j^m] \doteq r_1^m Z^m + r_1^m \bar{Z}^m$$
$$= r_1^m (Z^m + \bar{Z}^m)$$

If we let

(5.32)
$$Z = Re^{j\phi}$$

we then have

(5.33)
$$[r_i^m r_j^m] = 2r_1^m R^m \cos m\phi$$

This shows that the coefficient of the x^3 term will fluctuate in sign as the number m takes in succession a set of increasing values because of the cosine term.   We also have

(5.34)
$$[r_i^m r_j^m r_k^m] \doteq r_1^m Z^m \bar{Z}^m = r_1^m R^{2m}$$

Proceeding in this manner, we see that when m is large enough so that only the dominant part of the coefficient of each power of x is retained the equation whose Encke roots are the mth powers of the roots of the original equation is

(5.35) $$x^5 + r_1^m x^4 + (2r_1^m R^m \cos m\phi)x^3$$
$$+ r_1^m R^{2m} x^2 + r_1^m R^{2m} r_2^m x + r_1^m R^{2m} r_2^m r_3^m = 0$$

From this we may find r_1, r_2, r_3, and R.   To obtain the angle of the complex root, we write

(5.36)
$$Z = Re^{j\phi} = u + jv = R(\cos \phi + j \sin \phi)$$

But we know that the sum of the Encke roots of the original equation is given by

(5.37)
$$a_1 = r_1 + Z + \bar{Z} + r_2 + r_3$$
$$= r_1 + 2u + r_2 + r_3$$

Hence

(5.38)
$$u = \frac{a_1 - r_1 - r_2 - r_3}{2} = R \cos \phi$$

or

$$\phi = \cos^{-1}\left\{\frac{u}{R}\right\} \tag{5.39}$$

In the above example we saw that the fluctuation of the coefficient of the x^3 term indicated the presence of a pair of complex roots. If two coefficients fluctuate in sign, the presence of two pairs of complex roots may be inferred and the analysis modified accordingly. Rather than consider any fixed rules, it is well to consider the general nature of the root-squaring process in solving equations by this method.

The Case of Repeated Roots. The nature of the process in case the equation has repeated roots may be illustrated by the consideration of a special case. As before, let the Encke roots of the equation be denoted by $r_1, r_2, r_3, \ldots, r_m$. Let the root r_2 be equal to the root r_3,

$$r_2 = r_3 \tag{5.40}$$

That is, the equation has the repeated root r_2. In this case again the equation whose Encke roots are the mth powers of those of the given equation is

$$x^n + [r_i^m]x^{n-1} + [r_i^m r_j^m]x^{n-2} + [r_i^m r_j^m r_k^m]x^{n-3} + \cdots = 0 \tag{5.41}$$

If m is sufficiently large so that we may retain only the dominant term in each coefficient, we have

$$x^n + r_1^m x^{n-1} + 2r_1^m r_2^m x^{n-2} + r_1^{2m} r_2^m x^{n-3} + \cdots = 0 \tag{5.42}$$

We notice that the coefficient of the term x^{n-2} does not follow the usual law that when m is doubled the coefficient is approximately squared. In this case, when m is doubled, the new coefficient is approximately *half* the square of the old one. This is an indication of a repeated root. To compute r_2, let

$$\begin{aligned} b_1 &= r_1^m \\ b_2 &= 2r_1^m r_2^m \\ b_3 &= r_1^m r_2^{2m} \end{aligned} \tag{5.43}$$

If we divide b_3 by b_1, we obtain

$$\frac{b_3}{b_1} = r_2^{2m} \tag{5.44}$$

and hence

$$|r_2| = \sqrt[2m]{\frac{b_3}{b_1}} \tag{5.45}$$

The rest of the roots are computed as before. The foregoing discussion is the general theory of Graeffe's root-squaring method. In general, it is better to keep the basic concept of the method of root squaring in mind rather than to formulate elaborate rules for special cases.

PROBLEMS

1. Determine the roots of the equation $\tanh x = \tan x$.

2. Determine the roots of the equation $\tan x = x$.

3. Find the roots of $e^x = 5x$.

4. Solve the equation $x^3 - 2x - 1 = 0$.

5. Solve the equation $x^3 - 97x - 202 = 0$.

6. By using Graeffe's method, solve the equation $x^2 - 2x + 2 = 0$.

7. Solve the equation $x^3 + x^2 + x + 1 = 0$.

8. Find the roots of the equation $x^3 - 5x^2 + 6x - 1 = 0$

(a) By the formula for the solution of a cubic equation.

(b) By Graeffe's method.

9. Solve $\tan x = 10/x$.

10. The equation $x^3 - 2x - 5 = 0$ has a real root between 2 and 3. Determine the magnitude of this root by the use of the Newton-Raphson method.

11. Compute to four decimal places the real root of the equation $x^2 + 4 \sin x = 0$ by the use of the Newton-Raphson method. *Ans.* $x = -1.9338$.

12. Determine the roots of the equation $x \tan x = 10$ to three decimal places.

13. Find the smallest positive root of the equation $x^x + 2x = 6$ to three decimal places. *Ans.* $x = 1.723$.

REFERENCES

1. Whittaker, E. T., and G. Robinson: "The Calculus of Observations," Blackie & Son, Ltd., Glasgow, 1924.

2. Doherty, R. E., and G. Keller: "Mathematics of Modern Engineering," John Wiley & Sons, Inc., New York, 1936.

3. Burnside, R., and F. Panton: "Theory of Equations," 8th ed., vol. I, Hodges & Figgis & Co., Dublin, 1918.

4. Scarborough, J. B.: "Numerical Mathematical Analysis," Oxford University Press, New York, 1950.

5. Hartree, D. R.: "Numerical Analysis," Oxford University Press, New York, 1952.

6. Milne, W. E.: "Numerical Calculus," Princeton University Press, Princeton, N.J., 1949.

7. Soroka, W. W.: "Analog Methods in Computation and Simulation," McGraw-Hill Book Company, Inc., New York, 1954.

8. Cowley, W. L.: "Advanced Practical Mathematics," Pitman Publishing Corporation, New York, 1934.

CHAPTER 6

LINEAR DIFFERENTIAL EQUATIONS WITH CONSTANT COEFFICIENTS

1. Introduction. *Linear Differential Equations of the First Order.* In applied mathematics the most important and frequently occurring differential equations are linear differential equations. A linear differential equation of order n is one of the form

$$(1.1) \quad a_0(x) \frac{d^n y}{dx^n} + a_1(x) \frac{d^{n-1} y}{dx^{n-1}} + \cdots + a_{n-1}(x) \frac{dy}{dx} + a_n(x)y = f(x)$$

where $a_0, a_1, \ldots, a_n$ and f are functions of the independent variable x and $a_0 \neq 0$.

If $n = 1$, we have the linear equation of the first order; this is written in the form

$$(1.2) \qquad \frac{dy}{dx} + P(x)y = Q(x)$$

If $Q(x) = 0$, we have

$$(1.3) \qquad \frac{dy}{dx} + P(x)y = 0$$

This equation is called a *homogeneous linear differential equation of the first order.* It may be put in the form

$$(1.4) \qquad \frac{dy}{y} = -P(x) \, dx$$

In this form the variables are said to be *separated,* and we may therefore integrate both members and obtain

$$(1.5) \qquad \ln y = -\int P(x) \, dx + c$$

where c is an arbitrary constant of integration. Therefore we have

$$(1.6) \qquad y = e^{-\int P(x) \, dx + c} = e^{-\int P(x) \, dx} e^c$$

but since e^c is an arbitrary constant, we may denote it by K. Hence the solution of (1.3) is

$$(1.7) \qquad y = Ke^{-\int P(x) \, dx}$$

To solve the more general differential equation (1.2), let us place

$$(1.8) \qquad\qquad y = u(x)v(x)$$

where u and v are functions of x to be determined.   Placing this form for y in (1.2), we obtain

$$(1.9) \qquad\qquad \frac{du}{dx} v + u \frac{dv}{dx} + P(x)uv = Q(x)$$

This may be written in the form

$$(1.10) \qquad\qquad v\left[\frac{du}{dx} + P(x)u\right] + u\frac{dv}{dx} = Q(x)$$

Since u and v are at our disposal, let us place the term in brackets equal to zero.   We then obtain

$$(1.11) \qquad\qquad \frac{du}{dx} + P(x)u = 0$$

and

$$(1.12) \qquad\qquad u\frac{dv}{dx} = Q(x)$$

However, (1.11) is of the same form as (1.3), and therefore its solution is

$$(1.13) \qquad\qquad u = Ke^{-\int P(x)\,dx}$$

If we substitute this value of u into (1.12), we obtain

$$(1.14) \qquad\qquad dv = \frac{1}{K} e^{+\int P(x)\,dx}Q(x)\,dx$$

Since the right-hand member is a function of x alone, we may integrate both sides and thus obtain

$$(1.15) \qquad\qquad v = \frac{1}{K} \int e^{+\int P(x)\,dx}Q(x)\,dx + C_1$$

where C_1 is an arbitrary constant.

Substituting these values of u and v into (1.8), we obtain

$$(1.16) \qquad\qquad y = Ke^{-\int P(x)\,dx}\left[\frac{1}{K} \int e^{\int P(x)\,dx}Q(x)\,dx + C_1\right]$$

This may be written in the form

$$(1.17) \qquad\qquad y = Ce^{-\int P\,dx} + e^{-\int P\,dx} \int e^{\int P(x)\,dx}Q(x)\,dx$$

where C is an arbitrary constant.

We thus see that the solution of Eq. (1.2) consists of two parts. One part is the solution of the homogeneous equation with the right-hand member equal to zero. This is called the *complementary function;* it contains an arbitrary constant. The other part involves an integral of the right-hand member $Q(x)$. This is called the *particular integral.* The general solution is the sum of these two parts and is given by (1.17).

2. The Reduced Equation, the Complementary Function. In the last section the solution of the general linear differential equation with variable coefficients of the first order was obtained. Equation (1.17) gives a formula by means of which the solution may be obtained, provided the indicated integrations may be performed.

If the linear differential equation with variable coefficients is of order higher than the first, it is not possible to obtain an explicit solution in closed form in the general case. In general a series solution must be resorted to in this case. Fortunately a great many of the problems of applied mathematics such as the study of small-amplitude mechanical oscillations and the analysis of electrical networks lead to the solution of linear differential equations with constant coefficients. Accordingly in this chapter we shall study methods of solution of this type of equation.

If the various coefficients $a_r(x)$, $r = 0, 1, 2, \ldots, n$ of (1.1) are constants, we may write this equation in the form

$$(2.1) \qquad \frac{d^n y}{dx^n} + a_1 \frac{d^{n-1} y}{dx^{n-1}} + \cdots + a_{n-1} \frac{dy}{dx} + a_n y = F(x)$$

provided $a_0 = 1$.

It is convenient to introduce the symbol of operation

$$(2.2) \qquad D^r = \frac{d^r}{dx^r} \qquad r = 1, 2, \ldots, n$$

We may then write (2.1) in the form

$$(2.3) \qquad D^n y + a_1 D^{n-1} y + \cdots + a_n y = F(x)$$

This may also be written in the form

$$(2.4) \qquad (D^n + a_1 D^{n-1} + \cdots + a_{n-1} D + a_n) y = F(x)$$

where the significance of the term in parentheses of the left-hand member is that it constitutes an operator that when operating on $y(x)$ leads to the left-hand member of (2.3).

To save writing, we may condense our notation further by letting

$$(2.5) \qquad L_n(D) = D^n + a_1 D^{n-1} + a_2 D^{n-2} + \cdots + a_{n-1} D + a_n$$

We may then write (2.4) concisely in the form

$$(2.6) \qquad L_n(D) y = F(x)$$

If $F(x)$ in (2.6) is placed equal to zero, we obtain the equation

$$(2.7) \qquad\qquad L_n(D)y = 0$$

This is called the reduced equation.

It will now be shown that the general solution of (2.6) consists of the sum of two parts y_c and y_P. y_c is the solution of the reduced equation and is called the complementary function. It then satisfies

$$(2.8) \qquad\qquad L_n(D)y_c = 0$$

The particular integral y_P satisfies the equation

$$(2.9) \qquad\qquad L_n(D)y_P = F(x)$$

If we add (2.8) and (2.9), we obtain

$$(2.10) \qquad\qquad L_n(D)y_c + L_n(D)y_P = F(x)$$

But this may be written in the form

$$(2.11) \qquad\qquad L_n(D)(y_c + y_P) = F(x)$$

If we now let

$$(2.12) \qquad\qquad y = y_c + y_P$$

we thus obtain

$$(2.13) \qquad\qquad L_n(D)y = F(x)$$

This proves the proposition.

It thus follows that the general solution of a linear differential equation with constant coefficients is the sum of a particular integral y_P and the complementary function y_c, the latter being the solution of the equation obtained by substituting zero for the function $F(x)$.

3. Properties of the Operator $L_n(D)$. *General Solution of the Linear Differential Equation.* We have seen that the general linear differential equation with constant coefficients may be written in the form

$$(3.1) \qquad\qquad L_n(D)y = F(x)$$

The expression $L_n(D)$ is known as a *linear differential operator of order n.* It is not an algebraic expression multiplied by y but a symbol that expresses the fact that certain operations of differentiation are to be performed on the function y.

Consider the particular linear operator

$$(3.2) \qquad\qquad L_2(D)y = 2\frac{d^2y}{dx^2} + 5\frac{dy}{dx} + 2y$$
$$= (2D^2 + 5D + 2)y$$

We shall also write this in the factorized form

$$(3.3) \qquad L(D)y = (2D + 1)(D + 2)y$$

factorizing the expression in D as if it were an ordinary algebraic quantity. Is this justifiable?

The operations of multiplication performed in ordinary algebra are based upon three laws:

1. The distributive law

$$m(a + b) = ma + mb$$

2. The commutative law

$$ab = ba$$

3. The index law

$$a^n a^m = a^{m+n}$$

Now D satisfies the first and third of these laws, for

$$(3.4) \qquad D(u + v) = Du + Dv$$
$$(3.5) \qquad D^m D^n u = D^{m+n} u$$

As for the second law,

$$(3.6) \qquad D(cu) = cD(u)$$

is true if c is a constant, but not if c is a variable.   We also have

$$(3.7) \qquad D^m(D^n u) = D^n(D^m u)$$

if m and n are positive integers.

Thus D satisfies the fundamental laws of algebra except in that it is not commutative with variables.   It follows that we are justified in performing any operations depending on the fundamental laws of algebra on the linear operator.

$$(3.8) \qquad L_n(D) = D^n + a_1 D^{n-1} + \cdots + a_{n-1}D + a_n$$

In view of this, the solution of the general linear differential equation with constant coefficients may be written symbolically in the form

$$(3.9) \qquad y = \frac{1}{L_n(D)} F(x)$$

We must now investigate the interpretation of the symbol $1/L_n(D)$ when operating on $F(x)$.

Let us consider the case $n = 1$.   That is,

$$(3.10) \qquad y = \frac{1}{L_1(D)} F(x) = \frac{1}{D + a_1} F(x)$$

This is the solution of the equation

$$(3.11) \qquad \frac{dy}{dx} + a_1 y = F(x)$$

This is a special case of the general linear equation of the first order (1.2) with $P(x) = a_1$, $Q(x) = F(x)$. Accordingly the solution of this equation is given by (1.17) with the above values for $P(x)$ and $Q(x)$. The solution is

$$(3.12) \qquad y = Ce^{-a_1 x} + e^{-a_1 x} \int e^{a_1 x} F(x)\, dx$$

We see that the solution consists of two parts. One part is the solution of Eq. (3.11) if $F(x) = 0$. This is the complementary function, so that, using the notation of Sec. 2, we have

$$(3.13) \qquad y_c = Ce^{-a_1 x}$$

This part contains the arbitrary constant C. The second part, which involves $F(x)$, is the particular integral; so we have

$$(3.14) \qquad y_P = e^{-a_1 x} \int e^{a_1 x} F(x)\, dx$$

Decomposition of $L(D)$ into Partial Fractions [*Distinct Roots of $L_n(D) = 0$*]

$$(3.15) \qquad \frac{1}{D - a} F(x) = Ce^{ax} + e^{ax} \int e^{-ax} F(x)\, dx$$

for the operator $1/(D - a)$ operating on $F(x)$.

Let us return to the general problem of interpreting $\dfrac{1}{L_n(D)} F(x)$, where $L_n(D)$ is a linear operator of the nth order.

Consider the equation

$$(3.16) \quad L_n(D)y = (D^n + a_1 D^{n-1} + \cdots + a_{n-1}D + a_n)y = 0$$

regarding $L_n(D)$ as a polynomial in D. Now, if this equation has n *distinct* roots $(m_1, m_2, \ldots, m_n)$, it is known from the theory of partial fractions that we may decompose $1/L_n(D)$ into the simple factors

$$(3.17) \qquad \frac{1}{L_n(D)} = \frac{A_1}{D - m_1} + \frac{A_2}{D - m_2} + \cdots + \frac{A_n}{D - m_n}$$

This is an algebraic identity, and the A_r $(r = 1, 2, \ldots, n)$ quantities are constant, given by

$$(3.18) \qquad A_r = \frac{1}{(d/dD)L_n(D)} \bigg|_{D = m_r} = \frac{1}{L_n'(m_r)}$$

In this case the solution of the equation becomes

$$(3.19) \qquad y = \frac{1}{L_n(D)} F(x) = \sum_{r=1}^{r=n} \frac{A_r}{D - m_r} F(x)$$

But by (3.15) we have

$$(3.20) \qquad \frac{1}{D - m_r} F(x) = C_r e^{m_r x} + e^{m_r x} \int e^{-m_r x} F(x)\, dx$$

Hence the general solution is

$$(3.21) \quad y = \frac{1}{L_n(D)} F(x) = \sum_{r=1}^{r=n} K_r e^{m_r x} + \sum_{r=1}^{r=n} A_r e^{m_r x} \int e^{-m_r x} F(x)\, dx$$

where the K_r quantities are *arbitrary* constants and the A_r quantities are given by (3.18).

The Case of Repeated Roots of $L_n(D) = 0$. If the equation $L_n(D) = 0$ has repeated roots, then the above partial-fraction expansion of $1/L_n(D)$ is no longer possible. Let us first consider the case in which *all* the roots of $L_n(D)$ are repeated. Let the multiple root be equal to m. In this case the equation to be solved is

$$(3.22) \qquad L_n(D)y = (D - m)^n y = F(x)$$

To solve this equation, let us assume a solution of the form

$$(3.23) \qquad y = e^{mx} v(x)$$

where $v(x)$ is a function of x to be determined. Let us consider the effect of operating with the operator $D - m$ on $e^{mx} v(x)$. We have

$$(3.24) \qquad \begin{aligned} (D - m)e^{mx} v(x) &= m e^{mx} v(x) + e^{mx} Dv - m e^{mx} v \\ &= e^{mx} Dv \end{aligned}$$

If we operate again with $D - m$, we obtain

$$(3.25) \qquad (D - m)^2 e^{mx} v(x) = (D - m)e^{mx} Dv = e^{mx} D^2 v$$

If we repeat this procedure n times, we obtain

$$(3.26) \qquad (D - m)^n e^{mx} v = e^{mx} D^n v$$

In view of this, we see that Eq. (3.22), because of the assumption (3.23), becomes

$$(3.27) \qquad e^{mx} D^n v = F(x)$$

In order to satisfy this, we must have

$$(3.28) \qquad D^n v = e^{-mx} F(x)$$

If we integrate Eq. (3.28) n times, we obtain

$$(3.29) \quad v = \underset{n}{\iint \cdots \iint} e^{-mx}F(x)\, dx \cdots dx$$

$$+ C_1 + C_2 x + \cdots + C_n x^{n-1}$$

where the factor $e^{-mx}F(x)$ must be integrated n times and the quantities C_r $(r = 1, 2, \ldots, n)$ are *arbitrary* constants.

We thus see from (3.22) that the result of the operator $1/(D - m)^n$ operating on $F(x)$ may be written in the form

$$(3.30) \quad \frac{1}{(D - m)^n} F(x) = e^{mx} \iint \cdots \iint e^{-mx}F(x)\, dx \cdots dx$$

$$+ e^{mx}(C_1 + C_2 x + \cdots + C_n x^{n-1})$$

Here the term involving the integrals is the particular integral of Eq. (3.22), and the term involving the arbitrary constants is the complementary function.

Let us consider the case in which the operator $L_n(D)$ is such that $(D - m)^r$ is a factor of $L_n(D)$ and that $D - m_1$, $D - m_2$, etc., are simple factors of $L_n(D)$.

To solve the equation $L_n(D)y = F(x)$, we must expand

$$(3.31) \quad \frac{1}{L_n(D)} = \frac{1}{(D - m)^r (D - m_1)(D - m_2) \cdots (D - m_s)}$$

where $s = n - r$, into partial fractions. In this case the partial-fraction expansion is of the form

$$(3.32) \quad \frac{1}{L_n(D)} = \frac{A_1}{(D - m)^r} + \frac{A_2}{(D - m)^{r-1}} + \cdots + \frac{A_r}{D - m}$$

$$+ \frac{B_1}{D - m_1} + \frac{B_2}{D - m_2} + \cdots + \frac{B_s}{D - m_s}$$

The coefficients A_P $(P = 1, 2, \ldots, r)$ are given by

$$(3.33) \quad A_P = \frac{\phi^{P-1}(m)}{(P - 1)!}$$

where

$$(3.34) \quad \phi(D) = \frac{(D - m)^r}{L_n(D)}$$

and

$$(3.35) \quad \phi^{P-1}(m) = \frac{d^{P-1}}{dD^{P-1}} \phi(D) \bigg|_{D=m}$$

The coefficients B_r $(r = 1, 2, \ldots, s)$ are given by

$$(3.36) \quad B_r = \frac{1}{(d/dD)L_n(D)} \bigg|_{D=m_r} = \frac{1}{L_n'(m_r)}$$

We thus see that the solution of the equation

$$(3.37) \qquad\qquad y = \frac{1}{L_n(D)} F(x)$$

when the equation

$$(3.38) \qquad\qquad L_n(D) = 0$$

has multiple roots, contains terms of the form

$$(3.39) \qquad \frac{B_r F(x)}{D - m_r} = C_r e^{m_r x} + B_r e^{m_r x} \int e^{-m_r x} F(x) \, dx$$

as in the solution of (3.21).

The term involving the repeated roots gives rise to terms of the form given by (3.30).

We thus have an explicit solution for the general linear differential equation of the nth order with constant coefficients. The difficulties that arise in using the general formulas are due to the difficulties in evaluating the integrals involved in various special cases.

As example of the general theory, consider the equation

$$\frac{d^2 y}{dx^2} - 3 \frac{dy}{dx} + 2y = x e^x$$

or
$$(D^2 - 3D + 2)y = x e^x$$

Here
$$L_2(D) = D^2 - 3D + 2$$
$$= (D - 2)(D - 1)$$

Accordingly the two roots are

$$\left. \begin{array}{l} m_1 = 2 \\ m_2 = 1 \end{array} \right\} \qquad \frac{d}{dD} L_2(D) = 2D - 3$$

By (3.18) we have
$$A_1 = \tfrac{1}{1} = 1$$
$$A_2 = \frac{1}{-1} = -1$$
$$y = \left(\frac{1}{D - 2} - \frac{1}{D - 1} \right) x e^x$$

By (3.21) we then have

$$y = K_1 e^{2x} + K_2 e^x + e^{2x} \int e^{-2x} x e^x \, dx - e^x \int e^{-x} x e^x \, dx$$
$$= K_1 e^{2x} + K_2 e^x - (1 + x)e^x - \frac{x^2}{2} e^x$$
$$= K_1 e^{2x} + K_1 e^x - \left(1 + x + \frac{x^2}{2} \right) e^x$$

As another example, consider

$$\frac{d^2y}{dx^2} + 2\frac{dy}{dx} + y = x$$

or
$$(D + 1)(D + 1)y = x$$

$$y = \frac{1}{(D + 1)^2}\, x$$

This is a special case of (3.30), for

$$m = -1 \quad \text{and} \quad n = 2$$

We therefore have

$$y = e^{-x}\!\int\!\int e^x x \,(dx)^2 + e^{-x}(C_1 + C_2 x)$$
$$= x - 2 + e^{-x}(C_1 + C_2 x)$$

4. The Method of Undetermined Coefficients. The labor involved in performing the integrations in the general method to obtain the particular integral may sometimes be avoided by the use of a method known as the *method of undetermined coefficients*.

This may be illustrated by an example. Consider the differential equation

$$(4.1) \qquad \frac{d^2y}{dx^2} + 3\frac{dy}{dx} + 2y = x^3 + x$$

To obtain the particular integral, let us assume a general polynomial of the third degree of the form

$$(4.2) \qquad y = ax^3 + bx^2 + cx + d$$

Substituting this into (4.1), we obtain

$$(4.3) \quad (6ax + 2b) + 3(3ax^2 + 2bx + c) + 2(ax^3 + bx^2 + cx + d)$$
$$= x^3 + x$$

Equating coefficients of like powers of x, we obtain

$$(4.4) \qquad \begin{aligned} 2a &= 1 \\ 9a + 2b &= 0 \\ 6a + 6b + 2c &= 1 \\ 2b + 3c + 2d &= 0 \end{aligned}$$

Solving these equations, we obtain

$$(4.5) \qquad \begin{aligned} a &= \tfrac{1}{2} \\ b &= -\tfrac{9}{4} \\ c &= \tfrac{23}{4} \\ d &= -\tfrac{51}{8} \end{aligned}$$

Substituting these values into (4.2), we obtain the particular integral

$$(4.6) \qquad y = \tfrac{1}{8}(4x^3 - 18x^2 + 46x - 51)$$

The substitution (4.2) was successful because it did not give in the first member of (4.1) any new types of terms. Both members are linear combinations of the functions x^3, x^2, x, and 1; hence we could equate coefficients of like powers of x.

The method of undetermined coefficients for obtaining the particular integral is particularly well adapted when the function $F(x)$ is a sum of terms such as sines, cosines, exponentials, powers of x, and their products whose derivatives are combinations of a finite number of functions. In this case we assume for y a linear combination of all terms entering with undetermined coefficients and then substitute it into the equation and equate coefficients of like terms.

As another example, consider the equation

$$\text{(4.7)} \qquad \frac{d^3y}{dx^3} + y = e^{2x} \cos 3x$$

In this case we assume

$$\text{(4.8)} \qquad y = ae^{2x} \cos 3x + be^{2x} \sin 3x$$

Substituting this into the equation, we obtain

$$\text{(4.9)} \qquad (9b - 45a)e^{2x} \cos 3x - (9a + 45b)e^{2x} \sin 3x = e^{2x} \cos 3x$$

We equate coefficients of like terms and obtain

$$\text{(4.10)} \qquad \begin{aligned} 9b - 45a &= 1 \\ 9a + 45b &= 0 \end{aligned}$$

Solving for a and b and substituting them into (4.8), we obtain

$$\text{(4.11)} \qquad y = \frac{e^{2x}}{234} (\sin 3x - 5 \cos 3x)$$

The Use of Complex Numbers to Find the Particular Integral. In the analysis of electrical networks or mechanical oscillations we are usually interested in finding the particular integral of an equation of the type

$$\text{(4.12)} \qquad L_n(D)y = B_0 \sin \omega x \qquad \text{or} \qquad B_0 \cos \omega x$$

We can obtain the particular solution in this case by replacing the right-hand member by a complex exponential. The success of the method depends on the following theorem:

Consider the equation

$$\text{(4.13)} \qquad L_n(D)y = F_1(x) + jF_2(x)$$

where $F_1(x)$ and $F_2(x)$ are real functions of x and $j = \sqrt{-1}$. Then the particular integral of (4.13) is of the form

$$\text{(4.14)} \qquad y = y_1 + jy_2$$

where y_1 satisfies

$$(4.15) \qquad\qquad L_n(D)y_1 = F_1(x)$$

and y_2 satisfies

$$(4.16) \qquad\qquad L_n(D)y_2 = F_2(x)$$

To prove this, it is necessary only to substitute (4.14) into (4.13), and, on equating the real and imaginary coefficients, we obtain (4.15) and (4.16). To illustrate the method, let us solve (4.7) by making the substitution

$$(4.17) \qquad\qquad e^{2x} \cos 3x = \operatorname{Re} e^{(2+j3)x}$$

where Re denotes the "real part of." We thus replace the right-hand member of (4.7) by $e^{(2+j3)x}$ and take the real part of the solution; that is, we have

$$(4.18) \qquad\qquad \frac{d^3y}{dx^3} + y = e^{(2+j3)x}$$

instead of (4.7).

To solve this, assume

$$(4.19) \qquad\qquad y = Ae^{(2+j3)x}$$

where A is a complex constant to be determined. Substituting this into (4.18) and dividing both members by the common factor $e^{(2+j3)x}$, we obtain

$$(4.20) \qquad\qquad A[(2 + j3)^3 + 1] = 1$$

We therefore have

$$(4.21) \qquad\qquad A = \frac{1}{-45 + 9j} = \frac{-45 - 9j}{2,106} = \frac{-5 - j}{234}$$

Substituting this into (4.19), we have

$$(4.22) \qquad\qquad y = \frac{-5 - j}{234} e^{2x}(\cos 3x + j \sin 3x)$$

If we take the real part of this expression, we have

$$(4.23) \qquad\qquad y_1 = \frac{e^{2x}}{234} (\sin 3x - 5 \cos 3x)$$

This is the required particular integral.

To solve the equation

$$(4.24) \qquad\qquad L_n(D)y = B_0 \sin \omega x$$

we replace $\sin \omega x$ by $e^{j\omega x}$ and consider

$$(4.25) \qquad\qquad L_n(D)y = B_0 e^{j\omega x}$$

We now assume a solution of the form

(4.26)
$$y = A e^{j\omega x}$$

We note that, if we operate on $A e^{j\omega x}$ with D, we have the result

(4.27)
$$D A e^{j\omega x} = A(j\omega) e^{j\omega x}$$

and

(4.28)
$$D^s A e^{j\omega x} = A(j\omega)^s e^{j\omega x}$$

We therefore note that the result of these operations merely replaces D by $j\omega$; accordingly we have

(4.29)
$$L_n(D) A e^{j\omega x} = L_n(j\omega) A e^{j\omega x}$$

Hence, on substituting (4.26) into (4.25), we have

(4.30)
$$L_n(j\omega) A e^{j\omega x} = B_0 e^{j\omega x}$$

and thus

(4.31)
$$A = \frac{B_0}{L_n(j\omega)}$$

provided $L_n(j\omega) \neq 0$.

Now $L_n(j\omega)$ is in general a complex number and may be written in the form

(4.32)
$$L_n(j\omega) = R e^{j\phi}$$

where

(4.33)
$$R = |L_n(j\omega)|$$

(4.34)
$$\phi = \tan^{-1} \frac{\operatorname{Im} L_n(j\omega)}{\operatorname{Re} L_n(j\omega)}$$

and Im denotes the "imaginary part of." Hence A may be written in the form

(4.35)
$$A = \frac{B_0}{R} e^{-j\phi}$$

Substituting this into (4.26), we have

(4.36)
$$y = \frac{B_0}{R} e^{j(\omega x - \phi)}$$

The solution of (4.24) is obtained by taking the imaginary part of (4.36) to correspond to $B_0 \sin \omega x$. Hence

(4.37)
$$y_2 = \frac{B_0}{R} \sin (\omega x - \phi)$$

is the required particular integral.

If we had taken the real part, we would obtain the solution of the equation

$$(4.38) \qquad L_n(D)y = B_0 \cos \omega x$$

This method is of extreme importance in the field of electrical engineering and mechanical oscillations and forms the basis of the use of complex numbers in the field of alternating currents. These matters will be discussed more fully in Chaps. 7 and 8.

5. The Simple Direct Laplace-transform, or Operational, Method of Solving Linear Differential Equations with Constant Coefficients. The method for solving differential equations mentioned in the heading of this section is essentially the same as that known under the name of *Heaviside's operational calculus.* The modern approach to this method is based on the Laplace transformation. This method provides a most convenient means for solving the differential equations of electrical networks and mechanical oscillations.

The chief advantage of this method is that it is very direct and does away with tedious evaluations of arbitrary constants. The procedure in a sense reduces the solution of a differential equation to a matter of looking up a particular transformation in a table of transforms. In a way this procedure is much like consulting a table of integrals in the process of performing integrations.

Only a brief account of the theory of the Laplace transformation will be given in this section. A fuller account will be found in Chap. 21.

Consider the functional relation between a function $g(p)$ and another function $h(t)$ expressed in the form

$$(5.1) \qquad g(p) = p \int_0^\infty e^{-pt} h(t)\, dt \qquad \text{Re } p > 0$$

where p is a complex number whose real part is greater than zero and $h(t)$ is a function such that the infinite integral of (5.1) converges and such that it satisfies the condition that

$$(5.2) \qquad h(t) = 0 \qquad \text{for } t < 0$$

In most of the modern literature on operational, or Laplace-transform, methods the functional relation expressed between $g(p)$ and $h(t)$ is written in the following form:

$$(5.3) \qquad g(p) = Lh(t)$$

The L denotes the "Laplace transform of" and greatly shortens the writing. The relation between $h(t)$ and $g(p)$ is also written in the form

$$(5.4) \qquad h(t) = L^{-1} g(p)$$

In this case we speak of $h(t)$ as being the inverse Laplace transform of $h(t)$.

The Transforms of Derivatives. Let us suppose that we have the functional relation

$$(5.5) \qquad y(p) = p \int_0^\infty e^{-pt} x(t) \, dt$$

or, symbolically,

$$(5.6) \qquad y(p) = Lx(t)$$

Let us now determine $L(dx/dt)$ in terms of $y(p)$. To do this, we have

$$(5.7) \qquad L\left(\frac{dx}{dt}\right) = p \int_0^\infty e^{-pt} \left(\frac{dx}{dt}\right) dt$$

By integrating by parts we obtain

$$(5.8) \qquad p \int_0^\infty e^{-pt} \left(\frac{dx}{dt}\right) dt = pe^{-pt} x \Big|_0^\infty + p^2 \int_0^\infty e^{-pt} x \, dt$$

Now, if we assume that

$$(5.9) \qquad \lim_{t \to \infty} (e^{-pt} x) = 0$$

and that $\int_0^\infty e^{-pt} x \, dt$ exists when p is greater than some fixed positive number, then (5.8) becomes

$$(5.10) \qquad L\left(\frac{dx}{dt}\right) = -px_0 + py$$

where

$$(5.11) \qquad x_0 = x(0)$$

Equation (5.10) gives the value of the Laplace transform of dx/dt in terms of the transform of x and the value of x at $t = 0$.

In order to compute the Laplace transform of d^2x/dt^2, let

$$(5.12) \qquad u = \frac{dx}{dt}$$

Then in view of (5.10) we have

$$(5.13) \qquad L\left(\frac{d^2x}{dt^2}\right) = L\left(\frac{du}{dt}\right) = -pu_0 + pL\left(\frac{dx}{dt}\right)$$
$$= -px_1 - p^2 x_0 + p^2 y$$

where x_1 is the value of dx/dt at $t = 0$.

Repeating the process, we obtain

$$(5.14) \qquad L\frac{d^3x}{dt^3} = p^3 y - p^3 x_0 - p^2 x_1 - px_2$$

$$(5.15) \qquad L\frac{d^4x}{dt^4} = p^4 y - p^4 x_0 - p^3 x_1 - p^2 x_2 - px_3$$

and

(5.16) $\quad L\dfrac{d^s x}{dt^s} = p^s y - (p^s x_0 + p^{s-1} x_1 + p^{s-2} x_2 + \cdots + p x_{s-1})$

where

(5.17) $\qquad\qquad x_s = \dfrac{d^s x}{dt^s} \qquad$ evaluated at $x = 0$

The above formulas for the transforms of derivatives are of great importance in the solution of linear differential equations with constant coefficients.

To illustrate the general theory, let it be required to solve the simple differential equation

(5.18) $\qquad\qquad\qquad \dfrac{dx}{dt} + ax = 0$

subject to the initial condition that

(5.19) $\qquad\qquad\qquad x = x_0 \qquad$ at $t = 0$

To solve this by the Laplace-transform method, we let

(5.20) $\qquad\qquad\qquad y = Lx$

and use (5.10); then, in terms of y, the equation becomes

(5.21) $\qquad\qquad\qquad py - px_0 + ay = 0$

or

(5.22) $\qquad\qquad\qquad y = \dfrac{px_0}{p + a} = L(x)$

The solution of one equation could be written symbolically in the form

(5.23) $\qquad\qquad\qquad x = L^{-1}\dfrac{px_0}{p + a}$

Consulting the table of transforms on page 152, we find that transform 7 gives

(5.24) $\qquad\qquad\qquad L^{-1}\dfrac{p}{p + a} = e^{-at}$

Accordingly we have

(5.25) $\qquad\qquad\qquad x = x_0 e^{-at}$

as the solution of the differential equation (5.19) subject to the given initial conditions.

As another example, let us solve the equation

(5.26) $\qquad\qquad\qquad \dfrac{d^2 x}{dt^2} + \omega^2 x = \cos \omega t \qquad t > 0$

subject to the initial conditions that

$$(5.27) \qquad \left.\begin{array}{r} x = x_0 \\ \dfrac{dx}{dt} = x_1 \end{array}\right\} \quad \text{at } t = 0$$

As before, we let $y = Lx$ and replace every member of (5.20) by its transform. Consulting the table of transforms, we find from No. 10 that

$$(5.28) \qquad L(\cos \omega t) = \frac{p^2}{p^2 + \omega^2}$$

Using (5.13), Eq. (5.20) is transformed to

$$(5.29) \qquad (p^2 y - p^2 x_0 - p x_1) + \omega^2 y = \frac{p^2}{p^2 + \omega^2}$$

or

$$(5.30) \qquad y = \frac{p^2 x_0}{p^2 + \omega^2} + \frac{p x_1}{p^2 + \omega^2} + \frac{p^2}{(p^2 + \omega^2)^2}$$

Consulting the table of transforms, we find that Nos. 10, 11, and 21 give the required information, and we have

$$(5.31) \qquad x = x_0 \cos \omega t + x_1 \frac{\sin \omega t}{\omega} + \frac{t}{2\omega} \sin \omega t$$

as the required solution.

The General Case. To solve the general equation with constant coefficients

$$(5.32) \qquad \frac{d^n x}{dt^n} + a_1 \frac{d^{n-1} x}{dt^{n-1}} + \cdots + a_{n-1} \frac{dx}{dt} + a_n x = F(t)$$

we introduce $y = Lx$ and $\phi_1(p) = LF(t)$ and replace the various derivatives of x by their transforms given by (5.16). We then obtain

$$(5.33) \qquad (p^n + a_1 p^{n-1} + \cdots + a_n) y = \phi_1(p) + \phi_2(p)$$

where

$$(5.34) \qquad \begin{aligned} \phi_2(p) = {}&(p x_{n-1} + p^2 x_{n-2} + \cdots + p^n x_0) \\ &+ a_1(p x_{n-2} + p^2 x_{n-3} + \cdots + p^{n-1} x_0) \\ &+ a_2(p x_{n-3} + p^2 x_{n-4} + \cdots + p^{n-2} x_0) \\ &+ \cdots\cdots\cdots\cdots\cdots\cdots\cdots\cdots \\ &+ a_{n-1}(p x_0) \end{aligned}$$

If we write

$$(5.35) \qquad L_n(p) = p^n + a_1 p^{n-1} + \cdots + a_n$$

Eq. (5.33) may be written concisely in the form

$$(5.36) \qquad y(p) = \frac{\phi_1(p)}{L_n(p)} + \frac{\phi_2(p)}{L_n(p)} = Lx(t)$$

To obtain the solution of the differential equation (5.32), we must obtain in some manner the inverse transform of $y(p)$, and we would then have

$$(5.37) \qquad\qquad x(t) = L^{-1}y(p)$$

If $F(t)$ is a constant, e^{at}, $\cos \omega t$, $\sin \omega t$, t^s where s is a positive integer, $e^{at} \sin \omega t$, $e^{at} \cos \omega t$, $t^s e^{at}$, $t^s \cos \omega t$, or $t^s \sin \omega t$, then $\phi_1(p)$ is a polynomial in p. The procedure in such a case is to decompose the expressions $\phi_1(p)/L_n(p)$ and $\phi_2(p)/L_n(p)$ into partial fractions, examine the table of transforms, and obtain the appropriate inverse transforms.

6. The Direct Computation of Transforms. A brief discussion of the manner in which the transforms given in the table are obtained will be given in this section. A more complete discussion using the theory of contour integration will be given in Chap. 21.

By the fundamental definition the notation

$$(6.1) \qquad\qquad g(p) = Lh(t)$$

signifies that $g(p)$ and $h(t)$ are related in the following manner,

$$(6.2) \qquad\qquad g(p) = p \int_0^\infty e^{-pt} h(t) \, dt$$

where the integral exists when p is greater than some fixed positive number. If we are given a definite function $h(t)$ and can perform the integration, we immediately obtain the Laplace transform of $h(t)$.

Transform of the "Unit Function." As a simple example of the computation of a direct transform, consider the function

$$(6.3) \qquad\qquad h(t) = \begin{cases} 1 & t \geqq 0 \\ 0 & t < 0 \end{cases}$$

Let us denote this function by the symbol $1(t)$. We then have

$$(6.4) \qquad L1(t) = p \int_0^\infty e^{-pt} \, dt = p \left. \frac{-e^{-pt}}{p} \right|_0^\infty = 1$$

We thus see that the transform of the unit function is unity. This is the transform pair No. 1 of the table of transforms.

As another example, let us consider the transform of the function e^{-at}. In this case we have

$$(6.5) \qquad Le^{-at} = p \int_0^\infty e^{-pt} e^{-at} \, dt = \frac{p}{p + a}$$

This gives us transform pair No. 7.

If in (6.5) we let

(6.6) $a = j\omega$ where $j = \sqrt{-1}$

we obtain

(6.7) $L(e^{-i\omega t}) = L(\cos \omega t - j \sin \omega t) = \dfrac{p}{p + j\omega}$

$$= \frac{p^2 - pj\omega}{p^2 + \omega^2}$$

If we now equate real coefficients, we obtain

(6.8) $L(\cos \omega t) = \dfrac{p^2}{p^2 + \omega^2}$

Equating imaginary coefficients, we have

FIG. 6.1

(6.9) $L(\sin \omega t) = \dfrac{p\omega}{p^2 + \omega^2}$

These are transform pairs 10 and 11. In the same manner, other transform pairs are computed.

Impulse Functions. Consider the transform of the function given by Fig. 6.1.

In this case we have

(6.10) $Lh(t) = Ap \displaystyle\int_{t_1}^{t_2} e^{-pt} \, dt = (e^{-pt_1} - e^{-pt_2})A$

If $t_1 = 0$, this becomes

(6.11) $Lh(t) = (1 - e^{-pt_2})A$

Now let t_2 tend to zero in such a manner that

(6.12) $\lim_{\substack{t_2 \to 0 \\ A \to \infty}} At_2 = 1$

That is, we shrink the rectangle represented by $h(t)$ in such a manner that its area tends to unity as its height tends to infinity.   Now

(6.13) $\lim_{\substack{t_2 \to 0 \\ A \to \infty}} (1 - e^{-pt_2})A = \lim_{\substack{t_2 \to 0 \\ A \to \infty}} (1 - 1 + pt_2 + \cdots)A$

$$= p = Lh(t)$$

We thus see that p is the transform of a function that is zero everywhere except at $t = $ zero, where it is infinite; we denote this function by $\delta(t)$, and we have

(6.14) $L\delta(t) = p$

where

(6.15) $$\delta(t) = \begin{cases} 0 & \text{if } t \neq 0 \\ \infty & \text{if } t = 0 \end{cases}$$

and

(6.16) $$\int_{-\infty}^{+\infty} \delta(t)\, dt = 1$$

This is the transform pair given by No. 2 of the table. A more thorough account of these Laplace transforms will be given in Chap. 21.

7. Systems of Linear Differential Equations with Constant Coefficients. In the study of dynamical systems, whether electrical or mechanical, the analysis usually leads to the solution of a system of linear differential equations with constant coefficients. The Laplace-transform method is well adapted for solving systems of equations of this type. The method will be made clear by an example. Consider the system of linear differential equations with constant coefficients given by

(7.1)
$$3\frac{dx_1}{dt} + 2x_1 + \frac{dx_2}{dt} = 1 \qquad t \geq 0$$
$$\frac{dx_1}{dt} + 4\frac{dx_2}{dt} + 3x_2 = 0$$

Let us solve these equations subject to the initial conditions

(7.2) $$\left. \begin{array}{r} x_1 = 0 \\ x_2 = 0 \end{array} \right\} \quad \text{at } t = 0$$

To solve these equations by the Laplace-transform method, let

(7.3)
$$Lx_1 = y_1$$
$$Lx_2 = y_2$$

Then, in view of (5.10) and the fact that the Laplace transform of unity is 1, the equations transform to

(7.4)
$$(3p + 2)y_1 + py_2 = 1$$
$$py_1 + (4p + 3)y_2 = 0$$

Solving these two simultaneous equations for y_1, we obtain

(7.5) $$y_1 = \frac{4p + 3}{(p + 1)(11p + 6)} = Lx_1$$

Using the transform pair No. 36 of the table, we obtain

(7.6) $$x_1 = \tfrac{1}{2} - \tfrac{1}{5}e^{-t} - \tfrac{3}{10}e^{-6t/11}$$

Solving for y_2, we have

(7.7) $$y_2 = \frac{-p}{(11p + 6)(p + 1)} = Lx_2$$

By the use of the transform pair No. 14, we obtain

$$(7.8) \qquad x_2 = \tfrac{1}{5}(e^{-t} - e^{-6t/11})$$

This example illustrates the general procedure. In Chaps. 7 and 8 the systems of differential equations arising in the study of electrical networks and mechanical oscillations are considered in detail.

PROBLEMS

Solve the equations:

1. $\dfrac{dy}{dx} + y = x.$

2. $\dfrac{dy}{dx} - \dfrac{2y}{x+1} = (x+1)^{\frac{3}{2}}.$

3. $x\dfrac{dy}{dx} - 2y = 2x.$

4. $\dfrac{dy}{dx} + y = x^2 + 2.$

5. Show that the equation $dy/dx + Py = Qy^n$ is reduced to a linear equation by the substitution $v = y^{1-n}$.

6. Solve $x(dy/dx) - 2y = 4x^3 \sqrt{y}$.

7. Solve the equation $d^4y/dx^4 + ky = 0$ subject to the initial conditions that $y = y_0$ at $x = 0$ and that the first three derivatives of y are zero at $x = 0$.

8. Find the general solution of $(D - a)^n y = \sin bx$, where $D = d/dx$, n is a positive integer, and a and b are real and unequal.

Find the solution of the following equations which satisfy the given conditions:

9. $\dfrac{d^2x}{dt^2} + 3\dfrac{dx}{dt} + 2x = 0$ $\left.\begin{array}{c} x = 0 \\ \dfrac{dx}{dt} = 1 \end{array}\right\}$ $t = 0$.

10. $\dfrac{d^2x}{dt^2} + n^2x = 0$ $\left.\begin{array}{c} x = a \\ \dfrac{dx}{dt} = 0 \end{array}\right\}$ $t = 0$.

11. $\dfrac{d^2x}{dt^2} + 9x = t + \tfrac{1}{2}$ $\left.\begin{array}{c} x = \tfrac{1}{18} \\ \dfrac{dx}{dt} = \tfrac{1}{9} \end{array}\right\}$ $t = 0$.

12. $\dfrac{d^2x}{dt^2} + 9x = 5\cos 2t$ $\left.\begin{array}{c} x = 1 \\ \dfrac{dx}{dt} = 3 \end{array}\right\}$ $t = 0$.

13. $\dfrac{d^2x}{dt^2} + 4\dfrac{dx}{dt} + 4x = 4e^{2t}$ $\left.\begin{array}{c} x = 0 \\ \dfrac{dx}{dt} = 0 \end{array}\right\}$ $t = 0$.

14. Solve $d^3x/dt^3 + d^2x/dt^2 = 6t^2 + 4$.

15. Find the general solution of the equation $(D^{2n+1} - 1)y = 0$, where n is a positive integer.

16. Solve $d^2x/dt^2 + 4x = \sin 2x$ subject to the conditions

$$\left.\begin{array}{c} x = x_0 \\ \dfrac{dx}{dt} = v_0 \end{array}\right\} \qquad t = 0$$

17. Solve $d^2x/dt^2 + b^2x = k \cos bt$, if

$$\left.\begin{array}{c} x = 0 \\ \dfrac{dx}{dt} = 0 \end{array}\right\} \quad t = 0$$

REFERENCES

1. Ince, E. L.: "Ordinary Differential Equations," Longmans, Green & Co., Inc., New York, 1927.
2. Ford, L. R.: "Differential Equations," 1st ed., McGraw-Hill Book Company, Inc., New York, 1933.
3. Piaggio, H. T. H.: "An Elementary Treatise on Differential Equations and Their Applications," George Bell & Sons, Ltd., London, 1929.
4. Forsythe, A. R.: "A Treatise on Differential Equations," The Macmillan Company, New York, 1929.
5. Cohen, A.: "An Elementary Treatise on Differential Equations," 2d ed., D. C. Heath and Company, Boston, 1933.
6. Jeffreys, H.: "Operational Methods in Mathematical Physics," Cambridge University Press, New York, 1927.
7. Pipes, L. A.: The Operational Calculus, *Journal of Applied Physics*, vol. 10, pp. 172–180, 1939.
8. McLachlan, N. W.: "Complex Variable and Operational Calculus with Technical Applications," Cambridge University Press, New York, 1939.
9. Carslaw, H. S., and J. C. Jaeger: "Operational Methods in Applied Mathematics," Oxford University Press, New York, 1941.

APPENDIX: LAPLACE TRANSFORMS OF USE IN THE SOLUTION OF DIFFERENTIAL EQUATIONS

Introduction. The modern theory of the operational calculus, a mathematical technique that has proved to be such a powerful mathematical tool in the solution of the differential equations of applied mathematics, is based on the Laplace transformation. This transformation is usually written in the form

$$(1) \qquad g(p) = p \int_0^\infty e^{-pt} h(t)\, dt \qquad \mathrm{Re}\ p > 0$$

In the usual applications of the theory $h(t)$ is a function for which the definite integral (1) exists and satisfies the condition

$$(2) \qquad h(t) = 0 \qquad \text{for } t < 0$$

A rigorous discussion of the restrictions that must be imposed on a function $h(t)$ in order that it may have a Laplace transformation will be found in the following books:

1. McLachlan, N. W.: "Complex Variable and Operational Calculus," Cambridge University Press, New York, 1939.
2. Gardner, M. F., and J. L. Barnes: "Transients in Linear Systems," John Wiley & Sons, Inc., New York, 1942.

It may be said, however, that the functions encountered in the various physical problems where the transform method is applicable satisfy the required conditions.

A concise survey of the various applications of the Laplace-transform, or operational, method will be found in the following paper:

3. Pipes, L. A.: The Operational Calculus, *Journal of Applied Physics*, vol. 10, nos. 3–5, 1939.

The utility of the method in the solution of differential equations with constant coefficients, whether ordinary or partial, follows from the fact that by the introduction of a Laplace transformation an ordinary differential equation becomes an algebraic equation in the transform, while the number of independent variables is reduced in the case of partial differential equations.

Notation. In most of the modern literature on operational or Laplace-transform methods the functional relation expressed between $g(p)$ and $h(t)$ is written in the following form:

$$(3) \qquad g(p) = Lh(t)$$

The L denotes the Laplace transform and greatly shortens the writing. The relation between $h(t)$ and $g(p)$ is also written in the form

$$(4) \qquad h(t) = L^{-1}g(p)$$

In such a case we say that $h(t)$ is the inverse Laplace transform of $h(t)$.

Some writers, notably van der Pol, express the relation (1) in the form

$$(5) \qquad h(t) \doteqdot g(p)$$

However, notations (3) and (4) are becoming more standard.

Basic Theorems. The utility of the Laplace transformation is based on some important relations which follow as a consequence of the fundamental equation (1). The most important of these theorems will be listed here for reference. They are established in references 1 to 3 above.

If $Lh(t) = g(p)$, then

$$(I) \qquad Lh(st) = g\left(\frac{p}{s}\right)$$

where s is a constant, $s > 0$.

$$(II) \qquad L\frac{dh}{dt} = pg(p) - ph(0)$$

where $h(0)$ is the value of $h(t)$ at $t = 0$.

$$(III) \qquad L\frac{d^2h}{dt^2} = p^2g - ph'(0) - p^2h(0)$$

where $h'(0)$ is dh/dt evaluated at $t = 0$.

$$(IV) \qquad L\frac{d^nh}{dt^n} = p^ng(p) - \sum_{k=0}^{k=n-1} h^{[k]}(0)p^{n-k}$$

where $h^{[k]}(0)$ denotes the value of the kth derivative of $h(t)$ evaluated at $t = 0$.

$$(V) \qquad L\int_{-\infty}^{t} h(t)\,dt = \frac{g(p)}{p} + \int_{-\infty}^{0} h(t)\,dt$$

$$(VI) \qquad Le^{-at}h(t) = \frac{pg(p+a)}{p+a}$$

(VII) $L^{-1}e^{-ap}g(p) = \begin{cases} 0 & t < a \\ h(t-a) & t > a \end{cases}$ a is a positive constant

(VIII) $L^{-1}e^{ap}g(p) = h(t+a)$ if $h(t) = 0$ $0 < t < a$

(IX) $\lim_{|(p)| \to 0} g(p) = \lim_{t \to \infty} h(t)$, an ordinary equality

(X) $\lim_{|(p)| \to \infty} g(p) = \lim_{t \to 0} h(t)$, an ordinary equality

If $L^{-1}g_1(p) = h_1(t)$ and $L^{-1}g_2(p) = h_2(t)$, then

(XI)
$$L^{-1}g_1(p)\frac{g_2(p)}{p} = \int_0^t h_1(u)h_2(t-u)\, du$$
$$= \int_0^t h_2(u)h_1(t-u)\, du$$

Many more theorems may be established. The above set of theorems is of great utility in the solution of differential equations by the Laplace transformation. The method will be illustrated by some worked examples.

Illustrative Examples. To illustrate the use of the table of Laplace transforms in the solution of differential equations, the following examples are appended:

1. Suppose it is required to solve the equation

$$\frac{d^2y}{dt^2} + a^2y = ce^{-bt}$$

subject to the initial conditions

$$\left. \begin{array}{l} y = 0 \\ \dfrac{dy}{dt} = y_1 \end{array} \right\}   \text{at } t = 0$$

To solve the equation, we let

$$Ly = Y(p)$$

By the basic theorem (III) we have

$$L\frac{d^2y}{dt^2} = p^2Y - py_1$$

and by No. 7

$$L(ce^{-bt}) = \frac{cp}{p+b}$$

The equation to be solved is thus transformed to

$$p^2Y - py_1 + a^2Y = \frac{cp}{p+b}$$

Therefore
$$Y(p) = \frac{cp}{(p^2+a^2)(p+b)} + \frac{py_1}{p^2+a^2}$$

Using Nos. 46 and 11, we have the inverse transform of $Y(p)$,

$$y(t) = \frac{c}{a^2+b^2}\left(e^{-bt} - \cos at + \frac{b}{a}\sin at\right) + \frac{y_1}{a}\sin at$$

This is the required solution.

2. A constant electromotive force E is applied at $t = 0$ to an electrical circuit consisting of an inductance L, resistance R, and capacitance c in series. The initial values of the current i and the charge on the capacitor q are zero. It is required to find the current.

TABLE OF LAPLACE TRANSFORMS

$$g(p) = p \int_0^\infty e^{-pt} h(t)\, dt$$

No.	$g(p)$	$h(t)$
1	1	$1(t)$ Heaviside unit function $1(t) = 1$ $t > 0$ $1(t) = 0$ $t < 0$
2	p	$\delta(t)$ Dirac impulse function $\delta(t) = \infty$ $t = 0$ $\delta(t) = 0$ $t \neq 0$
3	$1/p^n$ n a positive integer	$t^n/n!$
4	p^n except for n a positive integer	$t^{-n}/\Gamma(1-n)$ $\Gamma(1-n)$ is the gamma function
5	$p^{\frac{1}{2}}$	$1/\sqrt{\pi t}$
6	$p^{-\frac{1}{2}}$	$2\sqrt{t}/\sqrt{\pi}$
7	$p/(p+a)$	e^{-at} valid for a complex
8	$1/(p+a)$	$(1 - e^{-at})/a$
9	$1/p(p+a)$	$t/a - 1/a^2 + e^{-at}/a^2$
10	$p^2/(p^2 + a^2)$	$\cos at$
11	$ap/(p^2 + a^2)$	$\sin at$
12	$p^2/(p^2 - a^2)$	$\cosh at$
13	$ap/(p^2 - a^2)$	$\sinh at$
14	$p/(p+a)(p+b)$	$(e^{-bt} - e^{-at})/(a-b)$
15	$\dfrac{p^2}{(p+a)(p+b)}$	$\dfrac{ae^{-at} - be^{-bt}}{a-b}$
16	$\dfrac{p(p+b)}{(p+b)^2 + a^2}$	$e^{-bt} \cos at$ $a^2 > 0$
17	$\dfrac{pa}{(p+b)^2 + a^2}$	$e^{-bt} \sin at$ $a^2 > 0$
18	$\dfrac{p}{(p+a)^2}$	te^{-at}

TABLE OF LAPLACE TRANSFORMS (*Continued*)

No.	$g(p)$	$h(t)$
19	$\dfrac{p}{(p+a)^n}$	$\dfrac{t^{n-1}e^{-at}}{(n-1)!}$ n a positive integer
20	$\dfrac{p^2}{(p+a)^2}$	$e^{-at}(1-at)$
21	$\dfrac{p^2}{(p^2+a^2)^2}$	$\dfrac{t}{2a}\sin\,(at)$
22	$\dfrac{pa^2}{(p^2+a^2)^2}$	$\dfrac{1}{2a}(\sin at - at\cos at)$
23	$\dfrac{p}{p^3+a^3}$	$\dfrac{1}{3a^2}\left[e^{-at} + e^{at/2}\left(\cos\dfrac{1}{2}\sqrt{3}\,at \right.\right.$ $\left.\left. -\sqrt{3}\sin\dfrac{1}{2}\sqrt{3}\,at\right)\right]$
24	$\dfrac{p^2}{p^3+a^3}$	$\dfrac{1}{3a}\left[e^{-at} + e^{at/2}\left(\cos\dfrac{1}{2}\sqrt{3}\,at \right.\right.$ $\left.\left. -\sqrt{3}\sin\dfrac{1}{2}\sqrt{3}\,at\right)\right]$
25	$\dfrac{p^3}{p^3+a^3}$	$\dfrac{1}{3}\left(e^{-at} - 2e^{at/2}\cos\dfrac{1}{2}\sqrt{3}\,at\right)$
26	$\dfrac{p}{p^4+4a^4}$	$\dfrac{1}{4a^3}(\sin at\cosh at - \cos at\sinh at)$
27	$\dfrac{p^2}{p^4+4a^4}$	$\dfrac{1}{2a^2}\sin at\sinh at$
28	$\dfrac{p^3}{p^4+4a^4}$	$\dfrac{1}{2a}(\sin at\cosh at + \cos at\sinh at)$
29	$\dfrac{p^4}{p^4+4a^4}$	$\cos at\cosh at$
30	$\dfrac{p}{p^4-a^4}$	$\dfrac{1}{2a^3}(\sinh\,at - \sin at)$
31	$\dfrac{p^2}{p^4-a^4}$	$\dfrac{1}{2a^2}(\cosh at - \cos at)$

TABLE OF LAPLACE TRANSFORMS (*Continued*)

No.	$g(p)$	$h(t)$
32	$\dfrac{p^3}{p^4 - a^4}$	$\dfrac{1}{2a}\,(\sinh at + \sin at)$
33	$\dfrac{p^4}{p^4 - a^4}$	$\tfrac{1}{2}(\cosh at + \cos at)$
34*	$\dfrac{p^2 + a_0 p}{(p + a)(p + b)}$	$\dfrac{(a_0 - a)e^{-at} - (a_0 - b)e^{-bt}}{b - a}$
35	$\dfrac{p}{p(p + a)(p + b)}$	$\dfrac{1}{ab} + \dfrac{be^{-at} - ae^{-bt}}{ab(a - b)}$
36	$\dfrac{p^2 + cp}{p(p + a)(p + b)}$	$\dfrac{c}{ab} + \dfrac{c - a}{a(a - b)}\,e^{-at} + \dfrac{c - b}{b(b - a)}\,e^{-bt}$
37	$\dfrac{p^3 + c_1 p^2 + c_0 p}{p(p + a)(p + b)}$	$\dfrac{c_0}{ab} + \dfrac{(a^2 - c_1 a + c_0)^{-at}}{a(a - b)} - \dfrac{(b^2 - c_1 b + c_0)^{-bt}}{b(a - b)}$
38	$\dfrac{p}{(p + a)(p + b)(p + c)}$	$\dfrac{e^{-at}}{(b - a)(c - a)} + \dfrac{e^{-bt}}{(a - b)(c - b)}$ $+ \dfrac{e^{ct}}{(a - c)(b - c)}$
39	$\dfrac{p^2 + c_0 p}{p^2 + b^2}$	$\dfrac{1}{b}\,(c_0 + b^2)^{\frac{1}{2}} \sin\,(bt + \theta)$ $\theta = \tan^{-1}\dfrac{b}{c_0}$
40	$\dfrac{1}{p^2 + b^2}$	$\dfrac{1}{b^2}\,(1 - \cos bt)$
41	$\dfrac{p^2 + c_0 p}{p(p^2 + b^2)}$	$\dfrac{c_0}{b^2} - \dfrac{(c_0^2 + b^2)^{\frac{1}{2}}}{b^2} \cos\,(bt + \theta)$ $\theta = \tan^{-1}\dfrac{b}{c_0}$

* Let

$$N(a) = \frac{1}{p - a} \qquad N(b) = \frac{1}{p - b}$$

Then, if $a \neq b$,

$$N(a)N(b) = \frac{1}{a - b}\,N(a) + \frac{1}{b - a}\,N(b)$$

This enables transforms of the type $p^2/(p + a)(p + b)(p + c)(p - d)$, etc., to be decomposed into simpler ones.

Table of Laplace Transforms (*Continued*)

No.	$g(p)$	$h(t)$
42	$\dfrac{p^3 + c_1 p^2 + c_0 p}{p(p^2 + b^2)}$	$\dfrac{c_0}{b^2} - \dfrac{[(c_0 - b^2)^2 + c_1^2 b^2]^{\frac{1}{2}}}{b^2} \cos(bt + \theta)$ $\theta = \tan^{-1} \dfrac{c_1 b}{c_0 - b^2}$
43	$\dfrac{p^2}{(p^2 + b^2)(p^2 + a^2)}$	$\dfrac{\cos bt - \cos at}{a^2 - b^2}$
44	$\dfrac{p^2}{[p^2 + (b + a)^2][p^2 + (b - a)^2]}$	$\dfrac{1}{2ab} \sin at \sin bt$
45	$\dfrac{1}{(p + a)^2 + b^2}$	$\dfrac{1}{b_0^2} + \dfrac{1}{b_0 b} e^{-at} \sin(bt - \theta)$ $\theta = \tan^{-1} \dfrac{b}{-a}$ $b_0^2 = a^2 + b^2$
46	$\dfrac{p}{(p + c)[(p + a)^2 + b^2]}$	$\dfrac{e^{-ct}}{(c - a)^2 + b^2} + \dfrac{e^{-at} \sin(bt - \theta)}{b[(c - a)^2 + b^2]^{\frac{1}{2}}}$ $\theta = \tan^{-1} \dfrac{b}{c - a}$
47	$\dfrac{1}{p(p^2 + b^2)}$	$\dfrac{1}{b^2} t - \dfrac{1}{b^3} \sin bt$
48	$\dfrac{1}{p(p^2 - b^2)}$	$\dfrac{1}{b^3} \sin bt - \dfrac{1}{b^2} t$
49	$\dfrac{p^2}{p^2 + 2ap + \omega_0^2}$	$\dfrac{-\omega_0}{\omega} e^{-at} \sin(\omega t - \phi) \quad$ if $\omega_0^2 > a^2$ where $\omega^2 = \omega_0^2 - a^2$, $\tan \phi = \dfrac{\omega}{a}$ <hr> $e^{-at}(1 - at) \quad$ if $a^2 = \omega_0^2$ <hr> $\dfrac{1}{n - m} (n e^{-nt} - m e^{-mt}) \quad$ if $a^2 > \omega_0^2$ where $-m, -n$ are the roots of $p^2 + 2ap + \omega_0^2 = 0$
50	$\dfrac{p}{p^2 + 2ap + \omega_0^2}$	$\dfrac{e^{-at}}{\omega} \sin \omega t \quad$ if $\omega_0^2 > a^2$ $\omega^2 = \omega_0^2 - a^2$ <hr> $\dfrac{1}{n - m} (e^{-mt} - e^{-nt}) \quad a^2 > \omega_0^2$ m and n defined above <hr> $t e^{-at} \quad$ if $a^2 = \omega_0^2$

TABLE OF LAPLACE TRANSFORMS (*Continued*)

No.	$g(p)$	$h(t)$
51†	$\dfrac{1}{p^2 + 2ap + \omega_0^2}$	$\dfrac{1}{\omega_0^2}\left[1 - \dfrac{\omega_0}{\omega}e^{-at}\sin(\omega t + \phi)\right]\qquad \omega_0^2 > a^2$ $\omega^2 = \omega_0^2 - a^2 \qquad \tan\phi = \dfrac{\omega}{a}$ $\dfrac{1}{\omega_0^2}\left[1 - \dfrac{\omega_0^2}{n-m}\left(\dfrac{e^{-mt}}{m} - \dfrac{e^{-nt}}{n}\right)\right]\qquad a^2 > \omega_0^2$ m, n defined in No. 49 $\dfrac{1}{\omega_0^2}[1 - e^{-at}(1 + at)]\qquad a^2 = \omega_0^2$
52	$\dfrac{N(p)}{D(p)}$, where $N(p)$ and $D(p)$ are polynomials in p; the degree of the polynomial $D(p)$ is at least as high as the degree of the polynomial $N(p)$; $D(p) = 0$ has n *distinct* roots $p_1, \ldots, p_n$; and $p = 0$ is not a root of $D(p) = 0$	Heaviside Expansion Formula‡ $\dfrac{N(0)}{D(0)} + \displaystyle\sum_{r=1}^{r=n} \dfrac{N(p_r)e^{p_r t}}{p_r D^1(p_r)}$ where $D^1(p_r) = \dfrac{dD}{dp}\qquad p = p_r$
53	$\dfrac{p^2 + 2\omega^2}{p^2 + 4\omega^2}$	$\cos^2 \omega t$
54	$p\tan^{-1}\dfrac{a}{p}$	$\dfrac{\sin at}{t}$
55	$p\log\dfrac{p+b}{p+a}$	$\dfrac{e^{-at} - e^{-bt}}{t}$

† In some cases it is simpler to decompose the ratio of the two polynomials in p into partial fractions and then to use transforms found in this table. In doing this the following identities are helpful:

$(a)\qquad \dfrac{1}{(a + bp^2)(a_1 + b_1 p^2)} \equiv \dfrac{1}{a_1 b - a b_1}\left(\dfrac{b}{a + bp^2} - \dfrac{b_1}{a_1 + b_1 p^2}\right)$

$(b)\qquad \dfrac{m + np}{(k + sp)(a + bp + cp^2)} \equiv \dfrac{1}{as^2 + ck^2 - bks}\left[\dfrac{s(ms - nk)}{k + sp}\right.$

$$\left. + \dfrac{c(nk - ms)p + asn + ckm - bsm}{a + bp + cp^2}\right]$$

$(c)\qquad \dfrac{s + mp^n}{(a + bp^n)(a_1 + b_1 p^n)} \equiv \dfrac{1}{a_1 b - a b_1}\left(\dfrac{bs - am}{a + bp^n} + \dfrac{a_1 m - b_1 s}{a_1 + b_1 p^n}\right)$

$(d)\qquad \dfrac{1}{(p + a)(p + b)(p + c)} \equiv \dfrac{A}{p + a} + \dfrac{B}{p + b} + \dfrac{C}{p + c}$

where $A = \dfrac{1}{(a - b)(a - c)}\qquad B = \dfrac{1}{(b - c)(b - a)}\qquad C = \dfrac{1}{(c - a)(c - b)}$

‡ This formula enables one to evaluate inverse transforms not found in this table.

Table of Laplace Transforms (Continued)

No.	$g(p)$	$h(t)$
56	$\dfrac{p}{\sqrt{p^2 + a^2}}$	$J_0(at)$ Bessel function of the first kind, zeroth order
57	$\dfrac{p}{\sqrt{p^2 + a^2}\,(\sqrt{p^2 + a^2} - p)^{-n}}$	$\dfrac{1}{a^n} J_n(at)$ for $n = 0, 1, 2, 3, \ldots$ Bessel function of first kind, nth order
58	$\dfrac{1}{\sqrt{p^2 + a^2}\,(\sqrt{p^2 + a^2} - p)^{-n}}$	$\dfrac{1}{a^n} \displaystyle\int_0^t J_n(at)\,dt$ for $n = 0, 1, 2, 3, \ldots$
59	$\dfrac{p}{\sqrt{p^2 + a^2} + p}$	$\dfrac{1}{a}\dfrac{J_1(at)}{t}$
60	$\dfrac{p}{(\sqrt{p^2 + a^2} + p)^n}$	$\dfrac{n}{a^n}\dfrac{J_n(at)}{t}$ $n = 1, 2, 3, \ldots$
61	$\dfrac{1}{(\sqrt{p^2 + a^2} + p)^n}$	$\dfrac{n}{a^n} \displaystyle\int_0^t \dfrac{J_n(at)\,dt}{t}$ $n = 1, 2, 3, \ldots$
62	$e^{-a/p}$	$J_0(2\sqrt{at})$
63	$\cos \dfrac{1}{p}$	Ber $(2\sqrt{t})$ Ber is the Bessel real function of Lord Kelvin
64	$\sin \dfrac{1}{p}$	Bei $(2\sqrt{t})$
65	$p^{-n}e^{-1/p}$	$t^{n/2}J_n(2\sqrt{t})$ Re $n > -1$
66	$pe^{-a\sqrt{p}}$ $a > 0$	$\dfrac{a}{2\sqrt{\pi t^3}} e^{-a^2/4t}$
67	$p^{\frac{1}{2}}e^{-a\sqrt{p}}$ $a > 0$	$\dfrac{1}{\sqrt{\pi t}} e^{-a^2/4t}$
68	$e^{-a\sqrt{p}}$ $a > 0$	$1 - \mathrm{erf}\left(\dfrac{a}{2\sqrt{t}}\right)$ where erf (y) is the error function defined by $\mathrm{erf}\,(y) = \dfrac{2}{\sqrt{\pi}} \displaystyle\int_0^y e^{-u^2}\,du$

TABLE OF LAPLACE TRANSFORMS (*Continued*)

No.	$g(p)$	$h(t)$
69	$\dfrac{pe^{-a\sqrt{p}}}{p + b\sqrt{p}}$ $a > 0$	$e^{b^2 t + ab}\left[1 - \mathrm{erf}\left(b\sqrt{t} + \dfrac{a}{2\sqrt{t}}\right)\right]$
70	$pK_0(a\sqrt{p})$ where $K_0(y)$ is the modified Bessel function of the second kind of order zero $a > 0$	$\dfrac{1}{2t}\,e^{-a^2/4t}$
71	$pK_0(ap)$	$0 \qquad\qquad 0 < t < a$ $\sqrt{t^2 - a^2} \qquad\quad t > a$
72	$\dfrac{p}{\sqrt{p^2 - 1}}$	$I_0(t)$ modified Bessel function of the first kind and zeroth order
73	$\dfrac{p(p - \sqrt{p^2 - 1})^n}{\sqrt{p^2 - 1}}$	$I_n(t)$ modified Bessel function of the first kind and nth order
74	$\dfrac{pe^{-a\sqrt{p^2 + b^2}}}{\sqrt{p^2 + b^2}}$ $a > 0$	$0 \qquad\qquad\qquad$ when $0 < t < a$ $J_0(b\sqrt{t^2 - a^2})$ when $t > a$
75	$\dfrac{pe^{-a\sqrt{p^2 - b^2}}}{\sqrt{p^2 - b^2}}$ $a > 0$	$0 \qquad\qquad\qquad$ when $0 < t < a$ $I_0(b\sqrt{t^2 - a^2})$ when $t > a$
76	$\dfrac{1}{\sqrt{1 + p}}$	$\mathrm{erf}\,(\sqrt{t})$
77	$\dfrac{pe^{-(x/v)\sqrt{(p+s)^2 - \sigma^2}}}{\sqrt{(p + s)^2 - \sigma^2}}$	$0 \qquad\qquad\qquad\qquad t < x/v$ $e^{-st}I_0(\sigma\sqrt{t^2 - x^2/v^2})$ $t > x/v$
78	$e^{-ap} - e^{-bp}$	
79	$\dfrac{m}{p}(1 - e^{-ap}) - mae^{-ap}$	

TABLE OF LAPLACE TRANSFORMS (*Continued*)

No.	$g(p)$	$h(t)$
80	$\tanh \dfrac{ap}{2}$	Meander function
81	$\dfrac{m}{p} - \dfrac{ma}{2}\left(\coth \dfrac{ap}{2} - 1\right)$	Saw-tooth function Slope $= m$
82	$\dfrac{1}{2}\left(1 + \coth \dfrac{ap}{2}\right)$	Stepped function
83	$\dfrac{1}{\sinh ap}$	
84	$\left(\dfrac{p-a}{p}\right)^n$	$L_n(at) = e^{-at}\dfrac{d^n}{dt^n}\left(\dfrac{t^n}{n!}e^{-at}\right)$ $=$ Laguerre polynomial of nth order

More complicated transforms will be found in the following references:

1. Campbell, G. A., and R. M. Foster: Fourier Integrals for Practical Applications, *Bell System Technical Journal*, September, 1931, pp. 312–408.
2. Pipes, L. A.: The Transient Behaviour of Four-terminal Networks, *Philosophical Magazine*, ser. 7, vol. 33, p. 174, March, 1942.
3. Gardner, M. F., and J. L. Barnes: "Transients in Linear Systems," John Wiley & Sons, Inc., New York, 1942.
4. McLachlan, N. W.: "Complex Variable and Operational Calculus," Cambridge University Press, New York, 1939.

The current is given by the equation

$$L\frac{di}{dt} + Ri + \frac{q}{c} = E$$

where $dq/dt = i$.

Let $\mathcal{L}i(t) = I(p)$, $\mathcal{L}q(t) = Q(p)$.

NOTE: The script $\mathcal{L}$ is used to denote the Laplace transform in order not to confuse it with the inductance parameter L.

By (III) the equations are transformed to

$$LpI + RI + \frac{Q}{c} = E$$
$$pQ = I$$

Therefore we have

$$LpI + RI + \frac{I}{pc} = E$$

Therefore

$$I = \frac{pE}{L(p^2 + R/Lp + 1/Lc)} = \frac{pE}{L[(p + a)^2 + \omega^2]}$$

where

$$a = \frac{R}{2L} \qquad \omega^2 = \frac{1}{Lc} - \frac{R^2}{4L^2}$$

By No. 17 we have

$$i = \frac{E}{\omega L} e^{-at} \sin \omega t \qquad \text{if } \omega^2 > 0$$

or by No. 18

$$i = \frac{E}{L} te^{-at} \qquad \text{if } \omega^2 = 0$$

$$i = \frac{E}{kL} e^{-at} \sinh kt \qquad \text{if } \omega^2 < 0 \qquad k^2 = -\omega^2$$

3. Resonance of a Pendulum. A simple pendulum, originally hanging in equilibrium, is disturbed by a force varying harmonically. It is required to determine the motion.

The differential equation is

$$\ddot{x} + \omega_0^2 x = F_0 \sin nt$$

Let the pendulum start from rest at its equilibrium position. In such a case we have the initial conditions

$$\left.\begin{array}{l} x = 0 \\ \dot{x} = 0 \end{array}\right\} \qquad \text{at } t = 0$$

Let $Lx = y$; then by (III) $L\ddot{x} = p^2 y$.

Using No. 11, the differential equation of motion is transformed to

$$(p^2 + \omega_0^2)y = \frac{F_0 pn}{p^2 + n^2}$$

or

$$y = \frac{F_0 pn}{(p^2 + n^2)(p^2 + \omega_0^2)} = \frac{F_0 n}{\omega_0^2 - n^2}\left(\frac{p}{p^2 + n^2} - \frac{p}{p^2 + \omega_0^2}\right)$$

By No. 11 we obtain

$$x = \frac{F_0 n}{\omega_0^2 - n^2}\left(\frac{\sin nt}{n} - \frac{\sin \omega_0 t}{\omega_0}\right) \qquad \text{if } \omega_0^2 \neq n^2$$

If $\omega_0^2 = n^2$,

$$y = \frac{F_0 p n}{(p^2 + n^2)^2}$$

and by No. 22

$$x = \frac{F_0}{2n^2} (\sin nt - nt \cos nt) \qquad \text{the case of resonance}$$

4. Linear flow of heat in a semi-infinite solid, $x > 0$; the boundary $x = 0$ kept at constant temperature v_0; the initial temperature of the solid zero.

In this problem we have to solve

$$\text{(1)} \qquad \frac{\partial v}{\partial t} = K \frac{\partial^2 v}{\partial x^2} \qquad x > 0 \qquad t > 0$$

with $v = v_0$ when $x = 0$, $t > 0$; $v = 0$ when $x > 0$, $t = 0$.

Let $Lv(x,t) = V(g,p)$.

By Theorem (II) $L(\partial v / \partial t) = pV$.

Equation (1) is transformed to

$$\text{(2)} \qquad \frac{d^2 V}{dx^2} - \frac{p}{k} V = 0 \qquad x > 0$$

with

$$\text{(3)} \qquad V = v_0 \qquad \text{when } x = 0$$

The solution of (2) which satisfies (3) and remains finite at $x \to \infty$ is

$$V = v_0 e^{-x\sqrt{p/K}}$$

By No. 68 the inverse transform of V is

$$v(x,t) = v_0 \left(1 - \text{erf} \frac{x}{2\sqrt{Kt}} \right)$$

The above examples are typical of the manner in which linear differential equations with constant coefficients may be solved by the use of these tables.

CHAPTER 7

OSCILLATIONS OF LINEAR LUMPED
ELECTRICAL CIRCUITS

1. Introduction. A large part of the analysis in engineering and physics is concerned with the study of vibrating systems. The electrical circuit is the most common example of a vibrating system. By analogy the electrical circuit serves as a model for the study of mechanical and acoustical vibrating systems. Historically the equations of motion of mechanical systems were developed a long time before any attention was given to the equations for electrical circuits. It was because of this that in the early days of electrical-circuit theory it was natural to explain the action in terms of mechanical phenomena. At the present time electrical-circuit theory has been developed to a much higher state than the theory of corresponding mechanical systems. Mathematically the elements in an electrical network are the coefficients in the differential equations describing the network. In the same way the coefficients in the differential equations of a mechanical or acoustical system may be looked upon as mechanical or acoustical elements. Kirchhoff's electromotive-force law plays the same role in setting up the electrical equations as D'Alembert's principle does in setting up the mechanical and acoustical equations. Therefore a mechanical or acoustical system may be represented by an analogous electrical network, and the problem may be solved by electrical-circuit theory.

2. Electrical-circuit Principles. The differential equations for electrical circuits with lumped parameters are of the same form as the equations for mechanical systems. Kirchhoff's first law is the application of the conservation-of-electricity principle to the circuit and may be stated in the following form:

1. The algebraic sum of all the currents into the junction point of a network is zero.

Kirchhoff's second law is a statement concerning the conservation of energy in the circuit and is usually stated in the following form:

2. The algebraic sum of the electromotive forces around a closed circuit is zero.

Let us apply the above Kirchhoff laws to the simple series circuit of Fig. 2.1.

The parameters R, L, and S of the circuit are expressed symbolically in the diagram below and are called the *resistance, inductance,* and *elastance* coefficients, respectively. From basic principles, we have

$$E_R = iR = \text{electromotive-force drop due to resistance}$$

$$(2.1) \quad E_L = L\frac{di}{dt} = \text{electromotive-force drop due to inductance}$$

$$E_S = Sq = \text{electromotive-force drop due to elastance}$$

Where q is the charge on the capacitor whose elastance is S, it is related to the current i by the equation

$$(2.2) \qquad i = \frac{dq}{dt}$$

The capacitance of the capacitor C is related to S by the equation

$$(2.3) \qquad C = \frac{1}{S}$$

Fig. 2.1

Applying Kirchhoff's second law to the circuit, we have

$$(2.4) \qquad\qquad L\frac{di}{dt} + Ri + Sq = e(t)$$

or, in terms of q, it is written in the form

$$(2.5) \qquad\qquad L\ddot{q} + R\dot{q} + Sq = e(t)$$

where $\ddot{q} = d^2q/dt^2$ and $\dot{q} = dq/dt$.

If $R = 0$ and $S = 0$, the above equation reduces to

$$(2.6) \qquad\qquad L\ddot{q} = e(t)$$

This equation has the same form as that governing the displacement x of a mass M when it is acted upon by a force F as shown in Fig. 2.2.

Fig. 2.2   Fig. 2.3

In the mechanical case, we have by Newton's law $(F = Ma)$ the equation

$$(2.7) \qquad\qquad M\ddot{x} = F$$

If the mass is attached to a linear spring as shown in Fig. 2.3, we have by Newton's law

$$(2.8) \qquad M\ddot{x} + kx = F$$

where k is the spring constant of the spring. This is analogous to Eq. (2.5) if we place $R = 0$. If in addition to the spring the mass of Fig. 2.3 were retarded by a force proportional to its velocity of the form $B\dot{x}$, then its equation of motion would be given by

$$(2.9) \qquad M\ddot{x} + B\dot{x} + kx = F$$

This equation has exactly the same form as Eq. (2.5); we therefore see that we have the following equivalence between electrical and mechanical quantities:

$$(2.10) \qquad \begin{aligned} e &\rightarrow F \\ L &\rightarrow M \\ R &\rightarrow B \\ S &\rightarrow k \\ q &\rightarrow x \\ i &\rightarrow \dot{x} = v \end{aligned}$$

This correspondence between electrical and mechanical quantities is the basis of the electrical and mechanical analogies.

3. Energy Considerations. The energy of an oscillating electrical or mechanical system is of importance in studying the behavior of the system. The potential energy stored in the spring of Fig. 2.3 when the mass has been displaced by a distance x is given by

$$(3.1) \qquad V_M = \int_0^x F\,dx = \int_0^x kx\,dx = \frac{kx^2}{2}$$

In the electrical case the energy involved in charging the capacitor plays the same role as the elastic energy in the mechanical case. This is given by

$$(3.2) \qquad V_E = \int_0^t ei\,dt = \int_0^t Sqi\,dt = S \int_0^q q\,dq = \frac{Sq^2}{2}$$

The kinetic energy of motion of the mass is given by

$$(3.3) \qquad T_M = \int_0^x F\,dx = \int_0^x M\ddot{x}\,dx = \int_0^v Mv\,dv = \frac{Mv^2}{2}$$

where $v = \dot{x}$ is the velocity of the mass.

In the electrical case we have

$$(3.4) \qquad T_E = \tfrac{1}{2}Li^2$$

The power dissipated in friction in the mechanical case is given by

$$(3.5) \qquad P_M = v^2 B$$

and the power dissipated in the electrical circuit is

(3.6) $$P_E = i^2 R$$

4. Analysis of General Series Circuit. We have seen in Sec. 2 that the equation governing the current of the general series circuit of Fig. 2.1 is given by

(4.1) $$L \frac{di}{dt} + Ri + Sq = e(t)$$

where

(4.2) $$i = \dot{q}$$

This is a linear differential equation with constant coefficients, and we may solve it by the methods discussed in Chap. 6. The Laplace-transform method is particularly well suited for solving this equation. To do this, we let

(4.3) $$\mathcal{L}i = I \qquad \mathcal{L}q = Q$$

NOTE: In order to avoid confusion with the inductance parameter, the Laplace transforms will be denoted by a script $\mathcal{L}$.

We therefore have from Chap. 6, Eq. (5.10),

(4.4) $$\mathcal{L}\left(\frac{di}{dt}\right) = pI - pi_0$$

From (4.2) we have

(4.5) $$\mathcal{L}i = \mathcal{L}\dot{q} = I = pQ - pq_0$$

where i_0 is the initial current flowing in the circuit and q_0 is the initial charge on the capacitor. From (4.5) we obtain

(4.6) $$Q = \frac{I}{p} + q_0$$

Equation (4.1) is transformed to

(4.7) $$L(pI - pi_0) + RI + SQ = \mathcal{L}e(t)$$

Eliminating Q, we obtain

(4.7a) $$\left(Lp + R + \frac{S}{p}\right) I + Sq_0 - Lpi_0 = \mathcal{L}e(t)$$

Solving for I, we obtain

(4.8) $$I = \frac{1}{p^2 + \frac{R}{L} p + \frac{S}{L}} \cdot \frac{p\mathcal{L}e(t) + Lp^2 i_0 - Spq_0}{L}$$

The Case of Free Oscillations. Let us first consider the case when there is no external electromotive force applied to the system. In this case $e(t)$ is equal to zero. To simplify the equation, let

$$(4.9) \qquad a = \frac{R}{2L}$$

$$(4.10) \qquad \omega_0 = \sqrt{\frac{S}{L}} = \sqrt{\frac{1}{LC}}$$

In this case we have

$$(4.11) \qquad I = \frac{1}{p^2 + 2ap + \omega^2} \frac{Lp^2 i_0 - Spq_0}{L}$$

To obtain the inverse transform of this expression, we use equations Nos. 49 and 50 of our table of transforms. There are three cases to consider:

(a) $\omega_0^2 > a^2$
(b) $\omega_0^2 = a^2$
(c) $\omega_0^2 < a^2$

Case a is called the *oscillatory case*. For this case we obtain from the table

$$(4.12) \qquad i(t) = -\frac{i_0 \omega_0}{\omega_s} e^{-at} \sin (\omega_s t - \phi) - \frac{q_0}{LC} \frac{e^{-at} \sin \omega_s t}{\omega_s}$$

where

$$(4.13) \qquad \omega_s = \sqrt{\omega_0^2 - a^2} \qquad \tan \phi = \frac{\omega_s}{a}$$

We thus see that the current is given as a damped oscillation, where i_0 and q_0 are the initial current and charge of the system.

If $\omega_0 = a$, we have case b. This is called the *critically damped case*. We then obtain

$$(4.14) \qquad i(t) = i_0 e^{-at}(1 - at) - \frac{q_0}{LC} t e^{-at}$$

In this case there are no oscillations, and the current dies down in an exponential manner.

Case c is the *overdamped case*, and the solution for this case may be easily obtained from Nos. 49 and 50 of the table.

If there is no resistance present in the circuit, then $a = 0$ and our transform becomes

$$(4.15) \qquad I = \frac{1}{p^2 + \omega^2} \frac{Lp^2 i_0 - Spq_0}{L}$$

We may compute the inverse transform of this equation by the use of transforms Nos. 10 and 11 of the table of transforms. We then have

$$(4.16) \qquad i(t) = i_0 \cos \omega_0 t - \omega_0 q_0 \sin \omega_0 t$$

where now

(4.17)
$$\omega_0 = \frac{1}{\sqrt{LC}}$$

The foregoing equations give the velocity of the mass of the analogous mechanical system. In this case q_0 corresponds to the initial displacement x_0, and i_0 corresponds to the initial velocity of the mass of the mechanical system. The quantity $\omega_0 = 1/\sqrt{LC}$ in the case where we have no resistance is called the *natural angular frequency* of the electrical system. This corresponds to

(4.18)
$$\omega_0 = \sqrt{\frac{k}{M}}$$

for the mechanical system. Here k is the spring constant, and M is the mass of the system.

Forced Oscillations. If $e(t)$ is not equal to zero, we must add to the preceding expressions the transform of

(4.19)
$$I = \frac{p\mathcal{L}e(t)}{L(p^2 + 2ap + \omega_0^2)}$$

The inverse transform of (4.19) gives the current in a general series circuit that has no initial current and no initial charge but has impressed on it an electromotive force $e(t)$ at $t = 0$. Let us compute this for the case in which $e(t)$ is an alternating potential of the form

(4.20)
$$e(t) = E_0 \sin \omega t$$

By No. 11 of the tables we obtain

(4.21)
$$\mathcal{L}e(t) = \frac{E_0 \omega p}{p^2 + \omega^2}$$

Substituting this into (4.19), we obtain

(4.22)
$$I = \frac{E_0 \omega}{L} \frac{p^2}{(p^2 + \omega^2)(p^2 + 2ap + \omega_0^2)}$$

The inverse transform of this expression may be most simply computed by the use of No. 52 of the table of transforms. For this case, we have

(4.23)
$$N(p) = p^2$$
$$D(p) = (p^2 + \omega^2)(p^2 + 2ap + \omega_0^2)$$

The roots of $D(p)$ are

(4.24)
$$
\begin{aligned}
p_1 &= -a + j\omega_s \\
p_2 &= -a - j\omega_s \qquad \text{where } \omega_s = \sqrt{\omega_0^2 - a^2} \\
p_3 &= +j\omega \\
p_4 &= -j\omega
\end{aligned}
$$

We also have $N(0)/D(0) = 0$, and

$$(4.25) \qquad D'(P) = 2p(p^2 + 2ap + \omega_0^2) + (p^2 + \omega^2)(2p + 2a)$$

Hence, substituting into No. 52 of the table, we obtain

$$(4.26) \qquad i = \frac{E_0 \omega}{2L} \left[\frac{p_1 e^{p_1 t}}{(p + a)(p^2 + \omega^2)} + \frac{p_2 e^{p_2 t}}{(p_2 + a)(p_2^2 + \omega^2)} \right]$$
$$+ \frac{E_0 \omega}{2L} \left(\frac{e^{j\omega t}}{\omega_0^2 + 2aj\omega - \omega^2} + \frac{e^{-j\omega t}}{\omega_0^2 - 2aj\omega - \omega^2} \right)$$

Since the roots p_1 and p_2 have a negative real part, the expression within the brackets vanishes ultimately as time increases. The second expression may be denoted by i_s. It may be easily transformed to the form

$$(4.27) \qquad i_s = \frac{E_0 \sin (\omega t - \theta)}{\sqrt{R^2 + \left(\omega L - \frac{1}{\omega C} \right)^2}} \qquad \theta = \tan^{-1} \frac{\omega L - \dfrac{1}{\omega C}}{R}$$

This term persists with the passage of time and is called the *steady-state term*. If R is zero so that the circuit is devoid of resistance, this becomes

$$(4.28) \qquad i_s = \frac{E_0 \sin (\omega t \pm \pi/2)}{\omega L - 1/\omega C}$$

If $\omega = 1/\sqrt{LC} = \omega_0$, the denominator of (4.28) vanishes and the steady-state current amplitude becomes indefinitely great. This is the phenomenon of resonance and occurs when the impressed electromotive force has a frequency equal to that of the natural frequency of the circuit. If the circuit has resistance, then the denominator of (4.27) does not vanish and we do not have true resonance.

It may be noted that the steady-state current may be obtained more simply directly from the differential equation of the circuit

$$(4.29) \qquad L \frac{di}{dt} + Rt + \frac{q}{C} = E_0 \sin \omega t$$

by the method of undetermined coefficients explained in Chap. 6, Sec. 4. The steady-state current is the particular integral of this equation. We replace the right-hand member of (4.29) by Im $E_0 e^{j\omega t}$, where "Im" means the "imaginary part of."

We let

$$(4.30) \qquad i = \text{Im } A e^{j\omega t}$$

where A is a complex number to be determined by (4.22). Suppressing

the Im symbol and realizing that

$$(4.31) \qquad q = \int i \, dt = \int A e^{j\omega t} \, dt = \frac{A e^{j\omega t}}{j\omega}$$

substitution into (4.29) gives

$$(4.32) \qquad \left(j\omega L + R + \frac{1}{j\omega C} \right) A = E_0$$

where we have divided both sides by the common factor $e^{j\omega t}$. Hence we have

$$(4.33) \qquad A = \frac{E_0}{R + j(\omega L - 1/\omega C)}$$

It is convenient to introduce the notation

$$(4.34) \qquad Z = R + j \left(\omega L - \frac{1}{\omega C} \right)$$

This complex number is called the *complex impedance* of the circuit. It may be written in the polar form

$$(4.35) \qquad Z = |Z| e^{j\theta}$$

where

$$(4.36) \quad |Z| = \sqrt{R^2 + \left(\omega L - \frac{1}{\omega C} \right)^2} \quad \text{and} \quad \tan \theta = \frac{\omega L - \dfrac{1}{\omega C}}{R}$$

We thus have

$$(4.37) \qquad A = \frac{E_0}{|Z|} e^{-j\theta}$$

The steady-state current is now given by (4.30) in the form

$$(4.38) \qquad i = \text{Im } E_0 \frac{e^{-\theta j} e^{j\omega t}}{|Z|} = \frac{E_0}{|Z|} \sin (\omega t - \theta)$$

This is the steady-state current given in (4.27) obtained more directly. The solution (4.26), however, contains both the steady-state solution and the transient response of the system produced by the sudden application of the potential $E_0 \sin \omega t$ on the system at $t = 0$.

FIG. 5.1

5. Discharge and Charge of a Capacitor. An interesting application of the differential equations governing the distribution of charges and currents in electrical networks is the following one: Consider the electrical circuit of Fig. 5.1.

Let a charge q_0 be placed on the capacitor, and let the switch S be closed at $t = 0$. Let it be required to determine the charge on the capacitor at any instant later.

When the switch is closed, we have, by Kirchhoff's law, the equation

$$(5.1) \qquad L\frac{d^2q}{dt^2} + R\frac{dg}{dt} + \frac{q}{C} = 0$$

To solve this, let us introduce the transform

$$(5.2) \qquad \mathcal{L}q = Q$$

The initial conditions of the problem are

$$(5.3) \qquad \left.\begin{array}{l} q = q_0 \\ i = \dfrac{dq}{dt} = 0 \end{array}\right\} \quad \text{at } t = 0$$

Hence we have

$$(5.4) \qquad \begin{aligned} \mathcal{L}\frac{dq}{dt} &= pQ - pq_0 \\ \mathcal{L}\frac{d^2q}{dt^2} &= p^2Q - p^2q_0 \end{aligned}$$

Hence Eq. (5.1) transforms to

$$(5.5) \qquad L(p^2Q - p^2q_0) + R(pQ - pq_0) + \frac{Q}{C} = 0$$

or

$$(5.6) \qquad \left(p^2L + pR + \frac{1}{C}\right)Q = Lp^2q_0 + Rpq_0$$

As before, let

$$(5.7) \qquad a = \frac{R}{2L} \qquad \omega_0 = \sqrt{\frac{1}{LC}}$$

We, therefore, have

$$(5.8) \qquad Q = \frac{p^2q_0}{p^2 + 2ap + \omega_0^2} + \frac{2apq}{p^2 + 2ap + \omega_0^2}$$

By the use of transforms Nos. 49 and 50, we obtain

$$(5.9) \qquad \begin{aligned} q &= q_0e^{-at}\left(\cosh \beta t + \frac{a}{\beta}\sinh \beta t\right) && \text{if } a > \omega_0 \\ q &= q_0e^{-at}(1 + at) && \text{if } a = \omega_0 \\ q &= q_0e^{-at}\left(\cos \omega_s t + \frac{a}{\omega_s}\sin \omega_s t\right) && \text{if } a < \omega_0 \end{aligned}$$

where $\omega_s = \sqrt{\omega_0^2 - a^2}$ and $\beta = \sqrt{a^2 - \omega_0^2}$.

The Charging of a Capacitor. Let us consider the circuit of Fig. 5.2.

In this case, at $t = 0$, the switch is closed and the potential E of the battery is impressed on the circuit. It is required to determine the manner in which the charge on the capacitor behaves.

The equation satisfied by the charge is now

FIG. 5.2

(5.10) $\ddot{q} + 2a\dot{q} + \omega_0^2 q = \dfrac{E}{L}$

To solve this equation, we again let

(5.11) $\mathcal{L}q = Q$

and since E is a constant, we have

(5.12) $\mathcal{L}\dfrac{E}{L} = \dfrac{E}{L}$

The initial conditions are now

(5.13) $\left.\begin{array}{r} q = 0 \\ \dot{q} = 0 \end{array}\right\}$ at $t = 0$

Hence we have

(5.14) $\begin{array}{l} \mathcal{L}\ddot{q} = p^2 Q \\ \mathcal{L}\dot{q} = pQ \end{array}$

Equation (5.10) transforms to

(5.15) $(p^2 + 2ap + \omega_0^2)Q = \dfrac{E}{L}$

and hence

(5.16) $Q = \dfrac{E}{L(p^2 + 2ap + \omega_0^2)}$

To obtain the inverse transform of (5.16), we use transform No. 51 of the table of transforms and thus obtain

(5.17)
$$q = CE\left[1 - e^{-at}\left(\cosh \beta t + \frac{a}{\beta}\sinh \beta t\right)\right] \quad \text{if } a > \omega_0$$
$$q = CE[1 - e^{-at}(1 + at)] \qquad\qquad\qquad \text{if } a = \omega_0$$
$$q = CE\left[1 - e^{-at}\left(\cos \omega_s t + \frac{a}{\omega_s}\sin \omega_s t\right)\right] \quad \text{if } a < \omega_0$$

where β and ω_s are as defined in (5.9).

In each case, the charging current is given by $i = \dot{q}$. The analogous mechanical problem is that of determining the motion of a mass when it has been given an initial displacement and is acted upon by a spring and retarded by viscous friction or if the mass has a sudden force applied to it.

6. Circuit with Mutual Inductance. Let us consider the circuits of Fig. 6.1.

In this case we have two circuits coupled magnetically. The coefficient L_{12} is termed the *mutual inductance coefficient*. It is positive if the magnetic fields of i_1 and i_2 add. If they are opposed, then the coefficient L_{12} is negative. In any case the equations governing the currents in the two circuits are given by applying Kirchhoff's laws to the two loops and are

FIG. 6.1

$$L_{11}\frac{di_1}{dt} + L_{12}\frac{di_2}{dt} + R_{11}i_1 = E$$
$$(6.1)$$
$$L_{22}\frac{di_2}{dt} + L_{12}\frac{di_1}{dt} + R_{22}i_2 = 0$$

We wish to determine the currents i_1 and i_2 on the supposition that at $t = 0$ the switch s is closed and the initial currents are zero.

Let us introduce the transforms

$$(6.2) \qquad \begin{aligned} \mathcal{L}i_1 &= I_1 \\ \mathcal{L}i_2 &= I_2 \end{aligned}$$

Now since we have

$$(6.3) \qquad \left. \begin{aligned} i_1 &= 0 \\ i_2 &= 0 \end{aligned} \right\} \quad \text{at } t = 0$$

and also E is a constant, Eq. (6.1) transforms to

$$(6.4) \qquad \begin{aligned} pL_{11}I_1 + pL_{12}I_2 + R_{11}I_1 &= E \\ pL_{22}I_2 + pL_{12}I_1 + R_{22}I_2 &= 0 \end{aligned}$$

We now solve these two algebraic equations by using Cramer's rule and obtain

$$(6.5) \qquad I_1 = \frac{\begin{vmatrix} E & pL_{12} \\ 0 & pL_{22} + R_{22} \end{vmatrix}}{\begin{vmatrix} pL_{11} + R_{11} & pL_{12} \\ pL_{12} & pL_{22} + R_{22} \end{vmatrix}}$$

$$I_2 = \frac{\begin{vmatrix} pL_{11} + R_{11} & E \\ pL_{12} & 0 \end{vmatrix}}{\begin{vmatrix} pL_{11} + R_{11} & pL_{12} \\ pL_{12} & pL_{22} + R_{22} \end{vmatrix}}$$

Hence we have

$$(6.6) \qquad I_1 = \frac{E(pL_{22} + R_{22})}{(L_{11}L_{22} - L_{12}^2)p^2 + (R_{11}L_{22} + R_{22}L_{11})p + R_{11}R_{22}}$$
$$I_2 = \frac{-EpL_{12}}{(L_{11}L_{22} - L_{12}^2)p^2 + (R_{11}L_{22} + R_{22}L_{11})p + R_{11}R_{22}}$$

If we let

(6.7)
$$a = \frac{R_{11}L_{22} + R_{22}L_{11}}{2(L_{11}L_{22} - L_{12}^2)}$$

and

(6.8)
$$\omega_0^2 = \frac{R_{11}R_{22}}{L_{11}L_{22} - L_{12}^2}$$

we then have

(6.9)
$$I_1 = \frac{E}{L_{11}L_{22} - L_{12}^2} \frac{pL_{22} + R_{22}}{p^2 + 2ap + \omega_0^2}$$
$$I_2 = \frac{-E}{L_{11}L_{22} - L_{12}^2} \frac{pL_{12}}{p^2 + 2ap + \omega_0^2}$$

In this case

(6.10)
$$a^2 > \omega_0^2 \qquad \sqrt{a^2 - \omega_0^2} = \beta$$

Using the transforms Nos. 50 and 51 of the table, we obtain after some algebraic reductions

(6.11)
$$i_1 = \frac{E}{R_{11}} \left[1 - e^{-at} \cosh \beta t + \frac{(a^2 - \beta^2)L_{22} - aR_{22}}{\beta R_{22}} e^{-at} \sinh \beta t \right]$$
$$i_2 = \frac{(\beta^2 - a^2)L_{12}E}{\beta R_{11}R_{22}} e^{-at} \sinh \beta t$$

for the transforms of I_1 and I_2. We see that, as time elapses, i_1 approaches its final value E/R_{11}. If we set $di_2/dt = 0$ and solve for t, we find that i_2 rises to a maximum value when

(6.12)
$$t = \frac{1}{\beta} \tanh^{-1} \frac{\beta}{a}$$

and then approaches zero asymptotically. An interesting special case is the symmetrical one. In this case the resistances of each mesh are equal, and the self-inductances are equal. We then have

(6.13)
$$R_{11} = R_{22} = R \qquad L_{11} = L_{22} = L$$
$$L_{12} = M$$

Equations (6.4) then become

(6.14)
$$pLI_1 + pMI_2 + RI_1 = E$$
$$pLI_2 + pMI_1 + RI_2 = 0$$

If we add the two equations, we obtain

(6.15)　　$$pL(I_1 + I_2) + pM(I_1 + I_2) + R(I_1 + I_2) = E$$

If we subtract the second equation from the first one, we have

(6.16)　　$$pL(I_1 - I_2) + pM(I_1 - I_2) + R(I_1 - I_2) = E$$

If we now let

$$(6.17) \qquad x_1 = I_1 + I_2 \qquad x_2 = I_1 - I_2$$

we have

$$(6.18) \qquad \begin{aligned} p(L + M)x_1 + Rx_1 &= E \\ p(L - M)x_2 + Rx_2 &= E \end{aligned}$$

Hence

$$(6.19) \qquad x_1 = \frac{E}{p(L + M) + R} \qquad x_2 = \frac{E}{p(L - M) + R}$$

If we let

$$(6.20) \qquad a_1 = \frac{R}{L + M} \qquad a_2 = \frac{R}{L - M}$$

we obtain

$$(6.21) \qquad x_1 = \frac{E}{L + M}\frac{1}{p + a_1} \qquad x_2 = \frac{E}{L - M}\frac{1}{p + a_2}$$

Using transform No. 8 of the table in Chap. 6, we have

$$(6.22) \qquad \mathcal{L}^{-1}x_1 = \frac{E}{R}\left(1 - e^{-a_1 t}\right) \qquad \mathcal{L}^{-1}x_2 = \frac{E}{R}\left(1 - e^{-a_2 t}\right)$$

Hence

$$(6.23) \qquad \begin{aligned} i_1 + i_2 &= \frac{E}{R}\left(1 - e^{-a_1 t}\right) \\ i_1 - i_2 &= \frac{E}{R}\left(1 - e^{-a_2 t}\right) \end{aligned}$$

and adding the two equations we obtain

$$(6.24) \qquad i_1 = \frac{E}{R}\frac{2 - e^{-a_1 t} - e^{-a_2 t}}{2}$$

Subtracting the second equation from the first equation, we obtain

$$(6.25) \qquad i_2 = \frac{E}{2R}\left(e^{-a_2 t} - e^{-a_1 t}\right)$$

These are the currents in the symmetrical case.

FIG. 7.1

7. Circuits Coupled by a Capacitor. Let us consider the circuit of Fig. 7.1. In this case, we have two coupled circuits. The coupling element is now a capacitor. Let the switch S be closed at $t = 0$, and let it be required to determine the current in the system.   We write Kirchhoff's law for both meshes.   We then obtain

(7.1)
$$L_1 \frac{di_1}{dt} + R_1 i_1 + \frac{q_1}{C_1} + \frac{q_1 - q_2}{C_{12}} = E$$
$$L_2 \frac{di_2}{dt} + R_2 i_2 + \frac{q_2}{C_2} + \frac{q_2 - q_1}{C_{12}} = 0$$

where

(7.2)
$$i_1 = \frac{dq_1}{dtv} \qquad i_2 = \frac{dq_2}{dtv}$$

Let us introduce the transforms

(7.3)
$$\mathcal{L}i_1 = I_1 \qquad \mathcal{L}q_1 = Q_1$$
$$\mathcal{L}i_2 = I_2 \qquad \mathcal{L}q_2 = Q_2$$

If we assume

(7.4)
$$\left. \begin{array}{ll} i_1 = 0 & q_1 = 0 \\ i_2 = 0 & q_2 = 0 \end{array} \right\} \quad \text{at } t = 0$$

Eqs. (7.1) transform into

(7.5)
$$pL_1 I_1 + R_1 I_1 + \frac{I_1}{pC_1} + \frac{I_1 - I_2}{pC_{12}} = E$$
$$pL_2 I_2 + R_2 I_2 + \frac{I_2}{pC_2} + \frac{I_2 - I_1}{pC_{12}} = 0$$

We now solve these equations algebraically for the transforms I_1 and I_2. We thus obtain

(7.6)
$$I_1 = \frac{\begin{vmatrix} E & -\dfrac{1}{pC_{12}} \\ 0 & pL_2 + R_2 + \dfrac{1}{pC_2} + \dfrac{1}{pC_{12}} \end{vmatrix}}{\begin{vmatrix} pL_1 + R_1 + \dfrac{1}{pC_1} + \dfrac{1}{pC_{12}} & -\dfrac{1}{pC_{12}} \\ -\dfrac{1}{pC_{12}} & pL_2 + R_2 + \dfrac{1}{pC_2} + \dfrac{1}{pC_{12}} \end{vmatrix}}$$

$$I_2 = \frac{\begin{vmatrix} pL_1 + R_1 + \dfrac{1}{pC_1} + \dfrac{1}{pC_{12}} & E \\ -\dfrac{1}{pC_{12}} & 0 \end{vmatrix}}{\begin{vmatrix} pL_1 + R_1 + \dfrac{1}{pC_1} + \dfrac{1}{pC_{12}} & -\dfrac{1}{pC_{12}} \\ -\dfrac{1}{pC_{12}} & pL_2 + R_2 + \dfrac{1}{pC_2} + \dfrac{1}{pC_{12}} \end{vmatrix}}$$

Expanding the determinants, we obtain the transforms I_1 and I_2 as the ratios of polynomials in p.   The inverse transforms of I_1 and I_2 give the currents in the system.   In this case, the determinant in the denominator of (7.6) of the system is a polynomial of the fourth degree in p. The inverse transforms may now be calculated by the use of No. 52 in the table.   This entails the solution of a quartic equation in p.   If numerical values are given, this may be done by the Graeffe root-squaring method described in Chap. 5.   The trend of the general solution may be determined by solving the symmetrical case in which we have

$$(7.7) \qquad R_1 = R_2 = R \qquad C_1 = C_2 = C \qquad L_1 = L_2 = L$$

In this case Eqs. (7.5) reduce to

$$(7.8)$$
$$pLI_1 + RI_1 + \frac{I_1}{pC} + \frac{I_1}{pC_{12}} - \frac{I_2}{pC_{12}} = E$$
$$pLI_2 + RI_2 + \frac{I_2}{pC} + \frac{I_2}{pC_{12}} - \frac{I_1}{pC_{12}} = 0$$

If we add the two equations, we obtain

$$(7.9) \qquad pL(I_1 + I_2) + R(I_1 + I_2) + \frac{1}{pC}(I_1 + I_2) = E$$

If we subtract the second equation from the first, we have

$$(7.10) \quad pL(I_1 - I_2) + R(I_1 - I_2) + \frac{1}{pC}(I_1 - I_2)$$
$$+ \frac{1}{pC_{12}}(I_1 - I_2) + \frac{1}{pC_{12}}(I_1 - I_2) = E$$

If we let

$$(7.11)$$
$$x_1 = I_1 + I_2$$
$$x_2 = I_1 - I_2$$

we obtain

$$(7.12)$$
$$pLx_1 + Rx_1 + \frac{1}{pC}x_1 = E$$
$$pLx_2 + Rx_2 + \frac{1}{p}\left(\frac{1}{C} + \frac{2}{C_{12}}\right)x_2 = E$$

If we let

$$(7.13) \qquad \frac{R}{2L} = a \qquad \omega_1^2 = \frac{1}{LC} \qquad \omega_2^2 = \frac{1}{L}\left(\frac{1}{C} + \frac{2}{C_{12}}\right)$$

the two equations become

$$(7.14)$$
$$(p^2 + 2ap + \omega_1^2)x_1 = p\frac{E}{L}$$
$$(p^2 + 2ap + \omega_2^2)x_2 = p\frac{E}{L}$$

The inverse transforms of x_1 and x_2 may now be calculated by No. 50. In the case

$$(7.15) \qquad \omega_1^2 > a^2 \qquad \omega_2^2 > a^2$$

we have

$$(7.16) \quad \begin{aligned} \mathcal{L}^{-1}x_1 &= \frac{E}{L\omega_a}\,(e^{-at}\sin\omega_a t) & \omega_a &= \sqrt{\omega_1^2 - a^2} \\ \mathcal{L}^{-1}x_2 &= \frac{E}{L\omega_b}\,(e^{-at}\sin\omega_b t) & \omega_b &= \sqrt{\omega_2^2 - a^2} \end{aligned}$$

Hence, adding the two equations (7.16), we have

$$(7.17) \quad \begin{aligned} i_1 &= \frac{Ee^{-at}}{2L}\left(\frac{\sin\omega_a t}{\omega_a} + \frac{\sin\omega_b t}{\omega_b}\right) \\ i_2 &= \frac{E}{2L}\,e^{-at}\left(\frac{\sin\omega_a t}{\omega_a} - \frac{\sin\omega_b t}{\omega_b}\right) \end{aligned}$$

If there is no resistance in the circuit, then $a = 0$ and the currents oscillate without loss of amplitude with the angular frequencies ω_1 and ω_2.

8. The Effect of Finite Potential Pulses.   It frequently happens that the response of an electrical circuit is desired when a potential pulse is

FIG. 8.1   FIG. 8.2

applied to it.   The general procedure may be illustrated by the following example.

Consider the circuit of Fig. 8.1.   Let $e(t)$ be a pulse of the form given by Fig. 8.2.

It is required to find the current in the circuit.   For generality, let us assume that the capacitor has an initial charge q_0 at $t = 0$.   The current satisfies the equation

$$(8.1) \qquad Ri + \frac{q}{C} = e(t) \qquad i = \frac{dq}{dt}$$

We introduce the transforms

$$(8.2) \quad \begin{aligned} \mathcal{L}i &= I \\ \mathcal{L}q &= Q \\ \mathcal{L}e &= E \end{aligned}$$

We now have

$$(8.3) \qquad \mathcal{L}\,\frac{dq}{dt} = pQ - pq_0 = I$$

Hence

(8.4)
$$Q = \frac{I}{p} + q_0$$

The transform of the potential $e(t)$ is given by

(8.5)
$$E = p \int_{t_1}^{t_2} E_0 e^{-pt} \, dt = E_0(e^{-pt_1} - e^{-pt_2})$$

Accordingly, Eq. (8.1) is transformed:

(8.6)
$$RI + \frac{1}{C}\left(\frac{I}{p} + q_0\right) = E_0(e^{-pt_1} - e^{-pt_2})$$

If we let

(8.7)
$$a = \frac{1}{RC}$$

we obtain

(8.8)
$$I = \frac{E_0 p}{R} \frac{e^{-pt_1} - e^{-pt_2}}{p + a} - aq_0 \frac{p}{p + a}$$

To obtain the inverse transform of I, we use No. 7 of the table of transforms and Theorem (VII) (Chap. 6, Appendix). We thus obtain

(8.9)
$$
\begin{aligned}
i &= -aq_0 e^{-at} & 0 < t < t_1 \\
i &= -aq_0 e^{-at} + \frac{E_0}{R} e^{-at(t-t_1)} & t_1 < t < t_2 \\
i &= -aq_0 e^{-at} + \frac{E_0}{R} e^{-a(t-t_1)} - \frac{E_0}{R} e^{-a(t-t_2)} & t > t_2
\end{aligned}
$$

This example illustrates the general procedure.

9. Analysis of the General Network. In this section the analysis of a general n-mesh network will be considered. Given a network, we can draw n independent circulating currents so that they permit a different current in each branch of the network. We shall use the following notation:

  a. The Resistance Coefficients. R_{rs} is the resistance common to the i_r and i_s circuits. R_{rr} is the total resistance in the i_r circuit.

  b. The Inductance Coefficients. The inductance notation is complicated by the possibility of mutual inductance. If L_{rs}^1 is the total self-inductance common to i_r and i_s, and M_{rs} is the mutual inductance between the i_r and i_s circuits, then we define L_{rs} to be

(9.1)
$$L_{rs} = L_{rs}^1 \pm M_{rs}$$

The negative sign is used if M_{rs} opposes L_{rs}^1. We define L_{rr} as the *total self-inductance* in the i_r circuit.

  c. The Elastance Coefficients. In the circuits that we are considering, every capacitor will be traversed by one or more circulating currents.

For a given current, capacitors appear in series but not in parallel. It is convenient if we write the equations in terms of the elastance coefficients rather than in terms of the capacitance coefficients. The elastance coefficients are the reciprocals of the capacitance coefficients and are denoted by the symbol S.

Let us denote by S_{rs} the elastance common to the i_r and i_s circuits. We shall denote by S_{rr} the sum of the elastances in the i_r circuit.

The Reciprocity Relations. With the notations defined above, we have

$$(9.2) \qquad R_{rs} = R_{sr} \qquad L_{rs} = L_{sr} \qquad S_{rs} = S_{sr}$$

These coefficients are called the *mutual parameters* of the network, and S_{rr}, L_{rr}, and R_{rr} are called the *mesh parameters*.

The General Equations. The set of differential equations describing the behavior of the general n-mesh networks may be written conveniently if we introduce the operators

$$(9.3) \qquad Z_{rs}(D) = L_{rs}\frac{d}{dt} + R_{rs} + S_{rs}\int (\qquad)\,dt$$

$$= L_{rs}D + R_{rs} + \frac{S_{rs}}{D}$$

If now $(e_1, e_2, \ldots, e_n)$ denote the potentials impressed on the contours of the meshes $1, 2, \ldots, n$, and $(i_1, i_2, \ldots, i_n)$ are the mesh currents of the corresponding n meshes, we have

$$(9.4) \qquad \begin{aligned} Z_{11}(D)i_1 + Z_{12}(D)i_2 + \cdots + Z_{1n}(D)i_n &= e_1(t) \\ Z_{21}(D)i_1 + Z_{22}(D)i_2 + \cdots + Z_{2n}(D)i_n &= e_2(t) \\ \cdots\cdots\cdots\cdots\cdots\cdots\cdots\cdots\cdots\cdots\cdots \\ Z_{n1}(D)i + Z_{n2}(D)i + \cdots + Z_{nn}(D)i &= e_n(t) \end{aligned}$$

A concise form of these equations may be obtained by the use of matrix notation, as explained in Chap. 4. To do this, we introduce the following square matrices:

$$(9.5) \qquad [L] = \begin{bmatrix} L_{11} & L_{12} & \cdots & L_{1n} \\ L_{21} & L_{22} & \cdots & L_{2n} \\ \cdots & \cdots & \cdots & \cdots \\ L_{n1} & L_{n2} & \cdots & L_{nn} \end{bmatrix} \qquad [R] = \begin{bmatrix} R_{11} & R_{12} & \cdots & R_{1n} \\ R_{21} & R_{22} & \cdots & R_{2n} \\ \cdots & \cdots & \cdots & \cdots \\ R_{n1} & R_{n2} & \cdots & R_{nn} \end{bmatrix}$$

$$[S] = \begin{bmatrix} S_{11} & S_{12} & \cdots & S_{1n} \\ S_{21} & S_{22} & \cdots & S_{2n} \\ \cdots & \cdots & \cdots & \cdots \\ S_{n1} & S_{n2} & \cdots & S_{nn} \end{bmatrix}$$

In terms of these matrices we construct the square matrix $[Z(D)]$ by

$$(9.6) \qquad [Z(D)] = [L]D + [R] + \frac{[S]}{D}$$

We also introduce the column matrices

$$(9.7) \qquad \{e\} = \begin{Bmatrix} e_1 \\ e_2 \\ \cdot \\ \cdot \\ \cdot \\ e_n \end{Bmatrix} \qquad \{i\} = \begin{Bmatrix} i_1 \\ i_2 \\ \cdot \\ \cdot \\ \cdot \\ i_n \end{Bmatrix}$$

The set of differential equations (9.4) may then be written concisely in the form

$$(9.8) \qquad [Z(D)]\{i\} = \{e\}$$

In the usual network problem we are given the various mesh charges and mesh currents of the system at $t = 0$, and the various mesh potentials $(e_1 e_2 \cdots e_n)$ are assumed impressed on the system at $t = 0$. We desire to find the subsequent distribution of currents in the system.

Let us introduce a column matrix $\{E(p)\}$ whose elements are the transforms of the elements of the matrix $\{e\}$. That is,

$$(9.9) \qquad \mathcal{L}\{e\} = \{E(p)\}$$

In the same way introduce the column matrix $\{I(p)\}$.

$$(9.10) \qquad \{I(p)\} = \mathcal{L}\{i\}$$

If we now introduce the column matrices

$$(9.11) \qquad \{i^0\} = \begin{Bmatrix} i_1^0 \\ i_2^0 \\ i_3^0 \\ \cdot \\ \cdot \\ \cdot \\ i_n^0 \end{Bmatrix} \qquad \{q^0\} = \begin{Bmatrix} q_1^0 \\ q_2^0 \\ \cdot \\ \cdot \\ \cdot \\ q_n^0 \end{Bmatrix}$$

where $(i_1^0, i_2^0, \ldots, i_n^0)$ are the initial currents of the corresponding meshes of the system at $t = 0$ and $(q_1^0, q_2^0, \ldots, q_n^0)$ are the corresponding initial mesh charges of the system at $t = 0$, then the set of differential equations (9.8) transforms into

$$(9.12) \qquad [Z(p)]\{I\} = \{E(p)\} + p[L]\{i^0\} - [S]\{q^0\}$$

If we now premultiply both sides of this equation by the inverse matrix $[Z(p)]^{-1}$, we obtain

$$(9.13) \qquad I = [Z(p)]^{-1}\{E(p)\} + p[Z(p)]^{-1}[L]\{i^0\} - [Z(p)]^{-1}[S]\{q^0\}$$

We now obtain the various mesh currents from the equation

$$(9.14) \qquad \{i\} = L^{-1}\{I\}$$

This formally completes the solution of the problem. In general the above algebraic procedure will give the elements of the matrix I as the ratios of polynomials in p. The inverse transforms of these elements must be evaluated by using transform No. 52 of the table of transforms. The procedure involves the computation of the roots of the polynomial equation

$$(9.15) \qquad\qquad |Z(p)| = 0$$

In the general case this polynomial cannot be factored, and it is of the $2n$th degree. The roots may be determined by the Graeffe root-squaring method of Chap. 5.

If there are no initial mesh charges and mesh currents in the system, we have

$$(9.16) \qquad\qquad \{i^0\} = \{q^0\} = \{0\}$$

and we have

$$(9.17) \qquad\qquad \{I\} = [Z(p)]^{-1}\{E(p)\}$$

The solution in this case is that of a system initially at rest that has the potentials $\{e\}$ impressed on it at $t = 0$.

10. The Steady-state Solution. *Alternating Currents.* The equations of the last section give the complete solution of a system having initial charges and potentials and also impressed electromotive forces of arbitrary form at $t = 0$.

There is one case of extreme practical importance in electrical engineering. This is the case where it is desired to find the so-called "steady-state current distribution" when the various mesh electromotive forces have the form

$$(10.1) \qquad \{e\} = \begin{Bmatrix} E_1 \sin(\omega t + \phi_1) \\ E_2 \sin(\omega t + \phi_2) \\ E_3 \sin(\omega t + \phi_3) \\ \cdots\cdots\cdots \\ E_n \sin(\omega t + \phi_n) \end{Bmatrix} = \mathrm{Im} \begin{Bmatrix} E_1 e^{j\phi_1} \\ E_2 e^{j\phi_2} \\ E_3 e^{j\phi_3} \\ \cdots \\ E_n e^{j\phi_n} \end{Bmatrix} e^{j\omega t}$$

This is the case that occurs in alternating-current theory. For generality, we shall assume that the various mesh potentials have the same frequency but differ in phase. To determine the steady-state mesh currents, it is necessary to determine the particular integral of the set of equations

$$(10.1a) \qquad\qquad [Z(D)]\{i\} = \{e\}$$

It is convenient to write

$$(10.2) \qquad\qquad \{e\} = \mathrm{Im}\ \{e\}_a e^{j\omega t}$$

where Im denotes the "imaginary part of" and

$$(10.3) \qquad \{e\}_a = \begin{Bmatrix} E_1 e^{j\phi_1} \\ E_2 e^{j\phi_2} \\ \dots \\ E_n e^{j\phi_n} \end{Bmatrix}$$

$$(10.4) \qquad \{i\} = \mathrm{Im}\ \{I\}_a e^{j\omega t}$$

where $\{I\}_a$ is a column matrix whose elements are the unknown complex amplitudes of the steady-state currents to be determined by Eq. (10.1). Substituting (10.4) into (10.1) and suppressing the Im symbol, we obtain

$$(10.5) \qquad [Z(j\omega)]\{I\}_a = \{e\}_a$$

Hence we have

$$(10.6) \qquad \{I\}_a = [Z(j\omega)]^{-1}\{e\}_a$$

The steady-state currents are now given by (10.4). The elements of the column matrix $\{I\}_a$ are called the *complex currents* of the system. The above procedure is a generalization of the method of Sec. 4 for the single-mesh case. We have

$$(10.7) \qquad [Z(j\omega)] = j\omega[L] + [R] + \frac{[S]}{j\omega}$$

This is called the *impedance matrix*. The terms

$$(10.8) \qquad Z_{rr} = j\omega L_{rr} + R_{rr} + \frac{S_{rr}}{j\omega}$$

are called the *mesh impedances*, and the terms

$$(10.9) \qquad Z_{rs} = j\omega L_{rs} + R_{rs} + \frac{S_{rs}}{j\omega} \qquad r \neq s$$

$$= Z_{sr}$$

are called the *mutual impedances*.

11. Four-terminal Networks in the Alternating-current Steady State.
A special form of the general network discussed in Secs. 9 and 10 is one that has a pair of input and a pair of output terminals. It is customary to refer to such a network as a *four-terminal network* or a *two-terminal-pair network*.

FIG. 11.1. Four-terminal network.

A four-terminal network is illustrated schematically by Fig. 11.1 as a box with two pairs of terminals.

The reference directions for voltage and current will be taken as those shown in Fig. 11.1. The four-terminal network will be supposed to consist of an n-mesh network having two pairs of accessible terminals as shown. The potentials E_1 and E_2 are complex potentials produced by sources external to the network, and the currents I_1 and I_2 are the complex currents in the corresponding meshes. The internal structure of the four-terminal network will be assumed to be quite general, and the n meshes will be supposed to have impedances Z_{kk} and complex mutual impedances Z_{ks} between the meshes. The restrictions on the component elements of the network are that they be linear and constant. It is further assumed that the network is passive; that is, the only sources of electromotive force are E_1 and E_2 produced by external agencies. It can be shown that, as a consequence of the general equations (10.5), we have the following linear relations:

(11.1) $$E_1 = AE_2 + BI_2 \qquad I_1 = CE_2 + DI_2$$

The coefficients A, B, C, D of Eqs. (11.1) are called *general four-terminal-network parameters*. It can be seen that as a consequence of the form of (11.1) A and D are in general complex numbers and that B has the dimension of an impedance and C the dimension of an admittance, or reciprocal impedance. As a result of Eq. (10.9) it can be shown that the following relation between the network parameters exists:

(11.2) $$AD - BC = 1$$

For many purposes it is convenient to express the pair of equations (11.1) as the following matrix equation,

(11.3) $$\begin{bmatrix} E_1 \\ I_1 \end{bmatrix} = \begin{bmatrix} A & B \\ C & D \end{bmatrix} \begin{bmatrix} E_2 \\ I_2 \end{bmatrix} = [T] \begin{bmatrix} E_2 \\ I_2 \end{bmatrix}$$

where $[T]$ is the square matrix

(11.4) $$[T] = \begin{bmatrix} A & B \\ C & D \end{bmatrix}$$

The square matrix $[T]$ is usually called the *transmission matrix* of the network. The determinant of $[T]$ is equal to unity as a consequence of the relation (11.2). The transmission matrix $[T]$ has the following inverse:

(11.5) $$[T]^{-1} = \begin{bmatrix} D & -B \\ -C & A \end{bmatrix}$$

Fig. 11.2. Four-terminal networks in cascade.

If two four-terminal networks of transmission matrices T_1, T_2 are connected in cascade as shown in Fig. 11.2, then the over-all relations between the input and output quantities are given by

(11.6) $$\begin{bmatrix} E_1 \\ I_1 \end{bmatrix} = [T]_1[T]_2 \begin{bmatrix} E_2 \\ I_2 \end{bmatrix} = [T] \begin{bmatrix} E_2 \\ I_2 \end{bmatrix}$$

where $[T]$ is the transmission matrix of the over-all network. It is given by

$$(11.7) \quad [T] = [T]_1[T]_2 = \begin{bmatrix} A_1 & B_1 \\ C_1 & D_1 \end{bmatrix} \begin{bmatrix} A_2 & B_2 \\ C_2 & D_2 \end{bmatrix}$$

$$= \begin{bmatrix} A_1A_2 + B_1C_2 & A_1B_2 + B_1D_2 \\ C_1A_2 + D_1C_2 & C_1B_2 + D_1D_2 \end{bmatrix}$$

It is thus seen that, in the cascade connection of several four-terminal networks, the over-all transmission matrix of the network is the matrix product of the transmission matrices of the individual networks taken in the order of connection. If a four-terminal network is *symmetrical* so that its input and output terminals may be interchanged without altering the current and potential distribution of the network, it may be shown that its transmission matrix has the property that $A = D$.

If the transmission matrices of several fundamental types of electrical circuits are known, then by matrix multiplication it is easy to obtain many useful properties of more complex structures formed by a cascade connection of fundamental circuits. The transmission matrices $[T]$ of several basic electrical circuits are listed in Table 1.

Wave Propagation along a Cascade of Symmetrical Structures. Many important problems of electrical-circuit theory such as those involving

FIG. 11.3. Cascade of four-terminal structures.

electric filters, delay lines, and transducers involve the determination of the nature of the current and potential distribution along a chain of identical symmetric four-terminal networks. Consider the cascade of n identical four-terminal networks as shown in Fig. 11.3. Let each of the four-terminal networks be a symmetrical one with the following transmission matrix:

$$(11.8) \qquad\qquad [T] = \begin{bmatrix} A & B \\ C & A \end{bmatrix}$$

Since each of the structures of the chain has the same matrix, the output potential and current E_n and I_n of the nth structure are related to the input potential and current E_0 and I_0 of the first structure by the following equation:

$$(11.9) \qquad\qquad \begin{bmatrix} E_0 \\ I_0 \end{bmatrix} = \begin{bmatrix} A & B \\ C & A \end{bmatrix}^n \begin{bmatrix} E_n \\ I_n \end{bmatrix}$$

In order to obtain a form for the transmission matrix $[T]$ that is convenient for computing powers of $[T]$, introduce the new variables a and

TABLE 1. TRANSMISSION MATRICES OF FUNDAMENTAL
FOUR-TERMINAL STRUCTURES

No.	Network	Transmission matrix $\begin{bmatrix} A & B \\ C & D \end{bmatrix} = [T]$
1	Series impedance	$\begin{bmatrix} 1 & Z \\ 0 & 1 \end{bmatrix}$
2	Shunt admittance	$\begin{bmatrix} 1 & 0 \\ Y & 1 \end{bmatrix}$
3	Coupled circuits	$\begin{bmatrix} \dfrac{L_1}{M} & \dfrac{jw(L_1L_2 - M^2)}{M} \\ \dfrac{-j}{wM} & \dfrac{L_2}{M} \end{bmatrix}$
4	Ideal transformer $a = \dfrac{N_1}{N_2}$	$\begin{bmatrix} \dfrac{1}{a} & 0 \\ 0 & a \end{bmatrix}$
5		$\begin{bmatrix} 1 & Z \\ Y & 1 + YZ \end{bmatrix}$
6		$\begin{bmatrix} 1 + YZ & Z \\ Y & 1 \end{bmatrix}$

TABLE 1. TRANSMISSION MATRICES OF FUNDAMENTAL
FOUR-TERMINAL STRUCTURES (*Continued*)

No.	Network	Transmission matrix $\begin{bmatrix} A & B \\ C & D \end{bmatrix} = [T]$
7	T section	$\begin{bmatrix} 1 + YZ_1 & Z_1 + Z_2 + YZ_1Z_2 \\ Y & 1 + YZ_2 \end{bmatrix}$
8	π section	$\begin{bmatrix} 1 + ZY_2 & Z \\ Y_1 + Y_2 + ZY_1Y_2 & 1 + ZY_1 \end{bmatrix}$
9	$\longleftarrow S \longrightarrow$ Transmission line	$\begin{bmatrix} \cosh aS & Z_0 \sinh aS \\ \dfrac{\sinh aS}{Z_0} & \cosh aS \end{bmatrix}$ where a = propagation function Z_0 = characteristic impedance S = length of line
10	Cascade of symmetrical identical networks Matrix of individual networks $\begin{bmatrix} A & B \\ C & A \end{bmatrix}$	Over-all matrix of n networks $\begin{bmatrix} \cosh an & Z \sinh an \\ \dfrac{\sinh an}{Z_0} & \cosh an \end{bmatrix}$ where $a = \cosh^{-1} A$ = propagation function $Z_0 = \sqrt{\dfrac{B}{C}}$ = characteristic impedance

Z_0 by the equations

(11.10)
$$a = \cosh^{-1} A$$

and

(11.11)
$$Z_0 = \left(\frac{B}{C} \right)^{\frac{1}{2}}$$

With this notation the transmission matrix $[T]$ takes the following form:

$$(11.12) \qquad [T] = \begin{bmatrix} A & B \\ C & A \end{bmatrix} = \begin{bmatrix} \cosh a & Z_0 \sinh a \\ \dfrac{\sinh a}{Z_0} & \cosh a \end{bmatrix}$$

If the matrix $[T]$ is multiplied by itself, the following result is obtained:

$$(11.13) \quad [T][T] = [T]^2 = \begin{bmatrix} \sinh^2 a + \cosh^2 a & Z_0(2 \sinh a \cosh a) \\ \dfrac{2 \sinh a \cosh a}{Z_0} & \sinh^2 a + \cosh^2 a \end{bmatrix}$$

$$= \begin{bmatrix} \cosh 2a & Z_0 \sinh 2a \\ \dfrac{\sinh 2a}{Z_0} & \cosh 2a \end{bmatrix}$$

Similarly, by direct multiplication and by the use of the identities of hyperbolic trigonometry, it can be shown that

$$(11.14) \quad [T]^r = \begin{bmatrix} \cosh ra & Z_0 \sinh ra \\ \dfrac{\sinh ra}{Z_0} & \cosh ra \end{bmatrix} \qquad r = 0, \pm 1, \pm 2, \pm 3, \ldots$$

The result (11.14) is very useful in the study of the behavior of four-terminal networks and associated structures. By means of (11.14) Eq. (11.9) may be written in the form

$$(11.15) \qquad \begin{bmatrix} E_0 \\ I_0 \end{bmatrix} = \begin{bmatrix} \cosh an & Z_0 \sinh an \\ \dfrac{\sinh an}{Z_0} & \cosh an \end{bmatrix} \begin{bmatrix} E_n \\ I_n \end{bmatrix}$$

or

$$(11.16) \qquad \begin{bmatrix} E_n \\ I_n \end{bmatrix} = \begin{bmatrix} \cosh an & -Z_0 \sinh an \\ \dfrac{-\sinh an}{Z_0} & \cosh an \end{bmatrix} \begin{bmatrix} E_0 \\ I_0 \end{bmatrix}$$

The potential E_k and the current I_k along the chain of four-terminal structures of Fig. 11.3 are given by the equation

$$(11.17) \qquad \begin{bmatrix} E_k \\ I_k \end{bmatrix} = \begin{bmatrix} \cosh ak & -Z_0 \sinh ak \\ \dfrac{-\sinh ak}{Z_0} & \cosh ak \end{bmatrix} \begin{bmatrix} E_0 \\ I_0 \end{bmatrix}$$

If the chain of four-terminal networks is terminated by an impedance equal to Z_0, then

$$(11.18) \qquad I_n = \frac{E_n}{Z_0}$$

Then the impedance Z_i looking into the chain of structures may be obtained from (11.15) in the form

$$(11.19) \qquad Z_i = \frac{E_0}{I_0} = \frac{E_n \cosh an + Z_0 I_n \sinh an}{(E_n/Z_0) \sinh an + I_n \cosh an} = Z_0$$

The quantity Z_0 is called the *characteristic impedance* of the chain of four-terminal networks. Hence, if the cascade of networks is terminated by the characteristic impedance Z_0, the impedance Z_i looking into the cascade is also equal to the characteristic impedance. In this case the input current of the chain is

$$(11.20) \qquad I_0 = \frac{E_0}{Z_0}$$

The potential and currents along the cascade may be obtained by the use of (11.17) if I_0 is eliminated by (11.20). The results are

$$(11.21) \quad E_k = E_0 e^{-ak} \qquad I_k = \frac{E_0}{Z_0} e^{-ak} \qquad k = 0, 1, 2, 3, \ldots, n$$

The quantity a is the *propagation function* of the chain of four-terminal structures of Fig. 11.3.

Attenuation and Passbands. In general the propagation function a is a complex function of the angular frequency ω. It has the form

$$(11.22) \qquad a = \alpha + j\beta$$

The quantity α is called the *attenuation function*, and β is the *phase function* of the cascade. β gives the change of phase per section as one progresses along the cascade. If the cascade of four-terminal networks is to pass a certain band of frequencies without attenuation, the real part of the propagation function must be zero and hence the propagation function a must be a pure imaginary quantity. Therefore for a *passband* it is necessary that

$$(11.23) \qquad \alpha = 0 \qquad a = j\beta$$

The relation (11.10) is then

$$(11.24) \qquad \cosh a = \cosh j\beta = \cos \beta = A$$

It follows that the network constant A of the fundamental four-terminal network of the cascade must satisfy the two following conditions for a *passband*,

$$(11.25) \qquad A = \cos \beta = \text{real}$$

and since $\cos \beta$ can vary only between -1 and $+1$, the following inequality must be satisfied:

$$(11.26) \qquad |A| \leqq 1$$

A very important class of circuits are those which are devoid of resistance. Circuits of this class are called *dissipationless* circuits. It can be shown that the parameter A is a real number if the fundamental circuit in the box is dissipationless so that (11.25) is always satisfied for circuits of this class. If the inequality (11.26) is satisfied, the cascade passes currents and potentials without attenuation. If the inequality is not satisfied, the currents and potentials are attenuated along the cascade. In general the parameter A is a function $A(\omega)$ of the angular frequency of the applied alternating potential. The ranges in frequencies that are attenuated or passed without attenuation may be determined by the use of the inequality (11.26). This relation is fundamental in the theory of electrical filter circuits.

12. The Transmission Line as a Four-terminal Network. A very important type of circuit is the transmission line shown schematically in Fig. 12.1.

Fig. 12.1. Transmission line.

This figure depicts a two-wire transmission line. In the alternating steady state this transmission line may be regarded as a continuous distribution of series impedance Z and shunt admittance Y per unit length, defined by the equations

$$(12.1) \qquad Z = R + j\omega L \qquad Y = G + j\omega C$$

where R is the resistance of the line per unit length, L the inductance per unit length, C the capacitance per unit length, and G the leakage conductance per unit length.

Consider a length dx of the transmission line at a distance x from the sending end as shown in Fig. 12.1. This length of line contains a shunt admittance $Y\,dx$ and a series impedance $Z\,dx$. Let dI be the complex current that flows from one conductor to the other through the admittance $Y\,dx$, and let dE be the change in the complex potential difference between the conductors caused by the current $I(x)$ flowing in the impedance $Z\,dx$. If higher-order infinitesimals are neglected, it is seen that, by an application of Kirchhoff's laws to a section of the line of length dx, we obtain the following equations:

$$(12.2) \qquad dI = -EY\,dx \qquad dE = -IZ\,dx$$

The complex current $I(x)$ and the complex potential $E(x)$ therefore satisfy the following two differential equations:

$$(12.3) \qquad \frac{dI}{dx} = -YE \qquad \frac{dE}{dx} = -ZI$$

If these two simultaneous first-order differential equations are solved subject to the boundary conditions that $E = E_1$ and $I = I_1$ at $x = 0$, the result is

$$E(x) = E_1 \cosh ax - I_1 Z_0 \sinh ax$$
$$(12.4) \qquad I(x) = \frac{-E_1}{Z_0} \sinh ax + I_1 \cosh ax$$

where

$$(12.5) \qquad a = (ZY)^{\frac{1}{2}} = [(R + j\omega L)(G + j\omega C)]^{\frac{1}{2}} = \alpha + j\beta$$

and

$$(12.6) \qquad Z_0 = \left(\frac{Z}{Y}\right)^{\frac{1}{2}} = \left(\frac{R + j\omega L}{G + j\omega C}\right)^{\frac{1}{2}}$$

The quantity a is the *propagation function* of the line. The real part of a, α, is the *attenuation function*, and the imaginary part of a, β, is the *phase function* of the line. The impedance Z_0 is the *characteristic impedance* of the line.

If S is the length of the line and I_2 and E_2 the output complex current and potential of the line, Eqs. (12.4) yield the following values for E_2 and I_2:

$$E(S) = E_2 = E_1 \cosh aS - I_1 Z_0 \sinh aS$$
$$(12.7) \qquad I(S) = I_2 = - \frac{E_1}{Z_0} \sinh aS + I_1 \cosh aS$$

The two equations (12.7) may be written in the convenient matrix form

$$(12.8) \qquad \begin{bmatrix} E_2 \\ I_2 \end{bmatrix} = \begin{bmatrix} \cosh \theta & -Z_0 \sinh \theta \\ \dfrac{-\sinh \theta}{Z_0} & \cosh \theta \end{bmatrix} \begin{bmatrix} E_1 \\ I_2 \end{bmatrix} \qquad \theta = aS$$

Equation (12.8) may also be written in the alternative form

$$(12.9) \qquad \begin{bmatrix} E_1 \\ I_1 \end{bmatrix} = \begin{bmatrix} \cosh \theta & Z_0 \sinh \theta \\ \dfrac{\sinh \theta}{Z_0} & \cosh \theta \end{bmatrix} \begin{bmatrix} E_2 \\ I_2 \end{bmatrix}$$

It is thus evident from (12.9) that the transmission matrix of the two-wire line of Fig. 12.1 is given by

$$(12.10) \qquad [T] = \begin{bmatrix} \cosh \theta & Z_0 \sinh \theta \\ \dfrac{\sinh \theta}{Z_0} & \cosh \theta \end{bmatrix}$$

This matrix has the following inverse:

$$(12.11) \qquad [T]^{-1} = \begin{bmatrix} \cosh \theta & -Z_0 \sinh \theta \\ \dfrac{-\sinh \theta}{Z_0} & \cosh \theta \end{bmatrix}$$

Calculations involving transmission lines may be greatly simplified by the use of the matrices (12.10) and (12.11). The quantity $\theta = aS$ is called the *angle of the line* and is, in general, a complex number. As an example of the use of the transmission matrix $[T]$, consider a transmission line short-circuited at the end $x = S$. In this case $E_2 = 0$, and from Eq. (12.9) we have the relation

$$(12.12) \qquad E_1 = I_2 Z_0 \sinh \theta$$

Hence the current at the short-circuited end is given by the equation

$$(12.13) \qquad I_2 = \frac{E_1}{Z_0 \sinh \theta}$$

If, on the other hand, the end $x = S$ is open-circuited, $I_2 = 0$ and (12.9) gives $E_2 = E_1/\cosh \theta$ for the open-circuit potential.

PROBLEMS

1. What is the analogous electrical circuit for a mechanical pendulum that is subjected to very small displacements?

2. A circuit consisting of an inductance L in series with a capacitance C has impressed on it at $t = 0$ a potential $e(t) = E_0 t/T_0$ $(0 < t < T_0)$ and $e(t) = 0$, $t > T_0$. Find the current in the system.

3. Two circuits are coupled with a mutual inductance M. One contains an impressed potential E_0, R, L_1, and a switch in series; the other circuit has L_2 and C in series. For what value of the circuit constants are oscillations possible?

4. Each side of an equilateral triangular circuit contains a capacitance C, and each vertex is connected to a common central point by an inductance L. Show that the possible oscillations of this circuit have the period $T = 2\pi \sqrt{3LC}$.

5. Two points are connected by three branches, two of which contain both a capacitance C and an inductance L, and the third only a capacitance C. Show that the angular frequencies of oscillation of the network are $1/\sqrt{LC}$ and $\sqrt{3/LC}$.

6. Two circuits L_1, R_1 and L_2, R_2 are coupled by a mutual inductance M, where $M^2 = L_1 L_2$. A constant electromotive force E is applied at $t = 0$ in the primary circuit. The initial currents are zero. Determine the currents in the circuits.

7. An electromotive force $E \cos (\omega t + \theta)$ is applied at $t = 0$ to a circuit consisting of capacitance C and inductance L in series. The initial charge and current are zero. Find the current at time t.

8. An electromotive force $E \sin \omega t$, where $\omega = 1/\sqrt{LC}$, is applied at $t = 0$ to a circuit consisting of capacitance C and inductance L in series. The initial current and charge are zero. Find the current. (This is the case of resonance.)

9. Show that a combination of capacitance C shunted by resistance R in series with a combination of inductance L shunted by resistance R behaves as a pure resistance for all forms of applied electromotive force if $L = CR^2$.

10. Two resistanceless circuits L_1, C_1 and L_2, C_2 are coupled by mutual inductance M. If at $t = 0$, when the currents and charges are zero, a battery of electromotive force E_0 is applied in the primary, find the current in the secondary.

11. A circuit consists of a resistance, an inductance, and a capacitance in series. An electromotive force $e = E_1 \cos \omega_1 t + E_2 \cos \omega_2 t$ is impressed on the circuit. Find the steady-state current.

12. A series circuit consisting of an inductance capacitance and resistance has an electromotive force $e(t)$ of the "meander" type, as shown in the figure, impressed on it. Find the steady-state current.

FIG. P 12

13. Two transmission lines of series impedances Z_1 and Z_2 per length and shunt admittances Y_1 and Y_2 are connected in cascade. The transmission lines have lengths S_1 and S_2, respectively. Find the over-all transmission matrix of the combination. The receiving end of the second transmission line is short-circuited. Find the current at this end in terms of the complex potential applied to the sending end of the first transmission line.

14. A circuit is composed of a cascade connection of n four-terminal networks. All the four-terminal networks of the cascade are identical and contain the structure

FIG. P 14

shown in Fig. P 14. Obtain the over-all transmission matrix of the cascade, and determine the range in ω that gives the passband and the stopband.

15. The same as Prob. 14 for the case in which all four-terminal networks contain the structure shown in Fig. P 15.

FIG. P 15

16. The cascade of four-terminal networks of Prob. 14 is short-circuited at the receiving end. A potential $E_0 \sin \omega t$ is impressed at the sending end of the cascade. Determine the instantaneous value of the receiving current when ω lies in a stopband and when ω lies in a passband.

REFERENCES

1. Berg, E. J.: "Heaviside's Operational Calculus," McGraw-Hill Book Company, Inc., New York, 1929.
2. Bush, V.: "Operational Circuit Analysis," John Wiley & Sons, Inc., New York, 1929.
3. Carson, J. R.: "Electric Circuit Theory and the Operational Calculus," McGraw-Hill Book Company, Inc., New York, 1920.
4. Pierce, G. W.: "Electric Oscillations and Electric Waves," McGraw-Hill Book Company, Inc., New York, 1920.
5. Guillemin, E. A.: "Communication Networks," John Wiley & Sons, Inc., New York, 1931.
6. Pipes, L. A.: The Operational Calculus, *Journal of Applied Physics*, vol. 10, 1939.
7. Kerchner, R. M., and F. Corcoran: "Alternating Current Circuits," John Wiley & Sons, Inc., New York, 1943.
8. Bode, H. W.: "Network Analysis and Feedback Amplifier Design," D. Van Nostrand Company, Inc., Princeton, N.J., 1945.
9. Josephs, H. J.: "Heaviside's Electric Circuit Theory," John Wiley & Sons, Inc., New York, 1946.
10. Jackson, L. S.: "Wave Filters," John Wiley & Sons, Inc., New York, 1943.
11. LePage, W., and S. Seely: "General Network Analysis," McGraw-Hill Book Company, Inc., New York, 1952.
12. Pipes, L. A.: The Matrix Theory of Four-terminal Networks, *Philosophical Magazine*, ser. 7, vol. 30, pp. 370–395, November, 1940.
13. Institute of Radio Engineers: *Transactions on Circuit Theory*, vol. CT-2, no. 2, June, 1955.

CHAPTER 8

VIBRATIONS OF ELASTIC SYSTEMS WITH A FINITE
NUMBER OF DEGREES OF FREEDOM

1. Introduction. One of the most important and interesting subjects of applied mathematics is the theory of small oscillations of mechanical systems in the neighborhood of an equilibrium position or a state of uniform motion. In the last chapter we considered the oscillations of a very important vibrating system, the electrical circuit. By the analogy between electrical and mechanical systems all the methods discussed in the last chapter may be used in the analysis of mechanical systems. In the mechanical system we are usually concerned with the determination of the natural frequencies and modes of oscillation rather than the complete solution for the amplitudes subject to the initial conditions of the system. In this chapter we shall use the classical method of solution rather than the Laplace-transform method. By comparing the analysis of the equivalent electrical circuits of the last chapter which were analyzed by the Laplacian-transformation method and the classical analysis of the mechanical systems in this chapter, a proper perspective of the utility of the two methods will be apparent.

2. Oscillating Systems with One Degree of Freedom. Let us consider the vibrating systems of Fig. 2.1. System a represents a mass that

$$(a) \qquad\qquad (b) \qquad\qquad (c)$$

Fig. 2.1

is constrained to move in a linear path. It is attached to a spring of spring constant k and is acted upon by a dashpot mechanism that introduces a frictional constraint proportional to the velocity of the mass. The mass has exerted upon it an external force $P_0 \sin \omega t$. By Newton's law we have

$$(2.1) \qquad M\ddot{x} = -Kx - R\dot{x} + P_0 \sin \omega t \qquad \begin{cases} \dot{x} = \dfrac{dx}{dt} \\[2mm] \ddot{x} = \dfrac{d^2x}{dt^2} \end{cases}$$

where K is the spring constant and R is the friction coefficient of the dashpot.

System b represents a system undergoing torsional oscillations. It consists of a massive disk of moment of inertia J attached to a shaft of torsional stiffness K. The disk undergoes torsional damping proportional to its angular velocity $\dot{\theta}$. The disk has exerted upon it an oscillatory torque $T_0 \sin \omega t$. By Newton's law we have

$$(2.2) \qquad J\ddot{\theta} = -K\theta - R\dot{\theta} + T_0 \sin \omega t$$

System c is a series electrical circuit having inductance, resistance, and elastance. By Kirchhoff's law the equation satisfied by the mesh charge q is

$$(2.3) \qquad L\ddot{q} + R\dot{q} + Sq = E_0 \sin \omega t$$

By comparing these three equations, we obtain the following table of analogues:

Linear		Torsional		Electrical	
Mass	M	Moment of inertia	J	Inductance	L
Stiffness	K	Torsional stiffness	K	Elastance	$S = 1/C$
Damping	R	Torsional damping	R	Resistance	R
Impressed force	$F_0 \sin \omega t$	Impressed torque $T_0 \sin \omega t$		Impressed potential	
					$E_0 \sin \omega t$
Displacement	x	Angular displacement	θ	Capacitor charge	q
Velocity	$\dot{x} = v$	Angular velocity	$\dot{\theta} = \omega$	Current	$i = \dot{q}$

We see from this table of analogues that it is necessary only for us to analyze one system and then by means of the table we may obtain the corresponding solution for the others.

Free Vibrations. Let us consider the system a when no impressed force is present. In this case, Eq. (2.1) reduces to

$$(2.4) \qquad M\ddot{x} + Rx + Kx = 0$$

This equation describes the free vibrations of the mass of Fig. 2.1. To find the general solution of (2.4), we find two nontrivial solutions. An arbitrary linear combination of the two particular solutions will then be the desired solution.

Since Eq. (2.4) is linear and homogeneous, we know from the general theory of Chap. 6 that we can obtain a particular solution of the form e^{st}, where s is a constant to be determined. If we substitute e^{st} for x in (2.4) and divide out the factor e^{st}, we obtain the quadratic equation

$$(2.5) \qquad\qquad Ms^2 + Rs + K = 0$$

This equation determines the quantity s. Let us denote the two roots of the quadratic equation (2.5) by s_1 and s_2. We then have

$$(2.6) \qquad\qquad x = c_1 e^{s_1 t} + c_2 e^{s_2 t}$$

for the general solution of (2.5), where c_1 and c_2 are arbitrary constants. The nature of the solution depends on the nature of the roots. There are three cases to consider.

a. *The Case* $R^2 - 4MK > 0$. In this case s_1 and s_2 are real and unequal. The general solution is

$$(2.7) \qquad\qquad x = c_1 e^{s_1 t} + c_2 e^{s_2 t}$$

Both roots are negative, and (2.7) represents a disturbance that vanishes as t approaches infinity.

b. *The Case* $R^2 - 4MK = 0$. In this case the quadratic equation (2.5) has a double root

$$(2.8) \qquad\qquad s_1 = s_2 = \frac{-R}{2M}$$

Thus $c_1 e^{(-R/2M)t}$ is the only solution obtainable from (2.5). However, the general theory of repeated roots as discussed in Chap. 6 shows that there exists a second solution of the form $x = t e^{(-R/2M)t}$. The general solution is therefore

$$(2.9) \qquad\qquad x = (c_1 + c_2 t) e^{(-R/2M)t}$$

In both these cases we have the so-called "aperiodic motion." As time increases, the displacement of the mass approaches zero asymptotically without oscillating about $x = 0$. This means that the effect of damping is so great that it prevents the elastic force from setting up oscillatory motions.

c. *The Case* $R^2 - 4MK < 0$. In this case, the roots s_1 and s_2 are complex conjugates. If we let

$$(2.10) \qquad\qquad \omega_s^2 = \frac{K}{M} - \frac{R^2}{4M^2}$$

we may write the general solution in the form

$$(2.11) \qquad x = c_1 e^{s_1 t} + c_2 e^{s_2 t} = e^{(-R/2M)t}(c_1 e^{j\omega t} + c_2 e^{-j\omega_s t})$$

By using the Euler relation, this becomes

(2.12) $$x = e^{(-R/2M)t}(c_1' \cos \omega_s t + c_2' \sin \omega_s t)$$

where c_1' and c_2' are two new arbitrary constants. If we let

(2.13) $$c_1' = A \cos \omega_s \delta \quad \text{and} \quad c_2' = A \sin \omega_s \delta$$

where A and δ are two new arbitrary constants, then (2.12) becomes

(2.14) $$x = A e^{(-R/2M)t} \cos \omega_s (t - \delta)$$

The constant A is called the *amplitude of the motion*, and $\omega_s \delta$ is called the *phase*.

(2.15) $$\omega_s = \sqrt{\frac{K}{M} - \frac{R^2}{4M^2}}$$

is called the *angular frequency of the motion*. The motion represented by (2.14) is quite different from the aperiodic motion discussed in cases a and b. In this case the damping is small compared with the elastic force, and the motion of the mass is oscillatory. The damping is not so small as to be considered negligible. The motion is one of damped harmonic oscillations. The oscillations behave like cosine waves with an angular frequency of ω_s except that the maximum value of the displacement attained with each oscillation is not constant. The "amplitude" is given by the expression $A e^{(-R/2M)t}$ and decreases exponentially as t increases.

The quantity $R/2M$ is called the *logarithmic decrement*. It indicates that the logarithm of the maximum displacement decreases at the rate $R/2M$. If there is no damping present ($R = 0$), we obtain harmonic oscillations with natural angular frequency

(2.16) $$\omega_0 = \sqrt{\frac{K}{M}}$$

The amplitude A and the phase $\omega \delta$ must be determined from the initial state of the system.

If, for example,

(2.17) $$\left. \begin{array}{l} x = 0 \\ \dot{x} = \dot{x}_0 \end{array} \right\} \quad \text{at } t = 0$$

then

(2.18) $$x = \frac{\dot{x}_0}{\omega_s} e^{-Rt/2M} \sin \omega_s t$$

is the particular solution.

Forced Oscillations. If an external force $F(t)$ is impressed upon the physical system a above, the equation governing the displacement x of the mass is given by

(2.19) $$M\ddot{x} + R\dot{x} + Kx = F(t)$$

From the general theory of Chap. 6 we know that the general solution of (2.19) is the superposition of the general solution of the homogeneous equation (2.4) and the particular solution of (2.19). Let the force $F(t)$ be a periodic force of the form

$$(2.20) \qquad F_0 e^{j\omega t} = F_0 \cos \omega t + jF_0 \sin \omega t$$
$$= F(t)$$

Accordingly we have

$$(2.21) \qquad M\ddot{x} + R\dot{x} + Kx = F_0 e^{j\omega t}$$

Since this equation is linear, we attempt to find a solution of the form

$$(2.22) \qquad x = A e^{j\omega t}$$

We realize that the real part of the solution corresponds to the force function $F_0 \cos \omega t$ and the imaginary part to the force function $F_0 \sin \omega t$. Substituting the assumed form of the solution in Eq. (2.21), we obtain

$$(2.23) \qquad -M\omega^2 A + jR\omega A + KA = F_0$$

or

$$(2.24) \qquad A = \frac{F_0}{K - M\omega^2 + jR\omega}$$

The complex number

$$(2.25) \qquad Z = K - M\omega^2 + jR\omega$$

may be written in the polar form

$$(2.26) \qquad Z = |Z| e^{j\theta}$$

where

$$(2.27) \qquad |Z| = \sqrt{(K - M\omega^2)^2 + R^2\omega^2}$$
$$\theta = \tan^{-1} \frac{R\omega}{K - M\omega^2}$$

We then have

$$(2.28) \qquad A = \frac{F_0}{|Z|} e^{-j\theta}$$

Substituting this into Eq. (2.22), we have

$$(2.29) \qquad x = \frac{F_0}{|Z|} e^{j(\omega t - \theta)}$$

The physical meaning of this solution is that if a force of the form $F_0 \cos \omega t$ is impressed on the vibrating system the resulting steady-state motion is given by

$$(2.30) \qquad x = \frac{F_0}{|Z|} \cos (\omega t - \theta)$$

If a force $F_0 \sin \omega t$ is impressed on the system, then the steady-state response is

$$(2.31) \qquad x = \frac{F_0}{|Z|} \sin (\omega t - \theta)$$

The complex number Z is called the *mechanical impedance* of the system. It is a generalization of the spring constant to the case of oscillatory motion.

It is convenient to introduce the quantity μ, defined by

$$(2.32) \qquad \mu = \frac{1}{|Z|}$$

μ is called the *distortion factor*. The angle θ is the phase displacement. The solution (2.29) may be written in the form

$$(2.33) \qquad x = F_0 \mu e^{j(\omega t - \theta)}$$

We see that the resulting steady-state motion is given by a function of the same type as that of the impressed force. However, it differs from it in amplitude by the factor μ and in phase by the angle θ. The solution (2.33) represents the steady-state asymptotic motion after the superimposed free vibrations which are damped have disappeared.

The general solution is of the form

$$(2.34) \qquad x = A e^{-Rt/2M} \cos \omega_s(t - \delta) + F_0 \mu e^{j(\omega t - \theta)}$$

If the initial conditions at $t = 0$ are given, the arbitrary constants A and δ may be determined.

The Case of General Periodic External Forces. A very important case in practice is the one in which the impressed external force is periodic of fundamental period T. That is,

$$(2.35) \qquad F(t + T) = F(t)$$

In this case we may express $F(t)$ in the complex Fourier series

$$(2.36) \qquad F(t) = \sum_{n=-\infty}^{n=+\infty} c_n e^{jn\omega t} \qquad \omega = \frac{2\pi}{T}$$

as explained in Chap. 3.

The coefficients c_n are given by

$$(2.37) \qquad c_n = \frac{1}{T} \int_0^T F(t) e^{-jn\omega t} \, dt$$

To determine the response in this case, we assume a solution of the form

$$(2.38) \qquad z = \sum_{n=-\infty}^{n=+\infty} a_n e^{jn\omega t}$$

On substituting this assumed form of solution and equating the coefficients of the term $e^{jn\omega t}$, we obtain

(2.39)
$$a_n = \frac{c_n}{Z_n}$$

where

(2.40)
$$Z_n = K - Mn^2\omega^2 + jRn\omega$$

This may be written in the polar form

(2.41)
$$Z_n = |Z_n|e^{j\theta_n}$$

where

(2.42) $|Z_n| = \sqrt{(K - Mn^2\omega^2)^2 + R^2n^2\omega^2}$ $\theta_n = \tan^{-1}\dfrac{Rn\omega}{K - Mn^2\omega^2}$

If we write

(2.43)
$$\mu_n = \frac{1}{|Z_n|}$$

then we have

(2.44)
$$a_n = c_n\mu_n e^{-j\theta_n}$$

Substituting this into (2.38), we obtain

(2.45)
$$x = \sum_{n=-\infty}^{n=+\infty} c_n\mu_n e^{j(n\omega t - \theta_n)}$$

This represents the steady-state response to the general external periodic force $F(t)$. In this case the general harmonic n is magnified by the distortion factor μ_n. Equation (2.45) is of extreme importance in the theory of recording instruments. If the parameters M, K, and R are adjusted so that the μ_n's are as large as possible, then the apparatus is as sensitive as possible. If for the various frequencies $n\omega$ the μ_n's have approximately the same value, then there is a minimum amount of distortion. The phase displacements θ_n are of secondary importance in acoustical instruments since they are imperceptible to the human ear.

Resonance Phenomena. If we study the distortion factor μ of Eq. (2.32) as a function of the frequency ω, that is, if we write

(2.46)
$$\mu = \frac{1}{|Z|} = \mu(\omega)$$

we notice that

(2.47)
$$\lim_{\omega \to \infty} \mu(\omega) = 0$$

(2.48)
$$\lim_{\omega \to 0} \mu(\omega) = \frac{1}{K}$$

That is, if we impress on the system a force of very high frequency, the amplitude of vibration tends to zero. If we apply a steady force, the motion is of constant magnitude F_0/K.

Between $\omega = 0$ and $\omega = \infty$ there is a value where $\mu(\omega)$ has a maximum value. If we place

$$(2.49) \qquad \frac{d}{d\omega}\,\mu(\omega) = 0$$

we obtain

$$(2.50) \qquad 2M^2\omega^2 = 2MK - R^2$$

If we let ω_r be the value of ω that satisfies this equation, we have

$$(2.51) \qquad \omega_r = \sqrt{\frac{K}{M} - \frac{R^2}{2M^2}}$$

This value of ω_r makes $\mu(\omega)$ a maximum. If there is no friction, $R = 0$ and the above analysis fails. In this case the equation of motion is

$$(2.52) \qquad M\ddot{x} + Kx = F_0 e^{j\omega t}$$

If

$$(2.53) \qquad \omega = \sqrt{\frac{K}{M}} = \omega_0$$

this equation has the particular solution

$$(2.54) \qquad x = \frac{F_0 t e^{j\omega t}}{2jM\omega} = \frac{F_0 t e^{j\omega t}}{2j\sqrt{KM}}$$

We then see that in this case if the impressed force coincides with the natural frequency of the system, ω_0, then the amplitude increases without limit as t increases. If friction is present, $\mu(\omega)$ is always finite and has its maximum value when $\omega = \omega_r$. In the literature the frequency ω_r is called the *resonance frequency* of the system.

3. Two Degrees of Freedom. The system considered in the above section consisted of a mass restrained to move in a linear manner, and its

FIG. 3.1   FIG. 3.2

position at any instant was specified by the parameter x measured from the position of equilibrium.

Let us now consider the motion of the system of Fig. 3.1. This system is analogous to the electrical circuit of Fig. 3.2. The state of both of these systems is determined by two quantities. These are the linear displacements of the two masses of the mechanical system (x_1, x_2) or the mesh charges of the electrical system (q_1, q_2). We speak of a system whose motion and position are characterized by two independent quantities as a system having *two degrees of freedom*. If the position and motion of a system are characterized by n independent quantities, then the system is said to be one of n *degrees of freedom*.

The equations of motion of the systems of Figs. 3.1 and 3.2 may be obtained by D'Alembert's principle in the mechanical case or Kirchhoff's laws for the electrical case. We may pass from one system to the other one by means of the table of analogues of Sec. 2. It is usually simpler to write Kirchhoff's laws for the system and then translate the electrical quantities to mechanical ones.

Writing Kirchhoff's law for the fall of potential in the two meshes of the circuit, we have

$$(3.1) \qquad \begin{aligned} L_1\ddot{q}_1 + S_1 q_1 + S(q_1 - q_2) &= 0 \\ L_2\ddot{q}_2 + S_2 q_2 + S(q_2 - q_1) &= 0 \end{aligned}$$

Translated to mechanical quantities, we have

$$(3.2) \qquad \begin{aligned} M_1\ddot{x}_1 + K_1 x_1 + K(x_1 - x_2) &= 0 \\ M_2\ddot{x}_2 + K_2 x_2 + K(x_2 - x_1) &= 0 \end{aligned}$$

These equations are linear and homogeneous of the second order of the type discussed in Chap. 6. Their solutions are of the exponential type. To solve them, let us place

$$(3.3) \qquad \begin{aligned} x_1 &= A_1 e^{\alpha t} \\ x_2 &= A_2 e^{\alpha t} \end{aligned}$$

where A_1, A_2, and α may be real or complex.

Substituting this into (3.2) and dividing out the factor $e^{\alpha t}$, we obtain

$$(3.4) \qquad \begin{aligned} A_1(M_1\alpha^2 + K_1 + K) - A_2 K &= 0 \\ -A_1 K + A_2(M_2\alpha^2 + K_2 + K) &= 0 \end{aligned}$$

These are two homogeneous linear equations of the type discussed in Chap. 4. This system of equations has a solution other than the trivial one $A_1 = A_2 = 0$ if

$$(3.5) \qquad \Delta(\alpha) = \begin{vmatrix} M_1\alpha^2 + K_1 + K & -K \\ -K & M_2\alpha^2 + K_2 + K \end{vmatrix} = 0$$

Expanding the determinant, we have

$$(3.6) \qquad \Delta(\alpha) = (M_1\alpha^2 + K_1 + K)(M_2\alpha^2 + K_2 + K) - K^2 = 0$$

This is called the *characteristic equation* of the system. This equation may be written in the form

$$(3.7) \qquad \left(\alpha^2 + \frac{K_1 + K}{M_1}\right)\left(\alpha^2 + \frac{K_2 + K}{M_2}\right) - \frac{K^2}{M_1 M_2} = 0$$

It is convenient to introduce the notation

$$(3.8) \qquad \omega_{11}^2 = \frac{K_1 + K}{M_1} \qquad \omega_{22}^2 = \frac{K_2 + K}{M_2}$$

$$\omega_{12}^2 = \frac{K}{\sqrt{M_1 M_2}}$$

We may then write the characteristic equation in the form

$$(3.9) \qquad (\alpha^2 + \omega_{11}^2)(\alpha^2 + \omega_{22}^2) - \omega_{12}^4 = 0$$

or

$$(3.10) \qquad \alpha^4 + \alpha^2(\omega_{11}^2 + \omega_{22}^2) + \omega_{11}^2 \omega_{22}^2 - \omega_{12}^4 = 0$$

We therefore have

$$(3.11) \qquad \alpha^2 = -\tfrac{1}{2}(\omega_{11}^2 + \omega_{22}^2) \pm \tfrac{1}{2}\sqrt{(\omega_{11}^2 - \omega_{22})^2 + 4\omega_{12}^2}$$

The expression under the radical is positive, and the absolute value of the second term is less than that of the first term. Hence α^2 is real and negative. Accordingly let us write

$$(3.12) \qquad \alpha^2 = -\omega^2 \qquad \text{or} \qquad \alpha = \pm j\omega$$

Hence

$$(3.13) \qquad \omega^2 = \frac{\omega_{11}^2 + \omega_{22}^2}{2} \pm \frac{1}{2}\sqrt{(\omega_{11}^2 - \omega_{22}^2)^2 + 4\omega_{12}^4}$$

Equation (3.13) gives two values for ω^2; let us call them ω_1 and ω_2. From (3.12) we obtain *four* values for α: $j\omega_1$, $-j\omega_1$, $j\omega_2$, and $-j\omega_2$. We find from our original assumption (3.3) that the solutions for x_1 and x_2 are of an exponential form, and we obtained *four* values of α. The general solution may be written in the form

$$(3.14) \qquad \begin{aligned} x_1 &= A_{11}e^{j\omega_1 t} + \bar{A}_{11}e^{-j\omega_1 t} + A_{12}e^{j\omega_2 t} + \bar{A}_{12}e^{-j\omega_2 t} \\ x_2 &= A_{21}e^{j\omega_1 t} + \bar{A}_{21}e^{-j\omega_1 t} + A_{22}e^{j\omega_2 t} + \bar{A}_{22}e^{-j\omega_2 t} \end{aligned}$$

Since x_1 and x_2 are real, $\bar{A}_{11}$ must be the conjugate of A_{11} and similarly for A_{12} and $\bar{A}_{12}$, etc. If we write

$$A_{11} = \frac{c_{11}e^{j\theta_1}}{2} \qquad \bar{A}_{11} = \frac{c_{11}e^{-j\theta_1}}{2}$$

$$A_{12} = \frac{c_{12}e^{j\theta_2}}{2} \qquad \bar{A}_{12} = \frac{c_{12}e^{-j\theta_1}}{2}$$

(3.15)

$$A_{21} = \frac{c_{21}e^{j\theta_2}}{2} \qquad \bar{A}_{21} = \frac{c_{21}e^{-j\theta_1}}{2}$$

$$A_{22} = \frac{c_{22}e^{j\theta_2}}{2} \qquad \bar{A}_{22} = \frac{c_{22}e^{-j\theta_2}}{2}$$

where c_{11}, c_{12}, c_{21}, c_{22}, θ_1, and θ_2 are new arbitrary constants, we may then write the solution in the form

(3.16)
$$x_1 = c_{11} \cos (\omega_1 t + \theta_1) + c_{12} \cos (\omega_2 t + \theta_2)$$
$$x_2 = c_{21} \cos (\omega_1 t + \theta_1) + c_{22} \cos (\omega_2 t + \theta_2)$$

The ratios c_{11}/c_{21} and c_{12}/c_{22} are determined by Eqs. (3.4), since for each value of α the ratios of the quantities A_{11}/A_{21} and A_{12}/A_{22} are determined by these equations. It appears that in Eqs. (3.16) there are *four independent* arbitrary constants. We may take them to be c_{11}, c_{12}, θ_1, and θ_2. Equation (3.16) shows that the most general solution of the system is made up of the superposition of two pure harmonic oscillations. In each of these oscillations the two masses oscillate with the same frequency and in the same phase. The amplitudes of oscillation are in a definite ratio given by Eqs. (3.4).

The pure harmonic oscillations are called the *principal oscillations* or the *principal modes of oscillation* of the system.

Special Case $M_1 = M_2 = M$, $K_1 = K_2 = K_0$. A very interesting and illuminating special case of the above general theory occurs when the two masses of the system are equal, that is,

(3.17)
$$M_1 = M_2 = M$$

and

(3.18)
$$K_1 = K_2 = K_0$$

This is a very symmetric case. Rather than apply the above general theory, it is more convenient to begin with the differential equations of the system. The general equations (3.2) reduce in this case to

(3.19)
$$M\ddot{x}_1 + (K_0 + K)x_1 - Kx_2 = 0$$
$$M\ddot{x}_2 + (K_0 + K)x_2 - Kx_1 = 0$$

If we add the two equations, we have

(3.20)
$$M(\ddot{x}_1 + \ddot{x}_2) + K_0(\ddot{x}_1 + \ddot{x}_2) = 0$$

Let us introduce the new coordinate y_1 defined by

(3.21) $$y_1 = x_1 + x_2$$

We then have

(3.22) $$M\ddot{y}_1 + K_0 y_1 = 0$$

Hence the coordinate y_1 performs simple harmonic oscillations of the form

(3.23) $$y_1 = A_1 \sin \omega_1 t + B_1 \cos \omega_1 t$$

where

(3.24) $$\omega_1 = \sqrt{\frac{K_0}{M}}$$

This represents a motion where the two masses swing to the left and right with equal amplitudes in such a manner that the coupling spring is not stressed. If we now subtract the second equation from the first one and let

(3.25) $$y_2 = x_1 - x_2$$

we obtain

(3.26) $$M\ddot{y}_2 + (K_0 + 2K)y_2 = 0$$

This equation has a solution

(3.27) $$y_2 = A_2 \sin \omega_2 t + B_2 \cos \omega_2 t$$

where

(3.28) $$\omega_2 = \sqrt{\frac{K_0 + 2K}{M}}$$

This case represents the one in which the two masses move in opposite directions with the same amplitude. We may write the transformation from the x coordinates to the y coordinates in the matrix form

(3.29) $$\begin{Bmatrix} y_1 \\ y_2 \end{Bmatrix} = \begin{bmatrix} 1 & 1 \\ 1 & -1 \end{bmatrix} \begin{Bmatrix} x_1 \\ x_2 \end{Bmatrix}$$

and also

(3.30) $$\begin{Bmatrix} x_1 \\ x_2 \end{Bmatrix} = \begin{bmatrix} 1 & 1 \\ 1 & -1 \end{bmatrix}^{-1} \begin{Bmatrix} y_1 \\ y_2 \end{Bmatrix} = \frac{1}{2} \begin{bmatrix} 1 & 1 \\ 1 & -1 \end{bmatrix} \begin{Bmatrix} y_1 \\ y_2 \end{Bmatrix}$$

In this very simple case we see that by a linear transformation of the coordinates (x_1, x_2) to the coordinates (y_1, y_2) we have effected a separation of the variables so that the motions of the y_1 and y_2 coordinates are uncoupled.

These new coordinates y_1 and y_2 are called *normal coordinates*. They will be considered in greater detail in a later section.

The general solution of the system may be written in the form

(3.31)
$$x_1 = \tfrac{1}{2}(A_1 \sin \omega_1 t + B_1 \cos \omega_1 t + A_2 \sin \omega_2 t + B_2 \cos \omega_2 t)$$
$$x_2 = \tfrac{1}{2}(A_1 \sin \omega_1 t + B_1 \cos \omega_1 t - A_2 \sin \omega_2 t - B_2 \cos \omega_2 t)$$

Let us suppose that the motion begins in such a manner that

(3.32)
$$\left. \begin{array}{l} x_1 = x_0 \\ x_2 = 0 \\ \dot{x}_1 = 0 \\ \dot{x}_2 = 0 \end{array} \right\} \quad \text{at } t = 0$$

That is, the system is initially at rest, but at $t = 0$ the mass 1 is displaced a distance x_0. In this case the general solution (3.31) reduces to

(3.33)
$$x_1 = \frac{x_0}{2} (\cos \omega_1 t + \cos \omega_2 t)$$
$$x_2 = \frac{x_0}{2} (\cos \omega_1 t - \cos \omega_2 t)$$

This solution may also be written in the form

(3.34)
$$x_1 = x_0 \cos \frac{\omega_1 + \omega_2}{2} t \cos \frac{\omega_1 - \omega_2}{2} t$$
$$x_2 = x_0 \sin \frac{\omega_1 + \omega_2}{2} t \sin \frac{\omega_1 - \omega_2}{2} t$$

If the coupling spring k is weak, then k is small and we may write

(3.35)
$$\omega_2 = \omega_1 + 2\delta$$

where δ is small compared with ω_1, and we have approximately

(3.36)
$$\omega_1 + \omega_2 = 2\omega_1$$
$$\omega_2 - \omega_1 = 2\delta$$

We may then write (3.34) in the form

(3.37)
$$x_1 = x_0 \cos \omega_1 t \cos \delta t$$
$$x_2 = x_0 \sin \omega_1 t \sin \delta t$$

The motions of the two masses in this case produce a phenomenon called *beats*. Each mass executes a rapid vibration of angular frequency ω_1 with an amplitude that changes slowly with an angular frequency δ. The two masses move in opposite phases so that the amplitude of one reaches its maximum when the other is at rest.

4. Lagrange's Equations. In this section a simple exposition of Lagrange's equations for conservative systems will be given. For a more complete and detailed treatment the reader is referred to the standard treatises on mechanics.

Let us consider the simple mass-and-spring system of Fig. 4.1.

x is a linear coordinate measured from the position of equilibrium of the mass. If the mass is moving with a velocity $v = \dot{x}$, its kinetic energy T is given by

$$(4.1) \qquad\qquad T = \tfrac{1}{2}Mv^2 = \tfrac{1}{2}M(\dot{x})^2$$

When the spring is stretched a distance x from its position of equilibrium, then the elastic, or potential, energy stored in the spring is

$$(4.2) \quad V = \int_0^x F\,dx = \int_0^x Kx\,dx = \frac{Kx^2}{2}$$

By Newton's second law of motion the differential equation governing the motion of the mass is

$$(4.3) \qquad\qquad Ma = -F$$

FIG. 4.1

where $a = \dot{v}$ is the acceleration of the mass and F is the restoring force of the spring. The minus sign is introduced because the restoring force F acts in the opposite direction from x, since x is measured from the position of equilibrium. We may also write Eq. (4.3) in the more fundamental form

$$(4.4) \qquad\qquad \frac{d}{dt}(Mv) = -F$$

If we differentiate the kinetic energy T of (4.1) with respect to $v = \dot{x}$, we obtain

$$(4.5) \qquad\qquad \frac{\partial}{\partial \dot{x}}T = \frac{\partial}{\partial \dot{x}}\frac{1}{2}M(\dot{x})^2 = M\dot{x} = Mv$$

If we differentiate the potential energy V of (4.2) with respect to x, we have

$$(4.6) \qquad\qquad \frac{\partial V}{\partial x} = \frac{\partial}{\partial x}\left(\frac{Kx^2}{2}\right) = Kx = F$$

Hence, in terms of the energy functions, the equation of motion may be written in the form

FIG. 4.2

$$(4.7) \qquad \frac{d}{dt}\left(\frac{\partial T}{\partial \dot{x}}\right) + \frac{\partial V}{\partial x} = 0$$

This form of the equation of motion is called *Lagrange's equation of motion* and is simply a convenient way of writing Newton's second law of motion.

Let us now consider the system of Fig. 4.2.

This is the system analyzed in Sec. 3. In this case the kinetic energy is given by

$$(4.8) \qquad T = \tfrac{1}{2}M_1\dot{x}_1^2 + \tfrac{1}{2}M_2\dot{x}_2^2$$

The potential energy stored in the springs V is

$$(4.9) \qquad V = \tfrac{1}{2}K_1x_1^2 + \tfrac{1}{2}K(x_1 - x_2)^2 + \tfrac{1}{2}K_2x_2^2$$

In this case the kinetic and potential energies are quadratic functions of the linear displacements x_1 and x_2. In this case, if we form the partial derivative

$$(4.10) \qquad \frac{\partial T}{\partial \dot{x}_1} = M_1\dot{x}_1 = M_1v_1$$

we obtain the momentum of the first mass.

The derivative

$$(4.11) \qquad \frac{\partial V}{\partial x_1} = K_1x_1 + K(x_1 - x_2)$$

is exactly the restoring force acting on the mass M_1. We thus see that the first of Eqs. (3.2) may be written in the form

$$(4.12) \qquad \frac{d}{dt}\left(\frac{\partial T}{\partial \dot{x}_1}\right) + \frac{\partial V}{\partial x_1} = 0$$

In the same manner the second equation of motion may be written in the form

$$(4.13) \qquad \frac{d}{dt}\left(\frac{\partial T}{\partial \dot{x}_2}\right) + \frac{\partial V}{\partial x_2} = 0$$

In this case the motion of the system is given by the two Lagrange equations (4.12) and (4.13).

The importance of Lagrange's equations is that they hold with respect to any sort of coordinates, not merely the linear coordinates which we have used above. For example, in the symmetric case of Sec. 3 the kinetic and potential energies are given by

$$(4.14) \qquad \begin{aligned} T &= \tfrac{1}{2}M(\dot{x}_1^2 + \dot{x}_2^2) \\ V &= \tfrac{1}{2}K_0(x_1^2 + x_2^2) + \tfrac{1}{2}K(x_1 - x_2)^2 \end{aligned}$$

We saw that the analysis was vastly simplified by introducing the new coordinates y_1 and y_2 by the linear transformation

$$(4.15) \qquad \begin{aligned} y_1 &= x_1 + x_2 \\ y_2 &= x_1 - x_2 \end{aligned}$$

or

$$(4.16) \qquad \begin{aligned} x_1 &= \tfrac{1}{2}(y_1 + y_2) \\ x_2 &= \tfrac{1}{2}(y_1 - y_2) \end{aligned}$$

In terms of these new coordinates the kinetic and potential energies become

$$(4.17) \qquad \begin{aligned} T &= \tfrac{1}{4}M(\dot{y}_1^2 + \dot{y}_2^2) \\ V &= \tfrac{1}{4}K_0(y_1^2 + y_2^2) + \tfrac{1}{2}Ky_2^2 \end{aligned}$$

It was *asserted* that Lagrange's equations would hold for the y_1 and y_2 coordinates. We therefore have

$$(4.18) \qquad \frac{d}{dt}\left(\frac{\partial T}{\partial \dot{y}_1}\right) + \frac{\partial V}{\partial y_1} = 0$$

or

$$(4.19) \qquad \frac{M}{2}\ddot{y}_1 + \frac{K_0}{2}y_1 = 0$$

and

$$(4.20) \qquad \frac{d}{dt}\left(\frac{\partial T}{\partial \dot{y}_2}\right) + \frac{\partial V}{\partial y_2} = 0$$

or

$$(4.21) \qquad \frac{M}{2}\ddot{y}_2 + \tfrac{1}{2}K_0 y_2 + Ky_2 = 0$$

Hence the equations of motion are

$$(4.22) \qquad M\ddot{y}_1 + K_0 y_1 = 0$$

and

$$(4.23) \qquad M\ddot{y}_2 + (K_0 + 2K)y_2 = 0$$

These were the equations of motion of the symmetric system obtained directly.

In this simple example we see that the introduction of the two new coordinates y_1 and y_2 reduces the potential- and kinetic-energy expressions to sums of squares. This is a general property of *normal coordinates*. Each normal coordinate executes simple harmonic oscillations independently of the others.

FIG. 4.3

As another example, let us consider the motion of three pendulums of equal masses M and length l connected by springs at a distance h from the suspension points A, B, and C as shown in Fig. 4.3.

The masses of the springs and the bars of the pendulums are assumed so small that they can be neglected. The motion of the pendulums may be expressed in terms of the angles θ_1, θ_2, and θ_3 of the pendulums measured from the vertical in a clockwise direction. The kinetic energy of

the system is

(4.24) $$T = \tfrac{1}{2}Ml^2(\dot{\theta}_1^2 + \dot{\theta}_2^2 + \dot{\theta}_3^2)$$

The potential energy of the system consists of two parts: the energy due to the gravitational force and the strain energy of the springs. If we limit ourselves to a consideration of small oscillations, then θ_1, θ_2, and θ_3 are small quantities. The energy due to gravity is

(4.25) $$V_g = Mgl(1 - \cos\theta_1) + Mgl(1 - \cos\theta_2) + Mgl(1 - \cos\theta_3)$$
$$\doteq \tfrac{1}{2}Mgl(\theta_1^2 + \theta_2^2 + \theta_3^2)$$

For small oscillations the springs may be assumed to remain always horizontal.

FIG. 4.4

The elongations of the springs are then given by

(4.26) $$h(\sin\theta_2 - \sin\theta_1) \doteq h(\theta_2 - \theta_1)$$

and

$$h(\sin\theta_3 - \sin\theta_2) \doteq h(\theta_3 - \theta_2)$$

respectively.

The strain energy of the springs is accordingly

(4.27) $$V_s = \frac{K}{2}\, h^2[(\theta_2 - \theta_1)^2 + (\theta_3 - \theta_2)^2]$$

The total potential energy of the system is

(4.28) $$V = \tfrac{1}{2}Mgl(\theta_1^2 + \theta_2^2 + \theta_3^2) + \frac{Kh^2}{2}\,[(\theta_2 - \theta_1)^2 + (\theta_3 - \theta_2)^2]$$

This mechanical system is analogous to the electrical circuit of Fig. 4.4. The magnetic energy of the electrical circuit is

(4.29) $$T_M = \tfrac{1}{2}L(\dot{q}_1^2 + \dot{q}_2^2 + \dot{q}_3^2)$$

where $\dot{q}_r = i_r$, the mesh currents of the system. The electric energy of the system is

(4.30) $$V_E = \tfrac{1}{2}S(q_1^2 + q_2^2 + q_3^2) + \tfrac{1}{2}S_0(q_2 - q_1)^2 + \tfrac{1}{2}S_0(q_3 - q_2)^2$$

These expressions are completely analogous to the kinetic and potential energies of the mechanical system. In this case we have

(4.31) $$\begin{aligned} Mgl &\to S & Kh^2 &\to S_0 \\ l^2 M &\to L & \theta_r &\to q_r \end{aligned}$$

for the analogous electrical and mechanical quantities.   The currents are analogous to the angular velocities of the pendulums.   In this case there are three Lagrangian equations of motion of the system:

$$(4.32) \qquad \frac{d}{dt}\left(\frac{\partial T}{\partial \dot{\theta}_r}\right) + \frac{\partial V}{\partial \theta_r} = 0 \qquad r = 1, 2, 3$$

Performing the differentiation, we obtain

$$(4.33) \qquad \begin{aligned} l^2 M \ddot{\theta}_1 + Mgl\theta_1 + Kh^2(\theta_1 - \theta_2) &= 0 \\ l^2 M \ddot{\theta}_2 + Mgl\theta_2 + Kh^2(\theta_2 - \theta_1) + Kh^2(\theta_2 - \theta_3) &= 0 \\ l^2 M \ddot{\theta}_3 + Mgl\theta_3 + Kh^2(\theta_3 - \theta_2) &= 0 \end{aligned}$$

We may find the normal coordinates in this case rather simply.   If we add the three equations, we obtain

$$(4.34) \qquad l^2 M(\ddot{\theta}_1 + \ddot{\theta}_2 + \ddot{\theta}_3) + Mgl(\theta_1 + \theta_2 + \theta_3) = 0$$

If we let

$$(4.35) \qquad y_1 = \theta_1 + \theta_2 + \theta_3$$

Eq. (4.34) becomes

$$(4.36) \qquad \ddot{y}_1 + \frac{g}{l} y_1 = 0$$

The solution of this equation is

$$(4.37) \qquad y_1 = A_1 \sin \sqrt{\frac{g}{l}}\, t + B_1 \cos \sqrt{\frac{g}{l}}\, t$$

and represents an oscillation of all three pendulums in synchronism with an angular frequency of

$$(4.38) \qquad \omega_1 = \sqrt{\frac{g}{l}}$$

If we subtract the last equation (4.33) from the first one and let

$$(4.39) \qquad y_2 = \theta_1 - \theta_3$$

we obtain

$$(4.40) \qquad Ml^2 \ddot{y}_2 + (Mgl + Kh^2)y_2 = 0 .$$

The solution of this equation is

$$(4.41) \qquad y_2 = A_2 \sin \omega_2 t + B_2 \cos \omega_2 t$$

where

$$(4.42) \qquad \omega_2 = \sqrt{\frac{g}{l} + \frac{Kh^2}{Ml^2}}$$

If we now add the first and last equations (4.33) and subtract twice the second equation and let

$$(4.43) \qquad y_3 = \theta_1 - 2\theta_2 + \theta_3$$

we obtain

$$(4.44) \qquad Ml^2 \ddot{y}_3 + (Mgl + 3Kh^2)y_3 = 0$$

This equation has the solution

$$(4.45) \qquad y_3 = A_3 \sin \omega_3 t + B_3 \cos \omega_3 t$$

where

$$(4.46) \qquad \omega_3 = \sqrt{\frac{Mgl + K3h^2}{Ml^2}}$$

We have thus succeeded in obtaining the three normal coordinates y_1, y_2, and y_3. The three angular frequencies of the system are ω_1, ω_2, and ω_3. If we know the initial displacement and angular velocities of the pendulums, we may determine the six arbitrary constants A_r, B_r, $r = 1, 2, 3$. Then the θ_r coordinates are given by

$$(4.47) \qquad \begin{aligned} \theta_1 &= \frac{y_1}{3} + \frac{y_2}{2} + \frac{y_3}{6} \\ \theta_2 &= \frac{y_1}{3} - \frac{y_3}{3} \\ \theta_3 &= \frac{y_1}{3} - \frac{y_2}{2} + \frac{y_3}{6} \end{aligned}$$

These equations are obtained by solving the θ_r coordinates in terms of the y_r coordinates. It may be shown that the kinetic and potential energies (4.25) and (4.28) are reduced to sums of squares in the y_r coordinates by this transformation.

5. Proof of Lagrange's Equations. In the last section we considered a method of writing the equation of motion of oscillating systems in terms of the expressions for the kinetic and potential energy of the system. We saw that the state of motion of the system could be expressed in terms of different parameters or coordinates.

In this section a proof of Lagrange's equations will be given for a particle; the proof may be easily generalized to a system of particles and to rigid bodies.

Let us consider a particle of mass M. According to Newton's second law the equations of free motion of this particle referred to a set of rectangular coordinates are given by

$$(5.1) \qquad M\ddot{x} = F_x \qquad M\ddot{y} = F_y \qquad M\ddot{z} = F_z$$

where F_x, F_y, F_z represent the components of the effective force acting on the particle in the x, y, and z directions. Suppose we desire to express these equations of motion in terms of another set of coordinates (q_1,q_2,q_3) related functionally to the rectangular coordinates (x,y,z). We may then express the coordinates (x,y,z) in terms of the coordinates (q_1,q_2,q_3) by

$$(5.2) \qquad x = F_1(q_1,q_2,q_3) \qquad y = F_2(q_1,q_2,q_3) \qquad z = F_3(q_1,q_2,q_3)$$

With this notation, on differentiation with respect to time, the expression for the component velocities of the particle $(\dot{x}, \dot{y}, \dot{z})$ may be put in the form

$$\dot{x} = \frac{\partial x}{\partial q_1}\dot{q}_1 + \frac{\partial x}{\partial q_2}\dot{q}_2 + \frac{\partial x}{\partial q_3}\dot{q}_3$$

$$(5.3) \qquad \dot{y} = \frac{\partial y}{\partial q_1}\dot{q}_1 + \frac{\partial y}{\partial q_2}\dot{q}_2 + \frac{\partial y}{\partial q_3}\dot{q}_3$$

$$\dot{z} = \frac{\partial z}{\partial q_1}\dot{q}_1 + \frac{\partial z}{\partial q_2}\dot{q}_2 + \frac{\partial z}{\partial q_3}\dot{q}_3$$

where in general $\dot{x}$, $\dot{y}$, $\dot{z}$ are explicit functions of $(q_1,q_2,q_3,\dot{q}_1,\dot{q}_2,\dot{q}_3)$.

Now since

$$(5.4) \qquad\qquad x = F_1(q_1,q_2,q_3)$$

then

$$(5.5) \qquad\qquad \frac{\partial x}{\partial q_1} = \phi_1(q_1,q_2,q_3)$$

Hence

$$(5.6) \qquad \frac{d}{dt}\left(\frac{\partial x}{\partial q_1}\right) = \frac{\partial \phi_1}{\partial q_1}\dot{q}_1 + \frac{\partial \phi_1}{\partial q_2}\dot{q}_2 + \frac{\partial \phi_1}{\partial q_3}\dot{q}_3$$

$$= \frac{\partial^2 x}{\partial q_1^2}\dot{q}_1 + \frac{\partial^2 x}{\partial q_2\,\partial q_1}\dot{q}_2 + \frac{\partial^2 x}{\partial q_3\,\partial q_1}\dot{q}_3$$

Differentiating the first equation (5.3) with respect to q_1, we obtain

$$(5.7) \qquad \frac{\partial \dot{x}}{\partial q_1} = \frac{\partial^2 x}{\partial q_1^2}\dot{q}_1 + \frac{\partial^2 x}{\partial q_1\,\partial q_2}\dot{q}_2 + \frac{\partial^2 x}{\partial q_1\,\partial q_3}\dot{q}_3$$

If we now compare (5.6) and (5.7), we obtain

$$(5.8) \qquad\qquad \frac{d}{dt}\left(\frac{\partial x}{\partial q_1}\right) = \frac{\partial \dot{x}}{\partial q_1}$$

with similar relations for y and z.

It is also evident by differentiating the first equation (5.3) with respect to $\dot{q}_1$ that

$$(5.9) \qquad\qquad \frac{\partial \dot{x}}{\partial \dot{q}_1} = \frac{\partial x}{\partial q_1}$$

with similar relations for y and z.

Let us now assume that we hold the coordinates q_2 and q_3 fixed and give the coordinate q_1 an infinitesimal increment δq_1. If δx, δy, and δz are the increments that this produced in x, y, and z, then, if we let δW_1 be the work done by the effective forces when the particle undergoes this infinitesimal displacement, we have

$$(5.10) \qquad \delta W_1 = F_x\,\delta x + F_y\,\delta y + F_z\,\delta z$$
$$= M(\ddot{x}\,\delta x + \ddot{y}\,\delta y + \ddot{z}\,\delta z)$$

as a consequence of Eqs. (5.1). We also have·

$$(5.11) \qquad \delta x = \frac{\partial x}{\partial q_1}\,\delta q_1 \qquad \delta y = \frac{\partial y}{\partial q_1}\,\delta q_1 \qquad \delta z = \frac{\partial z}{\partial q_1}\,\delta q_1$$

Hence we may write (5.10) in the form

$$(5.12) \qquad \delta W_1 = M\left(\ddot{x}\,\frac{\partial x}{\partial q_1} + \ddot{y}\,\frac{\partial y}{\partial q_1} + \ddot{z}\,\frac{\partial z}{\partial q_1}\right)\delta q_1$$

The rule for the differentiation of a product yields

$$(5.13) \qquad \frac{d}{dt}\left(\dot{x}\,\frac{\partial x}{\partial q_1}\right) = \ddot{x}\,\frac{\partial x}{\partial q_1} + \dot{x}\,\frac{d}{dt}\left(\frac{\partial x}{\partial q_1}\right)$$

or

$$(5.14) \qquad \ddot{x}\,\frac{\partial x}{\partial q_1} = \frac{d}{dt}\left(\dot{x}\,\frac{\partial x}{\partial q_1}\right) - \dot{x}\,\frac{d}{dt}\left(\frac{\partial x}{\partial q_1}\right)$$

If we substitute the values of $\dfrac{\partial x}{\partial q_1}$ and $\dfrac{d}{dt}\left(\dfrac{\partial x}{\partial q_1}\right)$ given by (5.9) and (5.8), we obtain

$$(5.15) \qquad \ddot{x}\,\frac{\partial x}{\partial q_1} = \frac{d}{dt}\left(\dot{x}\,\frac{\partial \dot{x}}{\partial \dot{q}_1}\right) - \dot{x}\,\frac{\partial \dot{x}}{\partial q_1}$$
$$= \frac{d}{dt}\frac{\partial}{\partial \dot{q}_1}\left(\frac{\dot{x}^2}{2}\right) - \frac{\partial}{\partial q_1}\left(\frac{\dot{x}^2}{2}\right)$$

and similar relations for y and z. However, the kinetic energy of the particle is given by

$$(5.16) \qquad T = \frac{M}{2}\,(\dot{x}^2 + \dot{y}^2 + \dot{z}^2)$$

Hence as a consequence of (5.15) and (5.16) the expression (5.12) may be written in the form

$$(5.17) \qquad \delta W_1 = \left(\frac{d}{dt}\frac{\partial T}{\partial \dot{q}_1} - \frac{\partial T}{\partial q_1}\right)\delta q_1$$

Now if $Q_1\,\delta q_1$ is the work done in the specified displacement of the particle, then it is convenient to regard Q_1 as a sort of generalized force.

We may write

(5.18) $$\delta W_1 = Q_1 \, \delta q_1$$

and we have

(5.19) $$\frac{d}{dt}\left(\frac{\partial T}{\partial \dot{q}_1}\right) - \frac{\partial T}{\partial q_1} = Q_1$$

By the same reasoning, if q_1 and q_3 are held constant and q_2 is given an increment δq_2, we obtain the equation

(5.20) $$\frac{d}{dt}\left(\frac{\partial T}{\partial \dot{q}_2}\right) - \frac{\partial T}{\partial q_2} = Q_2$$

and in the same manner, holding q_1 and q_2 constant and giving q_3 an increment δq_3, we obtain

(5.21) $$\frac{d}{dt}\left(\frac{\partial T}{\partial \dot{q}_3}\right) - \frac{\partial T}{\partial q_3} = Q_3$$

We see that there are as many equations as there are degrees of freedom. The Q_r quantities are called *generalized forces*. The q_r quantities are the *generalized coordinates*.

Conservative Systems. If there is no loss of energy in the dynamical system under consideration, the generalized forces may be derived from the potential energy of the system V in the form

(5.22) $$Q_1 = -\frac{\partial V}{\partial q_1} \qquad Q_2 = -\frac{\partial V}{\partial q_2} \qquad Q_3 = -\frac{\partial V}{\partial q_3}$$

In this case the free motion of the particle is given by the three Lagrangian equations

(5.23) $$\frac{d}{dt}\left(\frac{\partial T}{\partial \dot{q}_r}\right) - \frac{\partial T}{\partial q_r} + \frac{\partial V}{\partial q_r} = 0 \qquad r = 1, 2, 3$$

By an extension of the above argument it may be shown that in the case of a conservative system having n degrees of freedom its Lagrangian equations are of the form (5.23). In this case there are n generalized coordinates $(q_1, q_2, \ldots, q_n)$, and there are n equations.

We notice that in the simple examples of Lagrange's equations discussed in Sec. 4 we had

(5.24) $$\frac{\partial T}{\partial q_r} = 0 \qquad r = 1, 2, \ldots, n$$

The reason for this was that the kinetic energy in the systems discussed in that section was not a function of the coordinates, but only of the velocities of the system. As an example of a system where the kinetic energy is a function of the generalized coordinates q_r as well as the generalized velocities $\dot{q}_r$, consider the two-dimensional motion of a particle in the xy plane as shown in Fig. 5.1.

In this case we have

$$(5.25) \qquad T = \tfrac{1}{2}M(\dot{x}^2 + \dot{y}^2)$$

Let us assume that the particle is attracted to the origin by a force proportional to the distance so that the particle has a radial force F_r directed toward the origin given by

FIG. 5.1

$$(5.26) \qquad F_r = Kr$$

In this case the potential energy is given by

$$(5.27) \qquad V = \frac{Kr^2}{2}$$

To describe the motion of the particle it is convenient to use the polar coordinates r and θ as the generalized coordinates. These coordinates are related to the cartesian coordinates x and y by the equations

$$(5.28) \qquad x = r \cos \theta \qquad y = r \sin \theta$$

In terms of these coordinates the kinetic energy becomes

$$(5.29) \qquad T = \frac{M}{2}(\dot{r}^2 + r^2\dot{\theta}^2)$$

The Lagrangian equations of motion are

$$(5.30) \qquad \frac{d}{dt}\left(\frac{\partial T}{\partial \dot{r}}\right) - \frac{\partial T}{\partial r} + \frac{\partial V}{\partial r} = 0$$

or

$$(5.31) \qquad M\ddot{r} - Mr\dot{\theta}^2 + Kr = 0$$

and

$$(5.32) \qquad \frac{d}{dt}\left(\frac{\partial T}{\partial \dot{\theta}}\right) - \frac{\partial T}{\partial \theta} + \frac{\partial V}{\partial \theta} = 0$$

or

$$(5.33) \qquad \frac{d}{dt}(Mr^2\dot{\theta}) = 0$$

Equations (5.31) and (5.33) are the equations of motion of the system. Equation (5.33) expresses the conservation of angular momentum of the system. The term $\partial T/\partial r$ is seen to give rise to the centrifugal-force term. Terms of the form $\partial T/\partial q_r$, which are absent in rectangular coordinates, may be regarded as a sort of fictitious force introduced by using generalized coordinates.

6. Small Oscillations of Conservative Systems. A very important class of problems in the theory of vibrations is that in which a dynamical system is performing free or forced oscillations without friction. The determination of the natural frequencies and modes of oscillations of the torsional vibrations of an engine, the oscillations of spring-mounted machinery, the oscillations of electrical networks whose resistance is so small as to be neglected, etc., are problems that fall in this category.

The Lagrangian equations of motion of a general conservative system of n degrees of freedom oscillating in the neighborhood of a position of equilibrium may be written in the form

(6.1)
$$M_{11}\ddot{q}_1 + \cdots + M_{1n}\ddot{q}_n + K_{11}q_1 + \cdots + K_{1n}q_n = 0$$
$$M_{21}\ddot{q}_1 + \cdots + M_{2n}\ddot{q}_n + K_{21}q_1 + \cdots + K_{2n}q_n = 0$$
$$\cdots \cdots \cdots \cdots \cdots \cdots \cdots \cdots \cdots \cdots \cdots \cdots \cdots$$
$$M_{n1}\ddot{q}_1 + \cdots + M_{nn}\ddot{q}_n + K_{n1}q_1 + \cdots + K_{nn}q_n = 0$$

where $(q_1, \ldots, q_n)$ are generalized coordinates, M_{rs} are inertia coefficients, and K_{rs} are stiffness coefficients. These are the equations governing the motion of the most general conservative system performing free oscillations in the neighborhood of a position of equilibrium. The examples discussed in Secs. 3 and 4 are special cases of this general system. The analysis of these equations is greatly facilitated by writing them in matrix notation. If we let

(6.2)
$$[M] = \begin{bmatrix} M_{11} & \cdots & M_{1n} \\ \cdots & \cdots & \cdots \\ M_{n1} & \cdots & M_{nn} \end{bmatrix} = \text{inertia matrix}$$

(6.3)
$$[K] = \begin{bmatrix} K_{11} & \cdots & K_{1n} \\ \cdots & \cdots & \cdots \\ K_{n1} & \cdots & K_{nn} \end{bmatrix} = \text{stiffness matrix}$$

(6.4)
$$\{q\} = \begin{Bmatrix} q_1 \\ \cdot \\ \cdot \\ \cdot \\ q_n \end{Bmatrix} = \text{coordinate matrix}$$

the set of Eqs. (6.1) may then be written in the convenient form

(6.5)
$$[M]\{\ddot{q}\} + [K]\{q\} = \{0\}$$

The coefficients M_{rs} and K_{rs} have the important property that

(6.6)
$$K_{rs} = K_{sr} \qquad M_{rs} = M_{sr}$$

Hence the matrices $[M]$ and $[K]$ are symmetric. The kinetic and potential energies of the system may be written in the convenient matrix form

(6.7)
$$T = \tfrac{1}{2}\{\dot{q}\}'[M]\{\dot{q}\} \qquad V = \tfrac{1}{2}\{q\}'[K]\{q\}$$

where $\{\dot{q}\}'$ and $\{q\}'$ are the transposed matrices of the column matrices $\{\dot{q}\}$ and $\{q\}$ and are hence row matrices. This is the notation used in Chap. 4.

Let us consider solutions of Eq. (6.5) corresponding to pure harmonic motion of the form

$$(6.8) \qquad \{q\} = \{A\} \sin (\omega t + \theta)$$

where $\{A\}$ is a column matrix of amplitude constants, ω is the angular frequency of the oscillation, and θ is an arbitrary phase angle. Substituting this into Eq. (6.5), we obtain

$$(6.9) \qquad ([K] - \omega^2[M])\{A\} = \{0\}$$

This represents a set of homogeneous algebraic equations in the arbitrary amplitude constants $\{A\}$.

It is convenient to premultiply both sides of Eq. (6.9) by $[K]^{-1}$, the inverse of K. We then obtain

$$(6.10) \qquad (I - \omega^2[K]^{-1}[M])\{A\} = \{0\}$$

where I is the unit matrix of the nth order. The matrix $[K]^{-1}[M]$ is usually called the *dynamical matrix*. That is, we have

$$(6.11) \qquad [U] = [K]^{-1}[M] = \text{dynamical matrix}$$

In terms of the dynamical matrix the set of Eqs. (6.10) may be written in the form

$$(6.12) \qquad (I - \omega^2[U])\{A\} = \{0\}$$

If we now write

$$(6.13) \qquad Z = \frac{1}{\omega^2}$$

then (6.12) may be written in the form

$$(6.14) \qquad (ZI - [U])\{A\} = \{0\}$$

This set of equations will have solutions other than the trivial one of zero if the determinant of the system vanishes. That is,

$$(6.15) \quad |ZI - U|$$
$$= \begin{vmatrix} Z - U_{11} & -U_{12} & -U_{13} - \cdots & -U_{1n} \\ -U_{21} & Z - U_{22} & -U_{23} - \cdots & -U_{2n} \\ -U_{n1} & -U_{n2} & - \cdots \cdots & Z - U_{nn} \end{vmatrix} = 0$$

This is an equation of the nth degree in Z. It may be proved that all the roots are real and positive. Ordinarily this equation will have n distinct roots $Z_1, Z_2, Z_3, \ldots, Z_n$. To each root Z_r there corresponds a value ω_r of ω, given by

$$(6.16) \qquad \omega_r = \sqrt{\frac{1}{Z_r}} \qquad r = 1, 2, \ldots, n$$

These are the natural angular frequencies of the system. We thus see that our original assumed solution (6.8) has led us to n values of ω. Each value ω_r of ω gives a solution of the form

$$(6.17) \qquad \{A^{(r)}\} \sin (\omega_r t + \theta_r)$$

Since the original set of equations is linear, we may write the general solution by summing solutions of the form (6.17). We then have the general solution

$$(6.18) \qquad \{q\} = \sum_{r=1}^{r=n} \{A^{(r)}\} \sin (\omega_r t + \theta_r)$$

The column matrices $\{A^{(r)}\}$ are called the *modal columns*. Every oscillation represented by each modal column is called a *principal mode of oscillation* of the system. The number of principal oscillations is equal to the number of degrees of freedom of the system.

Every principal oscillation is a pure harmonic motion. The most general form of oscillation of a system of n degrees of freedom consists of the superposition of n pure harmonic motions. The frequencies of the principal oscillations are called the *natural frequencies* of the system. The lowest frequency is called the *fundamental frequency*.

Orthogonality of the Principal Oscillations. The modal columns satisfy Eq. (6.9) with the proper value of ω. For example, the rth modal column satisfies the equation

$$(6.19) \qquad \omega_r^2 [M]\{A^{(r)}\} = [K]\{A^{(r)}\}$$

This equation fixes the *ratios* of the numbers of the rth modal column. If, for example, the first number $A_1^{(r)}$ is chosen arbitrarily, then by Eq. (6.19) the numbers $A_2^{(r)}$, $A_3^{(r)}$, $\ldots$, $A_n^{(r)}$ may be expressed in terms of $A_1^{(r)}$. We thus see that the general solution (6.18) contains only $2n$ arbitrary constants, since any number in any modal column may be specified arbitrarily and the phase angles θ_r are arbitrary.

The modal columns possess a very interesting and important property that will now be derived. Let us write the equation satisfied by the mode $\{A^{(s)}\}$. This equation is

$$(6.20) \qquad \omega_s^2 [M]\{A^{(s)}\} = [K]\{A^{(s)}\}$$

Let us premultiply Eq. (6.19) by $\{A^{(s)}\}'$ and Eq. (6.20) by $\{A^{(r)}\}'$.

We then obtain

$$(6.21) \qquad \omega_r^2\{A^{(s)}\}'[M]\{A^{(r)}\} = \{A^{(s)}\}'[K]\{A^{(r)}\}$$
$$(6.22) \qquad \omega_s^2\{A^{(r)}\}'[M]\{A^{(s)}\} = \{A^{(r)}\}'[K]\{A^{(s)}\}$$

Now, by a fundamental theorem of matrix algebra, if we have the product of three conformable matrices $[a][b][c]$, then the transpose of the product is given by

$$(6.23) \qquad ([a][b][c])' = [c]'[b]'[a]'$$

(see Chap. 4). If we then take the transpose of Eqs. (6.21) and use the reversal law of transposed products (6.23), we obtain

$$(6.24) \qquad \omega_r^2\{A^{(r)}\}'[M]\{A^{(s)}\} = \{A^{(r)}\}'[K]\{A^{(s)}\}$$

in view of the fact that the matrices $[M]$ and $[K]$ are symmetric, and hence $[M]' = M$ and $[K]' = [K]$.

If we now subtract Eq. (6.24) from Eq. (6.22), we obtain

$$(6.25) \qquad (\omega_s^2 - \omega_r^2)\{A^{(r)}\}'[M]\{A^{(s)}\} = 0$$

Now, by hypothesis, ω_s and ω_r are two *different* natural frequencies of the system; hence $\omega_s \neq \omega_r$. It follows that

$$(6.26) \qquad \{A^{(r)}\}'[M]\{A^{(s)}\} = 0$$

This relation is known as the *orthogonality* relation for the principal modes of oscillation.

7. Solution of the Frequency Equation and Calculation of the Normal Modes by the Use of Matrices. A very useful and important method for the determination of the roots of the frequency equation (6.15) and the determination of the normal modes of a conservative system has been presented by W. J. Duncan and A. R. Collar.* This method is most convenient in that it avoids the expansion of the determinantal equation (6.15) and the solution of the resulting high-degree equation. The modal columns $\{A^{(r)}\}$ are also most simply obtained. Because of its great utility and increasing usefulness a brief treatment of the method will be given in this section.

We see from Eq. (6.14) that the rth modal column satisfies the equation

$$(7.1) \qquad [U]\{A^{(r)}\} = Z_r\{A^{(r)}\}$$

where Z_r is the rth root of the frequency or determinantal equation (6.15). $[U]$ is the dynamical matrix of the system. If we premultiply Eq. (7.1) by U, we obtain

$$(7.2) \qquad [U]^2\{A^{(r)}\} = Z_r[U]\{A^{(r)}\} = Z_r^2\{A^{(r)}\}$$

* W. J. Duncan and A. R. Collar, A Method for the Solution of Oscillation Problems by Matrices, *Philosophical Magazine*, ser. 7, vol. 17, p. 865, 1934.

If we premultiply (7.1) by $[U]$ s times, we obtain

(7.3) $$[U]^s\{A^{(r)}\} = Z_r^s\{A^{(r)}\} \qquad r = 1, 2, \ldots, n$$

We have n equations of this type, one for each modal column $\{A^{(r)}\}$ and its associated root Z_r. Let us now construct a square matrix $[A]$ from the various modal columns $\{A^{(r)}\}$ in the following manner:

(7.4) $$[A] = [A^{(1)} A^{(2)} \cdots A^{(n)}] = [A_{rs}]$$

The set of Eqs. (7.3) may be conveniently written in the form

(7.5) $$[U]^s[A] = [A] \begin{bmatrix} Z_1^s & 0 & 0 & \cdots & & 0 \\ 0 & Z_2^s & 0 & \cdots & & 0 \\ 0 & 0 & Z_3^s & 0 & \cdots & 0 \\ \cdot & \cdot & \cdot & \cdot & \cdot & \cdot \\ 0 & 0 & & \cdots & & Z_n^s \end{bmatrix}$$

Postmultiplying (7.5) by $[A]^{-1}$, we obtain

(7.6) $$[U]^s = [A] \begin{bmatrix} Z_1^s & 0 & 0 & \cdots & 0 \\ 0 & Z_2^s & 0 & \cdots & 0 \\ 0 & 0 & Z_3^s & \cdots & 0 \\ \cdot & \cdot & \cdot & \cdot & \cdot \\ 0 & 0 & 0 & \cdots & Z_n^s \end{bmatrix} [A]^{-1}$$

For convenience let

(7.7) $$[B] = [A]^{-1}$$

Now let the roots Z_r of the determinantal equation be arranged in descending order of magnitude; that is, let Z_1 be the largest root of the determinantal equation, Z_2 the next largest, etc., or

(7.8) $$Z_1 > Z_2 > Z_3 \cdots > Z_n$$

assuming that the roots are all distinct. Now let us assume that s in Eq. (7.6) is so great that

(7.9) $$Z_1^s \gg Z_2^s, \text{ etc.}$$

If this is true, then only the terms corresponding to the dominant root Z_1 need be retained. By direct multiplication we have for s sufficiently large

(7.10) $$[U]^s \cong Z_1^s \begin{bmatrix} A_{11}B_{11} & A_{11}B_{12} & \cdots & A_{11}B_{1n} \\ A_{21}B_{11} & A_{21}B_{12} & \cdots & A_{21}B_{1n} \\ \cdot & \cdot & \cdots & \cdot \\ A_{n1}B_{11} & A_{n1}B_{12} & \cdots & A_{n1}B_{1n} \end{bmatrix}$$

As a consequence of this property of the dynamical matrix $[U]$ we may perform the following procedure, which will yield the dominant root Z_1 of the system as well as the modal column associated with this root.

Let us select an *arbitrary* column matrix $\{x\}_0$ and form the following sequence:

$$
\begin{aligned}
[U]\{x\}_0 &= \{x\}_1 \\
[U]\{x\}_1 &= [U]^2\{x\}_0 = \{x\}_2 \\
[U]\{x\}_2 &= [U]^3\{x\}_0 = \{x\}_3 \\
&\cdots\cdots\cdots\cdots\cdots \\
[U]\{x\}_{s-1} &= [U]^s\{x\}_0 = \{x\}_s
\end{aligned}
$$

(7.11)

In view of Eq. (7.10) we have *for a sufficiently large s*

(7.12)
$$
\{x\}_s = [U]^s\{x\}_0 = [U]^s
\begin{Bmatrix}
x_{10} \\ x_{20} \\ \cdot \\ \cdot \\ \cdot \\ x_{n0}
\end{Bmatrix}
$$

$$
\cong Z_1^s
\begin{Bmatrix}
A_{11}R_1 \\ A_{21}R_1 \\ \cdots \\ A_{n1}R_1
\end{Bmatrix}
$$

where

(7.13)
$$
R_1 = B_{11}x_{10} + B_{12}x_{20} + \cdots + B_{1n}x_{n0}
$$

That is, by repeated multiplication of the column matrix $\{x\}_0$ by the dynamical matrix $[U]$, we eventually reach a stage where further multiplication by $[U]$ merely multiplies every element of the column matrix $\{x\}_{s-1}$ by a common factor. This common factor is Z_1, the dominant root of the determinantal equation. By (6.16) the fundamental angular frequency ω_1 is given by

(7.14)
$$
\omega_1 = \sqrt{\frac{1}{Z_1}}
$$

We also see that the elements of the column matrix $\{x\}_s$ are proportional to those of the modal matrix $\{A^{(1)}\}$.

We now turn to a procedure by which we may obtain the next largest root Z_2 and its appropriate mode.

To do this, let us place $s = 1$ in Eq. (7.6) and premultiply both sides by $[A]^{-1}$. We then obtain, since $[A^{-1}] = [B]$,

$$(7.15) \qquad [B][U] = \begin{bmatrix} Z_1 & 0 & 0 & \cdots & 0 \\ 0 & Z_2 & 0 & \cdots & 0 \\ 0 & 0 & Z_3 & \cdots & 0 \\ \cdots & \cdots & \cdots & \cdots & \cdots \\ 0 & 0 & & \cdots & Z_n \end{bmatrix} [B]$$

The matrix B is given by

$$(7.16) \qquad [B] = \begin{bmatrix} B_{11} & B_{12} & B_{13} & \cdots & B_{1n} \\ B_{21} & B_{22} & B_{23} & \cdots & B_{2n} \\ \cdots & \cdots & \cdots & \cdots & \cdots \\ B_{n1} & B_{n2} & B_{n3} & \cdots & B_{nn} \end{bmatrix}$$

We thus see that if we take a typical *row* $[B_r]$ of the square matrix $[B]$ in the form

$$(7.17) \qquad [B_r] = [B_{r1} \quad B_{r2} \quad B_{r3} \quad \cdots \quad B_{rn}]$$

then as a consequence of Eq. (7.15) we have

$$(7.18) \qquad [B_r][U] = Z_r[B_r]$$

We also have, by (7.1), the relation

$$(7.19) \qquad [U]\{A^{(r)}\} = Z_r\{A^{(r)}\}$$

a relation satisfied by the modal column $\{A^{(r)}\}$. Now since the dynamical matrix $[U]$ is equal to $[K]^{-1}[M]$, we may write (7.19) in the form

$$(7.20) \qquad [K]^{-1}[M]\{A^{(r)}\} = Z_r\{A^{(r)}\}$$

If we premultiply both sides of this equation by M, take the transpose of both sides, and use the reversal law of transposed products, we obtain

$$(7.21) \qquad \{A^{(r)}\}'[M][U] = Z_r\{A^{(r)}\}'[M]$$

Comparing Eqs. (7.21) and (7.18), we see that they are identical in form; hence we have

$$(7.22) \qquad [B_r] = a_r\{A^{(r)}\}'[M]$$

where a_r is a proportionality factor. Equation (7.22) is of great importance in determining the higher roots of the determinantal equation as well as the modal columns corresponding to these roots.

We notice that since $[B] = [A]^{-1}$ we have

$$(7.23) \qquad [B][A] = I$$

where I is the unit matrix of the nth order. Hence the row matrices $[B_r]$ and the modal column matrices $\{A^{(r)}\}$ have the property that

$$(7.24) \qquad [B_r]\{A^{(s)}\} = \begin{cases} 0 & \text{if } r \neq s \\ 1 & \text{if } r = s \end{cases}$$

The general solution of the problem under consideration is given in terms of the natural angular frequencies ω_r and the modal columns $\{A^{(r)}\}$ in the form

$$(7.25) \qquad \{q\} = \sum_{r=1}^{r=n} C_r \{A^{(r)}\} \sin(\omega_r t + \theta_r)$$

where the θ_r are the arbitrary phase angles determined from the initial conditions of the system at $t = 0$. The C_r are arbitrary constants also determined from the initial conditions of the system.

This equation may also be written in the convenient matrix form

$$(7.26) \qquad \{q\} = [A] \begin{bmatrix} \sin(\omega_1 t + \theta_1) & 0 & \cdots & 0 \\ 0 & \sin(\omega_2 t + \theta_2) & 0 & \cdots & 0 \\ \hdotsfor{5} \\ 0 & \cdots & & \sin(\omega_n t + \theta_n) \end{bmatrix} \{C\}$$

Normal Coordinates. If we premultiply both sides of (7.26) by $[B] = [A]^{-1}$, we obtain

$$(7.27) \qquad \{y\} = [B]\{q\} = \begin{bmatrix} \sin(\omega_1 t + \theta_1) & 0 & \cdots & 0 \\ 0 & \sin(\omega_2 t + \theta_2) & \cdots & 0 \\ \hdotsfor{4} \\ 0 & \cdots & & \sin(\omega_n t + \theta_n) \end{bmatrix} \{C\}$$

Hence we have

$$(7.28) \qquad \begin{aligned} y_1 &= C_1 \sin(\omega_1 t + \theta_1) \\ y_2 &= C_2 \sin(\omega_2 t + \theta_2) \\ &\cdots\cdots\cdots\cdots\cdots \\ y_n &= C_n \sin(\omega_n t + \theta_n) \end{aligned}$$

The y_r quantities are the normal coordinates of the system.

Continuing the Solution. By Eq. (7.12) we have seen how the fundamental frequency ω_1 and the fundamental mode $\{A^{(1)}\}$ may be obtained. We shall now develop a procedure by which the higher angular frequencies and the corresponding modal columns may be obtained.

If we premultiply (7.25) by the row matrix $[B_1]$, we have in view of (7.24)

$$(7.29) \qquad [B_1]\{q\} = C_1 \sin(\omega_1 t + \theta_1)$$

If now the fundamental mode is absent, we have

$$(7.30) \qquad [B_1]\{q\} = 0$$

Hence, expanding this equation, we obtain

$$(7.31) \qquad B_{11}q_1 + B_{12}q_2 + \cdots + B_{1n}q_n = 0$$

or

$$q_1 = -\frac{B_{12}}{B_{11}} q_2 - \frac{B_{13}}{B_{11}} q_3 - \cdots - \frac{B_{1n}}{B_{11}} q_n$$

(7.32)
$$q_2 = q_2$$
$$q_3 = q_3$$
$$\cdots\cdots$$
$$q_n = q_n$$

This set of equations may be written in the matrix form

(7.33)
$$\begin{Bmatrix} q_1 \\ q_2 \\ \cdot \\ \cdot \\ \cdot \\ q_n \end{Bmatrix} = \begin{bmatrix} 0 & -\dfrac{B_{12}}{B_{11}} & -\dfrac{B_{13}}{B_{11}} & \cdots & -\dfrac{B_{1n}}{B_{11}} \\ 0 & 1 & 0 & \cdots & 0 \\ 0 & \cdots\cdots\cdots & \cdots & 1 \end{bmatrix} \begin{Bmatrix} q_1 \\ \cdot \\ \cdot \\ \cdot \\ q_n \end{Bmatrix}$$

Or if we call the square matrix above $[S]$, we have

(7.34) $\{q\} = [S]\{q\}$

This constrains the coordinates in such a manner that the fundamental mode is absent. The original differential equations of the system (6.5) may be written in terms of the *dynamical matrix* in the form

(7.35) $[U]\{\ddot{q}\} + I\{q\} = \{0\}$

where I is the unit matrix of the nth order. If we now differentiate Eq. (7.34) twice with respect to time, we have

(7.36) $\{\ddot{q}\} = [S]\{\ddot{q}\}$

Substituting this into (7.35), we obtain

(7.37) $[U][S]\{\ddot{q}\} + I\{q\} = 0$

If we let

(7.38) $[U][S] = [U]_1$

Eq. (7.37) becomes

(7.39) $[U]_1\{\ddot{q}\} + I\{q\} = \{0\}$

This set of equations has the same *form* as the original set (7.35). It represents a system whose dynamical matrix is $[U]_1$ and whose natural frequencies and modes are the same as those of the original system, but since we have used the constraint (7.34), the fundamental frequency and mode are now absent.

By carrying out the same procedure with the matrix $[U]_1$ that was performed with the matrix $[U]$, we obtain the root Z_2 and hence the next higher natural frequency ω_2 together with the corresponding mode. We then obtain a new row matrix $[B_2]$ by Eq. (7.22) and repeat the procedure until all the angular frequencies and all the modal columns of the system have been found. An example of the general procedure will now be given.

8. Numerical Example, the Triple Pendulum. As a simple numerical example of the above theory, let us consider the oscillations of a triple pendulum under gravity in a vertical plane. This example is given by

Duncan and Collar in their fundamental paper referred to in Sec. 7. The dynamical system under consideration is given by Fig. 8.1.

We shall consider the case of small oscillations, and for the coordinates of the system we shall take the small horizontal displacements of the masses M_1, M_2, M_3, respectively, from the equilibrium position. The first step in the procedure is to compute the dynamical matrix $[U]$.

Fig. 8.1

The Flexibility Matrix. If we apply a set of static forces F_1, F_2, F_3 in the direction of the coordinates q_1, q_2, and q_3, we may write the relation between the displacements q_1, q_2, and q_3 and the forces F_1, F_2, F_3 in the form

$$(8.1) \qquad \begin{Bmatrix} F_1 \\ F_2 \\ F_3 \end{Bmatrix} = \begin{bmatrix} K_{11} & K_{12} & K_{13} \\ K_{21} & K_{22} & K_{23} \\ K_{31} & K_{32} & K_{33} \end{bmatrix} \begin{Bmatrix} q_1 \\ q_2 \\ q_3 \end{Bmatrix}$$

where the square matrix $[K]$ is the stiffness matrix. We may premultiply by $[K]^{-1}$ and obtain the displacements in terms of the forces in the form

$$(8.2) \qquad \begin{Bmatrix} q_1 \\ q_2 \\ q_3 \end{Bmatrix} = \begin{bmatrix} \phi_{11} & \phi_{12} & \phi_{13} \\ \phi_{21} & \phi_{22} & \phi_{23} \\ \phi_{31} & \phi_{32} & \phi_{33} \end{bmatrix} \begin{Bmatrix} F_1 \\ F_2 \\ F_3 \end{Bmatrix}$$

where the matrix $[\phi] = [K]^{-1}$ is the flexibility matrix. Since $K_{rs} = K_{sr}$, we have

$$(8.3) \qquad\qquad \phi_{rs} = \phi_{sr}$$

That is, the flexibility matrix is a symmetric matrix.

In terms of the flexibility matrix the dynamical matrix is given by

$$(8.4) \qquad\qquad [U] = [K]^{-1}[M] = [\phi][M]$$

To determine the elements of the flexibility matrix, it is necessary only to impose a unit force F_1 on the system and compute or measure the corresponding deflections $(q_1 q_2 q_3)$. This gives the elements of the first column of $[\phi]$. Applying a unit force F_2 and obtaining the corresponding deflections yields the second column of $[\phi]$, etc.

If a static unit force is applied horizontally to mass M_1, then the three masses will each be displaced a distance a given by

$$(8.5) \qquad a = \frac{l_1}{g(M_1 + M_2 + M_3)}$$

Hence the first column of the flexibility matrix is given by

$$(8.6) \qquad a = \phi_{11} = \phi_{21} = \phi_{31}$$

When a unit force is applied horizontally to M_2, M_1 will again be displaced a distance a, but M_2 and M_3 will each be displaced a distance $a + b$, where

$$(8.7) \qquad b = \frac{l_2}{g(M_2 + M_3)}$$

Hence the second column of the matrix $[\phi]$ is given by

$$(8.8) \qquad \phi_{12} = a \qquad \phi_{22} = \phi_{32} = a + b$$

Applying a unit horizontal force to M_3 displaces M_1 a distance a; M_2 a distance $a + b$; and M_3 a distance $a + b + c$, where

$$(8.9) \qquad c = \frac{l_3}{gM_3}$$

The third column of the flexibility matrix is

$$(8.10) \qquad \phi_{13} = a \qquad \phi_{23} = a + b \qquad \phi_{33} = a + b + c$$

Hence the flexibility matrix is given by

$$(8.11) \qquad [\phi] = \begin{bmatrix} a & a & a \\ a & a + b & a + b \\ a & a + b & a + b + c \end{bmatrix}$$

The mass matrix, in this case, has the diagonal form

$$(8.12) \qquad [M] = \begin{bmatrix} M_1 & 0 & 0 \\ 0 & M_2 & 0 \\ 0 & 0 & M_3 \end{bmatrix}$$

Hence the dynamical matrix is given by

$$(8.13) \qquad [U] = [\phi][M]$$
$$= \begin{bmatrix} M_1a & M_2a & M_3a \\ M_1a & M_2(a + b) & M_3(a + b) \\ M_1a & M_2(a + b) & M_3(a + b + c) \end{bmatrix}$$

As a numerical example, let us take the case where all the masses are equal and the lengths of the pendulums are equal.   In this case we have

$$(8.14) \qquad M_1 = M_2 = M_3 = M \qquad l_1 = l_2 = l_3 = l$$

$$a = \frac{l}{3Mg} \qquad b = \frac{l}{2Mg} \qquad c = \frac{l}{Mg}$$

Hence the dynamical matrix in this case becomes

$$(8.15) \qquad U = \frac{l}{6g} \begin{bmatrix} 2 & 2 & 2 \\ 2 & 5 & 5 \\ 2 & 5 & 11 \end{bmatrix} = \frac{l}{6g}[u]$$

Equation (6.12) reduces in this case to

$$(8.16) \qquad \left(I - \frac{\omega^2 l}{6g}[u] \right) \{A\} = \{0\}$$

If we let

$$(8.17) \qquad \frac{6g}{l}\frac{1}{\omega^2} = \bar{Z}$$

then Eq. (6.14) becomes

$$(8.18) \qquad (\bar{Z}I - [u])\{A\} = \{0\}$$

where $[u]$ is the numerical part of the dynamical matrix $[U]$, and the factor $6g/l$ has been absorbed into $\bar{Z}$.

The angular frequencies are given by

$$(8.19) \qquad \omega_r = \sqrt{\frac{6g}{\bar{Z}_r l}}$$

To find the roots $\bar{Z}_r$, we begin the iterative procedure of Eq. (7.11). If we choose for our *arbitrary* column $\{x\}_0$ the column

$$(8.20) \qquad \{x\}_0 = \begin{Bmatrix} 1 \\ 1 \\ 1 \end{Bmatrix}$$

we begin the sequence

$$(8.21) \qquad [u]\{x\}_0 = \begin{bmatrix} 2 & 2 & 2 \\ 2 & 5 & 5 \\ 2 & 5 & 11 \end{bmatrix} \begin{Bmatrix} 1 \\ 1 \\ 1 \end{Bmatrix}$$

$$= \begin{Bmatrix} 6 \\ 12 \\ 18 \end{Bmatrix} = 18 \begin{Bmatrix} 0.3 \\ 0.6 \\ 1 \end{Bmatrix}$$

It is unnecessary to carry the common factor 18 in the further operations since it is the *ratios* of the successive elements in the multiplications that are important. Dropping the factor 18 and continuing, we have

$$
(8.22) \qquad
\begin{bmatrix} 2 & 2 & 2 \\ 2 & 5 & 5 \\ 2 & 5 & 11 \end{bmatrix}
\begin{Bmatrix} 0.3 \\ 0.6 \\ 1 \end{Bmatrix}
= \begin{Bmatrix} 4 \\ 9 \\ 15 \end{Bmatrix}
= 15 \begin{Bmatrix} 0.26 \\ 0.6 \\ 1 \end{Bmatrix}
$$

$$
\begin{bmatrix} 2 & 2 & 2 \\ 2 & 5 & 5 \\ 2 & 5 & 11 \end{bmatrix}
\begin{Bmatrix} 0.26 \\ 0.6 \\ 1 \end{Bmatrix}
= 14.53 \begin{Bmatrix} 0.25688 \\ 0.58716 \\ 1 \end{Bmatrix}
$$

After nine multiplications we have

$$
(8.23) \qquad
\begin{bmatrix} 2 & 2 & 2 \\ 2 & 5 & 5 \\ 2 & 5 & 11 \end{bmatrix}
\begin{Bmatrix} 0.254885 \\ 0.584225 \\ 1 \end{Bmatrix}
= 14.4309 \begin{Bmatrix} 0.254885 \\ 0.584225 \\ 1 \end{Bmatrix}
$$

Repeating the process merely multiplies the column matrix by the factor 14.4309; we therefore have

$$
(8.24) \qquad \bar{Z}_1 = 14.4309
$$

The fundamental frequency of the oscillation is given by

$$
(8.25) \qquad F_1 = \frac{\omega_1}{2\pi} = \frac{1}{2\pi}\sqrt{\frac{6g}{\bar{Z}_1 l}} = 0.102624 \sqrt{\frac{g}{l}}
$$

The modal column $\{A^{(1)}\}$ is proportional to the column

$$
\begin{Bmatrix} 0.254885 \\ 0.584225 \\ 1 \end{Bmatrix}
$$

To obtain the higher harmonics, we first make use of Eq. (7.22) to obtain the row B_1. In this case we have

$$
(8.26) \qquad [B_1] = a_1[0.254885,\ 0.584225,\ 1]
\begin{bmatrix} M & 0 & 0 \\ 0 & M & 0 \\ 0 & 0 & M \end{bmatrix}
$$

Since a_1 is an arbitrary factor and we are interested only in a row proportional to $[B_1]$, we may take B_1 equal to $[0.254885,\ 0.584225,\ 1]$. The matrix $[S]$ of (7.34) is now given by

$$
(8.27) \qquad [S] =
\begin{bmatrix} 0 & -2.29211 & -3.92334 \\ 0 & 1 & 0 \\ 0 & 0 & 1 \end{bmatrix}
$$

We then obtain

$$
(8.28) \qquad [u]_1 = [u][S] =
\begin{bmatrix} 0 & -2.58422 & -5.84668 \\ 0 & 0.41578 & -2.84668 \\ 0 & 0.41578 & 3.15332 \end{bmatrix}
$$

This is the dynamical matrix that has the fundamental mode absent. We now repeat the iterative procedure by again choosing an arbitrary column matrix $\{x\}_0$; we thus find

(8.29)

$$[u]_1 \begin{Bmatrix} 1 \\ 1 \\ 1 \end{Bmatrix} = \begin{Bmatrix} \cdots \\ -2.4309 \\ 3.5691 \end{Bmatrix} = 3.5691 \begin{Bmatrix} \cdots \\ -0.68110 \\ 1 \end{Bmatrix}$$

$$[u]_1 \begin{Bmatrix} \cdots \\ -0.68110 \\ 1 \end{Bmatrix} = \begin{Bmatrix} \cdots \\ -3.1299 \\ 2.8701 \end{Bmatrix} = 2.8701 \begin{Bmatrix} \cdots \\ -1.09049 \\ 1 \end{Bmatrix}$$

After 15 multiplications the column repeats itself, and the multiple factor is

(8.30) $\bar{Z}_2 = 2.6152$

The modal column $\{A^{(2)}\}$ for this approximation may be taken to be

(8.31) $\{A^{(2)}\} = \begin{Bmatrix} -0.95670 \\ -1.29429 \\ 1 \end{Bmatrix}$

Hence the first overtone has this mode and a frequency given by

(8.32) $F_2 = \dfrac{\omega_2}{2\pi} = \dfrac{1}{2\pi} \sqrt{\dfrac{6g}{\bar{Z}_2 l}} = 0.24107 \sqrt{\dfrac{g}{l}}$

Again by Eq. (7.22) we may take the row $\{B_2\}$ equal to $\{A^{(2)}\}'$. The condition for the absence of the second overtone is

(8.33) $[B_2]\{q\} = 0 = [-0.95670, -1.29429, 1]\{q\}$

Solving this for q_1, we have

(8.34) $q_1 = -1.35287q_2 + 1.04526q_3$

We may eliminate q_1 between this equation and the equation

(8.35) $[B_1]\{q\} = 0.254885q_1 + 0.584225q_2 + q_3 = 0$

We thus obtain

(8.36) $q_2 = -5.2900q_3$

This ensures that both the fundamental and first-overtone modes are absent from the oscillation. Equation (8.36) may be written in the convenient matrix form

(8.37) $\begin{Bmatrix} q_1 \\ q_2 \\ q_3 \end{Bmatrix} = \begin{bmatrix} 1 & 0 & 0 \\ 0 & 0 & -5.2900 \\ 0 & 0 & 1 \end{bmatrix} \begin{Bmatrix} q_1 \\ q_2 \\ q_3 \end{Bmatrix}$

$$= [S]_1\{q\}$$

We now construct a new dynamical matrix $[u]_2$ that has the fundamental and overtone modes absent; this new matrix is given by

$$(8.38) \qquad [u]_2 = [u]_1[S]_1 = \begin{bmatrix} 0 & 0 & 7.8238 \\ 0 & 0 & -5.0461 \\ 0 & 0 & 0.9539 \end{bmatrix}$$

We again repeat the iterative process and obtain

$$(8.39) \qquad [u]_2\{x\}_0 = \begin{bmatrix} 0 & 0 & 7.8238 \\ 0 & 0 & -5.0461 \\ 0 & 0 & 0.9539 \end{bmatrix} \begin{Bmatrix} 1 \\ 1 \\ 1 \end{Bmatrix}$$

$$= \begin{Bmatrix} 7.8238 \\ -5.0461 \\ 0.9539 \end{Bmatrix} = 0.9539 \begin{Bmatrix} 8.2019 \\ -5.2900 \\ 1 \end{Bmatrix}$$

Repeating the process merely repeats the factor 0.9539; so it is unnecessary to go further. We thus have

$$(8.40) \qquad \bar{Z}_3 = 0.9539$$

The highest frequency is given by

$$(8.41) \qquad F_3 = \frac{1}{2\pi} \sqrt{\frac{6g}{\bar{Z}_3 l}} = 0.39916 \sqrt{\frac{g}{l}}$$

The mode $\{A^{(3)}\}$ corresponding to this frequency may be taken to be

$$(8.42) \qquad \{A^{(3)}\} = \begin{Bmatrix} 8.2019 \\ -5.2900 \\ 1 \end{Bmatrix}$$

to a factor of proportionality. The modal matrix may be taken to be

$$(8.43) \qquad [A] = \begin{bmatrix} 0.254885 & -0.95670 & 8.2019 \\ 0.584225 & -1.29429 & -5.2900 \\ 1 & 1 & 1 \end{bmatrix}$$

In this case, because of the simplicity of the mass matrix $[M]$, we may take

$$(8.44) \qquad [B] = [A]'$$

the transpose of matrix $[A]$.

The normal coordinates are then given by

$$(8.45) \qquad \{y\} = [B]\{q\}$$

9. Nonconservative Systems. Vibrations with Viscous Damping. In the last few sections the general theory of conservative systems has been considered.   These systems are characterized completely by their kinetic- and potential-energy functions and are of great practical importance.   In many problems that arise in practice the frictional forces are relatively small and may be disregarded and the system treated as a conservative one.

The mathematical analyses of vibrating systems that contain frictional forces of a general nature usually lead to a formulation involving *non-linear* differential equations (see Chap. 22).   However, in a great many practical problems, the frictional forces involved are proportional to the velocities of the moving parts of the system.   Frictional forces of this type are present in systems that contain viscous friction.   The mathematical solution of vibration problems of systems involving viscous friction leads usually to the solution of sets of *linear* equations and is relatively simple.

The Lagrangian equations of Sec. 4 can be generalized to take into account viscous friction.   In order to do this, it is necessary to compute the rate at which energy is dissipated by the viscous frictional forces. This may be done by considering a single particle moving along the x axis undergoing damping so that the resisting frictional force impeding its motion is

$$(9.1) \qquad f_r = -c\dot{x}$$

The work done by the frictional force during a small displacement δx is $-(c\dot{x}\,\delta x)$, and the amount of energy δW dissipated is

$$(9.2) \qquad \delta W = f_r\,\delta x = c\dot{x}\,\delta x = (c\dot{x}^2)\,\delta t \qquad x = \dot{x}\,\delta t$$

The time rate at which energy is dissipated in this case is $\delta W/\delta t = c\dot{x}^2$. Let the function F be defined by the equation

$$(9.3) \qquad F = \frac{c\dot{x}^2}{2}$$

This function is called the *dissipation* function and represents half the rate at which the energy of the particle is dissipated by the viscous frictional force.   The frictional force f_r may therefore be obtained by the following equation:

$$(9.4) \qquad f_r = -\frac{dF}{d\dot{x}} = -c\dot{x}$$

By an extension of the above analysis to the case of a system having n degrees of freedom undergoing viscous friction, it can be shown that the dissipation function of the entire system in general has the form

$$(9.5) \qquad F = \tfrac{1}{2}(C_{11}\dot{q}_1 + 2C_{12}\dot{q}_1\dot{q}_2 + C_{22}\dot{q}_2^2 + \cdots)$$

where $(\dot{q}_1, \dot{q}_2, \dot{q}_3, \ldots)$ are the generalized velocities of the system and the coefficients $C_{11}, C_{12}, C_{22}, \ldots$ in general depend on the configuration of the system, though for the case of small vibrations in the neighborhood of a configuration of stable equilibrium these coefficients can be treated with good accuracy as being constant. In such cases it is convenient to introduce the *damping matrix*

$$(9.6) \qquad [C] = \begin{bmatrix} C_{11} & C_{12} & C_{13} & \cdots & C_{1n} \\ C_{21} & C_{22} & C_{23} & \cdots & C_{2n} \\ \cdots\cdots\cdots\cdots\cdots\cdots\cdots \\ C_{n1} & C_{n2} & C_{n3} & \cdots & C_{nn} \end{bmatrix} \qquad C_{ij} = C_{ji}$$

The elements of the damping matrix $[C]$ are the viscous-friction damping coefficients C_{ij}. The matrix $[C]$ is a symmetric matrix. In terms of this matrix the dissipation function F may be written in the following concise form,

$$(9.7) \qquad F = \tfrac{1}{2}(\dot{q})'[C](q)$$

where $(\dot{q})'$ is the transpose of the generalized velocity matrix $(\dot{q})$.

The dissipation function F represents half the rate at which energy is being dissipated from the entire system as it moves under the influence of viscous friction. The generalized forces f_i that arise from the viscous friction of the system are

$$(9.8) \qquad f_i = -\frac{\partial F}{\partial \dot{q}_i} \qquad i = 1, 2, 3, \ldots, n$$

The Lagrangian equations of the system then take the form

$$(9.9) \qquad \frac{d}{dt}\left(\frac{\partial T}{\partial \dot{q}_i}\right) - \frac{\partial T}{\partial q_i} = -\frac{\partial V}{\partial q_i} - \frac{\partial F}{\partial \dot{q}_i} + Q_i \qquad i = 1, 2, 3, \ldots$$

The left-hand member of (9.9) represents the effect of the inertia terms of the system; the terms of the right-hand member are the various generalized forces of the system. (1) The term $-(\partial V/\partial q_i)$ takes into account forces that may be derived from a potential function V such as gravitational forces, forces due to the presence of elastic springs, etc. (2) The term $-(\partial F/\partial \dot{q}_i)$ takes into account the effect of retarding forces due to viscous friction. (3) The term Q_i includes all other forces acting on the system, such as time-dependent disturbing forces.

In terms of the inertia matrix $[M]$, the stiffness matrix $[K]$, and the damping matrix $[C]$ of the system the Lagrangian equations (9.9) may be written in the following concise form:

$$(9.10) \qquad [M]\{\ddot{q}\} + [C]\{\dot{q}\} + [K]\{q\} = \{Q\}$$

The elements of the column matrix (Q) are the generalized forces Q_i of the system.

The electrical networks of Chap. 7 may be regarded as special dynamical systems that are characterized by the following functions:

$$(9.11) \quad T = \tfrac{1}{2}\{\dot{q}\}'[L]\{\dot{q}\} \qquad V = \tfrac{1}{2}\{q\}'[S]\{q\} \qquad F = \tfrac{1}{2}\{\dot{q}\}'[R]\{\dot{q}\}$$

In these expressions the $\{\dot{q}\}$ are the various mesh currents of the circuit, the elements of $\{q\}$ are the various mesh charges of the circuit, and the square matrices $[L]$, $[S]$, and $[R]$ are the inductance, elastance, and resistance matrices of the circuit. In this case T represents the magnetic energy of the system, V the electric energy of the system, and F is one-half the power dissipated by the resistances of the circuit. The Lagrangian equations (9.9) now take the following form:

$$(9.12) \qquad [L]\{\ddot{q}\} + [R]\{\dot{q}\} + [S]\{q\} = \{E\}$$

The elements of the column matrix $\{E\}$ are the various mesh potentials of the electrical circuit.

Classical Solution, Free Oscillations. If the generalized forces Q_i driving the nonconservative system are all equal to zero, then the set of Eqs. (9.10) reduce to

$$(9.13) \qquad [M]\{\ddot{q}\} + [C]\{\dot{q}\} + [K]\{q\} = \{0\}$$

This set of differential equations determines the nature of the free oscillations of the system. In order to solve this set of equations, assume a solution of the exponential form

$$(9.14) \qquad\qquad \{q\} = \{A\}e^{mt}$$

where m is a number to be determined and $\{A\}$ is a column of constants. If this assumed form of solution is substituted into (9.13), the following result is obtained:

$$(9.15) \qquad\qquad ([M]m^2 + [C]m + [K])\{A\}e^{mt} = \{0\}$$

If (9.15) is divided by the scalar factor e^{mt}, a set of linear homogeneous equations in the column of constants $\{A\}$ is obtained. For this set of equations to have a nontrivial solution, it is necessary that the determinant of the coefficients must vanish; hence we must have

$$(9.16) \qquad \Delta(m) = |[M]m^2 + [C]m + [K]| = 0$$

This equation is called *Lagrange's determinantal equation for m*. In general it is of degree $2n$. The following properties concerning the roots of $\Delta(m)$ may be proved:[*]

---

[*] See A. G. Webster, "The Dynamics of Particles and of Rigid Bodies," Teubner Verlagsgesellschaft, Leipzig, 1925.

1. None of the roots is real and positive.

2. If $[C] = [0]$, there is no dissipation of energy and the system is a conservative one. In this case the roots are all pure imaginaries.

3. If $[M] = [0]$ or $[K] = [0]$ so that the system is devoid of inertia or of stiffness and $[C] \neq [0]$, the roots are real and negative so that the motion dies away exponentially.

4. If the elements of the damping matrix $[C]$ are not too large, all the roots are conjugate complex numbers with a negative real part. This is the most frequent case in practice.

Let it be supposed that Eq. (9.16) has $2n$ distinct roots $(m_1, m_2, m_3, \ldots, m_{2n})$. Then as a consequence of (9.15) there are $2n$ equations of the following type,

$$(9.17) \quad ([M]m_r^2 + [C]m_r + [K])\{A_r\} = \{0\} \qquad r = 1, 2, 3, \ldots, 2n$$

where $\{A_r\}$ represents a column of constants associated with the root m_r. Each column $\{A_r\}$ has the form

$$(9.18) \qquad\qquad \{A_r\} = \begin{bmatrix} A_{1r} \\ A_{2r} \\ \cdot \\ \cdot \\ \cdot \\ A_{nr} \end{bmatrix}$$

Equation (9.5) fixes the ratios

$$(9.19) \qquad\qquad A_{1r} : A_{2r} : A_{3r} : \cdots : A_{nr}$$

The theory of linear differential equations indicates that to obtain a general solution of the set of Eqs. (9.13) we must take the sum of the particular solutions $\{A_r\}e^{m_r t}$ for all the roots m_r. We thus obtain the following general solution:

$$(9.20) \qquad\qquad (q) = \sum_{r=1}^{2n} \{A_r\}e^{m_r t}$$

It must be noted that the ratios of the A's in any one column are determined by the linear equations (9.17); therefore there is still a factor that is arbitrary for each column and hence $2n$ in all. Thus the general solution (9.20) contains $2n$ arbitrary constants, as it should.

If the roots of (9.16) are complex, they occur in conjugate complex pairs of the form

$$(9.21) \quad m_r = -a_r + j\omega_r \qquad \bar{m}_r = -a_r - j\omega_r \qquad r = 1, 2, 3, \ldots, n$$

In this case the general solution (9.20) contains terms of the following type:

$$(9.22) \quad \{A_r\}e^{m_r t} + \{\bar{A}_r\}e^{\bar{m}_r t}$$
$$= e^{-a_r t}\{B_r\} \cos (\omega_r t + \theta_r) \quad\quad r = 1, 2, 3, \ldots, n$$

where $\{B_r\}$ represents a column of constants and the θ_r are phase angles. In this case the general solution of (9.13) takes the form

$$(9.23) \quad\quad\quad \{q\} = \sum_{r=1}^{n} \{B_r\}e^{-a_r t} \cos (\omega_r t + \theta_r)$$

It may easily be shown that the $\{B_r\}$ columns satisfy (9.17) in the same manner as do the $\{A_r\}$ columns, and hence the ratios of the B's in each column are fixed. Each column then contains an arbitrary constant in the phase angle θ_r belonging to the column. The following results may be stated:

If the roots of the determinantal equation (9.16) are distinct and conjugate complex quantities, then the motion of a dynamical system having n degrees of freedom slightly displaced from a position of stable equilibrium may be described as follows:

Each coordinate performs the resultant of n damped harmonic oscillations of different periods. The phase and damping factors of any simple oscillation of a particular period are the same for all the coordinates. The absolute value of the amplitude of any particular coordinate is arbitrary, but the ratios of the amplitudes for a particular period for the different coordinates are determined solely by the nature of the system. The $2n$ arbitrary constants determine the n amplitudes and phases of the system. These arbitrary constants are found from the values of the n coordinates (q) and the n velocities $(\dot{q})$ for a particular instant of time.

The classical method of solution for the general nonconservative system consists in obtaining the determinantal equation (9.16), expanding the determinantal equation, then solving it for the $2n$ roots $(m_1, m_2, m_3, \ldots, m_{2n})$ by the Graeffe method of Chap. 5. Once the roots m_r of the determinantal equation have been found, the ratios of the columns (B_r) can be calculated by the use of (9.17). Finally the arbitrary constants are determined from a knowledge of the initial conditions of the system.

10. A Matrix Iterative Method for the Analysis of Nonconservative Systems. In a fundamental paper by Duncan and Collar* an iterative method similar to that discussed in Sec. 7 for the determination of the modes, decrement factors a_r, and frequencies ω_r of nonconservative sys-

---

* W. J. Duncan and A. R. Collar, Matrices Applied to the Motions of Damped Systems, *Philosophical Magazine*, ser. 7, vol. 19, p. 197, 1935.

tems is given.   The basic principle that underlies the method is to write the system of differential equations (9.13) as a first-order system by the introduction of the following partitioned matrix:

$$(10.1) \qquad \{y\} = \begin{bmatrix} (q) \\ (\dot{q}) \end{bmatrix}$$

The column matrix $\{y\}$ thus contains $2n$ elements, the n coordinates (q), and the n velocities $\{\dot{q}\}$.   If the following square partitioned matrix of the $2n$th order $2n$ is introduced,

$$(10.2) \qquad [v] = \begin{bmatrix} [0] & [I] \\ -[M]^{-1}[K] & -[M]^{-1}[C] \end{bmatrix}$$

where $[0]$ is the nth-order zero matrix and $[I]$ is the nth-order unit matrix, then the system of differential equations (9.13) may be written in the following form:

$$(10.3) \qquad \{\dot{y}\} = [v]\{y\}$$

In order to solve the first-order system of differential equations (10.3), assume a solution of the form

$$(10.4) \qquad \{y\} = e^{mt}\{A\}$$

If the assumed solution (10.4) is substituted into the differential equations (10.3), the following result is obtained:

$$(10.5) \qquad me^{mt}\{A\} = [v]e^{mt}\{A\}$$

If the scalar factor e^{mt} is divided out of Eq. (10.5), the result may be written in the form

$$(10.6) \qquad (mI - [v])\{A\} = \{0\}$$

where I is the unit matrix of order $2n$.   The matrix

$$(10.7) \qquad [c(m)] = mI - [v]$$

is the characteristic matrix of the matrix $[v]$.   The characteristic equation of $[v]$ is

$$(10.8) \qquad \det [c(m)] = |mI - [v]| = 0$$

The roots $m_1, m_2, m_3, \ldots, m_{2n}$ are the *eigenvalues* of the matrix $[v]$, and the columns $\{A_1\}, \{A_2\}, \{A_3\}, \ldots, \{A_{2n}\}$ satisfy equations of the form

$$(10.9) \qquad (m_rI - [v])\{A_r\} = \{0\} \qquad r = 1, 2, 3, 4, \ldots, 2n$$

The columns $\{A_r\}$ are therefore the *eigenvectors* of the matrix $[v]$.

The root m_r, having the largest modulus, may be determined by setting up a sequence similar to that of (7.11) of the form

$$(10.10) \qquad \{x\}_s = [v]^s \{x\}_0 \qquad s = 1, 2, 3, 4, \ldots$$

where $\{x\}_0$ is an *arbitrary* column matrix of the $2n$th order. It will be found that for a sufficiently large s continued multiplications give rise merely to multiplicative factors. These factors enable the eigenvalue having the largest modulus to be determined, and also the associated eigenvector can be found. The details of the practical numerical procedure are somewhat lengthy and will be found in the above paper and in the book by Frazer, Duncan, and Collar.[5]

11. Forced Oscillations of a Nonconservative System. Let us suppose that on each coordinate of the general nonconservative system there is impressed a harmonically varying force

$$(11.1) \cdot \qquad F_r \cos \omega t \qquad r = 1, 2, \ldots, n$$

In this case the differential equations (9.13) become

$$(11.2) \qquad [M]\{\ddot{q}\} + [R]\{\dot{q}\} + [K]\{q\} = \{F\} \cos \omega t$$

where $\{F\}$ is a column matrix whose elements are the amplitudes of the impressed forces F_r. We replace $\cos \omega t$ by $\mathrm{Re}\ e^{j\omega t}$ and solve the equation

$$(11.3) \qquad [M]\{\ddot{q}\} + [R]\{\dot{q}\} + [K]\{q\} = \{F\} e^{j\omega t} \qquad \prime$$

retaining only the real part of the particular solution. To do this, let us assume

$$(11.4) \qquad \{q\} = \{Q\} e^{j\omega t}$$

where $\{Q\}$ is a column of amplitude constants to be determined. Substituting this assumed solution into (11.4) and dividing by the common factor $e^{j\omega t}$, we have

$$(11.5) \qquad ([K] - \omega^2[M] + j\omega[R])\{Q\} = \{F\}$$

If we let

$$(11.6) \qquad [Z] = [K] - \omega^2[M] + j\omega[R] = [Y]^{-1}$$

then on premultiplying both sides of (11.6) by $[Z]^{-1} = [Y]$ we have

$$(11.7) \qquad \{Q\} = [Y]\{F\}$$

The steady-state solution of the forced oscillation is now given by

$$(11.8) \qquad \{q\} = \mathrm{Re}\ ([Y]\{F\} e^{j\omega t})$$

where Re signifies "the real part of." The matrix $[Z]$ is sometimes termed in the literature the *mechanical impedance matrix* and $[Y]$ the *mechanical admittance matrix.* Equation (11.8) represents the forced oscillations after the damped free oscillations have vanished.

It must be noted that, if $[R] = [0]$ and the system is conservative, then, if ω happens to coincide with one of the natural frequencies of the system, $[Z]$ as given by Eq. (11.6) vanishes and we have the case of resonance.

12. Dynamic Stability: The Routh-Hurwitz Stability Criterion. Consider a given dynamical system that is moving under the action of applied forces described by a set of differential equations. If any small disturbing influences are applied to the system, it may deviate only slightly from the previous condition of motion or it may depart from it further and further. If the deviation is slight, the system is said to be *dynamically stable;* otherwise, the system is *dynamically unstable.* The system is said to be dynamically stable if it is stable for all kinds of disturbances. In this section, criteria for the stability of linear dynamical systems will be given. These stability criteria are of great importance in determining the stability of many practical dynamical systems such as the stability of an aircraft in flight, the stability of certain electrical circuits used in communication and power engineering, and the stability of linear control systems.

Consider a linear dynamical system of n degrees of freedom whose differential equations of motion may be written in the following matrix form,

$$(12.1) \qquad [a]\{\ddot{x}\} + [b]\{\dot{x}\} + [c]\{x\} = \{0\}$$

where $\{x\}$ is a column matrix whose elements are the n coordinates of the system and the $[a]$, $[b]$, and $[c]$ matrices are square matrices whose elements are constants. The dots indicate differentiation with respect to time in the usual manner. Let a solution of the form

$$(12.2) \qquad \{x\} = \{A\}e^{st}$$

be assumed, where $\{A\}$ is a column of constants, e is the base of the natural logarithms, and s is a quantity to be determined. If this form of solution is substituted into (12.1), the result is

$$(12.3) \qquad ([a]s^2 + [b]s + [c])\{A\}e^{st} = \{0\}$$

If (12.3) is divided by the scalar factor e^{st}, the result is

$$(12.4) \qquad ([a]s^2 + [b]s + [c])\{A\} = \{0\}$$

This is a set of linear equations in the elements of the column matrix $\{A\}$. For a nontrivial solution the determinant of the coefficients $D(s)$ must be equal to zero so that

$$(12.5) \qquad D(s) = |[a]s^2 + [b]s + [c]| = 0$$

If the following notation is introduced,

(12.6) $$[g(s)] = [a]s^2 + [b]s + [c]$$

the determinant $D(s)$ can be expressed in the following form:

(12.7) $$D(s) = \det [g(s)] = \begin{vmatrix} g_{11}(s) & g_{12}(s) & \cdots & g_{1k}(s) \\ g_{21}(s) & g_{22}(s) & \cdots & g_{2k}(s) \\ \cdots & \cdots & \cdots & \cdots \\ g_{k1}(s) & g_{k2}(s) & \cdots & g_{kk}(s) \end{vmatrix}$$

If the determinant $D(s)$ is expanded, a polynomial in s of degree $n = 2k$ is obtained. This polynomial has the following form,

(12.8) $$D(s) = a_0 s^n + a_1 s^{n-1} + a_2 s^{n-2} + \cdots + a_{n-1} s + a_n = 0$$

where the constants a_i are functions of the constants of the dynamical system. The stability or instability of the dynamical system under consideration depends on the location of the roots of the polynomial $D(s)$ in the complex s plane. In general the roots of the polynomial equation $D(s) = 0$ will be complex numbers of the form $s_i = b_i + j\omega_i$, where $j = \sqrt{-1}$. If the real parts of all the roots b_i are negative numbers, there will be decrement factors $e^{b_i t}$ in the terms of the solution (12.2). This indicates that the solution is a decaying time function, and the solution will be *stable*. If, however, one or more roots s_i have a positive real part, then the solution (12.2) will contain one or more terms with the exponentially *increasing* factor $e^{b_i t}$, and the system will be *unstable*. An imaginary root of the form $s = j\omega$ will give rise to an oscillatory term of the form $e^{j\omega t}$ and thus represents a borderline case between stability and instability. If s_i is a multiple root, the above conclusions still hold unless $s_i = j\omega$ is a *multiple imaginary* root. In this case the solution contains the functions $e^{j\omega t}$, $te^{j\omega t}$, $t^2 e^{j\omega t}$, etc. The factor $te^{j\omega t}$ increases with time, and therefore a multiple root on the imaginary axis denotes instability. It is therefore apparent that, for the linear system characterized by the set of differential equations (12.1) to be stable, it is necessary and sufficient that the roots of the equation $D(s) = 0$ shall have nonpositive real parts and that, if any purely imaginary roots exist, they must not be multiple roots.

It is thus evident that the stability or instability of the dynamical system under consideration can be determined by obtaining the roots of $D(s) = 0$ by some procedure such as Graeffe's root-squaring method given in Chap. 5. This is a laborious procedure, and information concerning the stability of the system may be obtained with much less labor by applying a criterion known in the mathematical literature as the *Routh-Hurwitz stability criterion*.* The Routh-Hurwitz criterion will be

* See E. J. Routh, "Advanced Rigid Dynamics," pp. 223–231, The Macmillan Company, New York, 1905, and A. Hurwitz, Ueber die Bedingungen unter welchen

stated here without proof. The reader interested in the method of proof of the criterion is referred to the paper by Hurwitz.

Let the characteristic determinant $D(s)$ of the system of Eqs. (12.1) be written in the following form:

$$(12.9) \quad D(s) = a_0 s^n + a_1 s^{n-1} + a_2 s^{n-2} + \cdots + a_{n-1} s + a_n = 0$$

Then the conditions that *all* the roots of $D(s)$ have negative real parts are as follows:

1. A necessary but not sufficient condition is that all the a's in Eq. (12.9) have the same sign.

2. A necessary and sufficient condition for stability is that the following test functions T_i are all *positive* when the equation $D(s) = 0$ is put in such form that a_0 is positive:

$$T_1 = a_1 \qquad T_2 = \begin{vmatrix} a_1 & a_0 \\ a_3 & a_2 \end{vmatrix} \qquad T_3 = \begin{vmatrix} a_1 & a_0 & 0 \\ a_3 & a_2 & a_1 \\ a_5 & a_4 & a_3 \end{vmatrix}$$

$$(12.10) \quad T_4 = \begin{vmatrix} a_1 & a_0 & 0 & 0 \\ a_3 & a_2 & a_1 & a_0 \\ a_5 & a_4 & a_3 & a_2 \\ a_7 & a_6 & a_5 & a_4 \end{vmatrix} \qquad T_5 = \begin{vmatrix} a_1 & a_0 & 0 & 0 & 0 \\ a_3 & a_2 & a_1 & a_0 & 0 \\ a_5 & a_4 & a_3 & a_2 & a_1 \\ a_7 & a_6 & a_5 & a_4 & a_3 \\ a_9 & a_8 & a_7 & a_6 & a_5 \end{vmatrix}$$

$$T_i = \begin{vmatrix} a_1 & a_0 & 0 & 0 & \cdots \\ a_3 & a_2 & a_1 & a_0 & \cdots \\ a_5 & a_4 & a_3 & a_2 & \cdots \\ \cdots & \cdots & \cdots & \cdots & \cdots \\ a_{2i-1} & a_{2i-2} & \cdots & \cdots & a_i \end{vmatrix}$$

In constructing these test functions all the coefficients a_r with $r > n$ or $r < 0$ are replaced by zeros. It is evident that, in the nth determinant, the bottom-row terms are all zero except the last term; hence

$$(12.11) \qquad\qquad T_n = a_n T_{n-1}$$

Consequently, if $a_n > 0$, then T_n has the same sign as T_{n-1} and it is therefore necessary to test the determinants only from T_1 to T_{n-1}. If any of these determinants have negative values, the system is *unstable*.

Stability of a Third-order System. As an example of the use of the Routh-Hurwitz criterion, consider a system whose determinantal equation is the cubic equation

$$(12.12) \qquad\qquad D(s) = s^3 + a_1 s^2 + a_2 s + a_3 = 0$$

eine Gleichung nur Wurzeln mit negativen reelen Theilen besitzt, *Mathematische Annalen*, vol. 46, pp. 273–284, 1895.

where a_1, a_2, and a_3 are *all positive*. The Routh-Hurwitz criterion then assures stability if

$$(12.13) \qquad T_2 = \begin{vmatrix} a_1 & 1 \\ a_3 & a_2 \end{vmatrix} = a_1 a_2 - a_3 > 0$$

Hence, if $a_1 a_2 > a_3$, the stability of the third-order system is assured.

Stability of a Fourth-order System. If a dynamical system under consideration has a determinantal equation of the fourth degree of the form

$$(12.14) \qquad s^4 + a_1 s^3 + a_2 s^2 + a_3 s + a_4 = 0$$

then the Routh-Hurwitz criterion assures the stability of the system provided that a_1, a_2, a_3, and a_4 are *all positive* and

$$(12.15) \qquad T_2 = \begin{vmatrix} a_1 & 1 \\ a_3 & a_2 \end{vmatrix} > 0 \qquad T_3 = \begin{vmatrix} a_1 & 1 & 0 \\ a_3 & a_2 & a_1 \\ 0 & a_4 & a_3 \end{vmatrix} > 0$$

Since $T_3 = a_3 T_2 - a_4 a_1^2 > 0$, it is necessary that $T_2 > 0$ if a_3 is positive. Hence, if $T_3 > 0$, T_2 must be positive and hence the *complete* criterion for the stability of the fourth-order system is that all the a's must be positive and that

$$(12.16) \qquad a_1 a_2 a_3 > a_1^2 a_4 + a_3^2$$

Extensive use of the Routh-Hurwitz criterion in the study of the stability of control systems or governors has been made since the time of Routh and Maxwell.* The Routh-Hurwitz criterion has been used extensively in recent years in studies involving the stability of control systems and servomechanisms of various sorts.[12] Another method of determining the stability of dynamical systems based on the theory of the complex variable is given in Chap. 19.

PROBLEMS

1. Obtain the flexibility matrix of the three-pendulum system of Fig. 4.3. Write the dynamical matrix of the system.

2. An electric train is made up of three units: a locomotive and two passenger cars. Each unit has a mass M, and the spring constants of the coupling connecting them are equal to K. Write the Lagrangian equation of motion of the system. Draw the equivalent electrical circuit, and determine the natural frequencies of the system.

3. If in the system of Prob. 2 identical shock absorbers that act by viscous friction are placed between the three units, determine the smallest value of the damping factor R so that the relative motion of the locomotive and cars is not oscillatory.

4. A long train of n identical units of mass M coupled by springs of spring constants all equal to K is oscillating. Draw the equivalent electrical circuit, and write the frequency equation of the system.

---

* See the paper On Governors, "Scientific Papers of J. C. Maxwell," vol. II, pp. 105–120, reprinted, Dover Publications, New York, 1952.

5. A uniform shaft free to rotate in bearings carries five equidistant disks. The moments of inertia of four disks are equal to J, while the moment of inertia of one of the end disks is equal to $2J$. Set up the dynamical matrix, and obtain the lowest natural frequency by the iterative matrix method of Sec. 7. Draw the equivalent electrical circuit.

6. A particle of mass M is attracted to a center by a force proportional to the distance, or $F_x = -ax$, $F_y = -ay$. Write the equations of motion of the particle. Show that x and y execute independent simple harmonic vibrations of the same frequency.

7. Solve Prob. 6 by using polar coordinates.

8. Two balls, each of mass M, and three weightless springs, one of length $2d$ and the others of length d, are connected together in the arrangement spring d—ball—spring $2d$—ball—spring d, and the whole device is stretched in a straight line between two points, with a given tension in the spring. Gravity is neglected.

Investigate the small vibrations of the balls at right angles to the straight line, assuming motion only in one plane. Set up the equations of motion. Determine the natural frequencies and the normal modes. What are the normal coordinates?

9. One simple pendulum is hung from another; that is, the string of the lower pendulum is tied to the bob of the upper one. Discuss the small oscillations of the resulting system, assuming arbitrary lengths and masses. Determine the natural frequencies and obtain the normal coordinates in the case of equal masses and equal lengths of strings.

10. Consider the case of the three coupled pendulums of Fig. 4.3. In this case assume that each pendulum is retarded by a viscous force proportional to its angular velocity. Consider an equal retarding force on each pendulum. Draw the equivalent electrical circuit, and obtain the general solution of the equations of motion. Assume that the damping is so small that oscillations are possible.

11. A particle subject to a linear restoring force and a viscous damping is acted on by a periodic force whose frequency differs from the natural frequency of the system by a small quantity.

The particle starts from rest at $t = 0$ and builds up the motion. Discuss the whole problem, including initial conditions. Consider what happens when the frequency gets nearer and nearer the natural frequency and the damping gets smaller and smaller.

12. Show that for a particle subject to a linear restoring force and viscous damping the maximum amplitude occurs when the applied frequency is less than the natural frequency. Find this resonance frequency. Show that maximum energy is attained when the applied frequency is equal to the natural frequency.

13. Two small metal spheres A and B of equal mass m are suspended from two points A' and B' at a distance a apart on the same horizontal line by insulating threads of equal length s. They are then charged with equal charges $+q$. If A is pulled aside a *short* distance s_1 and B a *short* distance s_2 (both small in comparison with a) in the plane formed by the equilibrium position of both threads, determine the resulting motion in this plane. Determine the frequencies of oscillation of the system.

14. Two particles of mass m connected by a weightless spring of unstressed length s and spring constant k are set moving in an arbitrary manner on a smooth horizontal plane. Set up and solve Lagrange's equations for this case.

15. An eighth-order system has the following determinantal equation: $D(s) = s^8 + 2s^7 + 4s^6 + 4s^5 + 6s^4 + 6s^3 + 7s^2 + 4s + 2 = 0$. Determine whether the system is stable or unstable.

16. A sixth-order system has the following determinantal equation: $D(s) = s^6 + s^5 + 6s^4 + 5s^3 + 11s^2 + 6s + 6 = 0$. Discuss the stability of the system.

17. Discuss the oscillations of the three coupled pendulums of Sec. 4 by the matrix iteration method of Sec. 7. Determine the lowest and highest frequencies of the oscillation of the pendulums by matrix iteration.

REFERENCES

1. Timoshenko, S.: "Vibration Problems in Engineering," D. Van Nostrand Company, Inc., Princeton, N.J., 1937.
2. Den Hartog, J. P.: "Mechanical Vibrations," 3d ed., McGraw-Hill Book Company, Inc., New York, 1940.
3. Routh, E. J.: "Advanced Rigid Dynamics," The Macmillan Company, New York, 1905.
4. Kármán, T. V., and M. A. Biot: "Mathematical Methods in Engineering," McGraw-Hill Book Company, Inc., New York, 1940.
5. Frazer, R. A., W. J. Duncan, and A. R. Collar: "Elementary Matrices and Some Applications to Dynamics and Differential Equations," Cambridge University Press, New York, 1938.
6. Scanlan, R. H., and R. Rosenbaum: "Aircraft Vibration and Flutter," The Macmillan Company, New York, 1951.
7. Olson, H. F.: "Dynamical Analogies," D. Van Nostrand Company, Inc., Princeton, N.J., 1943.
8. Maxfield, J. P., and H. C. Harrison: Methods of High Quality Recording and Reproducing of Music and Speech Based on Telephone Research, *Bell System Technical Journal*, vol. 5, pp. 493–523, July, 1926.
9. W. P. Mason: "Electromechanical Transducers and Wave Filters," D. Van Nostrand Company, Inc., Princeton, N.J., 1948.
10. Goldstein, H.: "Classical Mechanics," Addison-Wesley Publishing Company, Cambridge, Mass., 1951.
11. Timoshenko, S. P., and D. H. Young: "Advanced Dynamics," McGraw-Hill Book Company, Inc., New York, 1948.
12. Brown, G. S., and D. P. Campbell: "Principles of Servomechanisms," John Wiley & Sons, Inc., New York, 1948. (This book contains an excellent bibliography on control systems.)

CHAPTER 9

THE DIFFERENTIAL EQUATIONS OF THE THEORY
OF STRUCTURES

1. Introduction. This chapter is devoted to the solution of the differential equations encountered in the determination of the deflection of loaded cords and beams and in the study of the transverse oscillations of beams subject to different boundary conditions. Since the differential equations encountered in these studies are linear, they may be solved simply by the use of the Laplace-transform, or operational, method.

2. The Deflection of a Loaded Cord. Perhaps the simplest problem encountered in the theory of structures is the determination of the deflec-

FIG. 2.1

tion of a cord stretched between supports under various conditions of loading.

Consider a section ds of a perfectly flexible cord as shown in Fig. 2.1.

Let $y(x)$ be the deflection curve of the cord, $w(x)$ be the load per unit length, and T be the tension of the cord. Then the equilibrium condition obtained by equating the net force on the segment in the y direction is

$$(2.1) \qquad T \sin \theta_1 - T \sin \theta_2 = w(x) \, dx$$

Equating the forces in the x direction, we have

$$(2.2) \qquad T \cos \theta_1 = T \cos \theta_2 = H$$

where H is the horizontal component of the tension T and is constant for the span. Dividing (2.1) by (2.2), we have

$$(2.3) \qquad \tan \theta_1 - \tan \theta_2 = \frac{w(x) \, dx}{H}$$

245

But we have

(2.4) $$\tan \theta_1 = \left(\frac{dy}{dx}\right)_x \qquad \tan \theta_2 = \left(\frac{dy}{dx}\right)_{x+dx}$$

Hence, by Taylor's expansion, we have

(2.5) $$\tan \theta_2 = \left(\frac{dy}{dx}\right)_x + \left(\frac{d^2y}{d^2x}\right)_x dx + \text{higher-order terms in } dx$$

Substituting this into (2.3), we obtain

(2.6) $$\frac{d^2y}{dx^2} = -\frac{w(x)}{H}$$

This is the fundamental differential equation governing the deflection of a cord under the influence of a load $w(x)$ per unit length and a horizontal component of tension H.

FIG. 2.2

Equation (2.6) may be solved most conveniently by the Laplace-transform, or operational, method. To do this, let us introduce the transforms

(2.7) $$Ly(x) = Y(p)$$
$$Lw(x) = W(p)$$

We then have

(2.8) $$L\left(\frac{d^2y}{dx^2}\right) = p^2Y - p^2y_0 - py_1$$

where

(2.9) $$y_0 = y(0) \qquad y_1 = \left(\frac{dy}{dx}\right)_{x=0}$$

Hence Eq. (2.6) is transformed into

(2.10) $$p^2Y - p^2y_0 - py_1 = -\frac{W(p)}{H}$$

a. *Uniform Load.* Let us first consider the case of a uniform load w_0 per unit length.

(2.11) $$w(x) = w_0$$

Let the cord be suspended from the points $x = 0$ and $x = s$ that are at equal heights, as shown in Fig. 2.2.

In this case we have

(2.12) $$W(p) = w_0 \qquad y_0 = 0 \qquad y(s) = 0$$

Hence (2.10) becomes

$$(2.13) \qquad Y = \frac{y_1}{p} - \frac{w_0}{Hp^2} = Ly(x)$$

To determine $y(x)$, we use the table of transforms, pages 152 to 159, and we have

$$(2.14) \qquad y(x) = L^{-1}Y(p) = y_1 x - \frac{w_0 x^2}{2H}$$

To determine y_1, we use the condition $y(s) = 0$ and obtain

$$(2.15) \qquad y_1 = \frac{w_0 s}{2H}$$

Substituting this into (2.14), we obtain

$$(2.16) \qquad y = \frac{w_0}{2H}(sx - x^2)$$

FIG. 2.3

for the deflection of the uniformly loaded cord.

b. *Uniform Load Extending over Part of the Span.* The power of the operational method is demonstrated in the solution of the case of Fig. 2.3. In this case we have

$$(2.17) \qquad W(p) = p \int_{x_1}^{x_2} e^{-px} w_0 \, dx = w_0(e^{-x_1 p} - e^{-x_2 p})$$

for the transform of the unit load w_0 extending from x_1 to x_2. In this case, Eq. (2.10) becomes

$$(2.18) \qquad Y(p) = \frac{y_1}{p} - \frac{w_0}{H} \frac{e^{-x_1 p} - e^{-x_2 p}}{p^2} = Ly(x)$$

By the use of the table of transforms and the rule that if

$$(2.19) \qquad L^{-1}g(p) = h(x)$$

then

$$(2.20) \qquad L^{-1}e^{-kp}g(p) = \begin{cases} 0 & x < k \\ h(x - k) & x > k \end{cases}$$

where $k > 0$, it is seen that we have

$$(2.21) \quad y(x) = \begin{cases} y_1 x & 0 < x < x_1 \\ y_1 x - \dfrac{w_0}{2H}(x - x_1)^2 & x_1 < x < x_2 \\ hy_1 x - \dfrac{w_0}{2H}(x - x_1)^2 + \dfrac{w_0}{2H}(x - x_2)^2 & x_2 < x < s \end{cases}$$

To determine y_1, we use $y(s) = 0$, and we find from (2.21) that

$$(2.22) \qquad y_1 = \frac{w_0}{2Hs}[(s - x_1)^2 - (s - x_2)^2]$$

Substituting this into (2.21), we obtain the deflection curve. The advantage of the operational method over the classical method is that we are able to write one differential equation for the entire span, while in the classical procedure it is necessary to write several equations depending on the discontinuous nature of the load and then evaluate the constants by using the condition that the deflection is continuous.

c. The Effect of a Concentrated Load. Let us compute the deflection of a flexible cord fixed at both ends and supporting a concentrated load P_0 as shown in Fig. 2.4.

FIG. 2.4   FIG. 2.5

The concentrated load is located at the point $x = a$.

In order to solve this problem operationally, we must compute the transform of the concentrated load. This may be done by considering the concentrated load P_0 as the limit of a distributed load w_0 distributed over a very small region, as shown in Fig. 2.5.

The transform of such a load is

$$(2.23) \qquad W(p) = p \int_a^{a+\delta} w_0 e^{-px} \, dx = w_0(e^{-pa} - e^{-p(a+\delta)})$$
$$= w_0 e^{-pa}(1 - e^{-p\delta})$$

Now we take the limit $\delta \to 0$ and $w_0 \to \infty$ in such a way that

$$(2.24) \qquad \lim_{\substack{w_0 \to \infty \\ \delta \to 0}} w_0 \delta = P_0$$

The exponential function $e^{-p\delta}$ may be expanded in the form

$$(2.25) \qquad e^{-p\delta} = 1 - p\delta + \frac{p^2\delta^2}{2!} - \frac{p^3\delta^3}{3!} + \cdots$$

Substituting this into (2.23), we have

$$(2.26) \qquad \lim_{\substack{\delta \to 0 \\ w_0 \to \infty}} W(p) = \lim_{\substack{\delta \to 0 \\ w_0 \to \infty}} e^{-pa} w_0 \, \delta p = p P_0 e^{-pa}$$

This is the transform of the concentrated load situated at the point $x = a$. Substituting this into Eq. (2.10), we have

$$(2.27) \qquad Y(p) = \frac{y_1}{p} - \frac{P_0}{H} \frac{e^{-ap}}{p} = Ly(x)$$

Computing the inverse transform of this expression by the table of transforms, we obtain

$$(2.28) \qquad y(x) = \begin{cases} y_1 x & 0 < x < a \\ y_1 x - \dfrac{P_0(x - a)}{H} & a < x < s \end{cases}$$

The constant y_1 may be determined by the condition $y(s) = 0$, and it is

$$(2.29) \qquad y_1 = \frac{P_0}{Hs}(s - a)$$

Substituting this value of y_1 into (2.28), we obtain the following equations for the deflection $y(x)$:

$$(2.30) \qquad y(x) = \begin{cases} \dfrac{P_0}{H} x \left(1 - \dfrac{a}{s}\right) & 0 < x < a \\ \dfrac{P_0}{H} a \left(1 - \dfrac{x}{s}\right) & a < x < s \end{cases}$$

d. *The Effect of an Arbitrary Load.* A useful relation may be easily obtained giving the deflection of an arbitrary load by the use of the Faltung theorem established in Chap. 21. The theorem states that if

$$(2.31) \qquad \begin{aligned} L^{-1} g_1(p) &= h_1(x) \\ L^{-1} g_2(p) &= h_2(x) \end{aligned}$$

then

$$(2.32) \qquad \begin{aligned} L^{-1} \frac{g_1 g_2}{p} &= \int_0^x h_1(u) h_2(x - u) \, du \\ &= \int_0^x h_2(u) h_1(x - u) \, du \end{aligned}$$

Returning to Eq. (2.10) with the initial deflection $y_0 = 0$, we have

$$(2.33) \qquad Y(p) = \frac{y_1}{p} - \frac{W(p)}{Hp^2} = Ly(x)$$

Now since

$$(2.34) \qquad L^{-1} \frac{1}{p} = x \qquad L^{-1} W(p) = w(x)$$

we have by the Faltung theorem

$$(2.35) \qquad L^{-1} \frac{W(p)}{Hp^2} = L^{-1} \frac{W(p)}{Hp \times p} = \int_0^x \frac{w(u)(x - u) \, du}{H}$$

Hence, from (2.33), we have

$$(2.36) \qquad y(x) = y_1 x - \frac{1}{H} \int_0^x w(u)(x - u) \, du$$

To determine y_1, we again use $y(s) = 0$, and we have

$$(2.37) \qquad y_1 = \frac{x}{Hs} \int_0^s w(u)(s - u) \, du - \frac{1}{H} \int_0^x w(u)(x - u) \, du$$

This gives the deflection of the cord in the span from $x = 0$ to $x = s$ due to the influence of a general load $w(x)$.

3. Stretched Cord with Elastic Support.   Let us assume that the vertical deflection of the cord is restrained by a large number of springs such

FIG. 3.1

that their effect can be considered as a distributed restoring force per unit length equal to ky, where k is a measure of the *spring constant* of the support and y is the deflection.   In this case we must add the amount $-ky$ to the vertical load of Eq. (2.6), and we obtain the differential equation

$$(3.1) \qquad H \frac{d^2y}{dx^2} - ky = -w(x)$$

for the deflection $y(x)$.   To solve this equation operationally, we again introduce the transforms

$$(3.2) \qquad\qquad\qquad Ly(x) = Y(p)$$
$$(3.3) \qquad\qquad\qquad Lw(x) = W(p)$$

and Eq. (3.1) transforms to

$$(3.4) \qquad\qquad (p^2 - c^2)Y = p^2 y_0 + p y_1 - \frac{W(p)}{H}$$

where

$$(3.5) \qquad\qquad\qquad c^2 = \frac{k}{H}$$

a. Cord Fixed at Its Ends, Concentrated Load.   Let us consider the case shown in Fig. 3.1.

In this case the transform of the concentrated load is by (2.26) $pe^{-ap}P_0$. Since $y_0 = 0$, Eq. (3.4) becomes

$$(3.6) \qquad Y(p) = \frac{p y_1}{p^2 - c^2} - \frac{P_0}{H} e^{-ap} \frac{p}{p^2 - c^2} = Ly(x)$$

Consulting the table of transforms, we find the inverse transform to be

$$(3.7) \qquad y(x) = \begin{cases} y_1 \dfrac{\sinh cx}{c} & 0 < x < a \\[2ex] y_1 \dfrac{\sinh cx}{c} - \dfrac{P_0}{Hc} \sinh c(x - a) & a < x < s \end{cases}$$

If we use the boundary condition $y(s) = 0$, we obtain

$$(3.8) \qquad y_1 = \frac{P_0}{H} \frac{\sinh c(s - a)}{\sinh cx}$$

Substituting this value of y_1 into (3.7), we obtain the following deflection of the cord:

$$(3.9) \qquad y(x) = \frac{P_0}{HC} \frac{\sinh c(s - a) \sinh cx}{\sinh sc} \qquad 0 < x < a$$

$$(3.10) \quad y(x) = \frac{P_0}{HC} \frac{\sinh c(s - a)}{\sinh cs} \sinh cx$$

$$- \frac{P_0}{HC} \sinh c(x - a) \qquad a < x < s$$

b. *Infinite Cord Elastically Supported, Concentrated Load.* The deflection of an infinitely long elastically supported cord under the influence of a concentrated load P_0 may be obtained as a special case of (3.10).

In order to obtain the deflection in this case, let

$$(3.11) \qquad z = x - a \qquad \text{and} \qquad a = \frac{s}{2}$$

Making these substitutions in (3.10), we obtain

$$(3.12) \quad y(z + a) = y_1(z)$$
$$= \frac{P_0}{Hc} \frac{\sinh (cs/2) \sinh [(cs/2) + cz]}{\sinh cs} - \frac{P_0}{Hc} \sinh cz \qquad -\frac{s}{2} < z < \frac{s}{2}$$

Now

$$(3.13) \qquad \lim_{s \to \infty} y_1(z) = \frac{P_0}{2Hc} e^{-cz} = \frac{P_0}{2\sqrt{Hk}} e^{-cz} \qquad -\frac{s}{2} < z < \frac{s}{2}$$

This is the required deflection where z is measured from the point of application of the load.

c. *Elastically Supported Cord with Uniform Load.* Let us consider the case of Fig. 3.2. In this case the cord is loaded with a uniform load w_0 per unit length. The load extends from $x = a$ to $x = b$.

FIG. 3.2

For this case we have

$$(3.14) \qquad Lw(x) = w_0(e^{-ap} - e^{-bp})$$

Then the general equation (3.4) becomes

$$(3.15) \qquad Y(p) = y_1 \frac{p}{p^2 - c^2} - \frac{w_0}{H} \frac{e^{-ap} - e^{-bp}}{p^2 - c^2} = Ly(x)$$

Consulting the table of transforms, we obtain

$$y(x) = y_1 \frac{\sinh cx}{c} \qquad\qquad 0 < x < a$$

$$y(x) = y_1 \frac{\sinh cx}{c} - \frac{w_0}{Hc^2} [\cosh c(x - a) - 1] \qquad a < x < b$$

(3.16)

$$y(x) = y_1 \frac{\sinh cx}{c} - \frac{w_0}{Hc^2} \cosh c(x - a)$$

$$+ \frac{w_0}{Hc^2} \cosh c(x - b) \qquad b < x < s$$

Using the boundary condition $y(s) = 0$, we obtain the following value for the constant y_1:

$$(3.17) \qquad y_1 = \frac{w_0}{Hc \sinh cs} [\cosh c(s - a) - \cosh c(s - b)]$$

Substituting this value of y_1 into (3.16) gives the required deflection.

d. *Elastically Supported Cord, General Loading.* The transform of the deflection of an elastically supported cord under the influence of a general load $w(x)$ is given by Eq. (3.4) in the form

$$(3.18) \qquad Y(p) = \frac{py_1}{p^2 - c^2} - \frac{1}{H} \frac{W(p)}{p^2 - c^2} = Ly(x)$$

where

$$(3.19) \qquad\qquad Lw(x) = W(p)$$

Now, by the Faltung theorem, we have

$$(3.20) \qquad L^{-1} \frac{W(p)}{p^2 - c^2} = \frac{1}{c} \int_0^x w(u) \sinh [c(x - u)] \, du$$

Hence the inverse transform of (3.18) is given by

$$(3.21) \qquad y(x) = y_1 \frac{\sinh cx}{c} - \frac{1}{Hc} \int_0^x w(u) \sinh [c(x - u)] \, du$$

Using the boundary condition $y(s) = 0$, we find the following value of y_1:

$$(3.22) \qquad y_1 = \frac{1}{H \sinh cs} \int_0^s w(u) \sinh [c(s - u)] \, du$$

Substituting this value of u_1 into (3.21) gives the required deflection produced by the general loading $w(x)$.

4. The Deflection of Beams by Transverse Forces. Consider a uniform straight beam supported as shown in Fig. 4.1.

Let us measure the deflection $y(x)$ of the beam at any point x down-

ward.   Then it is shown in works on elasticity* that $y(x)$ satisfies the
following differential equation,

$$(4.1) \qquad EI\frac{d^4y}{dx^4} = w(x)$$

where E is Young's modulus of elasticity of the material of the beam
and I is the moment of inertia of
the cross section of the beam with
respect to a line passing through the
center of gravity of the cross section and perpendicular to the x axis
and to the vertical direction y.   The

FIG. 4.1

quantity EI is called the *flexural rigidity* of the beam. $w(x)$ is the load
per unit length of the beam.

There also exist the two following relations,

$$(4.2) \qquad F(x) = -EI\frac{d^3y}{dx^3}$$

and

$$(4.3) \qquad M(x) = -EI\frac{d^2y}{dx^2}$$

where $F(x)$ is the *shear force* and $M(x)$ is the *bending moment*.   The
deflection $y(x)$ is measured positive downward, the load per unit length
$w(x)$ is measured positive downward, the shear force $F(x)$ is measured
positive upward, and the bending moment $M(x)$ positive clockwise.

To solve Eq. (4.1), let us introduce the transforms

$$(4.4) \qquad\qquad Ly(x) = Y(p)$$
$$(4.5) \qquad\qquad Lw(x) = W(p)$$

Hence, since

$$(4.6) \qquad L\frac{d^4y}{dx^4} = p^4Y - p^4y_0 - p^3y_1 - p^2y_2 - py_3$$

where

$$(4.7) \qquad y_r = \left(\frac{d^ry}{dx^r}\right) \qquad \text{evaluated at } x = 0$$

Eq. (4.1) transforms into

$$(4.8) \qquad\qquad Y(p) = \frac{W(p)}{EIp^4} + y_0 + \frac{y_1}{p} + \frac{y_2}{p^2} + \frac{y_3}{p^3}$$

* R. V. Southwell, "An Introduction to the Theory of Elasticity for Engineers and
Physicists," Oxford University Press, New York, 1936.

a. Uniform Beam Clamped Horizontally at Both Ends under the Influence of a Uniformly Distributed Load. Consider the deflection of the beam of Fig. 4.2.

FIG. 4.2

In this case, the deflection and slope at $x = 0$ are both equal to zero; hence

$$(4.9) \qquad y_0 = y_1 = 0$$

The transform of the uniform load w_0 is given by

$$(4.10) \qquad W(p) = w_0$$

Hence, in this case, (4.8) reduces to

$$(4.11) \qquad Y(p) = \frac{w_0}{EIp^4} + \frac{y_2}{p^2} + \frac{y_3}{p^3} = Ly(x)$$

The inverse transform of this gives

$$(4.12) \qquad y(x) = \frac{w_0}{EI}\frac{x^4}{4!} + y_2\frac{x^2}{2!} + y_3\frac{x^3}{3!}$$

The constants y_2 and y_3 are determined by the conditions

$$(4.13) \qquad y = \frac{dy}{dx} = 0 \qquad \text{at } x = s$$

These conditions give

$$(4.14) \qquad y_2 = +\frac{w_0 s^2}{12EI} \quad y_3 = -\frac{w_0 s}{2EI}$$

Substituting these values into (4.12), we obtain the following equation for the deflection:

$$(4.15) \qquad y(x) = \frac{w_0 x^2(s - x)^2}{24EI}$$

b. Uniform Beam Clamped Horizontally at Both Ends and Carrying a Concentrated Load. Consider the problem of determining the deflection of the beam shown in Fig. 4.3.

In this case the transform of the concentrated load is

$$(4.16) \qquad W(p) = pe^{-ap}P_0$$

FIG. 4.3

Since the deflection and slope are zero at $x = 0$, Eq. (4.8) in this case reduces to

$$(4.17) \qquad Y(p) = \frac{P_0}{EI}\frac{e^{-ap}}{p^3} + \frac{y_2}{p^2} + \frac{y_3}{p^3} = Ly(x)$$

The inverse transform of this is

$$(4.18) \qquad \begin{aligned} y(x) &= y_2\frac{x^2}{2!} + y_3\frac{x^3}{3!} & 0 < x < a \\ y(x) &= \frac{P_0}{6EI}(x - a)^3 + y_2\frac{x^2}{2} + y_3\frac{x^3}{6} & a < x < s \end{aligned}$$

The conditions that the deflection and slope must vanish at $x = s$ enable y_1 and y_2 to be determined. Inserting these values of y_2 and y_3 into (4.18), we obtain the following equations for the deflection:

(4.19)
$$y(x) = \frac{P_0}{6EIs^3} x^2 (s - a)^2 [3as - (s + 2a)x] \qquad 0 < x < a$$

$$y(x) = \frac{P_0 a^2}{6EIs^3} (a - s)^2 (3s - 2a - as) \qquad a < x < s$$

c. *Uniform Beam Clamped Horizontally at One End and Free at the Other and Carrying a Concentrated Load.* Let us determine the deflection of the beam shown in Fig. 4.4.

In this case, Eq. (4.8) becomes

(4.20) $$Y(p) = \frac{P_0 e^{-ap}}{EIp^3} + \frac{y_2}{p^2} + \frac{y_3}{p^3}$$

Fig. 4.4

The inverse transform of $Y(p)$ is

(4.21)
$$y(x) = y_2 \frac{x^2}{2} + y_3 \frac{x^3}{6} \qquad 0 < x < a$$

$$y(x) = \frac{P_0}{6EI} (x - a)^3 + y_2 \frac{x^2}{2!} + y_3 \frac{x^3}{6} \qquad a < x < s$$

In this case, since the end $x = s$ is free, it follows that the bending moment and shear force at that point must vanish. We therefore have by (4.2) and (4.3)

(4.22) $$\frac{d^2y}{dx^2} = \frac{d^3y}{dx^3} = 0 \qquad \text{at } x = s$$

Applying these conditions to (4.21), we obtain

(4.23)
$$y_2 = \frac{aP_0}{EI}$$

$$y_3 = - \frac{P_0}{EI}$$

Substituting these values into (4.21), we obtain the following equations for the deflection:

(4.24)
$$y(x) = \frac{P_0 x^2}{EI} \left(\frac{a}{2} - \frac{x}{6} \right) \qquad 0 < x < a$$

$$y(x) = \frac{P_0 a^2}{EI} \left(\frac{x}{2} - \frac{a}{6} \right) \qquad a < x < s$$

5. Deflection of Beams on an Elastic Foundation. Let us assume that a uniform beam is attached to a rigid base by means of a uniform elastic medium as shown in Fig. 5.1.

The action of the elastic medium may be taken into account by introducing a restoring force $-ky$ acting in a direction opposite to that of the
load $w(x)$. In this case Eq. (4.1)
becomes

FIG. 5.1

$$(5.1) \quad EI\frac{d^4y}{dx^4} + ky = w(x)$$

The constant k is called the *modulus of the foundation*.

Let us divide Eq. (5.1) by EI. We then obtain

$$(5.2) \qquad \frac{d^4y}{dx^4} + \frac{k}{EI}y = \frac{w(x)}{EI}$$

If we now let

$$(5.3) \qquad a = \left(\frac{k}{4EI}\right)^{\frac{1}{4}}$$

Eq. (5.2) may be written in the form

$$(5.4) \qquad \frac{d^4y}{dx^4} + 4a^4y = \frac{w(x)}{EI}$$

To solve this equation operationally, we write

$$(5.5) \qquad Ly(x) = Y(p)$$
$$(5.6) \qquad Lw(x) = W(p)$$

Equation (5.4) is then transformed to

$$(5.7) \qquad (p^4 + 4a^4)Y = \frac{W(p)}{EI} + p^4y_0 + p^3y_1 + p^2y_2 + py_3$$

*a. Beam on Elastic Foundation and Clamped Horizontally at Both
Ends under the Influence of a Concentrated Load.* Let us consider the
deflection of the beam shown in
Fig. 5.2.

In this case, the conditions that
the slope and deflection at $x = 0$
must vanish lead to

$$(5.8) \qquad y_1 = y_0 = 0$$

FIG. 5.2

The transform of the concentrated load P_0 acting at $x = b$ is

$$(5.9) \qquad W(p) = pP_0e^{-pb}$$

Hence, in this case, Eq. (5.7) becomes

$$(5.10) \qquad Y(p) = \frac{P_0}{EI}\frac{pe^{-pb}}{p^4 + 4a^4} + y_2\frac{p^2}{p^4 + 4a^4} + y_3\frac{p}{p^4 + 4a^4}$$

The transform of dy/dx is given by

$$(5.11) \quad L\left(\frac{dy}{dx}\right) = pY(p)$$

$$= \frac{P_0}{EI}\frac{p^2 e^{-pb}}{p^4 + 4a^4} + y_2\frac{p^3}{p^4 + 4a^4} + y_3\frac{p^2}{p^4 + 4a^4}$$

We have the following inverse transforms:

$$(5.12) \quad L^{-1}\frac{p}{p^4 + 4a^4} = \frac{1}{4a^3}(\sin ax \cosh ax - \cos ax \sinh ax)$$

$$= \phi_1(x)$$

$$(5.13) \quad L^{-1}\frac{p^2}{p^4 + 4a^4} = \frac{1}{2a^2}(\sin ax \sinh ax) = \phi_2(x)$$

$$(5.14) \quad L^{-1}\frac{p^3}{p^4 + 4a^4} = \frac{1}{2a}(\sin ax \cosh ax + \cos ax \sinh ax) = \phi_3(x)$$

$$(5.15) \quad L^{-1}\frac{p^4}{p^4 + 4a^4} = \cos ax \cosh ax = \phi_4(x)$$

In terms of these functions the inverse of $Y(p)$ in Eq. (5.10) is

$$(5.16) \quad \begin{aligned} y &= y_2\phi_2(x) + y_3\phi_1(x) & 0 < x < b \\ y &= \frac{P_0}{EI}\phi_1(x - b) + y_2\phi_2(x) + y_3\phi_1(x) & b < x < s \end{aligned}$$

The constants y_2 and y_3 may be found from the condition that the deflection and slope must vanish at $x = s$. From (5.16) we thus obtain

$$(5.17) \quad 0 = \frac{P_0}{EI}\phi_1(s - b) + y_2\phi_2(s) + y_3\phi_1(s)$$

From the transform of (5.11) we obtain

$$(5.18) \quad 0 = \frac{P_0}{EI}\phi_2(s - b) + y_2\phi_3(s) + y_3\phi_2(s)$$

These two equations may be solved for the constants y_2 and y_3. This gives

$$(5.19) \quad y_2 = \frac{P_0}{EI}\frac{\phi_1(s)\phi_2(s - b) - \phi_2(s)\phi_1(s - b)}{\phi_2^2(s) - \phi_3(s)\phi_1(s)}$$

$$(5.20) \quad y_3 = \frac{P_0}{EI}\frac{\phi_2(s)\phi_2(s - b) - \phi_3(s)\phi_1(s - b)}{\phi_1(s)\phi_2(s) - \phi_2^2(s)}$$

The deflection is obtained by substituting these values of y_2 and y_3 into (5.16).

b. *Beam on Elastic Foundation and Clamped Horizontally at Both Ends under the Influence of a General Load.* In this case, since the deflection and slope vanish at $x = 0$, Eq. (5.7) becomes

$$(5.21) \qquad Y(p) = \frac{W(p)}{EI(p^4 + 4a^4)} + \frac{p^2y_2}{p^4 + 4a^4} + \frac{py_3}{p^4 + 4a^4}$$

The inverse transform of the slope is given by

$$(5.22) \qquad L\left(\frac{dy}{dx}\right) = \frac{pW(p)}{EI(p^4 + 4a^4)} + \frac{p^3y_2}{p^4 + 4a^4} + \frac{p^2y_3}{p^4 + 4a^4}$$

Now, by the Faltung theorem, we have

$$(5.23) \qquad L^{-1}\frac{W(p)}{p^4 + 4a^4} = \int_0^x w(u)\phi_1(x - u)\, du$$

$$(5.24) \qquad L^{-1}\frac{pW(p)}{p^4 + 4a^4} = \int_0^x w(u)\phi_2(x - u)\, du$$

Hence the inverses of (5.21) and (5.22) give the following equations for the deflection and slope:

$$(5.25) \qquad y = \frac{1}{EI}\int_0^x w(u)\phi_1(x - u)\, du + y_2\phi_2(x) + y_3\phi_1(x)$$

$$(5.26) \qquad \frac{dx}{dy} = \frac{1}{EI}\int_0^x w(u)\phi_2(x - u)\, du + y_2\phi_3(u) + y_3\phi_2(x)$$

Now, if we let

$$(5.27) \qquad A = \frac{1}{EI}\int_0^s w(u)\phi_1(s - u)\, du$$

$$(5.28) \qquad B = \frac{1}{EI}\int_0^s w(u)\phi_2(s - u)\, du$$

and make use of the fact that the slope and deflection both vanish at $x = s$, we obtain the following values for the constants y_2 and y_3:

$$(5.29) \qquad y_2 = \frac{B\phi_1(s) - A\phi_2(s)}{\phi_2^2(s) - \phi_1(s)\phi_3(s)}$$

$$(5.30) \qquad y_3 = \frac{B\phi_2(s) - A\phi_3(s)}{\phi_1(s)\phi_2(s) - \phi_2^2(s)}$$

If these values of y_2 and y_3 are substituted into (5.25), the value of the deflection is obtained.

6. Buckling of a Uniform Column under Axial Load. Consider a column hinged at the point $x = s$ and supported at $x = 0$ in such a way that lateral deflection is prevented but free rotation is allowed as shown in Fig. 6.1.

Fig. 6.1

The column is under the influence of an axial load considered positive when acting in a downward direction to cause a compression. Let $y(x)$

be the deflection of the column.   The bending moment at any point x is given by

$$(6.1) \qquad EI \frac{d^2y}{dx^2} = -M$$

The bending moment at any point x due to the force P is given by

$$(6.2) \qquad M = Py$$

Hence, substituting this into (6.1), we have

$$(6.3) \qquad EI \frac{d^2y}{dx^2} + Py = 0$$

If we let

$$(6.4) \qquad a^2 = \frac{P}{EI}$$

we obtain

$$(6.5) \qquad \frac{d^2y}{dx^2} + a^2y = 0$$

The general solution of this equation is

$$(6.6) \qquad y = A \cos ax + B \sin ax$$

where A and B are arbitrary constants.   In order to satisfy the boundary condition $y(0) = 0$, we must have

$$(6.7) \qquad A = 0$$

so that the solution reduces to

$$(6.8) \qquad y = B \sin ax$$

To satisfy the condition $y(s) = 0$, we must have

$$(6.9) \qquad \sin as = 0$$

or

$$(6.10) \qquad as = k\pi \qquad k = 0, 1, 2, 3, \ldots$$

To each value of k, there corresponds a solution

$$(6.11) \qquad y_k = B_k \sin \frac{k\pi x}{s}$$

where the B_k's are arbitrary constants.   These deflections are called the *modes of buckling*.   To each mode there corresponds a load

$$(6.12) \qquad P_k = k^2\pi^2 \frac{EI}{s^2}$$

These loads are called the *critical loads*. For each of these loads the corresponding mode of buckling represents an equilibrium position with an arbitrary amplitude. The first critical load is obtained by placing $k = 1$ in (6.12), so that we have

$$(6.13) \qquad P_1 = \pi^2 \frac{EI}{s^2}$$

This equation is known as *Euler's formula*. It gives the upper limit for the stability of the undeflected equilibrium position of the column.

7. The Vibration of Beams. To find the equation of motion for the free vibrations of a uniform beam, we use D'Alembert's principle that states that any dynamical problem may be treated as a static problem by the addition of appropriate inertia forces. The equation giving the static deflection of a beam $y(x)$ under the influence of a static load $w(x)$ is

$$(7.1) \qquad EI \frac{d^4 y}{dx^4} = w(x)$$

The equation of the free vibration of a beam may be obtained from this equation by considering $-m(\partial^2 y/\partial t^2)$ as the load, where m is the mass per unit length. Accordingly, letting

$$(7.2) \qquad w(x) = -m \frac{\partial^2 y}{\partial t^2}$$

in (7.1), we obtain

$$(7.3) \qquad EI \frac{\partial^4 y}{\partial x^4} = -m \frac{\partial^2 y}{\partial t^2}$$

where partial differentiation symbols must be used because the deflection y is now a function of the two *independent* variables x and t.

Let us investigate oscillations of the harmonic type. To do this, we let

$$(7.4) \qquad y(x,t) = v(x) \sin \omega t$$

If we substitute (7.4) into (7.3), we obtain the following ordinary differential equation for the variable $v(x)$:

$$(7.5) \qquad EI \frac{d^4 v}{dx^4} = m\omega^2 v$$

If we let

$$(7.6) \qquad k^4 = \frac{m\omega^2}{EI}$$

Eq. (7.5) may be written in the form

$$(7.7) \qquad \frac{d^4 v}{dx^4} = k^4 v$$

This equation has solutions of the exponential type

$$(7.8) \qquad v = ce^{\theta x}$$

where c is an arbitrary constant. Substituting this into (7.7), we find that the possible values of θ are given by

$$(7.9) \qquad\qquad\qquad \theta^4 = k^4$$

or

$$(7.10) \qquad\qquad\qquad \theta^2 = \pm k^2$$

and hence

$$(7.11) \qquad\qquad \theta = \pm k \text{ or } \pm jk \qquad j = \sqrt{-1}$$

Therefore, the general solution of (7.7) is given by

$$(7.12) \qquad v = c_1 e^{kx} + c_2 e^{-kx} + c_3 e^{jkx} + c_4 e^{-jkx}$$

where the c_r quantities are *arbitrary* constants.

It is convenient to express the solution of (7.7) in terms of hyperbolic and trigonometric functions instead of exponential functions in the form

$$(7.13) \quad v(x) = A \cos kx + B \sinh kx \\ + C \cosh kx + D \sinh kx$$

where A, B, C, D are arbitrary constants.

FIG. 7.1

a. Natural Frequencies of a Cantilever. Let us determine the natural frequencies and modes of oscillation of the cantilever beam shown in Fig. 7.1.

To determine the natural frequencies of the cantilever beam, we have the boundary conditions

$$(a) \qquad\qquad \begin{array}{l} v = 0 \\ \dfrac{dv}{dx} = 0 \end{array} \qquad x = 0 \text{ (fixed end)}$$

$$(b) \qquad \frac{d^2v}{dx^2} = 0 \qquad \text{at } x = s \qquad \text{bending moment} = 0$$

$$(c) \qquad \frac{d^3v}{dx^3} = 0 \qquad \text{at } x = s \qquad \text{shear force} = 0$$

Imposing these conditions on the general solution (7.13), we have

$$(7.14) \qquad\qquad A + C = 0 \qquad B + D = 0$$

Hence we have

$$(7.15) \qquad\qquad A = -C \qquad B = -D$$
$$(7.16) \qquad C(\cosh ks + \cos ks) + D(\sinh ks + \sin ks) = 0$$
$$(7.17) \qquad C(\sinh ks - \sin ks) + D(\cosh ks + \cos ks) = 0$$

In order that these homogeneous linear equations in C and D may have a nontrivial solution, it is necessary that

(7.18)
$$\begin{vmatrix} \cosh ks + \cos ks & \sinh ks + \sin ks \\ \sinh ks - \sin ks & \cosh ks + \cos ks \end{vmatrix} = 0$$

or

(7.19)
$$1 + \cosh ks \cos ks = 0$$

Therefore

(7.20)
$$\cos ks = -\frac{1}{\cosh ks}$$

This equation may be solved graphically by letting $ks = Z$ and plotting $\cos Z$ and $-1/\cosh Z$ as shown in Fig. 7.2.

If the Z_r are the abscissas of the points of intersection of these curves, then they are the solutions of the Eq. (7.20). The first few roots of (7.20) are given by

(7.21)
$$\begin{array}{ccc} Z_1 = 1.8751 & Z_2 = 4.694 & Z_3 = 7.854 \\ Z_4 = 10.996 & Z_5 = 14.13, \text{ etc.} \end{array}$$

Each root Z_r fixes a value k_r of k by the equation

(7.22)
$$k_r = \frac{Z_r}{s}$$

By (7.6) each value k_r of k fixes a value of the possible natural frequency ω by the equation

(7.23)
$$\omega_r = k_r^2 \sqrt{\frac{EI}{m}} = \left(\frac{Z_r}{s}\right)^2 \sqrt{\frac{EI}{m}}$$

The lowest natural angular frequency is given by

(7.24)
$$\omega_1 = \left(\frac{1.875}{s}\right)^2 \sqrt{\frac{EI}{m}}$$

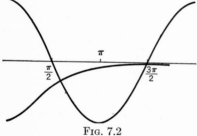

FIG. 7.2

b. Natural Frequencies of a Hinged Beam. Let us consider the determination of the natural frequencies of oscillation of a beam hinged at both ends $x = 0$ and $x = s$. The boundary conditions for this case are

(a)
$$\begin{array}{cc} v = 0 & v = 0 \\ x = 0 & x = s \end{array}$$

(b)
$$\begin{array}{cc} \dfrac{d^2v}{dx^2} = 0 & \dfrac{d^2v}{dx^2} = 0 \\ x = 0 & x = s \end{array}$$

Imposing two of these conditions on Eq. (7.13), we obtain the following equations

$$(7.25) \qquad \begin{aligned} 0 &= A + C \\ 0 &= -A + C \end{aligned}$$

Hence

$$(7.26) \qquad A = C = 0$$

and from the remaining conditions

$$(7.27) \qquad \begin{aligned} 0 &= B \sin ks + D \sinh ks \\ 0 &= -B \sin ks + D \sinh ks \end{aligned}$$

Now Eqs. (7.27) show that

$$(7.28) \qquad B \sin ks = 0$$

and

$$(7.29) \qquad D \sinh ks = 0$$

Now, since sinh ks cannot be zero for real values of its argument, other than $ks = 0$, it follows that $D = 0$. Then, for a nontrivial solution $B \neq 0$, we must have

$$(7.30) \qquad \sin ks = 0$$

Hence

$$(7.31) \quad ks = r\pi \qquad r = 0, 1, 2, 3, \ldots$$

Fig. 7.3

and to each value of r there corresponds a value k_r of k, given by

$$(7.32) \qquad k_r = \frac{r\pi}{s}$$

By (7.6) the natural frequencies are given by

$$(7.33) \qquad \omega_r = \left(\frac{r\pi}{s}\right)^2 \sqrt{\frac{EI}{m}} \qquad r = 1, 2, 3, 4, 5, \ldots$$

The natural modes are given by

$$(7.34) \qquad v_r(x) = B_r \sin \frac{r\pi x}{s} \qquad r = 1, 2, 3, \ldots$$

c. Beam Clamped at One End and Carrying a Mass at the Free End. As a more complicated example of the general method, let us consider the system of Fig. 7.3.

This represents a cantilever beam supporting a mass M at its free end. In this case we must adjust the general solution (7.13) to the boundary conditions

$$(a) \qquad \left.\begin{array}{r} v = 0 \\ \dfrac{dv}{dx} = 0 \end{array}\right\} \qquad x = 0 \qquad \text{clamped end}$$

$$(b) \qquad \dfrac{d^2v}{dx^2} = 0 \qquad \text{at } x = s \qquad \text{zero bending moment}$$

The fourth condition is that at the free end the shearing force is the force due to the inertia of the mass M. Now the shearing force F is given by

$$(7.35) \qquad F = -EI\,\frac{\partial^3 y}{\partial x^3}$$

in terms of the deflection $y(x,t)$. The inertia force of the mass is $-M(\partial^2 y/\partial t^2)_{x=s}$. Hence we have

$$(7.36) \qquad EI\left(\frac{\partial^3 y}{\partial x^3}\right)_{x=s} = M\left(\frac{\partial^2 y}{\partial t^2}\right)_{x=s}$$

To obtain the boundary condition in terms of the variable $v(x)$, we use the fact that

$$(7.37) \qquad y(x,t) = v(x)\sin\omega t$$

Hence, substituting this into (7.36) and dividing both sides by the common factor $\sin\omega t$, we obtain

$$(c) \qquad EI\left(\frac{d^3 v}{dx^3}\right)_{x=s} = -(M\omega^2 v)_{x=s}$$

This is the required boundary condition.

We now impose these boundary conditions on the general solution (7.13). Condition (a) gives

$$(7.38) \qquad \begin{array}{l} 0 = A + C \\ 0 = B + D \end{array}$$

Therefore we may write

$$(7.39) \qquad v(x) = A(\cos kx - \cosh kx) + B(\sin kx - \sinh kx)$$

Condition (b) gives

$$(7.40) \qquad -A(\cos ks + \cosh ks) - B(\sin ks + \sinh ks) = 0$$

and condition (c) gives

(7.41) $-k^3[A(\sinh ks - \sin ks) + B(\cosh ks + \cos ks)]$
$$= + \frac{M\omega^2}{EI}[A(\cosh ks - \cos ks) + B(\sinh ks - \sin ks)]$$

In order that Eqs. (7.40) and (7.41) may have solutions other than the trivial solution $A = B = 0$, the determinant of their coefficients must vanish. If we let

(7.42)
$$\phi = \frac{M}{ms} = \frac{M}{M_B}$$

so that ϕ is the ratio of the mass M to the mass of the beam M_B, and also let

(7.43)
$$Z = ks$$

we obtain, after some reductions, the equation

(7.44)
$$\frac{1 + \cosh Z \cos Z}{\cosh Z \sin Z - \sinh Z \cos Z} = \phi Z$$

This equation can be solved by plotting the curve

(7.45)
$$y_1 = \frac{1 + \cosh Z \cos Z}{\cosh Z \sin Z - \sinh Z \cos Z}$$
$$= \frac{\cos Z + \operatorname{sech} Z}{\sin Z - \cos Z \tanh Z}$$

and the straight line

(7.46)
$$y_2 = \phi Z$$

and finding the values of Z at the intersections.

If $\phi = 1$, the graph gives the following approximate values of Z for the intersection of y_1 and y_2:

(7.47)
$$Z = 1.238,\ 4.045,\ \frac{9\pi}{4},\ \frac{13\pi}{4},\ \cdots$$

If we call the rth root of (7.45) Z_r, then we have

(7.48)
$$\omega_r = \left(\frac{Z_r}{s}\right)^2 \sqrt{\frac{EI}{m}}$$

for the natural angular frequencies of the oscillations of the system.

If $M \gg M_B$ so that the supported mass is much larger than the mass of the beam, then $\phi \gg 1$. In this case the angular frequency is very small, and Z is small.   Now, when Z is small, we can use the following approximations:

$$(7.49) \qquad \cos Z \doteq 1 - \frac{Z^2}{2} \qquad \cosh Z \doteq 1 + \frac{Z^2}{2}$$

$$\sin Z \doteq Z - \frac{Z^3}{6} \qquad \sinh Z \doteq Z + \frac{Z^3}{6}$$

Using these approximations, Eq. (7.44) becomes

$$(7.50) \qquad 1 + 1 - \frac{Z^4}{4} = \phi Z^2 \left[1 + \frac{Z^2}{3} - \left(1 - \frac{Z^2}{3} \right) \right]$$

or

$$(7.51) \qquad 2 - \frac{Z^4}{4} = \frac{2}{3} \phi Z^4$$

Neglecting $Z^4/4$ in comparison with 2, we have

$$(7.52) \qquad Z_1 = \left(\frac{3}{\phi} \right)^{\frac{1}{4}}$$

In this case we have from (7.48)

$$(7.53) \qquad \omega_1 = \frac{1}{s^2} \sqrt{\frac{3EI}{m\phi}} = \frac{1}{s^2} \sqrt{\frac{3EIM_B}{mM}} = \sqrt{\frac{3EI}{s^3 M}}$$

for the fundamental frequency in the case that the supported mass is much greater than the mass of the beam.   This result may be computed more simply by computing the *effective spring constant* of the beam by impressing a unit force at the free end and computing the resulting deflection.

8. Rayleigh's Method of Calculating Natural Frequencies.   Lord Rayleigh[*] has given an approximate method for finding the lowest natural frequency of a vibrating system.   The method depends upon the energy considerations of the oscillating system.

From mechanics it is known that, if a conservative system (one that does not undergo loss of energy throughout its oscillation) is vibrating freely, then when the system is at its maximum displacement the kinetic energy is instantaneously zero, since the system is at rest at this instant. At this same instant the potential of the system is at its maximum value. This is evident since the potential energy is the work done against the elastic restoring forces, and this is clearly a maximum at the maximum displacement.

In the same manner, when the system passes through its mean position, the kinetic energy is a maximum and the potential energy is zero.   By

[*] Lord Rayleigh, "Theory of Sound," 2d ed., vol. I, pp. 111, 287, Dover Publications, New York, 1945.

realizing these facts it is possible to compute the natural frequencies of conservative systems.

To illustrate the general procedure, consider the simple mass-and-spring system shown in Fig. 8.1.

Let V be the potential energy and T be the kinetic energy of the system at any instant. We then have

$$(8.1) \qquad V = \int_0^x Kx \, dx = K \frac{x^2}{2}$$

Fig. 8.1

since the spring force is given by Kx, where K is the spring constant.

The kinetic energy is

$$(8.2) \qquad T = \frac{1}{2} M \left(\frac{dx}{dt} \right)^2$$

Let the system be executing free harmonic vibrations of the type

$$(8.3) \qquad x = a \sin \omega t$$

Now at the maximum displacement

$$(8.4) \qquad \sin \omega t = \pm 1 \qquad \cos \omega t = 0$$

Hence, from (8.1) and (8.2), we have

$$(8.5) \qquad V_M = \tfrac{1}{2} Ka^2$$

where V_M denotes the maximum potential energy.

Now, when the system is passing through its equilibrium position, we have

$$(8.6) \qquad \sin \omega t = 0 \qquad \cos \omega t = \pm 1$$

Hence we have

$$(8.7) \qquad T_M = \tfrac{1}{2} Ma^2 \omega^2$$

Now the total energy in the system is the sum of the kinetic and potential energies. In the absence of damping forces this total remains constant (conservative system). It is thus evident that the maximum kinetic energy is equal to the maximum potential energy, and hence

$$(8.8) \qquad T_M = V_M$$

or

$$(8.9) \qquad \tfrac{1}{2} Ka^2 = \tfrac{1}{2} Ma^2 \omega^2$$

We thus find

$$(8.10) \qquad \omega = \sqrt{\frac{K}{M}}$$

for the natural frequency of the harmonic oscillations. The above illustrative example shows the essence of Rayleigh's method of computing natural frequencies. The method is particularly useful in determining the lowest natural frequency of continuous systems in the absence of frictional forces.

The method will now be applied to determine the natural frequencies of uniform beams.

Kinetic Energy of an Oscillating Beam. Consider a section of length dx of a uniform beam having a mass m per unit length. The kinetic energy of this element of beam is given by

$$(8.11) \qquad dT = \tfrac{1}{2}m \left(\frac{\partial y}{\partial t}\right)^2 dx$$

since $\partial y/\partial t$ is the velocity of the element and $m\, dx$ is its mass. The entire kinetic energy is given by

$$(8.12) \qquad T = \tfrac{1}{2}m \int_0^s \left(\frac{\partial y}{\partial t}\right)^2 dx$$

where s is the length of the beam.

The Potential Energy of an Oscillating Beam. Consider an element of beam of length dx as shown in Fig. 8.2.

FIG. 8.2

If the left-hand end of the section is fixed, the bending moment M turns the right-hand end through the angle ϕ and the bending moment is proportional to ϕ; that is, we have

$$(8.13) \qquad M(\phi) = k\phi$$

where k is a constant of proportionality. If now the section is bent so that the right-hand end is turned through an angle θ, the amount of work done is given by

$$(8.14) \quad dV = \int_{\phi=0}^{\phi=\theta} M(\phi)\, d\phi = \int_{\phi=0}^{\phi=\theta} k\phi\, d\phi = \frac{k\theta^2}{2} = \frac{M(\theta)\theta}{2}$$

Now the slope of the displacement curve at the left end of the section is $\partial y/\partial x$, and the slope at the right-hand end is

$$(8.15) \qquad \left(\frac{\partial y}{\partial x}\right)_{x+dx} = \left(\frac{\partial y}{\partial x}\right)_x + \left(\frac{\partial^2 y}{\partial x^2}\right)_x dx + \cdots$$

by Taylor's expansion in the neighborhood of x.

Hence, neglecting higher-order terms, we have

$$(8.16) \qquad \theta = -\frac{\partial^2 y}{\partial x^2}\, dx$$

Substituting this into (8.14), we have

$$(8.17) \qquad dV = -\frac{M}{2}\frac{\partial^2 y}{\partial x^2}\,dx$$

for the potential energy of the section of the beam. However, we have

$$(8.18) \qquad M = -EI\frac{\partial^2 y}{\partial x^2}$$

Hence, substituting this into (8.17), we obtain

$$(8.19) \qquad dV = \frac{EI}{2}\left(\frac{\partial^2 y}{\partial x^2}\right)^2 dx$$

The potential energy of the whole beam is

$$(8.20) \qquad V = \frac{EI}{2}\int_0^s \left(\frac{\partial^2 y}{\partial x^2}\right)^2 dx$$

If now the beam is executing harmonic vibrations of the type

$$(8.21) \qquad y(x,t) = v(x)\sin \omega t$$

we have, on substituting this into (8.12),

$$(8.22) \qquad T_M = \tfrac{1}{2}m\omega^2 \int_0^s v^2(x)\,dx$$

for the *maximum* kinetic energy, and, substituting into (8.20), we obtain

$$(8.23) \qquad V_M = \frac{EI}{2}\int_0^s \left(\frac{d^2 v}{dx^2}\right)^2 dx$$

for the *maximum* potential energy.

The natural angular frequency ω can be found if the deformation curve $v(x)$ is known by equating the two expressions (8.22) and (8.23). The procedure is to guess a certain function $v(x)$ that satisfies the boundary conditions at the ends of the beam and then equate expressions (8.22) and (8.23) to determine ω.

As an example of the general procedure, consider the system of Fig. 8.3.

Fig. 8.3

This system consists of a heavy uniform beam simply supported at each end and carrying a concentrated mass M at the center of the span. The boundary conditions at the ends are

$$(8.24) \qquad \left.\begin{aligned} y &= 0 \\ \frac{\partial^2 y}{\partial x^2} &= 0 \end{aligned}\right\}\ x = 0 \qquad \left.\begin{aligned} y &= 0 \\ \frac{\partial^2 y}{\partial x^2} &= 0 \end{aligned}\right\}\ x = s$$

This expresses the fact that the displacement and bending moments at each end are zero. To determine the fundamental frequency, let us assume the curve

$$(8.25) \qquad v(x) = A \sin \frac{\pi x}{s}$$

where A is the maximum deflection at the center. This assumed curve satisfies the boundary conditions and approximates the first mode of oscillation.

From (8.22) the maximum kinetic energy of the beam is

$$(8.26) \qquad T_M = \frac{m\omega^2}{2} \int_0^s A^2 \sin^2 \frac{\pi x}{s} \, dx = \frac{m\omega^2 A^2 s}{4} = \frac{M_B \omega^2 A^2}{4}$$

where

$$(8.27) \qquad M_B = ms$$

is the mass of the beam.

The maximum kinetic energy of the central load is

$$(8.28) \qquad T'_M = \tfrac{1}{2} M \omega^2 A^2$$

Hence, for the whole system, the total maximum kinetic energy is

$$(8.29) \qquad \sum T_M = \tfrac{1}{2} \omega^2 A^2 \left(\frac{M_B}{2} + M \right)$$

From (8.23) the maximum potential energy of the system is

$$(8.30) \qquad V_M = \frac{EI}{2} \int_0^s \left(\frac{\partial^2 v}{\partial x^2} \right)^2 dx = \frac{EI A^2 \pi^4}{4s^4} \int_0^s 2 \sin^2 \frac{\pi x}{s} \, dx$$

We have

$$(8.31) \qquad \int_0^s 2 \sin^2 \frac{\pi x}{s} \, dx = s$$

Hence

$$(8.32) \qquad V_M = \frac{EI A^2 \pi^4}{4s^3}$$

Equating expressions (8.29) and (8.32), we obtain

$$(8.33) \qquad \omega^2 = \frac{48.7 EI}{s^3 (M_B/2 + M)}$$

This gives the fundamental angular frequency ω. There are two interesting special cases:

1. If the central load is zero, then $M = 0$ and we have

$$(8.34) \qquad \omega^2 = \frac{97.4 EI}{M_B s^3}$$

This turns out to be the exact expression obtained by the use of the differential equations of Sec. 7.

2. If the beam is light compared with the central load, then $M_B \ll M$ and we have

(8.35)
$$\omega^2 = \frac{48.7EI}{Ms^3}$$

Rayleigh's method is very useful in the computation of the lowest natural frequencies of systems having distributed mass and elasticity. The success of the method depends on the fact that a large error in the assumed mode $v(x)$ produces a small error in the frequency ω. If it happens that we choose $v(x)$ to be one of the true modes, then Rayleigh's method will give the exact value for ω. In general it may be shown that Rayleigh's method gives values of the fundamental frequency ω that are somewhat greater than the true values.

PROBLEMS

1. A flexible string is held under a horizontal component of tension H and extends between $x = 0$ and $x = s$. It is loaded by a uniformly distributed load w_0 per unit length, extending from $x = a$ to $x = b$. Find the location and magnitude of the maximum deflection.

2. Find the deflection of the string of Prob. 1 if two concentrated loads P_a and P_b act on it at $x = a$ and $x = b$.

3. A string extending from $x = 0$ to $x = s$ is under a horizontal component of tension H and rests on an elastic foundation of spring constant k. A load P_a at $x = a$ and a load P_b at $x = b$ act on the string. Determine the deflection of the string.

4. Determine the deflection of a cantilever beam of flexural rigidity EI under the influence of a uniform load w_0 per unit length extending from $x = a$ to $x = b$. The beam is clamped at $x = 0$ and extends to $x = s$.

5. An infinite beam of flexural rigidity EI rests on an elastic foundation. The modulus of the foundation is k. The beam extends from $x = -\infty$ to $x = +\infty$, and at $x = 0$ there is applied a concentrated load P_0. Determine the deflection of the beam.

6. Consider a beam of length s clamped at $x = 0$ and $x = s$. Let $v_i(x)$ be a mode of oscillation corresponding to an angular frequency ω_i and let $v_j(x)$ be a mode corresponding to an angular frequency ω_j. Show that

$$\int_0^s v_i(x)v_j(x)\, dx = 0 \qquad \text{if } i \neq j$$

7. Determine the natural frequencies of oscillation of a uniform beam with free ends.

8. Determine the natural frequencies of oscillation of a uniform beam with a built-in end at $x = 0$ and simply supported at $x = s$.

9. Derive the equation giving the natural frequencies of a beam clamped at $x = 0$ and $x = s$ resting on an elastic foundation of modulus equal to k.

10. A string of length s under a tension t carries a mass M at its mid-point. Using Rayleigh's method, determine the fundamental frequency of oscillation. (HINT: Obtain the total potential and kinetic energies, etc.)

11. A uniform beam is built in at one end and carries a mass M at its other end. Use Rayleigh's method to determine the fundamental angular frequency of oscillation.

12. A uniform beam is hinged at $x = 0$ and is elastically supported at $x = s$ by a spring whose constant is k. Find the natural frequencies of oscillation. Discuss the limiting cases $k = 0$ and $k = \infty$.

13. Apply Rayleigh's method to determine the fundamental frequency of the system of Prob. 12.

REFERENCES

1. Kármán, T., and M. A. Biot: "Mathematical Methods in Engineering," McGraw-Hill Book Company, Inc., New York, 1940.
2. Timoshenko, S.: "Vibration Problems in Engineering," D. Van Nostrand Company, Inc., Princeton, N.J., 1937.
3. Temple, G., and W. G. Bickley: "Rayleigh's Principle," Oxford University Press, New York, 1933.
4. Pipes, L. A.: Application of the Operational Calculus to the Theory of Structures, *Journal of Applied Physics*, September, 1943, pp. 486–495.

CHAPTER 10

THE CALCULUS OF FINITE DIFFERENCES AND LINEAR DIFFERENCE EQUATIONS WITH CONSTANT COEFFICIENTS

1. Introduction. A great many electrical and mechanical systems encountered in practice consist of many identical component parts. Such problems as the determination of the potential and current distribution along an electrical network of the ladder type or the determination of the natural frequencies of the torsional oscillations of systems consisting of identical disks attached to each other by identical lengths of shafting may be most simply solved by the use of difference equations.

The calculus of finite differences is of extreme importance in the theory of interpolation and numerical integration and differentiation. In this chapter some of the elementary procedures of the calculus of finite differences will be considered, and methods for the solution of linear difference equations will be developed.

2. The Fundamental Operators of the Calculus of Finite Differences. The calculus of finite differences is greatly facilitated by the use of certain *operators*. An operator may be defined as a symbol placed before a function to indicate the application of some process to the function to produce a new function. The symbol $D = d/dx$ is an example; we have

$$(2.1) \qquad Df(x) = \frac{df}{dx} = f'(x)$$

In the calculus of finite differences it is convenient to use the operators E, Δ, D, and k, any constant. These operators indicate the following processes:

$$(2.2) \qquad \begin{aligned} EF(x) &= F(x + h) \\ \Delta F(x) &= F(x + h) - F(x) \\ DF(x) &= F'(x) \\ kF(x) &= kF(x) \end{aligned}$$

The operator E when applied to a function means that the function is to be replaced by its value h units to the right, D indicates differentiation, and the constant operator k merely multiplies the function by a given constant.

If now an operator is applied to a function and a second operator is applied to the resulting function, etc., the several operators are written as a product. Each new operator is written to the left of those preceding it. It may be shown that the order in which the operators are applied is immaterial. For example,

$$(2.3) \qquad \Delta DF(x) = \Delta F'(x) = F'(x + h) - F'(x) = D\Delta F(x)$$

If an operator is repeated n times, this is indicated by an exponent. For example,

$$(2.4) \qquad E \times E \times E \times F(x) = E^3 F(x)$$

In this manner all positive and integral powers of operators may be defined. An operator with power zero produces no change in the function; for example,

$$(2.5) \qquad D^0 F(x) = F(x)$$

Products of powers of operators combine according to the law of exponents; that is,

$$(2.6) \qquad D^2 D^3 F(x) = D^5 F(x)$$

At present we shall restrict the powers of D and Δ to be integral and nonnegative numbers. However, all real powers of E may be admitted. The general power of E is defined by the equation

$$(2.7) \qquad E^n F(x) = F(x + nh)$$

These powers combine according to the law of exponents:

$$(2.8) \qquad E^m E^n F(x) = F(x + nh + mh) = E^{m+n} F(x)$$

The sum or difference of two operators applied to a function is defined to be the sum or difference of the functions resulting from the application of each operator; that is,

$$(2.9) \qquad (E + D)F(x) = EF(x) + DF(x) = F(x + h) + F'(x)$$

3. The Algebra of Operators. In the above section the definitions of the operators E, Δ, D, and k were given. The meaning of all operators found from E, Δ, D, and k by addition, subtraction, and multiplication was given. The question of separating these operators from the functions to which they apply and working with them as if they were algebraic quantities will now be considered.

Two operators are said to be *equal* if, when applied to an arbitrary function, they produce the same results. For example,

$$(3.1) \qquad \Delta = E - 1$$

These operators, which we may call A, B, C, etc., may be combined as if they were algebraic quantities provided they conform to the following five laws of algebra:

(a) $A + B = B + A$
(b) $A + (B + C) = (A + B) + C$ *Form a ring.*
(c) $AB = BA$
(d) $A(BC) = (AB)C$
(e) $A(B + C) = AB + AC$

It is easy to show that the operators satisfy these fundamental laws of algebra. For example, to prove that

(3.2) $$E^n D = DE^n$$

we have

(3.3) $$E^n DF(x) = E^n F'(x) = F'(x + nh)$$
$$= DF(x + nh) = DE^n F(x)$$

Since the operators satisfy the laws of algebra, operators can be combined according to the usual algebraic rules. For example,

(3.4)
$$(E^{\frac{1}{2}}\Delta - D)(E^{\frac{1}{2}}\Delta + D) = E\Delta^2 - D^2$$
$$(D - \Delta)(D - \Delta) = D^2 - 2D\Delta + \Delta^2$$
$$\text{etc.}$$

4. Fundamental Equations Satisfied by the Operators. As a consequence of the definition of the operators E and Δ, we have

(4.1) $$E = 1 + \Delta$$

The connection between the operator E and the derivative operator D may be obtained by means of the symbolic form of Taylor's series given in Chap. 1, Sec. 16. We saw there that Taylor's expansion could be written in the form

(4.2) $$EF(x) = F(x + h)$$
$$= \left(1 + hD + \frac{h^2 D^2}{2!} + \frac{h^3 D^3}{3!} + \cdots\right) F(x)$$
$$= e^{hD} F(x)$$

Comparing both members of Eq. (4.2), we see that we may write symbolically

(4.3) $$E = e^{hD}$$

We also have from (4.1)

(4.4) $$1 + \Delta = e^{hD}$$

or

(4.5) $$\Delta = e^{hD} - 1$$

5. Difference Tables. If a function is known for equally spaced values of the argument, the differences of the various entries may be obtained by subtraction. It is very convenient to write these differences in tabular form. For example, let us consider the function $F(x) = x^3$, and let the tabular difference be $h = 1$; we then construct the following table of differences:

$$F(x) = x^3$$

x	$F(x)$	$\Delta F(x)$	$\Delta^2 F(x)$	$\Delta^3 F(x)$	$\Delta^4 F(x)$
1	1	7	12	6	0
2	8	19	18	6	0
3	27	37	24	6	
4	64	61	30		
5	125	91			
6	216				

We see that the third differences of this function are constant and the fourth differences are zero. This is a special case of the following theorem:

The nth differences of a polynomial of nth degree are constant, and all higher differences are zero. The proof of this theorem is not difficult and is left as an exercise for the reader.

Difference tables are of extreme importance in the theory of interpolation. Interpolation in its most elementary aspects is sometimes described as "the science of reading between the lines of a mathematical table." However, by the use of the theory of interpolation, it is possible to find the derivative and the integral of a function specified by a table taken between any limits. The utility of a difference table depends on the fact that in the case of practically all tabular functions the differences of a certain order are all zero.

6. The Gregory-Newton Interpolation Formula. Let us consider a function $F(x)$ whose values at $x = a, x = a + h, x = a + 2h, x = a + 3h$, etc., are given. Suppose that from these given values of $F(x)$ we construct a difference table and that the differences of order m are constant. We desire to compute the value of the function at some intermediate value of the argument $a + nh$. By the use of the operator E of Sec. 2 we have

(6.1) $$E^n F(a) = F(a + nh)$$

By Eq. (4.1) we have

$$(6.2) \qquad\qquad E^n = (1 + \Delta)^n$$

But, by the binomial theorem, we obtain

$$(6.3) \qquad E^n = (1 + \Delta)^n = 1 + n\Delta + \frac{n(n-1)}{2} \Delta^2 + \cdots$$

Hence we have from Eq. (6.1)

$$(6.4) \quad F(a + nh) = F(a) + n\,\Delta F(a) + \frac{n(n-1)}{2} \Delta^2 F(a) + \cdots$$

Now, in order to compute the value of $F(x)$ corresponding to any intermediate value of the argument such as $a + \frac{1}{2}h$, we simply substitute the value of $n = \frac{1}{2}$ in Eq. (6.4). Equation (6.4) is often referred to as *Newton's formula of interpolation*. It was discovered by James Gregory in 1670.

7. The Derivative of a Tabulated Function. From Eq. (4.5) giving the relation between the derivative operator D and the difference operator Δ, we have

$$(7.1) \qquad\qquad e^{hD} = 1 + \Delta$$

Hence we have

$$(7.2) \qquad\qquad D = \frac{1}{h} \ln (1 + \Delta)$$

If we expand $\ln (1 + \Delta)$ into a formal Maclaurin series in powers of Δ, we have

$$(7.3) \qquad D = \frac{1}{h}\left(\Delta - \frac{\Delta^2}{2} + \frac{\Delta^3}{3} - \frac{\Delta^4}{4} + \cdots \right)$$

We thus have

$$(7.4) \quad DF(a) \doteq F'(a) = \frac{1}{h} \Delta F(a) - \frac{1}{2h} \Delta^2 F(a) + \frac{1}{3h} \Delta^3 F(a) - \cdots$$

for the derivative of the function $F(x)$ at $x = a$.

To obtain higher derivatives, we have, from (7.2),

$$(7.5) \qquad\qquad D^r = \frac{1}{h^r} [\ln (1 + \Delta)]^r \qquad r = 1, 2, \ldots$$

The second member is expanded and applied to $F(a)$.

8. The Integral of a Tabulated Function. It is sometimes required to obtain the integral of a tabulated function over a certain range of the variable. To do this, it is convenient to introduce the operator D^{-1} or $1/D$. This operator is defined as the operator which when followed by

D leaves the function unchanged; that is, we have

(8.1) $$D^{-1}F(x) = \int F(x)\,dx + c$$

since if we operate on (8.1) with D, we obtain

(8.2) $$D \times D^{-1}F(x) = \frac{d}{dx}\int F(x)\,dx + \frac{d}{dx}c = F(x)$$

We also have the definite integral

(8.3) $$\int_a^{a+h} F(x)\,dx = \frac{1}{D}F(x)\Big|_a^{a+h} = \frac{1}{D}[F(a+h) - F(a)]$$
$$= \frac{1}{D}\Delta F(a)$$

If we use Eq. (7.2) for D, we may write (8.3) in the form

(8.4) $$\int_a^{a+h} F(x)\,dx = \frac{h\Delta}{\ln(1+\Delta)}F(a)$$
$$= \frac{h\Delta}{\Delta - \Delta^2/2 + \Delta^3/3 - \Delta^5/5 + \cdots}F(a)$$

By division the right-hand member of (8.4) may be written in the form

(8.5) $$\int_a^{a+h} F(x)\,dx = h\left(1 + \frac{\Delta}{2} - \frac{\Delta^2}{12} + \frac{\Delta^3}{24} - \frac{19}{720}\Delta^4 + \cdots\right)F(a)$$

By similar reasoning we have

(8.6) $$\int_a^{a+nh} F(x)\,dx = \frac{1}{D}[F(a+nh) - F(a)] = \frac{1}{D}(E^n - 1)F(a)$$
$$= \frac{h[(1+\Delta)^n - 1]F(a)}{\ln(1+\Delta)}$$
$$= nh\left[1 + \frac{n}{2}\Delta + \frac{n(2n-3)}{12}\Delta^2 + \frac{n(n-2)^2}{24}\Delta^3\right.$$
$$\left. + \frac{n(6n^3 - 45n^2 + 110n - 90)}{720}\Delta^4 + \cdots\right]F(a)$$

If $n = 2$, we have

(8.7) $$\int_a^{a+2h} F(x)\,dx = h\left(2 + 2\Delta + \frac{\Delta^2}{3} - \frac{\Delta^4}{90} + \cdots\right)F(a)$$

If $F(x)$ is such that its fourth and higher differences may be neglected, we have

(8.8) $$\int_a^{a+2h} F(x)\,dx = h\left(2 + 2\Delta + \frac{\Delta^2}{3}\right)F(a)$$
$$= h[2 + 2(E - 1) + \tfrac{1}{3}(E - 1)^2]F(a)$$
$$= \frac{h}{3}(1 + 4E + E^2)F(a)$$

This is known as *Simpson's rule* for approximate integration.   If $F(x)$ is a polynomial of degree less than 4, formula (8.8) is *exact*.   If we place $n = 3$ in (8.6) and neglect fourth and higher differences, we obtain

$$(8.9) \quad \int_a^{a+3h} F(x)\, dx = \frac{3h}{8}(1 + 3E + 3E^2 + E^3)F(a)$$

$$= \frac{3h}{8}[F(a) + 3F(a + h) + 3F(a + 2h)$$
$$+ F(a + 3h)]$$

This is known as the *three-eighths rule of Cotes*.

9. A Summation Formula.   A formula of great utility for the summation of polynomials may be easily obtained by the use of the finite-difference operators.   Consider the sum of n terms:

$$(9.1) \quad S_n = F(a) + F(a + h) + \cdots + F[a + (n - 1)h]$$
$$= (1 + E + E^2 + \cdots + E^{n-1})F(a)$$

The geometric progression in E may be summed, and we have

$$(9.2) \quad S_n = \frac{E^n - 1}{E - 1}F(a)$$

$$= \frac{(1 + \Delta)^n - 1}{\Delta}F(a)$$

Expanding $(1 + \Delta)^n$ by the binomial theorem and dividing by Δ, we obtain

$$(9.3) \quad S_n = \left[n + \frac{n(n - 1)}{2}\Delta + \frac{n(n - 1)(n - 2)}{6}\Delta^2 + \cdots \right]F(a)$$

As an application of this equation, let it be required to find the sum of the first n cubes.   To do this, we let $F(x) = x^3$, $h = 1$, and we use the difference table of Sec. 5.   We then have

$$(9.4) \quad 1^3 + 2^3 + 3^3 + \cdots + n^3 = n + \frac{n(n - 1)}{2} \times 7$$

$$+ \frac{n(n - 1)(n - 2)}{6} \times 12 + \frac{n(n - 1)(n - 2)(n - 3)}{24} \times 6$$

$$= \frac{n^2}{4}(n + 1)^2$$

The summation formula is exact if $F(x)$ is a polynomial.

10. Difference Equation with Constant Coefficients.   An equation relating an unknown function $u(x)$ and its first n differences of the form

$$(10.1) \quad a_0 \Delta^n u(x) + a_1 \Delta^{n-1}u(x) + \cdots + a_{n-1} \Delta u(x) + a_n u(x) = \phi(x)$$

where the a_r's are constants, is called a linear *difference* equation of order n with constant coefficients.

This type of equation is of frequent occurrence in technical applications. It has many striking analogies with the linear differential equations discussed in Chap. 6. If $\phi(x) = 0$, the equation is said to be *homogeneous*. By the use of the relation (3.1), Eq. (10.1) may be written in terms of the operator E in the form

$$(10.2) \qquad (b_0 E^n + b_1 E^{n-1} + b_2 E^{n-2} + \cdots + b_n) u(x) = \phi(x)$$

where the b's are constants. This is the form in which difference equations occur in practice.

The Complementary Function. As in the case of linear *differential* equations, the solution of the difference equation (10.2) consists of the sum of the particular integral and the complementary function. The complementary function is the solution of the homogeneous equation

$$(10.3) \qquad (b_0 E^n + b_1 E^{n-1} + \cdots + b_n) u(x) = 0$$

In the usual applications of difference equations $h = 1$, that is,

$$(10.4) \qquad E u(x) = u(x + 1), \text{ etc.}$$

To solve the homogeneous difference equation (10.3), we assume a solution of the exponential form

$$(10.5) \qquad u(x) = c e^{mx}$$

where c is an arbitrary constant and m is a number to be determined. If we operate on Eq. (10.5) with E, we obtain

$$(10.6) \qquad E u(x) = E c e^{mx} = c e^{m(x+1)} = c e^{mx} e^m$$

In the same manner, we have

$$(10.7) \qquad E^2 u(x) = E c e^{mx} e^m = c e^{mx} e^{2m}$$

and in general

$$(10.8) \qquad E^s u(x) = c e^{mx} e^{sm}$$

We therefore see that if we substitute the assumed solution (10.5) into the homogeneous difference equation (10.3) we obtain

$$(10.9) \qquad c e^{mx} (b_0 e^{nm} + b_1 e^{(n-1)m} + \cdots + b_n) = 0$$

If we let

$$(10.10) \qquad q = e^m$$

Eq. (10.9) may be written in the form

$$(10.11) \qquad c q^x (b_0 q^n + b_1 q^{n-1} + \cdots + b_n) = 0$$

If we exclude the trivial solution $u(x) = 0$, then

$$(10.12) \qquad\qquad cq^x \neq 0$$

Hence the term in parentheses in (10.11) must vanish, and we have

$$(10.13) \qquad\qquad b_0 q^n + b_1 q^{n-1} + \cdots + b_n = 0$$

This is an algebraic equation that determines the possible values of q. There are three cases to be considered.

a. *The Case of Distinct Real Roots.* If the algebraic equation (10.13) has n distinct roots $(q_1, q_2, \ldots, q_n)$, then the general solution of the homogeneous difference equation (10.3) is

$$(10.14) \qquad\qquad u(x) = c_1 q_1^x + c_2 q_2^x + \cdots + c_n q_n^x$$

where the c's are arbitrary constants.

For example, let it be required to solve the equation

$$(10.15) \qquad\qquad (2E^2 + 5E + 2)u(x) = 0$$

In this case the algebraic equation determining the possible values of q is

$$(10.16) \qquad\qquad 2q^2 + 5q + 2 = 0$$

The two roots of this equation are

$$(10.17) \qquad\qquad q_1 = -\tfrac{1}{2} \qquad q_2 = -2$$

Hence the solution of (10.15) is

$$(10.18) \qquad\qquad u(x) = c_1(-2)^x + c_2(-\tfrac{1}{2})^x$$

where c_1 and c_2 are arbitrary constants.

b. *The Case of Complex Roots.* Let us suppose that the algebraic equation (10.13) has pairs of conjugate complex roots. Let

$$(10.19) \qquad\qquad q_1 = Re^{i\phi} \qquad q_2 = Re^{-i\phi}$$

be a pair of complex roots. The solutions of the difference equation corresponding to these terms are of the form

$$(10.20) \qquad c_1(q_1)^x + c_2(q_2)^x = c_1 R^x e^{i\phi x} + c_2 R^x e^{-i\phi x}$$
$$= R^x(A \cos \phi x + B \sin \phi x)$$

where A and B are two new arbitrary constants. As an example, consider the equation

$$(10.21) \qquad\qquad (E^2 - 2E + 4)u(x) = 0$$

The roots in this case are

$$(10.22) \qquad\qquad q_1 = 2e^{i\pi/3} \qquad \text{and} \qquad q_2 = 2e^{-i\pi/3}$$

Hence the solution of (10.21) is

$$(10.23) \qquad u = 2^x \left(A \cos \frac{\pi x}{3} + B \sin \frac{\pi x}{3} \right)$$

where A and B are arbitrary constants.

c. *The Case of Repeated Roots.* Suppose we have the difference equation

$$(10.24) \qquad (E - a)^2 u(x) = 0$$

In this case the algebraic equation has repeated roots equal to a. To solve this equation, assume the solution

$$(10.25) \qquad u(x) = a^x v(x)$$

We now have

$$(10.26) \qquad \begin{aligned} (E - a)u(x) &= (E - a)a^x v(x) \\ &= a^{x+1} v(x + 1) - a^{x+1} v(x) \\ &= a^{x+1}(E - 1)v(x) \end{aligned}$$

Similarly

$$(10.27) \qquad (E - a)^2 u(x) = a^{x+2}(E - 1)^2 v(x)$$

Hence the function $v(x)$ satisfies the difference equation

$$(10.28) \qquad (E^2 - 2E + 1)v(x) = 0$$

This equation is obviously satisfied by

$$(10.29) \qquad v(x) = A + Bx$$

where A and B are arbitrary constants. Hence the solution of (10.24) is given by

$$(10.30) \qquad u(x) = a^x(A + Bx)$$

In the same manner it may be demonstrated that if the algebraic equation (10.13) has a root a that is repeated r times then the part of the solution due to this root has the form

$$(10.31) \qquad u(x) = (c_1 + c_2 x + \cdots + c_r x^{r-1})a^x$$

where the c's are arbitrary constants.

The Particular Integral. The difference equations most frequently encountered in practice are of the linear homogeneous type. The methods used for obtaining the particular integrals of linear differential equations with constant coefficients have their counterpart in the theory of difference equations. To illustrate the general procedure of determining the particular integral, let us write the linear inhomogeneous difference equation (10.2) in the form

$$(10.32) \qquad \mathcal{L}(E)u(x) = \phi(x)$$

where $\mathcal{L}(E)$ denotes the linear operator involving the various powers of E expressed in Eq. (10.2).

a. $\phi(x)$ *Is of the Exponential Form* e^{mx}. In this case, to obtain the particular integral, assume the solution

$$(10.33) \qquad u(x) = Ae^{mx}$$

where A is to be determined. On substituting this into (10.32) we have

$$(10.34) \qquad Ae^{mx}\mathcal{L}(e^m) = e^{mx}$$

Hence, provided that

$$(10.35) \qquad \mathcal{L}(e^m) \neq 0$$

we have

$$(10.36) \qquad A = \frac{1}{\mathcal{L}(e^m)}$$

This case enables one to determine the solution when $\phi(x)$ is sin mx or cos mx by the use of Euler's relation.

b. $\phi(x)$ *Is of the Form* a^x. In this case we assume a solution of the form

$$(10.37) \qquad u = Aa^x$$

On substituting this into (10.32) we obtain

$$(10.38) \qquad Aa^x\mathcal{L}(a) = a^x$$

Hence

$$(10.39) \qquad A = \frac{1}{\mathcal{L}(a)}$$

provided that $\mathcal{L}(a) \neq 0$.

c. *Decomposition of* $1/\mathcal{L}(E)$ *into Partial Fractions*. It is sometimes convenient to decompose the operator $1/\mathcal{L}(E)$ into partial fractions. For example, consider the difference equation

$$(10.40) \qquad (E^2 - 5E + 6)u(x) = 5^x$$

In this case the operator $\mathcal{L}(E)$ has the factored form

$$(10.41) \qquad \mathcal{L}(E) = (E - 3)(E - 2)$$

We may write

$$(10.42) \qquad u(x) = \frac{5^x}{\mathcal{L}(E)} = \left(\frac{1}{E-3} - \frac{1}{E-2}\right)5^x$$

$$= \frac{5^x}{2} + c_1 3^x - \frac{5^x}{3} + c_2 2^x$$

$$= \frac{5^x}{6} + c_1 3^x + c_2 2^x$$

The decomposition of the operator $1/\mathfrak{L}(E)$ into partial fractions frequently facilitates the determination of the particular integral. Methods for the determination of the particular integral when $\phi(x)$ contains functions of special form will be found in the references at the end of the chapter.

11. Oscillations of a Chain of Particles Connected by Strings. The calculus of finite differences may be applied to the solution of dynamical problems, whether electrical or mechanical. This calculus has great power when the system under consideration has a great many component parts arranged in some order. It may be that there are so many component parts that to write down all their equations of motion would be impossible. If there exists a certain amount of similarity between the successive component parts of the system, it may be possible to write down a few difference equations and in this manner include all the equations of motion. This may be illustrated by the following problem:

Consider a string of length $(n + 1)a$, whose mass may be neglected, which is stretched between two fixed points with a force τ and is loaded at intervals a with n equal masses M not under the influence of gravity, and which is slightly disturbed. Let it be required to determine the natural frequencies of the system and the modes of oscillation.

FIG. 11.1

Let (A,B) Fig. (11.1) be the fixed points and $(y_1, y_2, \ldots, y_n)$ be the ordinates at time t of the n particles.

Consider small displacements only and hence the tensions of all the strings as equal to τ.

The force on the kth mass is given by

$$(11.1) \qquad F_k = \frac{\tau}{a} \left[(y_{k-1} - y_k) + (y_{k+1} - y_k) \right]$$

This is a restoring force acting in the negative direction. By Newton's second law the equation of motion of the kth particle is given by

$$(11.2) \qquad \frac{M \, d^2 y_k}{dt^2} + \frac{\tau}{a} \left(-y_{k-1} + 2y_k - y_{k+1} \right) = 0$$

Since each particle is vibrating, let us place

$$(11.3) \qquad y_k = A_k \cos(\omega t + \phi)$$

Substituting this into (11.2) and dividing out the common cosine term, we obtain

$$(11.4) \qquad -\omega^2 M A_k + \frac{\tau}{a} \left(-A_{k-1} + 2A_k - A_{k+1} \right) = 0$$

If we let

(11.5)
$$c = 2 - \frac{\omega^2 M a}{\tau}$$

we may write (11.4) in the convenient form

(11.6)
$$-A_{k+1} + cA_k - A_{k-1} = 0$$

This is a homogeneous difference equation of the second order with constant coefficients in the unknown amplitude A_k. To solve it, we use the method of Sec. 10 and assume a solution of the form

(11.7)
$$A_k = Be^{\theta k}$$

where B is an arbitrary constant and θ is to be determined. If we substitute this assumed form of the solution into (11.6), we obtain

(11.8)
$$Be^{\theta k}(-e^{\theta} + c - e^{-\theta}) = 0$$

Therefore, for a nontrivial solution, we must have

(11.9)
$$\frac{c}{2} = \frac{e^{\theta} + e^{-\theta}}{2} = \cosh \theta$$

This equation determines two values of θ since $\cosh \theta$ is an even function, and we also have

(11.10)
$$\cosh(-\theta) = \frac{c}{2} = \cosh \theta$$

Hence, $B_1 e^{\theta k}$ and $B_2 e^{-\theta k}$ are solutions of the difference equation (11.6), and the general solution is the sum of these two solutions. It is convenient to write the general solution in terms of hyperbolic functions rather than in terms of exponential functions. We thus write

(11.11)
$$A_k = P \sinh \theta k + Q \cosh \theta k$$

where P and Q are arbitrary constants. Equation (11.2) represents the amplitude of the motion of every particle except the first and last. In order that it may represent these also, it is necessary to suppose that y_0 and y_{n+1} are both zero, although there are no particles corresponding to the values of k equal to 0 and $n + 1$. With this understanding the solution (11.11) represents the amplitude of the oscillation of every particle from $k = 1$ to $k = n$.

Now, since $A_0 = 0$, we have from (11.11)

(11.12)
$$Q = 0$$

The fact that $A_{n+1} = 0$ gives

(11.13)
$$\sinh \theta(n + 1) = 0$$

This equation fixes the possible values of θ; they are

(11.14) $$\theta = \frac{r\pi j}{n+1} \qquad r = 1, 2, 3, \ldots, n$$

Having determined the possible values of θ, we now turn to Eq. (11.5) to determine the possible values of ω. We thus obtain

(11.15) $$c = 2 - \frac{\omega^2 M a}{\tau} = 2 \cosh \frac{r\pi j}{n+1}$$

$$= 2 \cos \frac{r\pi}{n+1}$$

Hence

(11.16) $$\omega^2 = \frac{2\tau}{Ma}\left(1 - \cos\frac{r\pi}{n+1}\right)$$

$$= \frac{4\tau}{Ma}\sin^2\frac{r\pi}{2(n+1)}$$

It is convenient to write ω_r to denote the value of ω that corresponds to the number r. We thus write

(11.17) $$\omega_r = 2\sqrt{\frac{\tau}{Ma}}\sin\frac{r\pi}{2(n+1)} \qquad r = 1, 2, 3, \ldots, n$$

The amplitude of the motion of each particle is given by Eq. (11.11) in the form

(11.18) $$A_k = P \sinh \theta k$$

The amplitude of the motion of the first particle is given by

(11.19) $$A_1 = P \sinh \theta$$

If, now, the value $r = 0$ were admitted, this would preclude the motion of the first particle. Similarly the value $r = n + 1$ is not admitted. The values of ω given by Eq. (11.17) are the n natural angular frequencies of the system. Giving r other values not multiples of $n + 1$, we merely repeat these frequencies. To each value θ_r of θ there corresponds a term of the amplitude of the kth particle. This may be written in the form

(11.20) $$A_k = P_r \sinh \theta_r k = P'_r \sin \frac{r\pi k}{n+1}$$

where P'_r is an arbitrary constant.

By (11.3) the coordinate of the kth particle corresponding to the value θ_r of θ is given by

(11.21) $$y_k = P'_r \sin \frac{r\pi k}{n+1} \cos (\omega_r t + \phi_r)$$

The general solution is then of the form

$$(11.22) \qquad y_k = \sum_{r=1}^{r=n} P'_r \sin \frac{r\pi k}{n+1} \cos (\omega_r t + \phi_r)$$

The $2n$ arbitrary constants P'_r and ϕ_r are determined by the initial displacements and velocities of the particles.

The problem of the loaded string is of historical interest. It is discussed by Lagrange in his "Mécanique analytique." He deduced the solution from his own equations of motion. By means of an extension of the above analysis Pupin treated the problem of the vibration of a *heavy* string loaded with beads, both for free and for forced vibrations, and by an electrical application solved a very important telephonic problem.*

12. An Electrical Line with Discontinuous Leaks. The following interesting electrical problem may be solved by the use of difference equations:

Let us suppose that the current for a load of resistance R is carried from the generator to the load by a single wire with an earth return.

Fig. 12.1

The wire is supported by n equally spaced identical insulators, as shown in Fig. 12.1.

The resistance of the sections of wire between insulators is r_0. The resistance of the earth return is negligible. Let us suppose that in dry weather when the insulators are perfect the current supplied by the generator is I_d but in wet weather it is necessary to supply a current I_w in order to receive a current I_d at the load R. Assuming that the leakage of all the insulators is the same, let it be required to find the resistance r of each.

If we write Kirchhoff's second law for the sth loop, we obtain the difference equation

$$(12.1) \qquad i_s r - i_{s-1}r + i_s r_0 + i_s r - i_{s+1}r = 0$$

This may be written in the form

$$(12.2) \qquad i_{s+1} - \left(2 + \frac{r_0}{r} \right) i_s + i_{s-1} = 0$$

* M. Pupin, Wave Propagation over Non-uniform Electrical Conductors, *Transactions of the American Mathematical Society*, vol. 1, p. 259, 1900.

If we assume a solution of the form

(12.3) $$i_s = ce^{\theta s}$$

where c is an arbitrary constant, and substitute this into the difference equation, we find that

(12.4) $$\cosh \theta = 1 + \frac{r_0}{2r}$$

The general solution of (12.2) may be written in the form

(12.5) $$i_s = A \cosh s\theta + B \sinh s\theta$$

To determine the arbitrary constants A and B, we have for the current in the first loop

(12.6) $$I_\omega = i_1 = A \cosh \theta + B \sinh \theta$$

Also in the $(n + 1)$st loop we have

(12.7) $$I_d = A \cosh (n + 1)\theta + B \sinh (n + 1)\theta$$

If we solve these two simultaneous equations for A and B, we obtain

(12.8)
$$A = \frac{I_\omega \sinh (n + 1)\theta - I_d \sinh \theta}{\sinh n\theta}$$
$$B = \frac{-I_\omega \cosh (n + 1)\theta + I_d \cosh \theta}{\sinh n\theta}$$

Substituting these values for A and B into (12.5), we obtain

(12.9) $$i_s = \frac{I_\omega \sinh (n - s + 1)\theta + I_d \sinh (s - 1)\theta}{\sinh n\theta}$$

If we write Kirchhoff's second law around the last loop, we obtain

(12.10) $$I_d \left(1 + \frac{r_0 + R}{r}\right) = i_n$$

If we solve Eq. (12.4) for r, we obtain

(12.11) $$r = \frac{r_0}{2(\cosh \theta - 1)} = \frac{r_0}{4 \sinh^2 (\theta/2)}$$

Substituting this value of r, and i_n from (12.9), into (12.10), we obtain after some reductions

(12.12) $$2I_d R \sinh n\theta \sinh \frac{\theta}{2} + r_0 I_d \cosh \frac{(2n + 1)\theta}{2} - r_0 I_\omega \cosh \frac{\theta}{2} = 0$$

This equation may be solved graphically for θ by the methods of Chap. 5. Substituting the value of θ determined by this equation into

Eq. (12.11) gives the desired value of r. If, as is usually the case, the line resistance r_0 is small in comparison with the insulator resistance, that is, if

$$(12.13) \qquad \frac{r_0}{r} \ll 1$$

then we have

$$(12.14) \qquad 4 \sinh^2 \frac{\theta}{2} \ll 1$$

and we may make the approximation

$$(12.15) \qquad 4 \sinh^2 \frac{\theta}{2} \doteq \theta^2$$

realizing that if x is small we have

$$(12.16) \qquad \sinh x \doteq x \qquad \cosh x \doteq 1 + \frac{x^2}{2}$$

Using these approximations in Eq. (12.12) and solving for θ, we obtain

$$(12.17) \qquad \theta^2 = \frac{8r_0(I_\omega - I_d)}{8nRI_d + r_0[I_d(2n+1)^2 - I_\omega]} = \frac{r_0}{r}$$

Hence

$$(12.18) \qquad r = \frac{8nRI_d + r_0[I_d(2n+1)^2 - I_\omega]}{8(I_\omega - I_d)}$$

for the required value of r.

13. Filter Circuits. In Chap. 7 the mathematical technique for the determination of the steady-state behavior of alternating-current networks was explained. A very important type of network is one in which

Fig. 13.1

numbers of similar impedance elements are assembled to form a recurrent structure. Networks of this type are called *filters* because they pass certain frequencies freely and stop others. Various forms of structure may be employed. A very common structure is the so-called "ladder" structure. This is shown in Fig. 13.1.

Except for the end meshes this structure consists of a number of identical series elements of complex impedance Z_1 and a number of shunt elements of complex impedance Z_2. The input and output impedances are Z_0 and Z_n, respectively, and there is a complex applied electromotive force

$$(13.1) \qquad e(t) = E_0 e^{j\omega t} \qquad j = \sqrt{-1}$$

applied to the first mesh. The real and imaginary parts of this complex electromotive force correspond to actual electromotive forces of the type $E_0 \cos \omega t$ or $E_0 \sin \omega t$. We assume that the instantaneous currents in the various meshes have the form

$$(13.2) \qquad i_s(t) = I_s e^{j\omega t}$$

where the I_s are the ordinary complex currents of steady-state alternating-current theory. The real or imaginary parts of (13.2) correspond to an applied potential of the form $E_0 \cos \omega t$ or $E_0 \sin \omega t$, respectively, with proper phase.

FIG. 13.2

The circuit of Fig. 13.1 is composed of n T sections of the type shown in Fig. 13.2.

As shown, the filter ends with half-series elements and is said to have *mid-series terminations*. It is sometimes more convenient to arrange the filter circuit as shown in Fig. 13.3. This circuit is said to have *mid-shunt terminations*. In this case we regard the filter as made up of $n - 1$ so-called "sections," as shown in Fig. 13.4.

FIG. 13.3

The type of termination affects the values of the currents in the different sections of the filter for given input and output impedances. However, it does not affect the frequency characteristics of the filter. It is therefore necessary to analyze only one case, and we shall choose the case of the mid-series termination. If we apply Kirchhoff's second law to the

FIG. 13.4

various meshes of Fig. 13.1, we obtain the following set of equations:

$$Z_0 I_0 + \frac{Z_1 I_0}{2} + Z_2(I_0 - I_1) = E_0$$

$$-Z_2 I_0 + (Z_1 + 2Z_2)I_1 - Z_2 I_2 = 0$$

$$\cdots \cdots \cdots \cdots \cdots \cdots \cdots \cdots$$

$$(13.3) \qquad -Z_2 I_{s-1} + (Z_1 + 2Z_2)I_s - Z_2 I_{s+1} = 0$$

$$\cdots \cdots \cdots \cdots \cdots \cdots \cdots \cdots$$

$$-Z_2 I_{n-1} + \left(Z_2 + Z_n + \frac{Z_1}{2}\right) I_n = 0$$

The equation for the sth mesh may be written in the form

$$(13.4) \qquad -I_{s-1} + \frac{Z_1 + 2Z_2}{Z_2} I_s - I_{s+1} = 0$$

This difference equation has a general solution of the form

$$(13.5) \qquad I_s = Ae^{as} + Be^{-as}$$

where A and B are arbitrary constants. The number a is given by

$$(13.6) \qquad \cosh a = \frac{Z_1 + 2Z_2}{2Z_2}$$

The quantity a is, in general, complex and is called the *propagation constant* of the filter. Since a is complex, let us write

$$(13.7) \qquad a = -\alpha - j\phi$$

The actual instantaneous current $i_s(t)$ is obtained by multiplying the complex amplitude I_s by $e^{j\omega t}$ in the form

$$(13.8) \qquad \begin{aligned} i_s(t) = I_s e^{j\omega t} &= (Ae^{as} + Be^{-as})e^{j\omega t} \\ &= Ae^{-\alpha s}e^{j(\omega t - \phi s)} + Be^{+\alpha s}e^{j(\omega t + \phi s)} \end{aligned}$$

Assuming that $\alpha > 0$, we thus see that there is an attenuation factor $e^{-\alpha}$ introduced into the amplitude of the first term by each section of the filter as we move away from the input end. Similarly, for the second term of (13.8), there is an attenuation for each section of the same amount as we move *toward* the input end. It is thus apparent that if α differs from zero for any frequency and the filter has an appreciable number of sections the current transmitted by the filter is effectively zero. On the other hand a current whose frequency is such that $\alpha = 0$ is freely transmitted. The quantity α is called the *attenuation constant*.

In the same manner ϕ is called the *phase constant* since it gives the change of phase per section (measured as a lag) in the currents as we move along the filter.

The physical significance of Eq. (13.8) is now clear. The first term represents a *space wave* of current traveling away from the input end, attenuated from section to section much as the time waves of the free oscillations of a circuit are attenuated from instant to instant. The second term represents a similar wave traveling back toward the input end, arising from reflection at the output end.

From Eq. (13.8) we see that there are two separate points of interest to be considered:

1. The dependence of the frequency characteristics upon the filter construction, that is, on the nature of Z_1 and Z_2

2. The dependence of the transmission characteristics upon the terminating impedances Z_0 and Z_n

The first matter involves only Eqs. (13.6) and (13.7), while the second matter involves the determination of the arbitrary constants A and B.

Frequency Characteristics. If the resistances of the elements Z_1 and Z_2 of the filter are so small that they may be neglected, then Z_1 and Z_2 are pure imaginary quantities. It follows, therefore, that

$$(13.9) \qquad \cosh a = 1 + \frac{Z_1}{2Z_2}$$

is *real*.

If we now express $\cosh a$ in terms of α and ϕ, we have

$$(13.10) \qquad \begin{aligned} \cosh a &= \cosh(-a) = \cosh(\alpha + j\phi) \\ &= \cosh \alpha \cos \phi + j \sinh \alpha \sin \phi \end{aligned}$$

Now since $\cosh a$ is *real*, either α must be zero or ϕ must be an integral multiple of π. Hence, since $\cosh \alpha$ is never less than unity and $\cos \phi$ is never greater than unity, we have three cases to consider.

(a)	$-1 \leq \cosh a \leq 1$	$\alpha = 0$	$a = -j\phi$
(b)	$\cosh a > 1$	$\phi = 0$	$a = -\alpha$
(c)	$\cosh a < -1$	$\phi = \pm\pi$	$a = -\alpha \pm j\pi$

In the frequency range corresponding to case a, currents are transmitted freely without attenuation. The range of frequencies for which this is the case is called a *passband*. Frequency ranges corresponding to the other two cases are called *stopbands*.

In terms of Z_1 and Z_2, the passbands are given by

FIG. 13.5

$$(13.11) \qquad -1 \leq \frac{Z_1 + 2Z_2}{2Z_2} \leq 1$$

or

$$(13.12) \qquad 0 \leq -\frac{Z_1}{Z_2} \leq 4$$

Stopbands are given by all other ranges of values.

The simplest filters of the types we are considering are given by Figs. 13.5 and 13.6.

For the arrangement of Fig. 13.5, we have

$$(13.13) \qquad Z_1 = j\omega L_1 \qquad Z_2 = \frac{-j}{\omega C_2}$$

The passband is given by

$$(13.14) \qquad 0 \leq L_1 C_2 \omega^2 \leq 4$$

or

(13.15) $$0 \le \omega \le \omega_c \qquad \omega_c = \frac{2}{\sqrt{L_1 C_2}}$$

Since all frequencies from 0 to a critical, or *cutoff*, frequency given by

$$\omega_c = \frac{2}{\sqrt{L_1 C_2}}$$

are passed without attenuation, we have a *low-pass* filter.

In the arrangement of Fig. 13.6 we have

(13.16) $$Z_1 = \frac{-j}{C_1 \omega} \qquad Z_2 = j\omega L_2$$

The passband is now determined by

(13.17) $$0 \le \frac{1}{L_2 C_1 \omega^2} \le 4$$

or

(13.18) $$\omega_c \le \omega \le \infty \qquad \omega_c = \frac{1}{2 \sqrt{L_2 C_1}}$$

Here all frequencies above a critical frequency are passed without attenuation. This arrangement is called a *high-pass* filter. More complicated arrangements may be treated in a similar manner.

Transmission Characteristics. The values of the arbitrary constants A and B of the solution of the difference equation (13.5) are most simply expressed in terms of the *characteristic impedance Z_k* of the given filter.

FIG. 13.6

By definition the characteristic impedance of a filter of the type we are considering is the input impedance of the filter when it has an *infinite* number of sections. It is evident that, in this case, the wave due to reflection at the output end, which is represented by the second term of (13.5), vanishes. The current in each section is now independent of the terminal impedance Z_n, and the general solution (13.5) reduces to

(13.19) $$I_s = A e^{as}$$

If $s = 0$, we have

(13.20) $$I_0 = A$$

Hence we may write

(13.21) $$I_s = I_0 e^{as}$$

The first of Eqs. (13.3) now becomes

$$(13.22) \qquad \left[-Z_2(e^a - 1) + \frac{Z_1}{2} + Z_0 \right] I_0 = E_0$$

But by definition, since Z_k is the impedance at the sending end of the entire filter that has an infinite number of sections, we have

$$(13.23) \qquad (Z_k + Z_0)I_0 = E_0$$

Comparing Eqs. (13.22) and (13.23) and using (13.9), we have

$$(13.24) \qquad Z_k = -Z_2(e^a - 1) + \frac{Z_1}{2} = -Z_2 \frac{e^a - e^{-a}}{2}$$

If we square this equation and use Eq. (13.6), we obtain

$$(13.25) \qquad \left(\frac{Z_k}{Z_2} \right)^2 = \left(\frac{Z_1 + 2Z_2}{2Z_2} \right)^2 - 1 = \frac{Z_1}{Z_2} + \frac{Z_1^2}{4Z_2^2}$$

Hence, finally,

$$(13.26) \qquad Z_k = \sqrt{Z_1 Z_2 + \frac{Z_1^2}{4}}$$

We can show that when we neglect the resistance parts of Z_1 and Z_2 then Z_k is *real* in the passbands and *imaginary* in the stopbands.

To determine the constants A and B for the actual filter with a finite number of sections, we substitute (13.5) in the first and last of the equations of (13.3). We then obtain

$$(13.27) \qquad \left[-Z_2(e^a - 1) + \frac{Z_1}{2} + Z_0 \right] A$$
$$+ \left[-Z_2(e^{-a} - 1) + \frac{Z_1}{2} + Z_0 \right] B = E_0$$
$$e^{an} \left[-Z_2(e^{-a} - 1) + \frac{Z_1}{2} + Z_n \right] A$$
$$+ e^{-an} \left[-Z_2(e^a - 1) + \frac{Z_1}{2} + Z_n \right] B = 0$$

However, from Eq. (13.24) we have

$$(13.28) \qquad Z_k = \frac{Z_1}{2} - Z_2(e^a - 1)$$

and, similarly,

$$(13.29) \qquad -Z_k = \frac{Z_1}{2} - Z_2(e^{-a} - 1)$$

Hence Eqs. (13.27) may be written in the convenient form

$$(13.30) \qquad \begin{array}{c} (Z_k + Z_0)A - (Z_k - Z_0)B = E_0 \\ -e^{an}(Z_k - Z_n)A + e^{-an}(Z_k + Z_n)B = 0 \end{array}$$

Solving these simultaneous equations for A and B and substituting the result into (13.5), we obtain

$$(13.31) \qquad I_s = \frac{E_0(e^{(n-s)a} - r_R e^{-(n-s)a})}{(Z_0 + Z_k)(e^{na} - r_s r_R e^{-na})}$$

where

$$(13.32) \qquad r_s = \frac{Z_0 - Z_k}{Z_0 + Z_k} \qquad r_R = \frac{Z_n - Z_k}{Z_n + Z_k}$$

The quantities r_s and r_R are called the sending-end and receiving-end *reflection coefficients*, respectively.

If the output impedance matches the characteristic impedance of the line, then

$$(13.33) \qquad Z_n = Z_k$$

Under this condition the filter with its terminating impedance behaves like an infinite filter. The reflection coefficient $r_R = 0$, and reflection is absent. In this case all the energy delivered to the filter at the input end is transmitted to Z_n, and the filter operates at maximum efficiency. In this case Eq. (13.31) reduces to

$$(13.34) \qquad I_s = \frac{E_0 e^{-sa}}{Z_0 + Z_k}$$

In practice one is more interested in the input and output currents than in the intermediate currents. The completeness of filtering is measured by the ratio

$$(13.35) \qquad \frac{I_n}{I_0} = e^{an}$$

14. Four-terminal Network Connection with Matrix Algebra.

In this section it will be shown that there exists an intimate connection between difference equations and matrix multiplication. To fix the ideas, we shall consider an application to electrical-circuit theory, and we shall see that in certain cases matrix multiplication has some advantages over the method of difference equations in that we

FIG. 14.1

need not solve for the arbitrary constants that appear in the solutions of the difference equations.

Consider the electrical circuit of Fig. 14.1.

This circuit consists of a series impedance and a perfect conductor return path. We suppose that an electromotive force

$$(14.1) \qquad e_1(t) = E_1 e^{j\omega t}$$

is impressed on one end of the circuit and that an electromotive force

$$(14.2) \qquad e_2(t) = E_2 e^{j\omega t}$$

is impressed on the other end of the circuit. This gives rise to a current

$$(14.3) \qquad i_1(t) = I_1 e^{j\omega t} = I_2 e^{j\omega t}$$

Since we are interested in steady-state values, we may suppress the factor $e^{j\omega t}$ as is customary in electrical-circuit theory. We then concern ourselves only with the complex amplitudes E_1, E_2, I_1, and I_2. By Kirchhoff's laws, we have the relations

$$(14.4) \qquad \begin{aligned} E_1 &= E_2 + ZI_2 \\ I_1 &= I_2 \end{aligned}$$

This may be written in the convenient matrix form

$$(14.5) \qquad \begin{Bmatrix} E_1 \\ I_1 \end{Bmatrix} = \begin{bmatrix} 1 & Z \\ 0 & 1 \end{bmatrix} \begin{Bmatrix} E_2 \\ I_2 \end{Bmatrix}$$

FIG. 14.2

This matrix equation expresses a relation between the input quantities E_1 and I_1 and the output quantities E_2 and I_2. We notice that the determinant of the square matrix of (14.5) is equal to unity.

Let us now consider the circuit of Fig. 14.2.

By Kirchhoff's laws, we now have the relations

$$(14.6) \qquad \begin{aligned} E_1 &= E_2 \\ I_1 &= YE_2 + I_2 \end{aligned}$$

where Y is the admittance of the circuit and is hence the reciprocal of the impedance. This relation may be written in the matrix form

$$(14.7) \qquad \begin{Bmatrix} E_1 \\ I_1 \end{Bmatrix} = \begin{bmatrix} 1 & 0 \\ Y & 1 \end{bmatrix} \begin{Bmatrix} E_2 \\ I_2 \end{Bmatrix}$$

We notice that, in this case also, the determinant of the square matrix is equal to unity.

Let us now consider the network of Fig. 14.3.

We may regard this circuit as being formed by a circuit of the type of Fig. 14.1 in series with a circuit of the type of Fig. 14.2 and another circuit of the type of Fig. 14.1.

FIG. 14.3

Since the output currents and voltage of one circuit are the input currents and voltages of the next network, we obtain

$$(14.8) \qquad \begin{aligned} \begin{Bmatrix} E_1 \\ I_1 \end{Bmatrix} &= \begin{bmatrix} 1 & Z_1 \\ 0 & 1 \end{bmatrix} \begin{bmatrix} 1 & 0 \\ Y & 1 \end{bmatrix} \begin{bmatrix} 1 & Z_2 \\ 0 & 1 \end{bmatrix} \begin{Bmatrix} E_2 \\ I_2 \end{Bmatrix} \\ &= \begin{bmatrix} 1 + Z_1 Y & Z_1 + Z_1 Z_2 Y + Z_2 \\ Y_1 & 1 + Z_2 Y \end{bmatrix} \begin{Bmatrix} E_2 \\ I_2 \end{Bmatrix} \end{aligned}$$

We thus may obtain the input and output quantities directly. The elements of the square matrix are functions of the impedances and admittances of the component parts of the network. Since the square matrix of (14.8) is the product of three matrices whose determinants are each equal to unity, its determinant also is equal to unity. The square matrix of Eq. (14.8) is called the *associated matrix* of the network.

Let us consider a box with four accessible terminals as shown in Fig. 14.4.

Let us assume that within the box there exist various impedance and admittance elements joined together in a general manner. Let us also assume that there are no potential sources within the box.

FIG. 14.4

It may then be shown by a repeated multiplication of the associated matrices of the individual elements within the box that the input and output potentials and currents are related by the equation

$$(14.9) \qquad \begin{Bmatrix} E_1 \\ I_1 \end{Bmatrix} = \begin{bmatrix} A & B \\ C & D \end{bmatrix} \begin{Bmatrix} E_2 \\ I_2 \end{Bmatrix}$$

where in general A, B, C, D are complex numbers and the determinant of the square matrix of (14.9) satisfies the relation

$$(14.10) \qquad AD - BC = 1$$

If we premultiply both sides of Eq. (14.9) by

$$\begin{bmatrix} A & B \\ C & D \end{bmatrix}^{-1}$$

we obtain

$$(14.11) \qquad \begin{Bmatrix} E_2 \\ I_2 \end{Bmatrix} = \begin{bmatrix} A & B \\ C & D \end{bmatrix}^{-1} \begin{Bmatrix} E_1 \\ I_1 \end{Bmatrix} = \begin{bmatrix} D & -B \\ -C & A \end{bmatrix} \begin{Bmatrix} E_1 \\ I_1 \end{Bmatrix}$$

If the network within the box is symmetrical so that it appears the

FIG. 14.5

same when viewed from the right as when viewed from the left, we have

$$(14.12) \qquad A = D$$

Cascade Connection of Symmetrical Networks. Let us suppose that we have a chain of n identical symmetrical networks connected as shown in Fig. 14.5.

Since the networks are identical and symmetrical, we have the relation

$$(14.13) \qquad \begin{Bmatrix} E_s \\ I_s \end{Bmatrix} = \begin{bmatrix} A & B \\ C & A \end{bmatrix}^n \begin{Bmatrix} E_r \\ I_r \end{Bmatrix}$$

There exists a very convenient manner of writing the matrix

$$\begin{bmatrix} A & B \\ C & A \end{bmatrix}$$

to enable one to raise it to a positive or negative integral power. To do this, we let

$$(14.14) \qquad A = \cosh a$$

$$(14.15) \qquad C = \frac{\sinh a}{Z_0}$$

Now since the determinant of

$$\begin{bmatrix} A & B \\ C & A \end{bmatrix}$$

equals unity, we have

$$(14.16) \qquad A^2 - BC = 1$$

or

$$(14.17) \qquad B = \frac{A^2 - 1}{C} = \frac{(\cosh^2 a - 1)Z_0}{\sinh a} = Z_0 \sinh a$$

Hence with these substitutions we write

$$(14.18) \qquad \begin{bmatrix} A & B \\ C & A \end{bmatrix} = \begin{bmatrix} \cosh a & Z_0 \sinh a \\ \dfrac{\sinh a}{Z_0} & \cosh a \end{bmatrix}$$

We now have

$$(14.19) \qquad \begin{bmatrix} A & B \\ C & A \end{bmatrix}^2 = \begin{bmatrix} \cosh a & Z_0 \sinh a \\ \dfrac{\sinh a}{Z_0} & \cosh a \end{bmatrix} \begin{bmatrix} \cosh a & Z_0 \sinh a \\ \dfrac{\sinh a}{Z_0} & \cosh a \end{bmatrix}$$

$$= \begin{bmatrix} \cosh^2 a + \sinh^2 a & 2Z_0(\cosh a \sinh a) \\ \dfrac{2}{Z_0} \cosh a \sinh a & \cosh^2 a + \sinh^2 a \end{bmatrix}$$

$$= \begin{bmatrix} \cosh 2a & Z_0 \sinh 2a \\ \dfrac{\sinh 2a}{Z_0} & \cosh 2a \end{bmatrix}$$

By mathematical induction it may be shown that

$$(14.20) \qquad \begin{bmatrix} A & B \\ C & A \end{bmatrix}^n = \begin{bmatrix} \cosh an & Z_0 \sinh an \\ \dfrac{\sinh an}{Z_0} & \cosh an \end{bmatrix}$$

The result (14.20) holds for n a positive or negative integer.

We therefore have

(14.21)
$$\begin{Bmatrix} E_s \\ I_s \end{Bmatrix} = \begin{bmatrix} \cosh an & Z_0 \sinh an \\ \dfrac{\sinh an}{Z_0} & \cosh an \end{bmatrix} \begin{Bmatrix} E_r \\ I_r \end{Bmatrix}$$

This gives the relation between the receiving-end quantities and the sending-end quantities. If we premultiply Eq. (14.13) by

$$\begin{bmatrix} A & B \\ C & A \end{bmatrix}^{-n}$$

we obtain

(14.22)
$$\begin{Bmatrix} E_r \\ I_r \end{Bmatrix} = \begin{bmatrix} \cosh an & -Z_0 \sinh an \\ -\dfrac{\sinh an}{Z_0} & \cosh an \end{bmatrix} \begin{Bmatrix} E_s \\ I_s \end{Bmatrix}$$

Expressions (14.21) and (14.22) are extremely useful in the field of electrical-circuit theory, and, by the electrical and mechanical analogues, they are of use in the field of mechanical oscillations.

15. Natural Frequencies of the Longitudinal Motions of Trains. As a simple mechanical example of the above general theory, let us consider the longitudinal motions of a train of n equal units as shown in Fig. 15.1.

FIG. 15.1

FIG. 15.2

For simplicity we shall assume that the mass of each unit is m and that the units are coupled together by coupling whose spring constant equals k. Friction will be neglected.

By the principles explained in Chap. 8, the mechanical system of Fig. 15.1 is analogous to the electrical system of Fig. 15.2.

This is a ladder network having n meshes. By the electrical-mechanical analogy principle, we have the following analogous quantities:

(15.1)
$$m \rightarrow L$$

(15.2)
$$k \rightarrow S = \frac{1}{C}$$

(15.3)
$$i_r \rightarrow \dot{x}_r = v_r$$

(15.4)
$$q_r \rightarrow x_r$$

where L is the inductance parameter of each mesh of the ladder network, S is the elastance of each capacitor of the network, i_r is the mesh current

FIG. 15.3

of the rth mesh, q_r is the mesh charge, x_r is the coordinate of the rth unit of the train, and v_r is the velocity of the rth unit.

The electrical circuit may be regarded as being composed of n units of the π type as shown in Fig. 15.3.

The associated matrix of the circuit of Fig. 15.3 is

$$(15.5) \quad \begin{bmatrix} A & B \\ C & A \end{bmatrix} = \begin{bmatrix} 1 & 0 \\ \dfrac{j\omega C}{2} & 1 \end{bmatrix} \begin{bmatrix} 1 & j\omega L \\ 0 & 1 \end{bmatrix} \begin{bmatrix} 1 & 0 \\ \dfrac{j\omega C}{2} & 1 \end{bmatrix}$$

$$= \begin{bmatrix} 1 - \dfrac{\omega^2 LC}{2} & j\omega L \\ j\omega C - \dfrac{j\omega^3 LC^2}{4} & 1 - \dfrac{\omega^2 LC}{2} \end{bmatrix}$$

We now let

$$(15.6) \quad \cosh a = 1 - \frac{\omega^2 LC}{2}$$

$$(15.7) \quad Z_0 = \frac{\sinh a}{j\omega C(1 - \omega^2 LC/4)}$$

in accordance with Eqs. (14.14) and (14.15).

We may then write the associated matrix of the circuit (15.5) in the form

$$(15.8) \quad \begin{bmatrix} A & B \\ C & A \end{bmatrix} = \begin{bmatrix} \cosh a & Z_0 \sinh a \\ \dfrac{\sinh a}{Z_0} & \cosh a \end{bmatrix}$$

To obtain the natural frequencies of the dynamical system of Fig. 15.1, we realize that when the train is oscillating freely there are no external forces exerted upon it at either end. Hence, in the equivalent electrical circuit, the sending-end and receiving-end potentials must be equal to zero. We thus have

$$(15.9) \quad \begin{Bmatrix} E_R \\ I_R \end{Bmatrix} = \begin{bmatrix} \cosh an & Z_0 \sinh an \\ \dfrac{\sinh an}{Z_0} & \cosh an \end{bmatrix} \begin{Bmatrix} E_s \\ I_s \end{Bmatrix}$$

Since $E_s = 0$, we have

$$(15.10) \quad E_R = I_s Z_0 \sinh an = 0$$

where I_s is arbitrary. The frequency equation of the system is therefore given by

$$(15.11) \quad Z_0 \sinh an = 0$$

If, in Eq. (15.6), we let

(15.12) $$a = jb \qquad j = \sqrt{-1}$$

and solve for ω, we find

(15.13) $$\omega = \frac{2}{\sqrt{LC}} \sin \frac{b}{2}$$

If we now substitute this into (15.7), we have

(15.14) $$Z_0 = \frac{\sin b}{\omega C \cos^2 b/2}$$

The frequency equation (15.11) then becomes

(15.15) $$\frac{j \sin b \sin bn}{\omega C \cos^2 b/2} = 0$$

This equation is satisfied if

(15.16) $$\sin bn = 0$$

or

(15.17) $$b = \frac{r\pi}{n} \qquad r = 0, 1, 2, \ldots, n - 1$$

Substituting this into (15.13), we obtain the n natural angular frequencies ω_r:

(15.18) $$\omega_r = \frac{2}{\sqrt{LC}} \sin \frac{r\pi}{2n} \qquad r = 0, 1, 2, \ldots, n - 1$$

Translating this result into mechanical language, we obtain

(15.19) $$\omega_r = 2 \sqrt{\frac{k}{m}} \sin \frac{r\pi}{2n} \qquad r = 0, 1, 2, \ldots, n - 1$$

for the natural angular frequencies of oscillation of the train of n units.

PROBLEMS

1. Find the successive differences of $F(x) = 1/x$, the interval h being unity.

2. Evaluate $\pi/4 = \int_0^1 dx/(1 + x^2)$ by integrating numerically.

3. A curve expressed by $F(x)$ has for $x = 0, 1, 2, 3, 4, 5, 6$ the ordinates 0, 1.17, 2.13, 2.68, 2.62, 1.77, -0.07, respectively. Find the slope of the curve at each of the seven points, and find the area under the curve from $x = 0$ to $x = 6$.

4. Show that $1^4 + 2^4 + 3^4 + \cdots + n^4 = (n/30)(6n^4 + 15n^3 + 10n^2 - 1)$.

5. Derive the formula

$$\int_a^{a+4h} F(x) \, dx = \frac{2h}{45} (7 + 32E + 12E^2 + 32E^3 + 7E^4)F(a)$$

6. Sum, to m terms, the series

$$(3^2 + 8) + (5^2 + 11) + (7^2 + 14) + (9^2 + 17) + \cdots$$

Solve the following difference equations:

7. $u(x + 2) - 3u(x + 1) - 4u(x) = m^x.$

8. $u(x + 2) + 4u(x + 1) + 4 = x.$

9. $\Delta u(x) + \Delta^2 u(x) = \sin x.$

10. $u(x + 2) + n^2 u(x) = \cos mx.$

11. A seed is planted. When it is one year old, it produces tenfold, and when two years old and upward, it produces eighteenfold. Every seed is planted as soon as produced. Find the number of grains at the end of the xth year.

$$Ans. \ \frac{1}{3\sqrt{17}} \left[\left(\frac{11 + 3\sqrt{17}}{2} \right)^{x+1} - \left(\frac{11 - 3\sqrt{17}}{2} \right)^{x+1} \right].$$

12. A low-pass filter with mid-series termination is constructed of elements $L_1 = 1/\pi$ henry, $C_2 = 1/\pi$ μf. Find the cutoff frequency. $Ans. \ F_c = 1,000$ cycles.

13. Draw the equivalent electrical circuit for the loaded string. Use the matrix method to compute the natural frequencies of the system.

14. Consider an infinitely extended string under tension F. The string carries equal equidistant masses m and is immersed in a viscous fluid. Draw the equivalent electrical circuit, and discuss the nature of wave propagation when a harmonic transverse force is impressed on the first mass.

15. A shaft of constant cross section carries n identical disks spaced at equal intervals of length a. The moment of inertia of each disk is denoted by J. The torsional stiffness of each section of shaft between two disks is determined by the constant c such that if the relative angular displacement of two neighboring disks is equal to θ the torque transmitted by the section is equal to $c\theta$. Determine the natural frequencies of the torsional oscillations of the system. If an oscillatory torque is applied to the first disk, determine the motion of the last disk.

16. A transmission-line conductor carries an alternating current of angular frequency ω. It is supported by a string insulator of n identical units attached to a metallic transmission-line tower that is at zero potential. Assume that the metallic conductors between two insulators forms an electrical capacitor of capacitance c_1; also, each metallic conductor and the tower form a capacitor of capacitance c_2. Determine the potential distribution along the chain of insulators.

17. A light elastic string of length ns and coefficient of elasticity E is loaded with n particles each of mass m ranged at intervals s along it, beginning at one extremity. If it is suspended by the other end, prove that the periods of its vertical oscillations are given by the formula

$$\pi \sqrt{\frac{sm}{E}} \ \csc \left(\frac{2r + 1}{2n + 1} \frac{\pi}{2} \right) \qquad \text{when } r = 0, 1, 2, \ldots, n - 1$$

18. A railway engine is drawing a train of equal carriages connected by spring couplings of strength μ, and the driving power is adjusted so that the velocity is $A + B \sin qt$. Show that, if $q^2[(M + 4m)b^2 + 4mk^2]$ is nearly equal to $2\mu b^2$, the couplings will probably break. M is the mass of a carriage that is supported on four equal wheels of mass m, radius b, and radius of gyration k. Are there any other values of q for which the couplings will probably break?

19. A regular polygon $A_1, A_2, \ldots, A_n$ is formed of n pieces of uniform wire, each of resistance r, and the center 0 is joined to each angular point by a straight piece of the same wire. Show that, if the point 0 is maintained at zero potential and the point A_1 at potential V, the current that flows in the conductor A_s, A_{s+1} is

$$I = \frac{2V \, \sinh \theta \, \sinh \, (n - 2s + 1)\theta}{r \, \cosh n\theta}$$

where θ is given by the equation $\cosh 2\theta = 1 + \sin \, (\pi/n)$.

REFERENCES

1. Boole, George: "A Treatise on the Calculus of Finite Differences," The Macmillan Company, New York, 1880.
2. Funk, P.: "Die Linearen Differenzengleichungen und ihre Anwendungen in der Theorie der Baukonstruktionen," Springer-Verlag OHG, Berlin, 1920.
3. Kármán, T. V., and M. A. Biot: "Mathematical Methods in Engineering," McGraw-Hill Book Company, Inc., New York, 1940.
4. Routh, E. J.: "Advanced Rigid Dynamics," The Macmillan Company, New York, 1905.

CHAPTER 11

PARTIAL DIFFERENTIATION

1. Introduction. A great many of the fundamental laws of the various branches of science are expressed most simply in terms of differential equations. For example, the motion of a particle of mass M, when acted upon by a force whose components along the three axes of a cartesian reference frame are F_x, F_y, and F_z, is given by the three differential equations

$$(1.1) \qquad M\frac{d^2x}{dt^2} = F_x \qquad M\frac{d^2y}{dt^2} = F_y \qquad M\frac{d^2z}{dt^2} = F_z$$

where x, y, z is the position of the particle at any time t. In this case the motion is given by a system of ordinary differential equations.

The physical laws governing the distribution of temperature in solids, the propagation of electricity in cables, and the distribution of velocities in moving fluids are expressed in terms of partial differential equations. It is therefore necessary that the student of applied mathematics should have a clear idea of the fundamental definitions and operations involving partial differentiation.

2. Partial Derivatives. A quantity $F(x,y,z)$ is said to be a function of the three variables x, y, z if the value of F is determined by the values of x, y, and z. If, for example, x, y, and z are the cartesian coordinates of a certain point in space, then $F(x,y,z)$ may be the temperature at that point, and as x, y, and z take on other values, $F(x,y,z)$ will give the temperature in the region under consideration.

Continuity. The function $F(x,y,z)$ is continuous at a point (a,b,c) for which it is defined if

$$(2.1) \qquad \lim_{\substack{x\to a \\ y\to b \\ z\to c}} F(x,y,z) = F(a,b,c)$$

independently of the manner in which x approaches a, y approaches b, and z approaches c.

Now, given $F(x,y,z)$, it is possible to hold y and z constant and allow x to vary; this reduces F to a function of x only which may have a derivative defined and computed in the usual way. This derivative is called the *partial derivative of F* with respect to x. Therefore, by definition,

$$(2.2) \qquad \frac{\partial F}{\partial x} = \lim_{h \to 0} \frac{F(x + h, y, z) - F(x,y,z)}{h}$$

The symbol $\partial F/\partial x$ denotes the partial derivative. Sometimes the alternative notations are used:

$$(2.3) \qquad \frac{\partial F}{\partial x} = F_x = \left(\frac{dF}{dx}\right)_{y,z}$$

Again, if we hold x and z constant, we make F a function of y alone whose derivative is the partial derivative of F with respect to y; this is written

$$(2.4) \qquad \frac{\partial F}{\partial y} = F_y = \left(\frac{dF}{dy}\right)_{x,z} = \lim_{k \to 0} \frac{F(x, y + k, z) - F(x,y,z)}{k}$$

In the same manner we define the partial derivative with respect to z.

$$(2.5) \qquad \frac{\partial F}{\partial z} = F_z = \left(\frac{dF}{dz}\right)_{x,y} = \lim_{q \to 0} \frac{F(x, y, z + q) - F(x,y,z)}{q}$$

If $F(x,y,z)$ has partial derivatives at each point of a domain, then those derivatives are themselves functions of x, y, and z and may have partial derivatives which are called the *second partial derivatives of the function F*. For example,

$$(2.6) \qquad \begin{aligned} \frac{\partial}{\partial x}\left(\frac{\partial F}{\partial x}\right) &= \frac{\partial^2 F}{\partial x^2} = F_{xx} \\ \frac{\partial}{\partial y}\left(\frac{\partial F}{\partial x}\right) &= \frac{\partial^2 F}{\partial y\,\partial x} = F_{yx} \\ \frac{\partial}{\partial y}\left(\frac{\partial F}{\partial z}\right) &= \frac{\partial^2 F}{\partial y\,\partial z} = F_{yz} \end{aligned}$$

etc.

Order of Differentiation. $\partial^2 F/(\partial x\,\partial y)$ denotes the derivative of $\partial F/\partial y$ with respect to x, while $\partial^2 F/(\partial y\,\partial x)$ denotes the derivative of $\partial F/\partial x$ with respect to y. It may be shown that if $F(x,y)$ and its derivatives $\partial F/\partial x$ and $\partial F/\partial y$ are *continuous* then the order of differentiation is immaterial, and we have

$$(2.7) \qquad \frac{\partial^2 F}{\partial x\,\partial y} = \frac{\partial^2 F}{\partial y\,\partial x}, \text{ etc.}$$

In general $\partial^{p+q} F/(\partial x^p\,\partial y^q)$ signifies the result of differentiating $F(x,y,z)$ p times with respect to x and q times with respect to y, the order of differentiation being immaterial. The extension to any number of variables is obvious.

3. The Symbolic Form of Taylor's Expansion. In Chap. 1, Sec. 16, we wrote Taylor's expansion of a function of one variable in the form

$$(3.1) \qquad e^{hD_x}f(x) = f(x + h)$$

where

$$(3.2) \qquad D_x = \frac{d}{dx}$$

and e is the base of the natural logarithms. The symbolic expansion of a function $F(x,y)$ of two variables written in the form

$$(3.3) \qquad e^{(hD_x+kD_y)}F(x,y) = F(x + h, y + k)$$

where

$$(3.4) \qquad D_x = \frac{\partial}{\partial x} \qquad D_y = \frac{\partial}{\partial y}$$

is to be interpreted by substituting

$$(3.5) \qquad u = hD_x + kD_y$$

in the Maclaurin expansion

$$(3.6) \qquad e^u = 1 + \frac{u}{1!} + \frac{u^2}{2!} + \cdots + \frac{u^n}{n!} + \cdots$$

and operating with the result on $F(x,y)$. Terms of the type D_x^r and $D_x^r D_y^s$, etc., are interpreted by

$$(3.7) \qquad D_x^r = \frac{\partial^r}{\partial x^r} \qquad D_x^r D_y^s = \frac{\partial^{r+s}}{\partial x^r \, \partial y^s}$$

The justification of (3.1) depends on the fact that the operators D_x and D_y satisfy certain laws of algebra and commute with constants, as discussed in Chap. 10. This form of Taylor's expansion is of great usefulness in applied mathematics.

4. Differentiation of Composite Functions. As a simple case of composite functions, let us consider

$$(4.1) \qquad F = F(x,y)$$

where x and y are both functions of the independent variable t, that is,

$$(4.2) \qquad x = x(t) \qquad y = y(t)$$

Now if t is given an increment Δt, then x and y receive increments Δx, Δy, and F receives an increment ΔF given by

$$(4.3) \qquad \Delta F = F(x + \Delta x, y + \Delta y) - F(x,y)$$

Now, by Taylor's expansion, we have

(4.4) $F(x + \Delta x, y + \Delta y) = e^{\Delta x\, D_x + \Delta y\, D_y} F(x,y)$

$$= F(x,y) + \frac{\partial F}{\partial x} \Delta x + \frac{\partial F}{\partial y} \Delta y + \delta_1 \Delta x + \delta_2 \Delta y$$

where

(4.5) $\lim_{\substack{\Delta x \to 0 \\ \Delta y \to 0}} \delta_1 = 0 \qquad \lim_{\substack{\Delta x \to 0 \\ \Delta y \to 0}} \delta_2 = 0$

Hence

(4.6) $\Delta F = \frac{\partial F}{\partial x} \Delta x + \frac{\partial F}{\partial y} \Delta y + \delta_1 \Delta x + \delta_2 \Delta y$

Dividing this by Δt and taking the limit as $\Delta t \to 0$, we have

(4.7) $\lim_{\Delta t \to 0} \frac{\Delta F}{\Delta t} = \lim_{\Delta t \to 0} \left(\frac{\partial F}{\partial x} \frac{\Delta x}{\Delta t} + \frac{\partial F}{\partial y} \frac{\Delta y}{\Delta t} + \delta_1 \frac{\Delta x}{\Delta t} + \delta_2 \frac{\Delta y}{\Delta t} \right)$

Now as $\Delta t \to 0$, $\Delta x \to 0$, and $\Delta y \to 0$, and if t is the only independent variable, we have

(4.8) $\lim_{\Delta t \to 0} \frac{\Delta F}{\Delta t} = \frac{dF}{dt} \qquad \lim_{t \to 0} \frac{\Delta x}{\Delta t} = \frac{dx}{dt}$, etc.

Therefore, provided the functions $x(t)$ and $y(t)$ are differentiable, (4.7) becomes

(4.9) $\frac{dF}{dt} = \frac{\partial F}{\partial x} \frac{dx}{dt} + \frac{\partial F}{\partial y} \frac{dy}{dt}$

If there are other independent variables besides t, then we must use the notation

(4.10) $\lim_{\Delta t \to 0} \frac{\Delta F}{\Delta t} = \frac{\partial F}{\partial t} \qquad \lim_{\Delta t \to 0} \frac{\Delta x}{\Delta t} = \frac{\partial x}{\partial t}$, etc.

and we have

(4.11) $\frac{\partial F}{\partial t} = \frac{\partial F}{\partial x} \frac{\partial x}{\partial t} + \frac{\partial F}{\partial y} \frac{\partial y}{\partial t}$

This formula may be extended to the case where F is a function of any number of variables $x, y, z, \ldots$ and $x, y, z, \ldots$, etc., are functions of the variables $t, r, s, p, \ldots$, etc.

The results may be stated in the following form:

If F is a function of the n variables $x_1, x_2, \ldots, x_n$ so that

(4.12) $F = F(x_1, x_2, x_3, \ldots, x_n)$

and each variable x is a function of the single variable t so that

(4.13) $x_r = x_r(t) \qquad r = 1, 2, 3, \ldots, n$

then

$$(4.14) \qquad \frac{dF}{dt} = \frac{\partial F}{\partial x_1}\frac{dx_1}{dt} + \frac{\partial F}{\partial x_2}\frac{dx_2}{dt} + \cdots + \frac{\partial F}{\partial x_n}\frac{dx_n}{dt}$$

If, however, each variable x is a function of the p variables $t_1, t_2, \ldots, t_p$ so that

$$(4.15) \qquad x_r = x_r(t_1, t_2, \ldots, t_p) \qquad r = 1, 2, 3, \ldots, n$$

then

$$(4.16) \qquad \begin{aligned} \frac{\partial F}{\partial t_1} &= \frac{\partial F}{\partial x_1}\frac{\partial x_1}{\partial t_1} + \frac{\partial F}{\partial x_2}\frac{\partial x_2}{\partial t_1} + \cdots + \frac{\partial F}{\partial x_n}\frac{\partial x_n}{\partial t_1} \\ \frac{\partial F}{\partial t_s} &= \frac{\partial F}{\partial x_1}\frac{\partial x_1}{\partial t_s} + \frac{\partial F}{\partial x_2}\frac{\partial x_2}{\partial t_s} + \cdots + \frac{\partial F}{\partial x_n}\frac{\partial x_n}{\partial t_s}, \text{ etc.} \end{aligned}$$

Second and Higher Derivatives. As an illustration of the manner in which higher derivatives may be computed from these fundamental formulas, let us differentiate (4.9) on the assumption that x and y are functions of the single variable t. We therefore have

$$(4.17) \qquad \frac{d^2F}{dt^2} = \frac{d}{dt}\left(\frac{\partial F}{\partial x}\right)\frac{dx}{dt} + \frac{\partial F}{\partial x}\frac{d^2x}{dt^2} + \frac{d}{dt}\left(\frac{\partial F}{\partial y}\right)\frac{dy}{dt} + \frac{\partial F}{\partial y}\frac{d^2y}{dt^2}$$

Now since $\partial F/\partial x$ and $\partial F/\partial y$ are functions of x and y, we apply (4.9) to $\partial F/\partial x$ and $\partial F/\partial y$ instead of to F and obtain

$$(4.18) \qquad \frac{d}{dt}\left(\frac{\partial F}{\partial x}\right) = \frac{\partial^2 F}{\partial x^2}\frac{dx}{dt} + \frac{\partial^2 F}{\partial x\,\partial y}\frac{dy}{dt}$$

and

$$(4.19) \qquad \frac{d}{dt}\left(\frac{\partial F}{\partial y}\right) = \frac{\partial^2 F}{\partial x\,\partial y}\frac{dx}{dt} + \frac{\partial^2 F}{\partial y^2}\frac{dy}{dt}$$

Substituting these in (4.17), we have

$$(4.20) \qquad \frac{d^2F}{dt^2} = \frac{\partial^2 F}{\partial x^2}\left(\frac{dx}{dt}\right)^2 + 2\frac{\partial^2 F}{\partial x\,\partial y}\frac{dx}{dt}\frac{dy}{dt} + \frac{\partial^2 F}{\partial y^2}\left(\frac{dy}{dt}\right)^2 + \frac{\partial F}{\partial x}\frac{d^2x}{dt^2} + \frac{\partial F}{\partial y}\frac{d^2y}{dt^2}$$

Expressions for the third and higher derivatives may be found in a similar manner.

5. Change of Variables. An important application of Eq. (4.11) is its use in changing variables; for example, let

$$(5.1) \qquad F = F(x, y)$$

and it is desired to replace x and y by the polar coordinates r and θ given by

$$(5.2) \qquad x = r\cos\theta \qquad y = r\sin\theta$$

Then F becomes a function of r and θ, and we have by (4.11)

(5.3)
$$\frac{\partial F}{\partial r} = \frac{\partial F}{\partial x}\frac{\partial x}{\partial r} + \frac{\partial F}{\partial y}\frac{\partial y}{\partial r} = \frac{\partial F}{\partial x}\cos\theta + \frac{\partial F}{\partial y}\sin\theta$$
$$\frac{\partial F}{\partial \theta} = \frac{\partial F}{\partial x}\frac{\partial x}{\partial \theta} + \frac{\partial F}{\partial y}\frac{\partial y}{\partial \theta} = \frac{\partial F}{\partial x}(-r\sin\theta) + \frac{\partial F}{\partial y}r\cos\theta$$

Solving these equations for $\partial F/\partial x$ and $\partial F/\partial y$, we have

(5.4)
$$\frac{\partial F}{\partial x} = \frac{\partial F}{\partial r}\cos\theta - \frac{\partial F}{\partial \theta}\frac{\sin\theta}{r}$$
$$\frac{\partial F}{\partial y} = \frac{\partial F}{\partial r}\sin\theta + \frac{\partial F}{\partial \theta}\frac{\cos\theta}{r}$$

The second derivatives may be computed by Eq. (4.20).

6. The First Differential.   For simplicity, let us consider

(6.1)
$$F = F(x,y)$$

a function of two variables x and y.   Now let us give x an increment Δx and y an increment Δy.   Then, as was stated in (4.6), F takes an increment ΔF, where

(6.2)
$$\Delta F = \frac{\partial F}{\partial x}\Delta x + \frac{\partial F}{\partial y}\Delta y + \delta_1\Delta x + \delta_2\Delta y$$

provided $\partial F/\partial x$ and $\partial F/\partial y$ are continuous.

In general the third term is an infinitesimal of higher order than the first term, and the fourth term is in general a higher-order infinitesimal than the second.

We take the first two terms of (6.2) and call them the *differential* of F and write

(6.3)
$$dF = \frac{\partial F}{\partial x}\Delta x + \frac{\partial F}{\partial y}\Delta y$$

The definition is completed by saying that if x and y are *independent* variables

(6.4)
$$dx = \Delta x \qquad dy = \Delta y$$

then (6.3) takes the form

(6.5)
$$dF = \frac{\partial F}{\partial x}dx + \frac{\partial F}{\partial y}dy$$

This expression is called the *total differential* of $F(x,y)$.   This definition may be extended to the case where F is a function of the n *independent variables* $x_1, x_2, \ldots, x_n$ to obtain

(6.6)
$$dF = \frac{\partial F}{\partial x_1}dx_1 + \frac{\partial F}{\partial x_2}dx_2 + \cdots + \frac{\partial F}{\partial x_n}dx_n$$

This definition (6.5) has been based on the assumption that x and y are independent variables. Let us now examine the case where this is not true. Let us suppose that x and y are functions of the three independent variables u, v, w, so that

$$(6.7) \qquad \begin{aligned} x &= x(u,v,w) \\ y &= y(u,v,w) \end{aligned}$$

Now since u, v, and w are independent, we have

$$(6.8) \qquad \begin{aligned} dx &= \frac{\partial x}{\partial u}\,du + \frac{\partial x}{\partial v}\,dv + \frac{\partial x}{\partial w}\,dw \\ dy &= \frac{\partial y}{\partial u}\,du + \frac{\partial y}{\partial v}\,dv + \frac{\partial y}{\partial w}\,dw \end{aligned}$$

And since F is a function of u, v, and w, we have

$$(6.9) \qquad dF = \frac{\partial F}{\partial u}\,du + \frac{\partial F}{\partial v}\,dv + \frac{\partial F}{\partial w}\,dw$$

But, by Eq. (4.16), we have

$$(6.10) \qquad \begin{aligned} \frac{\partial F}{\partial u} &= \frac{\partial F}{\partial x}\frac{\partial x}{\partial u} + \frac{\partial F}{\partial y}\frac{\partial y}{\partial u} \\ \frac{\partial F}{\partial v} &= \frac{\partial F}{\partial x}\frac{\partial x}{\partial v} + \frac{\partial F}{\partial y}\frac{\partial y}{\partial v} \\ \frac{\partial F}{\partial w} &= \frac{\partial F}{\partial x}\frac{\partial x}{\partial w} + \frac{\partial F}{\partial y}\frac{\partial y}{\partial w} \end{aligned}$$

Substituting these equations into (6.9), we have

$$(6.11) \qquad \begin{aligned} dF &= \frac{\partial F}{\partial x}\left(\frac{\partial x}{\partial u}\,du + \frac{\partial x}{\partial v}\,dv + \frac{\partial x}{\partial w}\,dw\right) \\ &\quad + \frac{\partial F}{\partial y}\left(\frac{\partial y}{\partial u}\,du + \frac{\partial y}{\partial v}\,dv + \frac{\partial y}{\partial w}\,dw\right) \\ &= \frac{\partial F}{\partial x}\,dx + \frac{\partial F}{\partial y}\,dy \end{aligned}$$

This is the same as (6.5). It thus follows that the differential of a function F of the variables $x_1, x_2, \ldots, x_n$ has the form (6.6) *whether the variables* $x_1, x_2, \ldots, x_n$ *are independent or not.*

Let us now consider the case where

$$(6.12) \qquad F(x_1, x_2, \ldots, x_n) = C$$

where C is a constant. This relation cannot exist when $x_1, x_2, \ldots, x_n$ are independent variables unless $F = C$. Let us suppose that $x_1, x_2, \ldots, x_n$ are functions of *independent* variables $u_1, u_2, \ldots, u_m$.

Hence F may be regarded as a function of the variables $u_1, u_2, \ldots, u_m$, and we write

(6.13) $$F(u_1, u_2, \ldots, u_m) = C$$

Hence

(6.14) $$dF = \frac{\partial F}{\partial u_1}\, du_1 + \frac{\partial F}{\partial u_2}\, du_2 + \cdots + \frac{\partial F}{\partial u_m}\, du_m$$

Now, since $u_1, u_2, \ldots, u_m$ are *independent* variables, u_1 may be changed without changing the value of the other variables or the value of F since $F = C$. Therefore

(6.15) $$F(u_1 + \Delta u_1, u_2, u_3, \ldots, u_m) = C$$

Hence

(6.16) $$\frac{\partial F}{\partial u_1} = \lim_{\Delta u_1 \to 0} \frac{F(u_1 + \Delta u_1, u_2, \ldots, u_m) - F(u_1, u_2, \ldots, u_m)}{\Delta u_1}$$
$$= 0$$

In the same manner we may prove that

(6.17) $$\frac{\partial F}{\partial u_r} = 0 \qquad r = 2, 3, \ldots, m$$

Hence, as a consequence of (6.14), we have

(6.18) $$dF = 0$$

and by (6.6) we have

(6.19) $$dF = \frac{\partial F}{\partial x_1}\, dx_1 + \frac{\partial F}{\partial x_2}\, dx_2 + \cdots + \frac{\partial F}{\partial x_n}\, dx_n = 0$$

7. Differentiation of Implicit Functions. If we have the relation

(7.1) $$F(x, y) = 0$$

we are accustomed to say that this equation defines y as an *implicit* function of x and is equivalent to the equation

(7.2) $$y = \phi(x)$$

If the functional relation (7.1) is simple, then we can actually solve (7.1) to obtain y in the form (7.2). For example, consider

(7.3) $$x^2 + y^2 - a^2 = 0$$

This equation may be solved for y to give

(7.4) $$y = \pm \sqrt{a^2 - x^2}$$

However, if Eq. (7.1) is complicated, it is in general not possible to solve it for y. It may be shown that y in (7.1) satisfies the definition of a function of x in the sense that when x is given (7.1) determines a value of y. It is convenient to be able to differentiate (7.1) with respect to either x or y without solving the equation explicitly for x or y.

To differentiate (7.1), let us take its first differential. As a special case of (6.19) we have

(7.5)
$$dF = \frac{\partial F}{\partial x}\,dx + \frac{\partial F}{\partial y}\,dy = 0$$

and hence

(7.6)
$$\frac{dy}{dx} = -\frac{\partial F/\partial x}{\partial F/\partial y} = y'$$

This may be written in the form

(7.7)
$$\frac{\partial F}{\partial x} + \frac{\partial F}{\partial y}\,y' = 0$$

To obtain the second derivative, let

(7.8)
$$\phi = \left(\frac{\partial F}{\partial x} + \frac{\partial F}{\partial y}\,y'\right)$$

Applying (7.7) to ϕ, we have

(7.9)
$$\frac{\partial \phi}{\partial x} + \frac{\partial \phi}{\partial y}\,y' = 0$$

Now

(7.10)
$$\frac{\partial \phi}{\partial x} = \frac{\partial^2 F}{\partial x^2} + \frac{\partial^2 F}{\partial x\,\partial y}\,y' + \frac{\partial F}{\partial y}\,\frac{\partial y'}{\partial x}$$

and

(7.11)
$$\frac{\partial \phi}{\partial y}\,y' = \frac{\partial^2 F}{\partial x\,\partial y}\,y' + \frac{\partial^2 F}{\partial y^2}\,(y')^2 + y'\,\frac{\partial F}{\partial y}\,\frac{\partial y'}{\partial y}$$

Substituting in (7.9), we obtain

(7.12)
$$\frac{\partial^2 F}{\partial x^2} + 2\,\frac{\partial^2 F}{\partial x\,\partial y}\,y' + \frac{\partial^2 F}{\partial y^2}\,(y')^2 + \frac{\partial F}{\partial y}\,y'' = 0$$

since
$$\frac{\partial y'}{\partial x} + y'\,\frac{\partial y'}{\partial y} = \frac{dy'}{dx} = y''$$

Repeating this process, we may find the derivatives y''', y'''', etc., provided the partial derivatives of $F(x,y)$ exist and provided that $\partial F/\partial y \neq 0$.

One Equation, More than Two Variables. The equation

(7.13)
$$F(x,y,z) = 0$$

defines any one of the variables, for example, x, in terms of the other two. If we take the differential of (7.13), we have

$$(7.14) \qquad dF = \frac{\partial F}{\partial x}\, dx + \frac{\partial F}{\partial y}\, dy + \frac{\partial F}{\partial z}\, dz = 0$$

If we place $y = $ const, then $dy = 0$, and we have

$$(7.15) \qquad \left(\frac{dz}{dx}\right)_y = -\,\frac{\partial F/\partial x}{\partial F/\partial z}$$

where the subscript denotes that y is held constant.   This is less ambiguous than the notation $\partial z/\partial x$.

If $x = $ const, we have

$$(7.16) \qquad \left(\frac{dy}{dz}\right)_x = -\,\frac{\partial F/\partial z}{\partial F/\partial y}$$

If $z = $ const, we obtain

$$(7.17) \qquad \left(\frac{dx}{dy}\right)_z = -\,\frac{\partial F/\partial y}{\partial F/\partial x}$$

Multiplying Eqs. (7.15), (7.16), and (7.17) together, we have

$$(7.18) \qquad \left(\frac{dx}{dy}\right)_z \left(\frac{dy}{dz}\right)_x \left(\frac{dz}{dx}\right)_y = -1$$

This is sometimes written in the form

$$(7.19) \qquad \left(\frac{\partial x}{\partial y}\right) \left(\frac{\partial y}{\partial z}\right) \left(\frac{\partial z}{\partial x}\right) = -1$$

The absurdity of using ∂x, ∂y, ∂z as symbols for *differentials* which may be canceled is apparent from Eq. (7.19).

8. Maxima and Minima.   Quite frequently in the application of mathematics to science it is necessary to determine the maximum or minimum values of a function of one or more variables.

Let us consider a function F of the single variable x, so that

$$(8.1) \qquad\qquad F = F(x)$$

A *maximum* of $F(x)$ is a value of $F(x)$ which is *greater* than those immediately preceding or immediately following, while a *minimum* of $F(x)$ is a value of $F(x)$ which is *less* than those immediately preceding or following.   In defining and discussing maxima and minima of $F(x)$, it is assumed that $F(x)$ and all necessary derivatives are continuous and single-valued functions of x.

In order to determine whether the function $F(x)$ has a maximum or a minimum at a point $x = a$, we may use Taylor's expansion of a function

of one variable in the form

$$(8.2) \quad F(x + h) = F(x) + \frac{h}{1!} F'(x) + \frac{h^2}{2!} F''(x) + \frac{h^3}{3!} F'''(x) + \cdots$$

Let $x = a$ be the critical point under consideration, and write

$$(8.3) \quad \Delta(h) = F(a + h) - F(a) = \frac{h}{1!} F'(a) + \frac{h^2}{2!} F''(a)$$

$$+ \frac{h^3}{3!} F'''(a) + \cdots$$

$\Delta(h)$ is thus the change in the value of the function when the argument of the function is changed by h. This is illustrated graphically, in the case that $F(a)$ is a maximum, by Fig. 8.1.

FIG. 8.1

Now, if $x = a$ is a point at which $F(x)$ has either a maximum or a minimum, we shall have for h sufficiently small

$$(8.4) \quad \text{Sign of } \Delta(h) = \text{sign of } \Delta(-h)$$

since for a maximum, if we move to the left of the critical point or to the right of the critical point, the function will decrease and for a minimum point the function will increase.   Now if

$$(8.5) \qquad\qquad F'(x) \neq 0$$

then for h sufficiently small

$$(8.6) \qquad\qquad \Delta(h) \cong hF'(a)$$

since the higher-order terms in (8.3) may be neglected.   In the same way

$$(8.7) \qquad\qquad \Delta(-h) \cong -hF'(a)$$

Hence, in order for (8.4) to be satisfied, we must have

$$(8.8) \qquad\qquad F'(a) = 0$$

at *either* a *maximum* or a *minimum*.   Now at a maximum $\Delta(h)$ must be negative and at a minimum $\Delta(h)$ must be positive for either positive or negative values of h.

Hence, if (8.8) is satisfied, for h sufficiently small,

$$(8.9) \qquad\qquad \Delta(h) \cong \frac{h^2}{2!} F''(a)$$

Since h^2 is always positive, then it is evident that at a *maximum* we must have

$$(8.10) \qquad\qquad F''(a) < 0$$

and at a *minimum*

(8.11) $$F''(a) > 0$$

Let us suppose that

(8.12) $$F''(a) = 0 \quad \text{and} \quad F'''(a) \neq 0$$

Then for h sufficiently small

(8.13) $$\Delta(h) \cong \frac{h^3}{3!} F'''(a)$$

Since, if $F'''(a) \neq 0$, the expression (8.13) changes sign with h, we cannot have a maximum or a minimum.

If, however,

(8.14) $$F'(a) = 0 \quad F''(a) = 0 \quad F'''(a) = 0$$

then for h sufficiently small

(8.15) $$\Delta(h) = \frac{h^4}{4!} F''''(a)$$

Hence $F(a)$ will be a *maximum* if

(8.16) $$F''''(a) < 0$$

and a *minimum* if

(8.17) $$F''''(a) > 0, \text{ etc.}$$

Maxima and Minima of Functions of Two Variables. We define the maximum and minimum values of a function $F(x,y)$ of two variables x, y in the following manner:

$F(a,b)$ is a *maximum* of $F(x,y)$ when, for all sufficiently small positive or negative values of h and k,

(8.18) $$\Delta(h,k) = F(a + h, h + k) - F(a,b) < 0$$

$F(a,b)$ is a minimum of $F(x,y)$ when, for all small positive or negative values of h and k,

(8.19) $$\Delta(h,k) = F(a + h, b + k) - F(a,b) > 0$$

By Taylor's expansion of a function of two variables, we have, if the necessary derivatives exist and are continuous,

(8.20) $$F(x + h, y + k) = F(x,y) + h\frac{\partial F}{\partial x} + k\frac{\partial F}{\partial y}$$
$$+ \frac{1}{2!}\left(h^2 \frac{\partial^2 F}{\partial x^2} + 2hk \frac{\partial^2 F}{\partial x\,\partial y} + k^2 \frac{\partial^2 F}{\partial y^2}\right) + \cdots$$

Letting $F_x = \partial F/\partial x$, $F_y = \partial F/\partial y$,

(8.21) $$A = \frac{\partial^2 F}{\partial x^2} \qquad B = \frac{\partial^2 F}{\partial x\,\partial y} \qquad C = \frac{\partial^2 F}{\partial y^2}$$

evaluated at the point $x = a$, $y = b$. Then

$$(8.22) \quad \Delta(h,k) = hF_x(a,b) + kF_y(a,b) + \frac{1}{2!}(h^2A + 2hkB + k^2C) + \cdots$$

It is thus evident that for small values of h and k, in order for $\Delta(h,k)$ to have the same sign independently of the signs of h and k, it is necessary for the coefficients of h and k in (8.22) to vanish. This gives

$$(8.23) \qquad\qquad \frac{\partial F}{\partial x} = 0 \qquad \frac{\partial F}{\partial y} = 0$$

evaluated at $x = a$, $y = b$ as a required condition for *either* a maximum or a minimum. If the conditions (8.23) are satisfied, then $\Delta(h,k)$ reduces to

$$(8.24) \qquad\qquad \Delta(h,k) = \frac{1}{2!}(h^2A + 2hkB + k^2C) + \cdots$$

To facilitate the discussion, we make use of the identity

$$(8.25) \qquad Ah^2 + 2Bhk + Ck^2 = \frac{(Ah + Bk)^2 + (AC - B^2)k^2}{A}$$

We may then write (8.24) in the form

$$(8.26) \qquad\qquad \Delta(h,k) = \frac{(Ah + Bk)^2 + (AC - B^2)k^2}{2!A}$$

The sign of $\Delta(h,k)$ given by (8.26) is *independent* of the signs of h and k provided that

$$(8.27) \qquad\qquad\qquad AC - B^2 > 0$$

or

$$(8.28) \qquad\qquad\qquad AC - B^2 = 0$$

This may be seen since $Ah + Bk^2$ is always positive or zero; therefore, if $AC - B^2$ is negative, the numerator of (8.26) will be positive when $k = 0$ and negative when $Ah + Bk = 0$.

Therefore a *second* condition for a maximum or a minimum of $F(x,y)$ is that at the point in question

$$(8.29) \qquad\qquad AC > B^2 \quad \text{or} \quad \frac{\partial^2 F}{\partial x^2}\frac{\partial^2 F}{\partial y^2} > \left(\frac{\partial^2 F}{\partial x\,\partial y}\right)^2$$

An investigation of the exceptional cases when (8.28) is satisfied or when

$$(8.30) \qquad\qquad\qquad A = B = C = 0$$

is beyond the scope of this discussion. The reader is referred to Goursat and Hedrick's "Mathematical Analysis."[1]   When condition (8.29) is satisfied at $x = a$, $y = b$, we see that $F(a,b)$ will have a *maximum* when

$$(8.31) \qquad \frac{\partial^2 F}{\partial x^2} < 0 \qquad \frac{\partial^2 F}{\partial y^2} < 0$$

evaluated at $x = a$, $y = b$. $F(a,b)$ will have a minimum when

$$(8.32) \qquad \frac{\partial^2 F}{\partial x^2} > 0 \qquad \frac{\partial^2 F}{\partial y^2} > 0$$

evaluated at $x = a$, $y = b$.
   If

$$(8.33) \qquad AC - B^2 < 0$$

then $F(x,y)$ has *neither* a maximum nor a minimum.   By a similar course of reasoning we obtain the conditions for maxima and minima of functions of three or more variables.   As an example of the above theory, let it be required to examine

$$(8.34) \qquad F(x,y) = x^2 y + xy^2 - axy$$

for maximum and minimum values.   Here

$$(8.35) \qquad \frac{\partial F}{\partial x} = (2x + y - a)y \qquad \frac{\partial F}{\partial y} = (2y + x - a)x$$

$$(8.36) \qquad \frac{\partial^2 F}{\partial x^2} = 2y \qquad \frac{\partial^2 F}{\partial y^2} = 2x$$

The conditions (8.23) are

$$(8.37) \qquad (2x + y - a)y = 0 \qquad (2y + x - a)x = 0$$

Condition (8.29) is

$$(8.38) \qquad 4xy > (2x + 2y - a)^2$$

The system of equations (8.37) has the four solutions

$$(8.39) \qquad \begin{matrix} x = 0 & x = a & x = 0 & x = \dfrac{a}{3} \\[2mm] y = 0 & y = 0 & y = a & y = \dfrac{a}{3} \end{matrix}$$

Only the last values satisfy (8.38), and a maximum or a minimum of $F(x,y)$ is located at

$$(8.40) \qquad x = \frac{a}{3} \qquad y = \frac{a}{3}$$

If a is positive, $\partial^2 F / \partial x^2$ is positive when $y = a/3$; therefore

$$(8.41) \qquad F\left(\frac{a}{3}, \frac{a}{3}\right) = -\frac{a^3}{27}$$

is a minimum.   If a is negative, $\partial^2 F / \partial x^2$ is negative when $y = a/3$; hence $-a^3/27$ is a maximum.

Lagrange's Method of Undetermined Multipliers.   In a great many practical problems it is desired to find the maximum or minimum value of a function of certain variables when the variables are not independent but are connected by some given relation.

For example, let it be required to find the maximum or minimum value of the function

$$(8.42) \qquad u = u(x,y,z)$$

and let the variables x, y, and z be connected by the relation

$$(8.43) \qquad \phi(x,y,z) = 0$$

In principle it should be possible to solve (8.43) for one variable in terms of the other two.   This variable may then be eliminated by substitution into (8.42).   Then the maximum or minimum values of u may be investigated by the methods discussed above since, by the elimination, u has been reduced to a function of two variables.   In many cases the solution of (8.43) for any of the variables may be extremely difficult or impossible.   To deal with such cases, Lagrange used an ingenious device which is known in the literature as the *method of undetermined multipliers*. This method will now be discussed.

If u is to have a maximum or minimum, it is necessary that

$$(8.44) \qquad \frac{\partial u}{\partial x} = 0 \qquad \frac{\partial u}{\partial y} = 0 \qquad \frac{\partial u}{\partial z} = 0$$

Hence

$$(8.45) \qquad \frac{\partial u}{\partial x}\, dx + \frac{\partial u}{\partial y}\, dy + \frac{\partial u}{\partial z}\, dz = 0$$

Differentiating the functional relation (8.43), we obtain

$$(8.46) \qquad \frac{\partial \phi}{\partial x}\, dx + \frac{\partial \phi}{\partial y}\, dy + \frac{\partial \phi}{\partial z}\, dz = 0$$

Let us now multiply (8.46) by the parameter λ and add the resulting equation to (8.45).   We thus obtain

$$(8.47) \qquad \frac{\partial u}{\partial x} + \lambda \frac{\partial \phi}{\partial x}\, dx + \frac{\partial u}{\partial y} + \lambda \frac{\partial \phi}{\partial y}\, dy + \frac{\partial u}{\partial z} + \lambda \frac{\partial \phi}{\partial z}\, dz = 0$$

This equation will be satisfied if

(8.48) $\dfrac{\partial u}{\partial x} + \lambda\,\dfrac{\partial \phi}{\partial x} = 0$ $\dfrac{\partial u}{\partial y} + \lambda\,\dfrac{\partial \phi}{\partial y} = 0$ $\dfrac{\partial u}{\partial z} + \lambda\,\dfrac{\partial \phi}{\partial z} = 0$

The three equations (8.48) and Eq. (8.43) furnish four equations to determine the proper values of the variables x, y, z and λ to assure the maximum or minimum value of the function u.

As an example of the use of this method, let it be required to find the volume of the largest parallelepiped that can be inscribed in the ellipsoid

(8.49) $\dfrac{x^2}{a^2} + \dfrac{y^2}{b^2} + \dfrac{z^2}{c^2} = 1$

In this case the function to be maximized is

(8.50) $u = 8xyz$

and Eqs. (8.48) are

$$8yz + \dfrac{2\lambda}{a^2}\,x = 0$$

(8.51) $$8xz + \dfrac{2\lambda}{b^2}\,y = 0$$

$$8xy + \dfrac{2\lambda}{c^2}\,z = 0$$

Multiplying the first equation by x, the second one by y, and the last one by z, and adding them, we obtain

(8.52) $3u + 2\lambda\left(\dfrac{x^2}{a^2} + \dfrac{y^2}{b^2} + \dfrac{z^2}{c^2}\right) = 0$

In view of (8.49) this becomes

(8.53) $3u + 2\lambda = 0$

Hence

(8.54) $2\lambda = -3u$

From the first equation (8.51) multiplied by x, we have

(8.55) $u\left(1 - \dfrac{3}{a^2}\,x^2\right) = 0$

or

(8.56) $x = \dfrac{a}{\sqrt{3}}$

Similarly

(8.57)
$$y = \frac{b}{\sqrt{3}} \qquad z = \frac{c}{\sqrt{3}}$$

Hence the required maximum volume is

(8.58)
$$u = \frac{8abc}{3\sqrt{3}}$$

9. Differentiation of a Definite Integral.   It is frequently required to differentiate a definite integral with respect to its limits or with respect to some parameter.   Let $F(x,u)$ be a continuous function of x, u, and consider

(9.1)
$$\phi(u) = \int_{a(u)}^{b(u)} F(x,u)\ dx$$

where u is a parameter appearing in the integrand and we assume that the limits a and b of the definite integral are continuous functions of the parameter u, so that

(9.2)
$$a = a(u) \qquad b = b(u) \qquad a + \Delta a = a(u + \Delta u)$$

The integral therefore defines a function $\phi(u)$ of the parameter u. We shall now show that differentiation of the function $\phi(u)$ yields the important equation

(9.3)
$$\frac{d\phi}{du} = \int_a^b \frac{\partial F}{\partial u}\ dx + F(b,u)\frac{db}{du} - F(a,u)\frac{da}{du}$$

To establish this equation, let u be given an increment Δu in (9.1). Hence

(9.4)
$$\phi(u + \Delta u) = \int_{a+\Delta a}^{b+\Delta b} F(x,\ u + \Delta u)\ dx$$

where Δa and Δb are the increments that a and b take when u is increased by Δu.   Then

(9.5) $\Delta\phi = \phi(u + \Delta u) - \phi(u)$
$$= \int_{a+\Delta a}^{a} F(x,\ u + \Delta u)\ dx + \int_a^b [F(x,\ u + \Delta u) - F(x,u)]\ dx$$
$$+ \int_b^{b+\Delta b} F(x,\ u + \Delta u)\ dx$$

Now by the concept of the definite integral of a continuous function, between the limits x_1 and x_2, we have

(9.6)
$$\int_{x_1}^{x_2} F(x)\ dx = F(x_0)(x_2 - x_1)$$

where x_0 is some intermediate point between x_2 and x_1 given by

(9.7)
$$x_1 < x_0 < x_2$$

This may be seen intuitively by the concept of the integral (9.6) giving the area under the curve $F(x)$ between the points x_1 and x_2. In this case $F(x_0)$ is a mean ordinate such that when it is multiplied by the length $x_2 - x_1$ it gives the same area as that given by the integral. We may apply Eq. (9.6) to the first integral of (9.5) and obtain

$$(9.8) \qquad \int_{a+a\Delta}^{a} F(x, u + \Delta u) \, dx = F(t_1, u + \Delta u)[a - (a + \Delta a)]$$
$$= -F(t_1, u + \Delta u) \, \Delta a$$

where

$$(9.9) \qquad\qquad a + \Delta a < t_1 < a$$

In the same way the last integral of (9.5) may be expressed in the form

$$(9.10) \qquad\qquad \int_{b}^{b+\Delta b} F(x, u + \Delta u) \, dx = \Delta b \, F(t_2, u + \Delta u)$$

where

$$(9.11) \qquad\qquad b < t_2 < b + \Delta b$$

Now

$$(9.12) \qquad \lim_{\Delta u \to 0} \int_{a}^{b} \frac{[F(x, u + \Delta u) - F(x,u)] \, dx}{\Delta u} = \int_{a}^{b} \frac{\partial F}{\partial u} \, dx$$

Hence, if we divide (9.5) by Δu, using the results (9.8), (9.10), and (9.12) and realizing that

$$(9.13) \qquad\qquad \lim_{\Delta u \to 0} t_1 = a \qquad \lim_{\Delta u \to 0} t_2 = b$$

we have

$$(9.14) \qquad \frac{d\phi}{du} = \int_{a}^{b} \frac{\partial F}{\partial u} \, dx + F(b,u) \frac{db}{du} - F(a,u) \frac{da}{du}$$

This is the required result.

In the special case that a and b are fixed, we have

$$(9.15) \qquad\qquad \frac{d\phi}{du} = \int_{a}^{b} \frac{\partial F}{\partial u} \, dx$$

If $F(x)$ does not contain the parameter u, and

$$(9.16) \qquad\qquad b = u \qquad a = \text{const}$$

we have

$$(9.17) \qquad\qquad \frac{\partial}{\partial b} \int_{a}^{b} F(x) \, dx = F(b)$$

In the same way, differentiating with respect to the lower limit gives

$$(9.18) \qquad\qquad \frac{\partial}{\partial a} \int_{a}^{b} F(x) \, dx = -F(a)$$

These equations are useful in evaluating certain definite integrals.

10. Integration under the Integral Sign. The possibility of differentiating under the integral sign leads to the converse possibility of integration.

Let

$$(10.1) \qquad \phi(u) = \int_a^b F(x,u) \, dx$$

where a and b are constants. Multiply by du and integrate with respect to u between u_0 and u. We then have

$$(10.2) \qquad \int_{u_0}^u \phi(u) \, du = \int_{u_0}^u du \int_a^b F(x,u) \, dx = Q(u)$$

The integrations are to be carried out first with respect to x and then with respect to u. Now let us consider

$$(10.3) \qquad P(u) = \int_a^b dx \int_{u_0}^u F(x,u) \, du$$

We wish to show that

$$(10.4) \qquad P(u) = Q(u)$$

Let us differentiate (10.3) with respect to u. By the results of the last section, when we carry out the differentiation on the right under the integral sign, we obtain

$$(10.5) \qquad \frac{\partial}{\partial u} \int_{u_0}^u F(x,u) \, du = F(x,u)$$

where the differentiation has been carried out with respect to the upper limit. Hence

$$(10.6) \qquad \frac{dP}{du} = \int_a^b F(x,u) \, dx = \phi(u)$$

Therefore

$$(10.7) \qquad \int_{u_0}^u \frac{\partial P}{\partial u} \, du = \int_{u_0}^u \phi(u) \, du = P(u) - P(u_0)$$

But, from (10.3), we have

$$(10.8) \qquad P(u_0) = 0$$

Hence

$$(10.9) \qquad P(u) = \int_{u_0}^u \phi(u) \, du = Q(u)$$

or

$$(10.10) \qquad \int_a^b dx \int_{u_0}^u F(x,u) \, du = \int_{u_0}^u du \int_a^b F(x,u) \, dx$$

as was to be proved. This shows the possibility of interchanging the order of multiple integrations. As an example of the use of the concept of integrating under the integral sign, consider

(10.11) $F(x,u) = x^u$ where $u > -1$

Now

(10.12) $\int_0^1 F(x,u)\ dx = \int_0^1 x^u\ dx = \dfrac{1}{u+1}$

Now multiply by du, and integrate between a and b.   Then

(10.13) $\int_a^b du \int_0^1 x^u\ dx = \int_a^b \dfrac{du}{u+1} = \ln\dfrac{b+1}{a+1}$

But

(10.14) $\int_a^b du \int_0^1 x^u\ dx = \int_0^1 dx \int_a^b x^u\ du = \ln\dfrac{b+1}{a+1}$

Now

(10.15) $\int_a^b x^u\ du = \dfrac{x^b - x^a}{\ln x}$

Hence

(10.16) $\int_0^1 \dfrac{x^b - x^a}{\ln x}\ dx = \ln\dfrac{b+1}{a+1}$

11. Evaluation of Certain Definite Integrals.   The evaluation of various definite integrals will illustrate some of the general principles discussed in Sec. 10.

Let us consider the integral

(11.1) $I = \int_0^\infty \dfrac{\sin bx}{x}\ dx$

If we change the sign of b, then the sign of the integral is changed. Placing $b = 0$ causes the integral to vanish.   However, if we let

(11.2) $bx = y$ $b > 0$

then we obtain

(11.3) $I = \int_0^\infty \dfrac{\sin y}{y}\ dy$

This shows that the integral does not depend on b but is a constant. Considered as a function of b, it has a discontinuity at $b = 0$.   Let us consider the integral

(11.4) $\int_0^\infty e^{-kx}\ dx = -\left.\dfrac{e^{-kx}}{k}\right|_0^\infty = \dfrac{1}{k}$ if $k > 0$

If we let k be the complex number

(11.5) $k = a + jb$

then we have

$$(11.6) \qquad \int_0^\infty e^{-(a+jb)x}\, dx = \frac{1}{a+jb} = \frac{a-jb}{a^2+b^2} \qquad a > 0$$

Separating the real and imaginary parts, we obtain the two integrals

$$(11.7) \qquad \int_0^\infty e^{-ax} \cos bx\, dx = \frac{a}{a^2+b^2}$$

$$(11.8) \qquad \int_0^\infty e^{-ax} \sin bx\, dx = \frac{b}{a^2+b^2}$$

Let us integrate (11.7) with respect to b and obtain

$$(11.9) \quad \int_0^b db \int_0^\infty e^{-ax} \cos bx\, dx = \int_0^\infty e^{-ax}\, dx \int_0^b \cos bx\, db$$

$$= \int_0^\infty e^{-ax} \frac{\sin bx}{x}\, dx = a \int_0^b \frac{db}{a^2+b^2} = \tan^{-1} \frac{b}{a}$$

Placing $a = 0$ in (11.9), we obtain the result

$$(11.10) \qquad \int_0^\infty \frac{\sin \cdot bx}{x}\, dx = \frac{\pi}{2} \qquad b > 0$$

The integral

$$(11.11) \qquad I_1 = \int_0^\infty e^{-x^2}\, dx$$

occurs very frequently in many branches of applied mathematics, particularly in the theory of probability. This integral represents the area of the so-called "probability curve"

$$(11.12) \qquad u = e^{-x^2}$$

Since the indefinite integral cannot be found except by a development in series, we are led to employ a certain device to evaluate the definite integral.

Since the variable of integration in a definite integral is of no importance, we have

$$(11.13) \qquad I_1 = \int_0^\infty e^{-x^2}\, dx \qquad I_1 = \int_0^\infty e^{-y^2}\, dy$$

Multiplying these integrals together, we obtain

$$(11.14) \qquad I_1^2 = \int_0^\infty e^{-x^2}\, dx \int_0^\infty e^{-y^2}\, dy$$

$$= \int_0^\infty \int_0^\infty e^{-x^2+y^2}\, dx\, dy$$

It is permissible to introduce e^{-x^2} under the sign of integration since x and y are to be considered as independent variables. If we consider

x and y as the coordinates of a cartesian reference frame and let z be a vertical coordinate, then the double integral (11.4) will represent the volume of a solid of revolution bounded by the surface

$$(11.15) \qquad z = e^{-x^2+y^2}$$

We may find this volume by introducing polar coordinates.   Then the element of area in the xy plane is

$$(11.16) \qquad ds = r\, dr\, d\theta \qquad \text{where } x^2 + y^2 = r^2$$

There may be some question concerning the validity of this process since the double integral (11.14) is the limit

$$(11.17) \qquad I_1^2 = \lim_{R \to \infty} \int_0^R \int_0^R e^{-x^2+y^2}\, dx\, dy$$

FIG. 11.1

which represents the volume over a square in the xy plane of sides equal to R (see Fig. 11.1).

It is easy to see that this volume is greater than that of the figure of revolution over the circle of radius R and less than that over the circle of radius $\sqrt{2}\, R$.   Hence if the integral

$$(11.18) \qquad \int_0^{\pi/2} \int_0^R e^{-r^2} r\, dr\, d\theta$$

approaches a limit for $R = \infty$, we have

$$(11.19) \qquad I_1^2 = \int_0^{\pi/2} \int_0^{\infty} e^{-r^2} r\, dr\, d\theta$$

The integration with respect to θ merely multiplies by $\pi/2$, while in the integral

$$(11.20) \qquad \int_0^R e^{-r^2} r\, dr = -\tfrac{1}{2} e^{-r^2} \Big|_0^R$$

the fact that we have an exact differential makes integration possible. Passing to the limit, we have

$$(11.21) \qquad I_1^2 = \lim_{R \to \infty} \frac{\pi}{2} \int_0^R e^{-r^2} r\, dr = \frac{\pi}{4} \lim_{R \to \infty} (1 - e^{-R^2}) = \frac{\pi}{4}$$

We therefore have the desired result

$$(11.22) \qquad I_1 = \int_0^{\infty} e^{-x^2}\, dx = \frac{\sqrt{\pi}}{2}$$

If in this integral we make the change in variable

$$(11.23) \qquad x = \sqrt{a}\, u \qquad a > 0$$

then we obtain

$$(11.24) \qquad I_1 = \int_0^\infty e^{-au^2} \sqrt{a}\, du = \frac{\sqrt{\pi}}{2}$$

or

$$(11.25) \qquad \int_0^\infty e^{-au^2}\, du = \frac{1}{2}\sqrt{\frac{\pi}{a}} \qquad a > 0$$

To illustrate a slightly different device, let us consider the integral

$$(11.26) \qquad I = \int_0^\infty e^{-x^2 + a^2/x^2}\, dx$$

This integral may be differentiated with respect to a to obtain

$$(11.27) \qquad \frac{dI}{da} = +2 \int_0^\infty \frac{a}{x^2} e^{-x^2 + a^2/x^2}\, dx$$

If we now change the variable of integration by putting

$$(11.28) \qquad x = \frac{a}{y} \qquad dx = -\frac{a\, dy}{y^2} = -\frac{x^2}{a}\, dy$$

then (11.27) becomes

$$(11.29) \qquad \frac{dI}{da} = -2 \int_0^\infty e^{-y^2 + a^2/y^2}\, dy = -2I$$

This is a linear differential equation with constant coefficients for I. Its general solution is

$$(11.30) \qquad I = Ce^{-2a}$$

where C is an arbitrary constant to be determined.

Placing $a = 0$, I reduces to

$$(11.31) \qquad \int_0^\infty e^{-x^2}\, dx = \frac{\sqrt{\pi}}{2}$$

Therefore

$$(11.32) \qquad C = \frac{\sqrt{\pi}}{2}$$

Hence we have finally

$$(11.33) \qquad \int_0^\infty e^{-x^2 + a^2/x^2}\, dx = \frac{\sqrt{\pi}}{2} e^{-2a} \qquad a > 0$$

The above examples illustrate typical procedures by which certain definite integrals may be evaluated.

12. The Elements of the Calculus of Variations. We have seen that a necessary condition for a function $F(x)$ to have a maximum or a minimum at a certain point is that the first derivative of the function shall vanish at that point; also a necessary condition for a maximum or a minimum of a function of several variables is that all its partial derivatives of the first order should vanish.

We now consider the following question: Given a definite integral whose integrand is a function of x, y and of the first derivatives $y' = dy/dx$,

$$(12.1) \qquad\qquad I = \int_{x_0}^{x_1} F(x,y,y') \, dx$$

for what function $y(x)$ is the value of this integral a maximum or a minimum? In contrast to the simple maximum or minimum problem of the differential calculus the function $y(x)$ is not known here but is to be determined in such a way that the integral is a maximum or a minimum. In applied mathematics we meet problems of this type very frequently. A very simple example is given by the question "What is the shortest curve that can be drawn between two given points?" In a plane, the answer is obviously a straight line. However, if the two points and their connecting curve are to lie on a given arbitrary surface, then the analytic equation of this curve, which is called a *geodesic*, may be found only by the solution of the above problem, which is called the *fundamental problem of the calculus of variations*.

Fig. 12.1

It will now be shown that the maximum or minimum problem of the calculus of variations may be reduced to the determination of the extreme value of a known function. To show this, consider functions $\bar{y}$ of x that are "neighboring" functions to the required function $y(x)$.

The function $\bar{y}$ is obtained as follows:

Let ϵ be a small quantity, and let $n(x)$ be an arbitrary function of x which is continuous and whose first two derivatives are continuous in the range of integration. We then introduce into the integral (12.1) in place of y and y' the neighboring functions

$$(12.2) \qquad\qquad \bar{y} = y + \epsilon n$$
$$(12.3) \qquad\qquad \bar{y}' = y' + \epsilon n'$$

We stipulate, however, that these functions $\bar{y}$ coincide with the function $y(x)$ at the end points of the range of integration, as shown in Fig. 12.1.

It must therefore be required that the arbitrary function $n(x)$ vanish at the end points of the interval.

If we substitute the function $\bar{y}$ into the integral, then the integral becomes a function of ϵ. We then require that $y(x)$ should make the integral a maximum or a minimum, that is, the function $I(\epsilon)$ must have a maximum or minimum value for $\epsilon = 0$.

That is,

$$(12.4) \qquad I(\epsilon) = \int_{x_0}^{x_1} F(x, y + \epsilon n, y' + \epsilon n') \, dx$$

should be a maximum or minimum for $\epsilon = 0$.

This gives us a simple method of determining the extreme value of a given integral. The condition is

$$(12.5) \qquad \left(\frac{dI}{d\epsilon}\right)_{\epsilon=0} = 0$$

We expand the integrand function F in a Taylor's series in the form

$$(12.6) \quad F(x, y + \epsilon n, y' + \epsilon n') = F(x,y,y') + \epsilon n \frac{\partial F}{\partial y} + \epsilon n' \frac{\partial F}{\partial y'}$$
$$+ \text{ terms in } \epsilon^2, \epsilon^3, \ldots$$

Therefore

$$(12.7) \quad I(\epsilon) = \int_{x_0}^{x_1} \left[F(x,y,y') + \epsilon n \frac{\partial F}{\partial y} + \epsilon n' \frac{\partial F}{\partial y'} \right.$$
$$\left. + \text{ terms in } \epsilon^2, \epsilon^3, \ldots \right] dx$$

If we differentiate (12.7) inside the integral sign with respect to ϵ, we obtain

$$(12.8) \qquad \frac{dI}{d\epsilon} = \int_{x_0}^{x_1} \left(n \frac{\partial F}{\partial y} + n' \frac{\partial F}{\partial y'} + \text{ terms in } \epsilon, \epsilon^2, \ldots \right) dx$$

This expression must vanish for $\epsilon = 0$. Since the terms in ϵ, ϵ^2, $\ldots$ vanish for $\epsilon = 0$, we have the condition

$$(12.9) \qquad \int_{x_0}^{x_1} \left(n \frac{\partial F}{\partial y} + n' \frac{\partial F}{\partial y'} \right) dx = 0$$

The second term of (12.9) may be transformed by integration by parts into the form

$$(12.10) \qquad \int_{x_0}^{x_1} n' \frac{\partial F}{\partial y'} \, dx = n \frac{\partial F}{\partial y'} \Big|_{x_0}^{x_1} - \int_{x_0}^{x_1} n \frac{d}{dx} \left(\frac{\partial F}{\partial y'} \right) dx$$

The first term vanishes since $n(x)$ must be zero at the limits. Hence, substituting back into (12.9), we obtain

$$(12.11) \qquad \int_{x_0}^{x_1} n \left(\frac{\partial F}{\partial y} - \frac{d}{dx} \frac{\partial F}{\partial y'} \right) dx = 0$$

Now, since $n(x)$ is *arbitrary*, the only way that the integral (12.11) can vanish is for the term in parentheses to vanish; hence we have

$$(12.12) \qquad \frac{\partial F(x,y,y')}{\partial y} - \frac{d}{dx} \frac{\partial F(x,y,y')}{\partial y'} = 0$$

This equation must be satisfied by y if y is to make the integral (12.1) either a maximum or a minimum. It is known in the literature as the *Euler-Lagrange differential equation.*

The investigation whether this equation leads to a maximum or a minimum is difficult but is seldom necessary in applied mathematics.

As an example of the application of Eq. (12.12), consider the problem of determining the curve between two given points A and B which by revolution about the x axis generates the surface of least *area.*

The area of the surface s is given by the equation

$$(12.13) \qquad s = 2\pi \int_a^b y \, ds = 2\pi \int_a^b y \sqrt{1 + y'^2} \, dx$$

Here we have

$$(12.14) \qquad F = y \sqrt{1 + y'^2}$$

Therefore Eq. (12.12) becomes

$$(12.15) \qquad \sqrt{1 + y'^2} - \frac{d}{dx}\left[\frac{yy'}{(1 + y'^2)^{\frac{1}{2}}} \right] = 0$$

This reduces to

$$(12.16) \qquad 1 + y'^2 - yy'' = 0$$

To integrate this equation, let

$$(12.17) \qquad y' = p \qquad y'' = p \frac{dp}{dy}$$

The equation then becomes

$$(12.18) \qquad \frac{p \, dp}{1 + p^2} = \frac{dy}{y}$$

and finally we have

$$(12.19) \qquad y = c_1 \cosh \frac{x - c_2}{c_1}$$

This is the equation of the catenary curve. The constants c_1 and c_2 must now be determined so that the curve (12.19) will pass through the points A and B as shown in Fig. 12.2.

This is the shape that a soap film assumes when stretched between two concentric parallel circular frames. It is obvious that, in this case, the surface s is a minimum.

The case where the function F is a function of several dependent variables y_k and their derivatives is of great importance. In this case we proceed as in the case of one variable and introduce as neighboring functions

$$(12.20) \quad \bar{y}_1 = y_1 + \epsilon_1 n_1 \qquad \bar{y}_2 = y_2 + \epsilon_2 n_2 \quad \cdots \quad \bar{y}_k = y_k + \epsilon_k n_k$$

where the functions $n_r(x)$ again vanish at the limits of the integral. The integral then becomes a function of the variables $\epsilon_1, \epsilon_2, \ldots, \epsilon_k$. The condition for a maximum or a minimum is

$$(12.21) \quad \frac{\partial I}{\partial \epsilon_r} = \int_{x_0}^{x_1} n_r \left(\frac{\partial F}{\partial y_r} - \frac{d}{dx} \frac{\partial F}{\partial y_r'} \right) dx = 0 \qquad r = 1, 2, \ldots, k$$

where $\epsilon_1 = \epsilon_2 = \cdots = \epsilon_r = \cdots = \epsilon_k = 0$.

It follows, therefore, that, as before, the coefficient of each of the functions n within the integral sign must vanish so that we have

$$(12.22) \quad \frac{d}{dx} \frac{\partial F}{\partial y_r'} - \frac{\partial F}{\partial y_r} = 0 \qquad r = 1, 2, \ldots, k$$

We thus see that the Euler-Lagrange equations hold for each of the independent variables.

FIG. 12.2

In literature the notation

$$(12.23) \quad \delta I = I(\epsilon) - I(0) = \epsilon \frac{dI}{d\epsilon}$$

for ϵ small is frequently used. δI is termed the *variation* of the integral. The condition that the integral have a maximum or a minimum is then expressed in the form

$$(12.24) \quad \delta \int_{x_0}^{x_1} F(x,y,y') \, dx = \int_{x_0}^{x_1} \delta F(x,y,y') \, dx = 0$$

δF is called the *variation* of F.

The Brachistochrone between Two Points. Perhaps the earliest problem in the calculus of variations was proposed in 1696 by the Swiss mathematician John Bernoulli. He proposed the following problem of the *brachistochrone:*

It is required to determine the equation of the plane curve down which a particle acted upon by gravity alone would

FIG. 12.3

descend from one fixed point to another in the shortest possible time.

Let A be the upper point and B the lower one. Assume the x axis of a cartesian reference frame to be measured vertically downward, and let A be the origin of coordinates as shown in Fig. 12.3.

Let s be the length of the required curve at any point measured from A. Let v be the velocity of the particle at the same point and t its time of descent from A to that point. We wish to determine the curve that will make T a minimum, where T is the total time of descent from A to B. Now, from mechanics, we have

(12.25) $$dt = \frac{ds}{v}$$

where

(12.26) $$ds = \sqrt{dx^2 + dy^2} = \sqrt{1 + y'^2}\, dx$$

We know that the particle loses no energy in passing from one point to another of a smooth curve, since the loss of gravitational potential energy is transformed into kinetic energy; hence

(12.27) $$v = \sqrt{2gx}$$

where it is assumed that the particle starts from rest and g is the acceleration due to gravity.

Therefore (12.25) becomes

(12.28) $$dt = \frac{\sqrt{1 + y'^2}}{\sqrt{2gx}}\, dx$$

and the total time T is

(12.29) $$T = \frac{1}{\sqrt{2g}} \int_{x=0}^{x=x_0} \frac{\sqrt{1 + y'^2}}{\sqrt{x}}\, dx$$

We must therefore minimize the integral

(12.30) $$I = \int_{x=0}^{x=x_0} \frac{\sqrt{1 + y'^2}}{\sqrt{x}}\, dx$$

Hence we have

(12.31) $$F = \frac{\sqrt{1 + y'^2}}{\sqrt{x}}$$

In this case the Euler-Lagrange equation becomes

(12.32) $$\frac{d}{dx}\frac{\partial F}{\partial y'} = \frac{d}{dx}\frac{y'}{\sqrt{x(1 + y'^2)}} = 0$$

Hence

(12.33) $$\frac{y'}{\sqrt{x(1 + y'^2)}} = c$$

where c is an arbitrary constant.

For simplicity, let

(12.34) $$c = \frac{1}{\sqrt{a}}$$

Squaring, clearing fractions, and transposing, we have

$$(12.35) \qquad y'^2 - \frac{xy'^2}{a} = \frac{x}{a}$$

Solving for y', we obtain

$$(12.36) \qquad y' = \frac{\sqrt{x}}{\sqrt{a-x}} = \frac{dy}{dx}$$

Hence

$$(12.37) \qquad dy = \frac{\sqrt{x}\,dx}{\sqrt{a-x}}$$

Therefore

$$(12.38) \qquad y = \int \frac{\sqrt{x}\,dx}{\sqrt{a-x}} + c_2$$

Integrating, we obtain

$$(12.39) \qquad y = a \sin^{-1}\sqrt{\frac{x}{a}} - \sqrt{ax - x^2} + c_2$$

The arbitrary constant c_2 is zero since we have $x = 0$ at $y = 0$. Hence the equation of the curve is

$$(12.40) \qquad y = a \sin^{-1}\sqrt{\frac{x}{a}} - \sqrt{ax - x^2}$$

This is the equation of a cycloid where a is the diameter of the generating circle. The constant a is determined by the condition that the cycloid must pass through the point x_0, y_0.

A more extended discussion of the calculus of variations is beyond the scope of this book. In recent years the application of the calculus of variations to problems of engineering and physics has proved of great value. Those interested will find the works listed in the references of value.

13. Summary of Fundamental Formulas of the Calculus of Variations. By the extension of the principles of Sec. 12 the Euler equations that cause various integrals to attain stationary values can be obtained. The following summary of results that are useful in various applications is given here for reference.

1. One *dependent* variable y; one *independent* variable x. Integrand contains first-order derivative.

$$(13.1) \qquad \delta I = \delta \int_{x_1}^{x_2} F(x,y,y_x)\,dx = 0 \qquad y_x = \frac{dy}{dx}$$

$$(13.2) \qquad \frac{\partial F}{\partial y} - \frac{d}{dx}\left(\frac{\partial F}{\partial y_x}\right) = 0$$

2. One *dependent* variable y, one *independent* variable x. Integrand contains derivatives $y_1, y_2, y_3, \ldots, y_n$, where $y_k = d^k y/dx^k$.

$$(13.3) \qquad \delta I = \delta \int_{x_1}^{x_2} F(x,y,y_1,y_2,y_3, \ldots ,y_n) \, dx = 0$$

$$(13.4) \quad \frac{\partial F}{\partial y} - \frac{d}{dx}\left(\frac{\partial F}{\partial y_1}\right) + \frac{d^2}{dx^2}\left(\frac{\partial F}{\partial y_2}\right) - \cdots + (-1)^n \frac{d^n}{dx^n}\left(\frac{\partial F}{\partial y_n}\right) = 0$$

3. Several *dependent* variables $x_1, x_2, x_3, \ldots, x_n$, one *independent* variable t, first-order derivatives $\dot{x}_k = dx_k/dt$.

$$(13.5) \quad \delta I = \delta \int_{t_1}^{t_2} F(t,x_1,x_2,x_3, \ldots ,x_n,\dot{x}_1,\dot{x}_2,\dot{x}_3, \ldots ,\dot{x}_n) \, dt = 0$$

$$(13.6) \qquad \frac{\partial F}{\partial x_k} - \frac{d}{dt}\left(\frac{\partial F}{\partial \dot{x}_k}\right) = 0 \qquad k = 1, 2, 3, \ldots, n$$

4. Higher derivatives, n *dependent* variables, one independent variable. In this case there are n Euler equations of a type similar to (13.4), one for each dependent variable.

5. One *dependent* variable u, two *independent* variables x and y.

$$(13.7) \qquad \delta I = \delta \int_{x_1}^{x_2} \int_{y_1}^{y_2} F(x,y,u,u_x,u_y,u_{xx},u_{xy},u_{yy}) \, dx \, dy = 0$$

where u_x, u_y are partial derivatives with respect to x and y and u_{xx}, u_{yy} are second partial derivatives with respect to x and y; u_{xy} is the mixed second partial derivative with respect to x and y.

$$(13.8) \quad F_u - \frac{\partial}{\partial x} F_{u_x} - \frac{\partial}{\partial y} F_{u_y} + \frac{\partial^2}{\partial x^2} F_{u_{xx}} + 2 \frac{\partial^2}{\partial x \, \partial y} F_{u_{xy}} + \frac{\partial^2}{\partial y^2} F_{u_{yy}} = 0$$

where $F_u = \partial F/\partial u$, $F_{u_{xx}} = \partial F/\partial u_{xx}$, $F_{u_{xy}} = \partial F/\partial u_{xy}$, etc.

14. Hamilton's Principle, Lagrange's Equations. There are several possible formulations of the laws of mechanics. The most elementary formulation involves the concept of force and leads to the Newtonian equations which are discussed in elementary textbooks on mechanics. Another alternative and very important formulation is *Hamilton's principle*. This formulation is based on the energy concept and is a very useful one, particularly in cases where Newton's laws are difficult to apply. Hamilton's principle assumes that the mechanical system under consideration is characterized by a kinetic-energy function T and a potential-energy function V. In the case of a mechanical system having n degrees of freedom the configuration of the system may be described in terms of the n general coordinates $q_1, q_2, q_3, \ldots, q_n$. The kinetic energy will be a function of the coordinates q_k ($k = 1, 2, 3, \ldots, n$) as well as the generalized velocities $\dot{q}_k$ (except when the q's are cartesian coordinates). Only conservative systems will be considered in this discussion. The potential energy V will be a function of the q's but will not depend on the velocities $\dot{q}_k$. We therefore have

$$(14.1) \qquad T = T(q_1, q_2, q_3, \ldots, q_n, \dot{q}_1, \dot{q}_2, \dot{q}_3, \ldots, \dot{q}_n)$$
$$(14.2) \qquad V = V(q_1, q_2, q_3, \ldots, q_n)$$

Hamilton's principle *postulates* that the integral

$$(14.3) \qquad I = \int_{t_1}^{t_2} (T - V) \, dt$$

where t_1 and t_2 are two instants in time, shall have a stationary value. The integrand $T - V$ is called the *Lagrangian function*. Therefore Hamilton's principle states that the motion of the dynamical system under consideration takes place in such a manner that

$$(14.4) \qquad \delta I = \delta \int_{t_1}^{t_2} (T - V) \, dt = \delta \int_{t_1}^{t_2} L \, dt = 0$$

The integrand of (14.4) contains the n *dependent* variables q_k and their time derivatives $\dot{q}_k$ and the single *independent* variable t. The requirement that this integral be stationary leads to a system of n Euler equations of the form (13.6). These equations are

$$(14.5) \qquad \frac{\partial L}{\partial q_k} - \frac{d}{dt}\left(\frac{\partial L}{\partial \dot{q}_k}\right) = 0 \qquad k = 1, 2, 3, \ldots, n$$

or

$$(14.6) \qquad \frac{\partial T}{\partial q_k} - \frac{\partial V}{\partial q_k} - \frac{d}{dt}\left(\frac{\partial T}{\partial \dot{q}_k}\right) = 0 \qquad k = 1, 2, 3, \ldots, n$$

These are the Lagrangian equations of motion of the system which were deduced in Chap. 8, Sec. 5, directly from Newton's laws without the use of the calculus of variations.

The Principle of Least Action. In a conservative system the sum of the potential and kinetic energy of the system is a constant c. Therefore

$$(14.7) \qquad T + V = c$$

Hence

$$(14.8) \qquad T - V = T - (c - T) = 2T - c$$

Hamilton's principle states that

$$(14.9) \quad \delta \int_{t_1}^{t_2} (T - V) \, dt = \delta \int_{t_1}^{t_2} (2T - c) \, dt = \delta \int_{t_1}^{t_2} 2T \, dt = 0$$

since the variation of a constant is zero. The integral

$$(14.10) \qquad A = 2 \int_{t_1}^{t_2} T \, dt$$

is called the *action*.   As a consequence of (14.9), we have

(14.11) $$\delta A = 0$$

In classical mechanics this is the celebrated *principle of least action*. It appears to have been first announced by De Maupertuis in 1744.*

Hamilton's principle is very useful in obtaining the equations of motion of continuous systems.   For example, consider a uniform string of mass m per unit length stretched between two supports from $x = 0$ to $x = s$ under the action of a constant tension k.   If the string is performing small oscillations in one plane of amplitude $u(x,t)$, it can be shown that, if the deflection u is small, the kinetic energy T and the potential energy V of the string may be expressed in the following form,

(14.12) $$T = \frac{m}{2} \int_0^s u_t^2 \, dx \qquad V = \frac{k}{2} \int_0^s u_x^2 \, dx$$

where u_t and u_x denote partial derivatives with respect to t and x, respectively.   Hence Hamilton's principle states that

(14.13) $$\delta \int_{t_1}^{t_2} (T - V) \, dt = \delta \int_{t_1}^{t_2} \int_0^s \left(\frac{m}{2} u_t^2 - \frac{k}{2} u_x^2 \right) dx \, dt$$

This is an integral of the type (13.7) with

(14.14) $$F = \frac{m}{2} u_t^2 - \frac{k}{2} u_x^2$$

Equation (13.8) in this case reduces to the equation

(14.15) $$\frac{\partial F}{\partial u} - \frac{\partial}{\partial t}\left(\frac{\partial F}{\partial u_t}\right) - \frac{\partial}{\partial x}\left(\frac{\partial F}{\partial x}\right) = -mu_{tt} + ku_{xx} = 0$$

or

(14.16) $$u_{tt} = a^2 u_{xx} \qquad a = \left(\frac{k}{m}\right)^{\frac{1}{2}}$$

This is the equation of motion of the string.   It is the equation for the propagation of waves in one dimension and is discussed in Chap. 16.

15. Variational Problems with Accessory Conditions: Isoperimetric Problems.   Problems in the calculus of variations sometimes arise that involve making one integral stationary while one or more other integrals involving the same variable and the same limits are to be kept constant. For example, the problem may be to bend a wire of fixed length so that it will enclose the maximum plane area.   There are many problems of this sort.   As a class they are called *isoperimetric* problems.

---

* See Cornelius Lanczos, "The Variational Principles of Mechanics," University of Toronto Press, Toronto, Canada, 1949.

For example, let it be required to find the stationary value of the integral

$$(15.1) \qquad I = \int_{x_1}^{x_2} F(x,y,y_x) \, dx$$

provided that the integral

$$(15.2) \qquad I_1 = \int_{x_1}^{x_2} F_1(x,y,y_x) \, dx = C_1 \qquad \text{a const}$$

To solve this problem, we consider the integral

$$(15.3) \qquad I_0 = \int_{x_1}^{x_2} F_0(x,y,y_x) \, dx$$

where

$$(15.4) \qquad F_0 = F + \mu F_1$$

and μ is a *parameter* to be determined.

It is clear that, since the integral I_1 is to remain constant, the integral I_0 will be stationary if I is stationary. The Euler equation that makes I_0 stationary is

$$(15.5) \qquad \frac{\partial F_0}{\partial y} - \frac{d}{dx}\left(\frac{\partial F_0}{\partial y_x}\right) = 0$$

The parameter μ can now be eliminated by the use of Eqs. (15.2) and (15.5). As an example, let it be required to find the shape of the plane curve that must be assumed by a wire of fixed length S_0 so that it encloses the maximum area. To solve this problem, it is convenient to express the shape of the curve in plane polar coordinates. We therefore seek the curve $r = r(\theta)$ that maximizes the integral

$$(15.6) \qquad I = \frac{1}{2} \int_0^{2\pi} r^2 \, d\theta$$

and has a fixed length

$$(15.7) \qquad I_1 = \int_0^{2\pi} (r^2 + r_\theta^2)^{\frac{1}{2}} \, d\theta = S_0$$

In this case we have

$$(15.8) \qquad F_0 = \frac{r^2}{2} + \mu(r^2 + r_\theta^2)^{\frac{1}{2}}$$

and

$$(15.9) \qquad \frac{\partial F_0}{\partial r} - \frac{d}{d\theta}\left(\frac{\partial F_0}{\partial r_\theta}\right) = r + \mu r(r^2 + r_\theta^2)^{-\frac{1}{2}} - \frac{d}{d\theta}\left[\mu r_\theta(r^2 + r_\theta^2)^{-\frac{1}{2}}\right] = 0$$

This equation may be written in the form

$$(15.10) \qquad \frac{rr_{\theta\theta} - 2r_\theta^2 - r^2}{(r^2 + r_\theta^2)^{\frac{3}{2}}} = \frac{1}{\mu}$$

The absolute value of the left-hand member of (15.10) will be recognized as the *curvature* of $r(\theta)$ expressed in polar coordinates. Hence $\rho = |\mu|$, a constant, and the curve is a circle. The value of the parameter μ may now be determined in terms of the given fixed length S_0 by the use of (15.7).

PROBLEMS

1. Find the first and second partial derivatives of the function $\tan^{-1}(x/y)$.

2. Show that, if $u = \ln(x^2 + y^2) + \tan^{-1}(y/x)$, then $\partial^2 u/\partial x^2 + \partial^2 u/\partial y^2 = 0$.

3. Show that, if $u = \tan(y + ax) + \sqrt{y - ax}$, then $\partial^2 u/\partial x^2 = a^2(\partial^2 u/\partial y^2)$.

4. If $u = F_1(x + jy) + F_2(x - jy)$, where $j = \sqrt{-1}$, show that $\partial^2 u/\partial x^2 + \partial^2 u/\partial y^2 = 0$.

5. If F is a function of x and y and $x + y = 2e^\theta \cos \phi$, $x - y = 2je^\theta \sin \phi$, where $j = \sqrt{-1}$, prove that $\partial^2 F/\partial\theta^2 + \partial^2 F/\partial\phi^2 = 4xy(\partial^2 F/\partial x\, \partial y)$.

6. Change the independent variable from x to z in $x^2(d^2y/dx^2) + ax(dy/dx) + by = 0$, where $x = e^z$, and show that the equation is transformed to $d^2y/dz^2 + (a - 1)(dy/dz) + by = 0$.

7. Find the maximum value of $V = xyz$ subject to the condition that $x^2/a^2 + y^2/b^2 + z^2/c^2 = 1$.   *Ans.* $V = abc/3\sqrt{3}$.

What is the geometric interpretation of this problem?

8. Divide 24 into three parts such that the continued product of the first, the square of the second, and the cube of the third may be a maximum.   *Ans.* 4, 8, 12.

9. Find the points on the surface $xyz = a^3$ which are nearest the origin.

10. Show that the necessary conditions for the maximum and minimum values of $\phi(x,y)$, where x and y are connected by an equation $F(x,y) = 0$, are that x and y should satisfy the two equations $F(x,y) = 0$ and

$$\frac{\partial\phi}{\partial x}\frac{\partial F}{\partial y} - \frac{\partial\phi}{\partial y}\frac{\partial F}{\partial x} = 0$$

11. Determine the equation of the shortest curve between two points in the xy plane.

12. Find the equation of the shortest line on the surface of a sphere, and prove that it is a great circle.

13. Show that the shortest lines on a right-circular cylinder are helices.

14. Find the equation of the shortest line on a cone of revolution.

15. Find the curve of given length between two fixed points which generates the minimum surface of revolution.

16. A cubic centimeter of brass is to be worked into a solid of revolution. It is desired to make its moment of inertia about the axis as small as possible. What shape should be given?

17. Find the curve of length 3 that joins the points $(-1,1)$ and $(1,1)$ which, when rotated about the x axis, will give minimum area.

18. Find the surface of revolution which encloses the maximum volume for a given surface area.

19. Use Hamilton's principle to derive the equation of motion of a particle moving in a straight line with potential energy $V = 1/x$, where x is the distance of the particle from some arbitrarily chosen origin.

20. Assuming that a string with fixed ends will hang in such a manner that its center of gravity has the lowest possible position, find the curve in which a string of given length will hang.

21. Prove by Hamilton's principle that the string in Prob. 20 will hang as stated.

22. Use Hamilton's principle to obtain the polar equations for the motion of a particle in space.

23. Find the surface of revolution which encloses the maximum volume in a given area.

24. Given a volume of homogeneous attracting gravitating matter, find the shape of the solid of revolution constituting the volume so that the attraction at a point on the axis of revolution shall be a maximum. $Ans.$ $r = (15V/4\pi)^{\frac{1}{3}} (\cos \theta)^{\frac{1}{3}}$.

25. Determine the shape of a curve of given length, so chosen that the area enclosed between the curve and its chord will be a maximum.

26. Consider a vibrating membrane, like a drumhead whose position of equilibrium is in the (x,y) plane. Let $u(x,y,t)$ be the small deflection of the membrane while it is performing oscillations. Find the potential energy V and the kinetic energy T under the assumption that the membrane is under constant tension P and has a mass m per unit area. Determine the equation of motion by Hamilton's principle.

27. Show that, if the integrand of (12.1) does not contain x explicitly so that it takes the form $I = \int_{x_0}^{x_1} F(y,y_x) \, dx$, then the Euler-Lagrange equation (12.12) takes the following form: $F - y(\partial F/\partial y_x) = \text{const}$. This is a very useful result that can be used when the integrand F does not depend explicitly on x.

REFERENCES

1. Goursat, E., and E. Hedrick: "A Course in Mathematical Analysis," vol. I, Ginn & Company, Boston, 1904.
2. Wilson, E. B.: "Advanced Calculus," Ginn & Company, Boston, 1911.
3. Bliss, G. A.: "Calculus of Variations," University of Chicago Press, Chicago, 1925.
4. Bolza, O.: "Lectures on the Calculus of Variations," University of Chicago Press, Chicago, reprinted, Stechert-Hafner, Inc., New York, 1931.
5. Forsythe, A. R.: "Calculus of Variations," Cambridge University Press, New York, 1927.
6. Osgood, William F.: "Advanced Calculus," chap. 17, The Macmillan Company, New York, 1933.
7. Courant, R., and D. Hilbert: "Methods of Mathematical Physics," Interscience Publishers, Inc., New York, 1953.
8. Weinstock, R. P.: "Calculus of Variations," McGraw-Hill Book Company, Inc., New York, 1952.
9. Fox, C.: "An Introduction to the Calculus of Variations," Oxford University Press, New York, 1950.
10. Hildebrand, F. B.: "Methods of Applied Mathematics," Prentice-Hall, Inc., Englewood Cliffs, N.J., 1952.
11. Polya, G., and G. Szego: "Isoperimetric Inequalities in Mathematical Physics," Princeton University Press, Princeton, N.J., 1951.

CHAPTER 12

THE GAMMA, BETA, AND ERROR FUNCTIONS

1. Introduction. In this chapter certain functions that arise in the solution of physical problems and are also of great importance in various branches of mathematical analysis will be considered.

It is, of course, impossible to give an extensive mathematical treatment of these functions in this limited space, and only the more important and fundamental properties will be developed.

2. The Gamma Function. The gamma function $\Gamma(n)$ has been defined by Euler to be the definite integral

$$(2.1) \qquad \Gamma(n) = \int_0^\infty x^{n-1} e^{-x}\, dx \qquad n > 0$$

This definite integral converges when n is positive and therefore defines a function of n for positive values of n. By direct integration it is evident that

$$(2.2) \qquad \Gamma(1) = \int_0^\infty e^{-x}\, dx = 1$$

By an integration by parts the following identity may be established:

$$(2.3) \quad \Gamma(n+1) = \int_0^\infty x^n e^{-x}\, dx = n \int_0^\infty x^{n-1} e^{-x}\, dx + (-x^n e^{-x})\Big|_0^\infty$$

$$= n \int_0^\infty x^{n-1} e^{-x}\, dx$$

Comparing the result (with 2.1), we have

$$(2.4) \qquad \Gamma(n+1) = n\Gamma(n)$$

This is the fundamental recursion relation satisfied by the gamma function. From this relation it is evident that if the value of $\Gamma(n)$ is known for n between any two successive positive integers the value of $\Gamma(n)$ for any positive value of n may be found by successive applications of (2.4). Equation (2.4) may be used to define $\Gamma(n)$ for values of n for which the definition (2.1) fails. We may write (2.4) in the form

$$(2.5) \qquad \Gamma(n) = \frac{\Gamma(n+1)}{n}$$

339

Then if

(2.6) $$-1 < n < 0$$

formula (2.5) gives us $\Gamma(n)$ since $n + 1$ is positive. We may then find $\Gamma(n)$ where $-2 < n < -1$ since now $n + 1$ on the right-hand side of (2.5) is known, and so on indefinitely. We then have in (2.1) and (2.5) the complete definition of $\Gamma(n)$ for all values of n except $n = 0$, -1, -2, ...

3. The Factorial, Gauss's Pi Function. From Eq. (2.2) we have

(3.1) $$\Gamma(1) = 1$$

Now, by the use of (2.4), we obtain

(3.2)
$$\Gamma(2) = 1 \times \Gamma(1) = 1$$
$$\Gamma(3) = 2 \times \Gamma(2) = 2 \times 1$$
$$\Gamma(4) = 3 \times \Gamma(3) = 3 \times 2 \times 1$$
. . . .
$$\Gamma(n + 1) = n!$$

provided n is a positive integer. From this it is convenient to define 0! in the form

(3.3) $$0! = \Gamma(1) = 1$$

Gauss's pi function is defined in terms of the gamma function by the equation

(3.4) $$\Pi(n) = \Gamma(n + 1)$$

We thus see that if n is a positive integer

(3.5) $$\Pi(n) = n!$$

If we place $n = 0$ in Eq. (2.5), we have

(3.6) $$\Gamma(0) = \frac{\Gamma(1)}{0} = \frac{1}{0} = \infty$$

By repeated application of (2.5) it is seen that the gamma function becomes infinite when n is zero or a negative integer.

4. The Value of $\Gamma(\frac{1}{2})$, Graph of the Gamma Function. If in the fundamental integral (2.1) we make the substitution

(4.1) $$x = y^2$$

we obtain

(4.2) $$\Gamma(n) = 2 \int_0^\infty y^{2n-1} e^{-y^2} \, dy$$

If now $n = \frac{1}{2}$, we have

(4.3) $$\Gamma(\tfrac{1}{2}) = 2 \int_0^\infty e^{-y^2}\, dy$$

By making use of Chap. 11, Eq. (11.22), we obtain

(4.4) $$\Gamma(\tfrac{1}{2}) = 2 \frac{\sqrt{\pi}}{2} = \sqrt{\pi}$$

From this result and (2.5) we obtain

(4.5) $$\Gamma(-\tfrac{1}{2}) = \frac{\Gamma(\tfrac{1}{2})}{-\tfrac{1}{2}} = -2\sqrt{\pi}$$

(4.6) $$\Gamma(-\tfrac{3}{2}) = \frac{\Gamma(-\tfrac{1}{2})}{-\tfrac{3}{2}} = -\tfrac{2}{3}(-2\sqrt{\pi}) = \frac{4\sqrt{\pi}}{3}$$

etc.

Figure 4.1 represents the graph of $\Gamma(n)$.

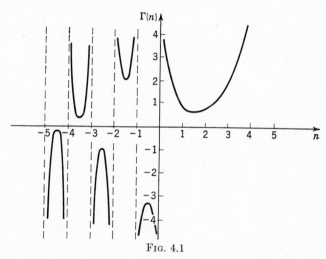

FIG. 4.1

5. The Beta Function. The beta function $\beta(m,n)$ is defined by the definite integral

(5.1) $$\beta(m,n) = \int_0^1 x^{m-1}(1 - x)^{n-1}\, dx \qquad \left\{ \begin{array}{l} m > 0 \\ n > 0 \end{array} \right.$$

This integral converges and thus defines a function of m and n provided that m and n are positive.

If we let

(5.2) $$x = 1 - y$$

in (5.1), we obtain

(5.3) $$\beta(m,n) = \int_0^1 (1 - y)^{m-1} y^{n-1}\, dy = \beta(n,m)$$

Other Forms of the Beta Function.   If in (5.1) we let $x = \sin^2 \phi$, we obtain

$$(5.4) \qquad \beta(m,n) = 2 \int_0^{\pi/2} (\sin \phi)^{2m-1}(\cos \phi)^{2n-1} \, d\phi$$

The substitution $x = y/a$ in (5.1) gives

$$(5.5) \qquad \beta(m,n) = \frac{1}{a^{m+n-1}} \int_0^a y^{m-1}(a - y)^{n-1} \, dy$$

If $x = y/(1 + y)$ in (5.1), we obtain

$$(5.6) \qquad \beta(m,n) = \int_0^\infty \frac{y^{n-1} \, dy}{(1 + y)^{m+n}}$$

These are the more common forms of the integral definition of the beta function.

6. The Connection of the Beta Function and the Gamma Function.
Consider the gamma function as given by (4.2),

$$(6.1) \qquad \Gamma(n) = 2 \int_0^\infty y^{2n-1}e^{-y^2} \, dy$$

We may also write

$$(6.2) \qquad \Gamma(m) = 2 \int_0^\infty x^{2m-1}e^{-x^2} \, dx$$

and hence

$$(6.3) \qquad \Gamma(m)\Gamma(n) = 4 \left(\int_0^\infty x^{2m-1}e^{-x^2} \, dx \right) \left(\int_0^\infty y^{2n-1}e^{-y^2} \, dy \right)$$
$$= 4 \int_0^\infty \int_0^\infty x^{2m-1}y^{2n-1}e^{-(x^2+y^2)} \, dx \, dy$$

If we now consider this integral as a surface integral in the first quadrant of the xy plane and introduce the polar coordinates

$$(6.4) \qquad \begin{aligned} x &= r \cos \theta \\ y &= r \sin \theta \end{aligned}$$

and introduce the surface element ds in the form

$$(6.5) \qquad ds = r \, dr \, d\theta$$

then (6.3) becomes

$$(6.6) \quad \Gamma(m)\Gamma(n) = 4 \int_0^{\pi/2} \int_0^\infty r^{2(m+n-1)}(\cos \theta)^{2m-1}(\sin \theta)^{2n-1}e^{-r^2}r \, d\theta \, dr$$
$$= 4 \int_0^{\pi/2} (\cos \theta)^{2m-1}(\sin \theta)^{2n-1} \, d\theta \int_0^\infty r^{2(m+n)-1}e^{-r^2} \, dr$$

Now from (5.4) we have

(6.7) $$\beta(n,m) = 2 \int_0^{\pi/2} (\cos \theta)^{2m-1} (\sin \theta)^{2n-1} \, d\theta$$
$$= \beta(m,n)$$

and from (6.2) we have

(6.8) $$\Gamma(m + n) = 2 \int_0^\infty r^{2(m+n)-1} e^{-r^2} \, dr$$

Hence (6.6) may be written in the form

(6.9) $$\Gamma(m)\Gamma(n) = \beta(m,n)\Gamma(m + n)$$

or

(6.10) $$\beta(m,n) = \frac{\Gamma(m)\Gamma(n)}{\Gamma(m + n)}$$

This formula is very useful for the evaluation of certain classes of definite integrals. For example, from (6.7) and (6.10) we obtain

(6.11) $$\int_0^{\pi/2} (\cos \theta)^{2m-1} (\sin \theta)^{2n-1} \, d\theta = \frac{\Gamma(m)\Gamma(n)}{2\Gamma(m + n)} \qquad \begin{cases} m > 0 \\ n > 0 \end{cases}$$

If in (6.11) we let

(6.12) $$2m - 1 = r \qquad \text{or} \qquad m = \frac{r + 1}{2}$$
$$2n - 1 = 0 \qquad \text{or} \qquad n = \tfrac{1}{2}$$

we obtain

(6.13) $$\int_0^{\pi/2} (\cos \theta)^r \, d\theta = \frac{\Gamma\left(\dfrac{r + 1}{2}\right)}{\Gamma(r/2 + 1)} \frac{\sqrt{\pi}}{2} \qquad r > -1$$

In a similar manner we obtain

(6.14) $$\int_0^{\pi/2} (\sin \theta)^r \, d\theta = \frac{\Gamma\left(\dfrac{r + 1}{2}\right)}{\Gamma(r/2 + 1)} \frac{\sqrt{\pi}}{2} \qquad r > -1$$

In a similar manner many other integrals may be evaluated in terms of the gamma functions. If a table of gamma functions is available, then the computation of these integrals is considerably simplified.

7. An Important Relation Involving Gamma Functions. Substituting (5.6) into the relation (6.10), we obtain

(7.1) $$\int_0^\infty \frac{y^{n-1} \, dy}{(1 + y)^{m+n}} = \frac{\Gamma(m)\Gamma(n)}{\Gamma(m + n)} \qquad \begin{cases} m > 0 \\ n > 0 \end{cases}$$

If we now let

(7.2) $$m = 1 - n \qquad 0 < n < 1$$

in (7.1), we obtain

(7.3) $$\int_0^\infty \frac{y^{n-1}\,dy}{1+y} = \frac{\Gamma(1-n)\Gamma(n)}{\Gamma(1)}$$

Now in Chap. 19 it is shown that

(7.4) $$\int_0^\infty \frac{y^{n-1}\,dy}{1+y} = \frac{\pi}{\sin n\pi} \qquad 0 < n < 1$$

Hence, since

(7.5) $$\Gamma(1) = 1$$

we have from (7.3) the important relation

(7.6) $$\Gamma(n)\Gamma(1-n) = \frac{\pi}{\sin n\pi} \qquad 0 < n < 1$$

8. The Error Function or Probability Integral.

Another very important function that occurs frequently in various branches of applied mathematics is the *error function*, erf (x), or the probability integral defined by

(8.1) $$\text{erf}\,(x) = \frac{2}{\sqrt{\pi}} \int_0^x e^{-n^2}\,dn$$

This integral occupies a central position in the theory of probability and arises in the solution of certain partial differential equations of physical interest.

From the definition of erf (x) we have

(8.2) $$\text{erf}\,(-x) = -\text{erf}\,(x)$$

(8.3) $$\text{erf}\,(0) = 0$$

(8.4) $$\text{erf}\,(\infty) = \frac{2}{\sqrt{\pi}} \int_0^\infty e^{-n^2}\,dn = \frac{2}{\sqrt{\pi}}\frac{\sqrt{\pi}}{2} = 1$$

(8.5) $$\text{erf}\,(jy) = \frac{2j}{\sqrt{\pi}} \int_0^y e^{n^2}\,dn \qquad j = \sqrt{-1}$$

PROBLEMS

1. Show that
$$\Gamma\left(\frac{2k+1}{2}\right) = \frac{1 \times 3 \times 5 \times \cdots \times (2k-1)}{2^k}\sqrt{\pi}$$
where k is a positive integer.

2. Show that
$$\int_0^1 \frac{x^n\,dx}{\sqrt{1-x^2}} = \frac{1 \times 3 \times 5 \times \cdots \times (n-1)}{2 \times 4 \times 6 \times \cdots \times n}\frac{\pi}{2}$$
if n is an even positive integer.

3. Show that

$$\int_0^1 \frac{x^n\, dx}{\sqrt{1 - x^2}} = \frac{2 \times 4 \times 6 \times \cdots \times (n - 1)}{1 \times 3 \times 5 \times \cdots \times n}$$

if n is an odd positive integer.

4. Show that

$$\int_0^1 \frac{dx}{\sqrt{1 - x^n}} = \frac{\sqrt{\pi}}{n} \frac{\Gamma(1/n)}{\Gamma(1/n + \frac{1}{2})}$$

5. Evaluate the following definite integrals:

(a) $\displaystyle\int_0^\infty e^{-x^4}\, dx.$

(b) $\displaystyle\int_0^\infty 4x^4 e^{-x^4}\, dx.$

(c) $\displaystyle\int_0^{\pi/2} \frac{\sqrt[3]{\sin^8 x}}{\sqrt{\cos x}}\, dx.$

6. Show that

$$\int_0^{\pi/2} \sqrt{\tan \theta}\, d\theta = \frac{\Gamma(\frac{1}{4})\Gamma(\frac{3}{4})}{2}$$

7. Show that

$$\frac{d^n \Gamma(y)}{dy^n} = \int_0^\infty x^{y-1} e^{-x} (\log y)^n\, dx$$

8. Show that by a suitable change in variable we have

$$\Gamma(n) = \int_0^1 \left(\log \frac{1}{y}\right)^{n-1} dy$$

9. Evaluate the integral $\displaystyle\int_0^x e^{-n^2}\, dn$ by expanding the integral in series, and show that

$$\int_0^x e^{-n^2}\, dn = x - \frac{x^3}{3 \times 1!} + \frac{x^5}{5 \times 2!} - \frac{x^7}{7 \times 3!} + \frac{x^9}{9 \times 4!} - R$$

where $R < x^{11}/1{,}320$.

10. Show by integrating by parts that

$$\int_0^x e^{-n^2}\, dn = \frac{\sqrt{\pi}}{2} - \frac{e^{-x^2}}{2x}\left(1 - \frac{1}{2x^2} + \frac{1 \times 3}{2^2 x^4}\right) + \frac{1 \times 3 \times 5}{2^3} \int_x^\infty \frac{e^{-n^2}\, dn}{n^6}$$

Show how this expression may be used to compute the value of erf (x) for large values of x.

REFERENCES

1. Whittaker, E. T., and G. N. Watson: "A Course in Modern Analysis," chap. 12, Cambridge University Press, New York, 1927.
2. Wilson, E. B.: "Advanced Calculus," chap. 14, Ginn & Company, Boston, 1911.
3. Woods, F. S.: "Advanced Calculus," chap. 7, Ginn & Company, Boston, 1926.

CHAPTER 13

BESSEL FUNCTIONS

1. Introduction. In the solution of a great many types of problems in applied mathematics we are led to the solution of linear differential equations or sets of linear differential equations. Usually these equations are equations having constant coefficients. In that case we are led to solutions of the exponential type, which include trigonometric and hyperbolic functions. This is the case in the study of small oscillations of dynamical systems or in the analysis of linear electrical circuits.

Next to the exponential, trigonometric, or hyperbolic functions the so-called "Bessel functions," or solutions of Bessel's differential equation, are perhaps most frequently encountered.

In this chapter we shall consider the fundamental properties of these functions in view of their practical importance.

2. Bessel's Differential Equation. As a starting point of the discussion, let us consider the linear differential equation

$$(2.1) \qquad x^2 \frac{d^2y}{dx^2} + x \frac{dy}{dx} + (x^2 - n^2)y = 0$$

where n is a constant.

This equation is known in the literature as *Bessel's differential equation*. Since it is a linear differential equation of the second order, it must have two linearly independent solutions. The standard form of the general solution of (2.1) is

$$(2.2) \qquad y = C_1 J_n(x) + C_2 Y_n(x)$$

where C_1 and C_2 are arbitrary constants and the function $J_n(x)$ is called the *Bessel function of order n of the first kind* and $Y_n(x)$ is the *Bessel function of order n of the second kind*. These functions have been tabulated and behave somewhat like trigonometric functions of damped amplitude. To see this qualitatively, let us transform the dependent variable by the substitution

$$(2.3) \qquad y = \frac{u}{\sqrt{x}}$$

346

This transformation converts (2.1) into

$$(2.4) \qquad \frac{d^2u}{dx^2} + \left(1 - \frac{n^2 - \frac{1}{4}}{x^2}\right) u = 0$$

In the special case in which

$$(2.5) \qquad n = \pm\tfrac{1}{2}$$

this becomes

$$(2.6) \qquad \frac{d^2u}{dx^2} + u = 0$$

Hence

$$(2.7) \qquad u = C_1 \sin x + C_2 \cos x$$

and

$$(2.8) \qquad y = C_1 \frac{\sin x}{\sqrt{x}} + C_2 \frac{\cos x}{\sqrt{x}}$$

where C_1 and C_2 are arbitrary constants. Also we see that as $x \to \infty$ in (2.4), and n is finite, we would expect the solution of (2.1) to behave qualitatively as (2.8) to a first approximation.

3. Series Solution of Bessel's Differential Equation. If we introduce the operator

$$(3.1) \qquad \theta = x \frac{d}{dx}$$

then Bessel's differential equation (2.1) may be written in the form

$$(3.2) \qquad \theta^2 y + (x^2 - n^2)y = 0$$

In order to solve this equation, let us assume an infinite-series solution in the form

$$(3.3) \qquad y = x^r \sum_{s=0}^{s=\infty} C_s x^s = \sum_{s=0}^{s=\infty} C_s x^{r+s}$$

Now

$$(3.4) \qquad \theta x^m = x \frac{d}{dx} x^m = xmx^{m-1} = mx^m$$

$$(3.5) \qquad \theta^2 x^m = \theta(mx^m) = m\theta x^m = m(mx^m) = m^2 x^m$$

Hence, on substituting (3.3) into (3.2), we have

$$(3.6) \qquad \theta^2 y + (x^2 - n^2)y = \sum_{s=0}^{s=\infty} [(r+s)^2 + x^2 - n^2]C_s x^{r+s} = 0$$

If we now equate the coefficients of the various powers of x, x^r, x^{r+1}, x^{r+2}, etc., to zero in (3.6), we obtain the set of equations

$$(3.7) \qquad C_s[(r+s)^2 - n^2] + C_{s-2} = 0$$

This is valid for $s = 0, 1, 2, \ldots$ in view of the fact that

$$(3.8) \qquad \begin{aligned} C_{-1} &= 0 \\ C_{-2} &= 0 \end{aligned}$$

since the leading coefficient in the expansion (3.3) is C_0.

Letting $s = 0$ in (3.7), we obtain

$$(3.9) \qquad C_0(r^2 - n^2) = 0$$

This equation is known as the *indicial equation*, and since

$$(3.10) \qquad C_0 \neq 0$$

it follows that

$$(3.11) \qquad r = \pm n$$

and from the equation

$$(3.12) \qquad C_1[(r + 1)^2 - n^2] = 0$$

it follows that

$$(3.13) \qquad C_1 = 0$$

The relation between C_s and C_{s-2} now shows, taking $s = 3, 5, \ldots$ in succession, that all coefficients of odd rank vanish.

Taking first of all $r = n$, we may write (3.7) in the form

$$(3.14) \qquad C_s = - \frac{C_{s-2}}{s(2n + s)} \qquad s = 2, 4, 6, \ldots$$

From (3.14) we see that the coefficients C_2, C_4, C_6, etc., are all determined in terms of C_0. Inserting these values of the coefficient into the assumed form of solution (3.3), we obtain the solution

$$(3.15) \qquad y = C_0 \left[x^n - \frac{x^{n+2}}{2^2(n + 1)} + \frac{x^{n+4}}{2^4(n + 1)(n + 2)2!} + \cdots \right.$$
$$\left. + \frac{(-1)^s x^{n+2s}}{2^{2s}(n + 1) \cdots (n + s)s!} + \cdots \right]$$

The coefficients are finite except when n is a negative integer. Excluding this case, we standardize the solution by taking

$$(3.16) \qquad C_0 = \frac{1}{2^n \Gamma(n + 1)} = \frac{1}{2^n \Pi(n)}$$

in general and

$$(3.17) \qquad C_0 = \frac{1}{2^n n!}$$

when n is a positive integer. Inserting this value of C_0 into (3.15) and generalizing the factorial numbers when n is not an integer by writing

$$(3.18) \qquad\qquad (n + s)! = \Pi(n + s)$$

we obtain

$$(3.19) \qquad J_n(x) = \sum_{s=0}^{s=\infty} \frac{(-1)^s}{\Pi(s)\Pi(n + s)} \left(\frac{x}{2}\right)^{n+2s}$$

This series converges for any finite value of x and represents a function $J_n(s)$ of x that is known as the *Bessel function of the first kind of order n.* When n is not an integer, the second solution may be obtained by replacing n by $-n$ in accordance with (3.11). It is therefore

$$(3.20) \qquad J_{-n}(x) = \sum_{s=0}^{s=\infty} \frac{(-1)^s}{\Pi(s)\Pi(s - n)} \left(\frac{x}{2}\right)^{2s-n}$$

The leading terms of $J_n(x)$ and $J_{-n}(x)$ are, respectively, finite (nonzero) multiples of x^n and x^{-n}; the two functions are not mere multiples of each other, and hence the general solution of the Bessel differential equation may be expressed in the form

$$(3.21) \qquad\qquad y = AJ_n(x) + BJ_{-n}(x)$$

where A and B are arbitrary constants provided that n is not an integer.

However, when n is an integer, and since n appears in the differential equation only as n^2 there is no loss of generality in taking it to be a positive integer, $J_{-n}(x)$ is not distinct from $J_n(x)$. In this case the denominators of the first n terms of the series for $J_{-n}(x)$ contain the factors

$$(3.22) \qquad\qquad \frac{1}{\Pi(s - n)} = 0$$

for $s = 0, 1, 2, \ldots, n - 1$. Hence these terms vanish. Therefore

$$(3.23) \qquad J_{-n}(x) = \sum_{s=n}^{s=\infty} \frac{(-1)^s}{\Pi(s)\Pi(s - n)} \left(\frac{x}{2}\right)^{2s-n}$$

If we now let

$$(3.24) \qquad\qquad r = s - n$$

then

$$(3.25) \qquad J_{-n}(x) = \sum_{r=0}^{r=\infty} \frac{(-1)^{r+n}}{\Pi(r + n)\Pi(r)} \left(\frac{x}{2}\right)^{2r+n} = (-1)^n J_n(x)$$

for $n = 0, 1, 2, 3, \ldots$ In this case we no longer have two linearly independent solutions of the differential equation, and an independent second solution must be found.

4. The Bessel Function of Order n of the Second Kind.   In the preceding section we have seen that, if n is not an integer, a general solution of the Bessel differential equation of order n is given by (3.21).   If, however, n is an integer, then in view of (3.25) we have

$$(4.1) \qquad \begin{aligned} y &= A J_n(x) + B(-1)^n J_n(x) \\ &= [A + B(-1)^n] J_n(x) \\ &= C J_n(x) \end{aligned}$$

where C is an arbitrary constant.   We therefore do not have the general solution of Bessel's differential equation, since such a solution must consist of two linearly independent functions multiplied by arbitrary constants.   Consider the function

$$(4.2) \qquad Y_n(x) = \frac{1}{\sin n\pi} \left[\cos n\pi J_n(x) - J_{-n}(x) \right]$$

Now if n is not an integer, the function $Y_n(x)$ is dependent on $J_n(x)$, and since it is a linear combination of $J_n(x)$ and $J_{-n}(x)$, it is a solution of Bessel's differential equation of order n.   If now n is an integer, because of the relation (3.25), we have

$$(4.3) \qquad Y_n(x) = \frac{0}{0}$$

Hence, when n is an integer, we define $Y_n(x)$ to be

$$(4.4) \qquad Y_n(x) = \lim_{r \to n} \frac{J_r(x) \cos r\pi - J_{-r}(x)}{\sin r\pi}$$

With this definition of $Y_n(x)$ we have, on carrying out the limiting process,

$$(4.5) \quad \frac{\pi}{2} Y_0(x) = J_0(x) \left(\log \frac{x}{2} + \gamma \right) + \left(\frac{x}{2} \right)^2 - \frac{(1 + \frac{1}{2})(x/2)^4}{(2!)^2} \\ + \left(1 + \frac{1}{2} + \frac{1}{3} \right) \frac{(x/2)^6}{(3!)^2} - \cdots$$

where γ is Euler's constant defined by

$$(4.6) \quad \gamma = \lim_{n \to \infty} \left(1 + \frac{1}{2} + \frac{1}{3} + \cdots + \frac{1}{n} - \log n \right) = 0.5772157$$

Also, when n is any positive integer, we have

$$(4.7) \quad \pi Y_n(x) = 2 J_n(x) \left(\log \frac{x}{2} + \gamma \right)$$

$$- \sum_{r=0}^{\infty} (-1)^r \frac{(x/2)^{n+2r}}{r!(n+r)!} \left(\sum_{m=1}^{n+r} m^{-1} + \sum_{m=1}^{r} m^{-1} \right)$$

$$- \sum_{r=0}^{n-1} \left(\frac{x}{2} \right)^{-n+2r} \frac{(n-r-1)!}{r!}$$

where, for $r = 0$, instead of $\sum_{m=1}^{n+r} m^{-1} + \sum_{m=1}^{r} m^{-1}$ we write $\sum_{m=1}^{n} m^{-1}$.

The presence of the logarithmic term in the function $Y_n(x)$ shows that these functions are infinite at $x = 0$. The general solution of Bessel's differential equation may now be written in the form

$$(4.8) \qquad\qquad y = C_1 J_n(x) + C_2 Y_n(x)$$

where C_1 and C_2 are arbitrary constants.

5. Values of $J_n(x)$ and $Y_n(x)$ for Large and Small Values of x. In Sec. 2 we saw that the transformation

$$(5.1) \qquad\qquad y = \frac{u}{\sqrt{x}}$$

transformed Bessel's differential equation into the form

$$(5.2) \qquad\qquad \frac{d^2 u}{dx^2} + \left(1 - \frac{n^2 - \frac{1}{4}}{x^2} \right) u = 0$$

We would suspect qualitatively that for large values of x the Bessel functions would behave as the solutions of the equation obtained from (5.2) by neglecting the $1/x^2$ term, that is, as solutions of the equation

$$(5.3) \qquad\qquad \frac{d^2 u}{dx^2} + u = 0$$

and hence as

$$(5.4) \qquad\qquad y = C_1 \frac{\sin x}{\sqrt{x}} + C_2 \frac{\cos x}{\sqrt{x}}$$

More precise analysis shows that

$$(5.5) \qquad \lim_{x \to \infty} J_n(x) \cong \frac{\cos (x - \pi/4 - n\pi/2)}{\sqrt{\pi x/2}}$$

$$(5.6) \qquad \lim_{x \to \infty} Y_n(x) \cong \frac{\sin (x - \pi/4 - n\pi/2)}{\sqrt{\pi x/2}}$$

That is, for large values of the argument x, the Bessel functions behave like trigonometric functions of decreasing amplitude.

From the series expansions of the functions $J_n(x)$ and $Y_n(x)$ we also have the following behavior for small values of x:

$$(5.7) \qquad \lim_{x \to 0} J_n(x) \cong \frac{x^n}{2^n \Pi(n)}$$

The value of $Y_n(x)$ is always infinite at $x = 0$. For small values of x this function is of the order $1/x^n$ if $n \neq 0$ and of the order $\log x$ if $n = 0$.

6. Recurrence Formulas for $J_n(x)$. Some important recurrence relations involving the function $J_n(x)$ may be obtained directly from the series expansion for the function. From (3.19) we have

$$(6.1) \qquad J_n(x) = \sum_{s=0}^{x=\infty} \frac{(-1)^s}{\Pi(s)\Pi(n+s)} \left(\frac{x}{2}\right)^{n+2s}$$

If we write

$$(6.2) \qquad J'_n = \frac{d}{dx} J_n(x)$$

we have

$$(6.3) \qquad xJ'_n = \sum_{s=0}^{s=\infty} \frac{(-1)^s(n+2s)}{\Pi(s)\Pi(n+s)} \left(\frac{x}{2}\right)^{n+2s}$$

$$= nJ_n + x \sum_{s=1}^{\infty} \frac{(-1)^s}{\Pi(s-1)\Pi(n+s)} \left(\frac{x}{2}\right)^{n+2s-1}$$

If in the last summation we place

$$(6.4) \qquad s = r + 1$$

we obtain

$$(6.5) \qquad xJ'_n = nJ_n - x \sum_{r=0}^{\infty} \frac{(-1)^r}{\Pi(r)\Pi(n+1+r)} \left(\frac{x}{2}\right)^{n+1+2r}$$

$$= nJ_n - xJ_{n+1}$$

In the same manner, we can prove that

$$(6.6) \qquad xJ'_n + nJ_n = xJ_{n-1}$$

If we add (6.5) to (6.6), we have

$$(6.7) \qquad 2J'_n = J_{n-1} - J_{n+1}$$

If we place $n = 0$ and use Eq. (3.25), we have

$$(6.8) \qquad J'_0 = -J_1$$

If we multiply (6.5) by x^{-n-1}, we obtain

(6.9) $$x^{-n}J'_n = x^{-n-1}nJ_n - x^{-n}J_{n+1}$$

Hence

(6.10) $$\frac{d}{dx}(x^{-n}J_n) = -x^{-n}J_{n+1}$$

Similarly, we may prove that

(6.11) $$\frac{d}{dx}(x^nJ_n) = x^nJ_{n-1}$$

If we subtract (6.6) from (6.5), we obtain

(6.12) $$\frac{2n}{x}J_n = J_{n-1} + J_{n+1}$$

Many other recurrence formulas may be obtained.

7. Expressions for $J_n(x)$ When n Is Half an Odd Integer.   The case when n is half an odd integer is of importance because these particular Bessel functions can be expressed in finite form by elementary functions.

If we place $n = \frac{1}{2}$ in the general series for $J_n(x)$ given by (3.19), we obtain

(7.1) $$J_{\frac{1}{2}}(x) = \sum_{s=0}^{s=\infty} \frac{(-1)^s}{\Pi(s)\Pi(s+\frac{1}{2})}\left(\frac{x}{2}\right)^{2s+\frac{1}{2}}$$

Now since

(7.2) $$\Pi(r) = r\Pi(r-1)$$

and

(7.3) $$\Pi(s) = s! \quad \text{if } s = 1, 2, 3, \ldots$$

we have

(7.4) $$J_{\frac{1}{2}}(x) = \frac{x^{\frac{1}{2}}}{2^{\frac{1}{2}}\Pi(\frac{1}{2})}\left(1 - \frac{x^2}{3!} + \frac{x^4}{5!} - \cdots\right)$$

However, we have

(7.5) $$\Pi\left(\frac{1}{2}\right) = \frac{\sqrt{\pi}}{2}$$

and

(7.6) $$\frac{\sin x}{x} = \left(1 - \frac{x^2}{3!} + \frac{x^4}{5!} - \cdots\right)$$

Hence from (7.4) we have

(7.7) $$J_{\frac{1}{2}}(x) = \sqrt{\frac{2}{\pi x}}\sin x$$

If we place $n = -\frac{1}{2}$ in the general series for $J_n(x)$, we may also show that

$$(7.8) \qquad\qquad J_{-\frac{1}{2}}(x) = \sqrt{\frac{2}{\pi x}} \cos x$$

If in the recurrence formula (6.12) we place $n = \frac{1}{2}$, we obtain

$$(7.9) \qquad\qquad \frac{J_{\frac{1}{2}}}{x} = J_{-\frac{1}{2}}(x) + J_{\frac{3}{2}}(x)$$

Hence

$$(7.10) \qquad\qquad J_{\frac{3}{2}}(x) = \frac{1}{x} J_{\frac{1}{2}}(x) - J_{-\frac{1}{2}}(x)$$

$$= \sqrt{\frac{2}{\pi x}} \left(\frac{\sin x}{x} - \cos x \right)$$

If in (6.12) we let $n = \frac{3}{2}$, we obtain

$$(7.11) \qquad\qquad \frac{3}{x} J_{\frac{3}{2}} = J_{\frac{1}{2}} + J_{\frac{5}{2}}$$

or

$$(7.12) \qquad J_{\frac{5}{2}} = \frac{3}{x} J_{\frac{3}{2}} - J_{\frac{1}{2}} = \sqrt{\frac{2}{\pi x}} \left(\frac{3 - x^2}{x^2} \sin x - \frac{3}{x} \cos x \right)$$

In the same way we may show that

$$(7.13) \qquad J_{-\frac{3}{2}} = \sqrt{\frac{2}{\pi x}} \left(- \sin x - \frac{\cos x}{x} \right)$$

$$(7.14) \qquad J_{-\frac{5}{2}} = \sqrt{\frac{2}{\pi x}} \left(\frac{3}{x} \sin x + \frac{3 - x^2}{x^2} \cos x \right), \text{ etc.}$$

8. The Bessel Functions of Order n of the Third Kind, or Hankel Functions of Order n. In some physical investigations we encounter complex combinations of Bessel functions of the first and second kinds so frequently that it has been found convenient to tabulate these combinations and thus define new functions.

These new functions are defined by the equations

$$(8.1) \qquad\qquad H_n^{(1)}(x) = J_n(x) + jY_n(x)$$
$$(8.2) \qquad\qquad H_n^{(2)}(x) = J_n(x) - jY_n(x) \qquad j = \sqrt{-1}$$

and are called *Bessel functions of order n of the third kind,* or *Hankel functions of order n.* These functions are complex quantities.

9. Differential Equations Whose Solutions Are Expressible in Terms of Bessel Functions. In applied mathematics differential equations whose solutions are expressible in terms of Bessel functions are frequently encountered.   Lists of these equations have been compiled.*   Several of these differential equations will be listed here for reference.

In order to shorten the writing, the notation

$$(9.1) \qquad Z_n(x) = C_1 J_n(x) + C_2 Y_n(x)$$

where C_1 and C_2 are arbitrary constants, will be introduced.   In terms of this notation the following differential equations have the indicated solutions:

$$(9.2) \qquad \frac{d^2y}{dx^2} + \left(b^2 - \frac{4n^2 - 1}{4x^2}\right)y = 0 \qquad y = x^{\frac{1}{2}}Z_n(bx)$$

$$(9.3) \qquad \frac{d^2y}{dx^2} + \frac{1 - 2a}{x}\frac{dy}{dx}$$
$$+ \left[(bcx^{c-1})^2 + \frac{a^2 - n^2c^2}{x^2}\right]y = 0 \qquad y = x^a Z_n(bx^c)$$

$$(9.4) \qquad \frac{d^2y}{dx^2} + bxy = 0 \qquad y = x^{\frac{1}{2}}Z_{\frac{1}{3}}[\tfrac{2}{3}(bx^3)^{\frac{1}{2}}]$$

$$(9.5) \qquad \frac{d^2y}{dx^2} + bx^2y = 0 \qquad y = x^{\frac{1}{2}}Z_{\frac{1}{4}}\left(\frac{x^2}{2}b^{\frac{1}{2}}\right)$$

$$(9.6) \qquad \frac{d^2y}{dx^2} + (k^2e^{2x} - n^2)y = 0 \qquad y = Z_n(ke^x)$$

Equation (9.4) is known in the mathematical literature as *Stokes's equation* and is of considerable importance in mathematical physics because of its occurrence in the theory of diffraction and refraction of waves as well as in the theory of transmission across potential barriers.†

10. Modified Bessel Functions.   Let us consider the differential equation

$$(10.1) \qquad \frac{d^2y}{dx^2} + \frac{1}{x}\frac{dy}{dx} + \left(-1 - \frac{n^2}{x^2}\right)y = 0$$

This equation is of the form (9.3) with

$$(10.2) \qquad a = 0 \qquad b = j \qquad c = 1$$

Hence $J_n(jx)$ is a solution of this equation.   The function

$$(10.3) \qquad I_n(x) = j^{-n}J_n(jx)$$

is taken as the standard form for one of the fundamental solutions of (10.1).   The function $I_n(x)$ defined in this manner is a real function

* See E. Jahnke and F. Emde, "Tables of Functions," pp. 146–147, Dover Publications, New York, 1943; W. G. Bickley, "Bessel Functions and Formulae," Cambridge University Press, New York, 1953.

† See "Tables of Modified Hankel Functions of Order One-third and Their Derivatives," Harvard University Press, Cambridge, Mass., 1945.

and is known as the *modified Bessel function of the first kind of order n.* Another fundamental solution of Eq. (10.1) is known as the *modified Bessel function of the second kind* and is defined by

(10.4) $$K_n(x) = \frac{\pi/2}{\sin n\pi} [I_{-n}(x) - I_n(x)]   \qquad n \text{ nonintegral}$$

The general solution of Eq. (10.1) may be written in the form

(10.5) $$y = A I_n(x) + B K_n(x)   \qquad n \text{ nonintegral}$$

where A and B are arbitrary constants.

In contrast to the Bessel function $J_n(x)$ and $Y_n(x)$ the functions $I_n(x)$ and $K_n(x)$ are not of the oscillating type, but their behavior is similar to that of the exponential functions. For large values of x we have

(10.6) $$I_0(x) \cong \frac{e^x}{\sqrt{2\pi x}}$$

(10.7) $$K_0(x) \cong \sqrt{\frac{\pi}{2x}} \, e^{-x}$$

For small values of x we have

(10.8) $$I_0(x) \cong 1$$

(10.9) $$K_0(x) \cong - \log \frac{x}{2}$$

11. The ber and bei Functions. In determining the distribution of alternating currents in wires of circular cross section the following differential equation is encountered:

(11.1) $$\frac{d^2y}{dx^2} + \frac{1}{x} \frac{dy}{dx} - jy = 0   \qquad j = \sqrt{-1}$$

This equation is a special case of Eq. (9.3) with

(11.2) $$a = 0   \qquad n = 0   \qquad c = 1$$

and

(11.3) $$b^2 = -j$$

Hence

(11.4) $$b = \sqrt{-j} = j\sqrt{j} = j^{\frac{3}{2}}$$

The general solution of Eq. (11.1) may therefore be written in the form

(11.5) $$y = A J_0(j^{\frac{3}{2}}x) + K_0(j^{\frac{3}{2}}x)$$

where A and B are arbitrary constants. The functions $J_0(j^{\frac{3}{2}}x)$ and $Y_0(j^{\frac{3}{2}}x)$ are complex functions. Decomposing them into their real and imaginary parts, we obtain

(11.6) $$J_0(j^{\frac{3}{2}}x) = \text{ber } (x) + j \text{ bei } (x)$$

and

(11.7) $$K_0(j^{\frac{1}{2}}x) = \text{ker } (x) + j \text{ kei } (x)$$

These equations define the functions ber (x), bei (x) and ker (x), kei (x).

12. Expansion in Series of Bessel Functions. In Chap. 3 it was pointed out that the expansion of an arbitrary function into a Fourier series is only a special case of the expansion of an arbitrary function in a series of orthogonal functions under certain restrictions. It will now be shown that it is possible to expand an arbitrary function in a series of Bessel functions. If in Eq. (2.4) we place ax instead of x, we obtain

(12.1) $$\frac{d^2u}{dx^2} + \left(a^2 - \frac{n^2 - \frac{1}{4}}{x^2}\right) u = 0$$

This equation has one solution,

(12.2) $$u = \sqrt{x}\, J_n(ax)$$

In the same manner

(12.3) $$v = \sqrt{x}\, J_n(bx)$$

satisfies the equation

(12.4) $$\frac{d^2v}{dx^2} + \left(b^2 - \frac{n^2 - \frac{1}{4}}{x^2}\right) v = 0$$

If we multiply (12.1) by v and (12.4) by u and subtract the second product from the first, we obtain

(12.5) $$(b^2 - a^2)uv = u''v - v''u$$

Let us now integrate both members of (12.5) with respect to x from 0 to x. We thus obtain

(12.6) $$(b^2 - a^2) \int_0^x uv\, dx = \int_0^x (u''v - v''u)\, dx$$

However, we have

(12.7) $$\frac{d}{dx} (vu' - uv') = u''v - v''u$$

Hence

(12.8) $$(b^2 - a^2) \int_0^x uv\, dx = \int_0^x \frac{d}{dx} (vu' - uv')\, dx$$
$$= (vu' - uv') \Big|_0^x$$

That is,

$$(12.9) \quad (b^2 - a^2) \int_0^x x J_n(ax) J_n(bx) \, dx$$
$$= x[a J_n(bx) J_n'(ax) - b J_n(ax) J_n'(bx)]$$

If we now differentiate the last equation with respect to b and then set

$$(12.10) \qquad\qquad b = a$$

we obtain

$$(12.11) \quad 2a \int_0^x x J_n^2(ax) \, dx = x[ax J_n'^2(ax) - J_n(ax) J_n'(ax)$$
$$- ax J_n(ax) J_n''(ax)]$$

From (12.9) we have

$$(12.12) \quad (b^2 - a^2) \int_0^1 x J_n(ax) J_n(bx) \, dx = a J_n(b) J_n'(a) - b J_n(a) J_n'(b)$$

Now the second member vanishes if a and b are roots of the equation

$$(12.13) \qquad\qquad J_n(\alpha) = 0$$

That is, if a and b are distinct positive zeros of $J_n(\alpha)$, we have

$$(12.14) \qquad (b^2 - a^2) \int_0^1 x J_n(ax) J_n(bx) \, dx = 0$$

and since

$$(12.15) \qquad\qquad a \neq b$$

we have

$$(12.16) \qquad\qquad \int_0^1 x J_n(ax) J_n(bx) \, dx = 0$$

We are now in a position to expand an arbitrary function $F(x)$ in the interval from $x = 0$ to $x = 1$ in a series of the form

$$(12.17) \qquad\qquad F(x) = \sum_{s=1}^{s=\infty} C_s J_n(\alpha_s x)$$

where the α_s are the successive positive roots of (12.13). To obtain the general coefficient C_k of this expansion, we multiply both members of (12.17) by $x J_n(\alpha_k x) \, dx$ and integrate from $x = 0$ to $x = 1$. We have by virtue of (12.16)

$$(12.18) \qquad \int_0^1 x J_n(\alpha_k x) F(x) \, dx = C_k \int_0^1 x J_n^2(\alpha_k x) \, dx$$

The last integral, which is independent of x, may be evaluated by means of (12.11), (12.3), and (6.9). Its value is

$$(12.19) \qquad\qquad \int_0^1 x J_n^2(\alpha_k x) \, dx = \tfrac{1}{2} J_{n+1}^2(\alpha_k)$$

Hence the typical coefficient of the series expansion (12.17) is given by

$$(12.20) \qquad C_s = \frac{2}{J_{n+1}^2(\alpha_s)} \int_0^1 x J_n(\alpha_s x) F(x)\, dx$$

This expansion is analogous to the expansion of an arbitrary function in a Fourier series. In later chapters we shall have occasion to use this type of expansion in problems of physical interest.

13. The Bessel Coefficients. The functions $J_n(x)$ of *integral* order are sometimes called the *Bessel coefficients*. These functions occur as coefficients in the expansion of the following function in powers of t:

$$(13.1) \qquad F(t) = e^{x(t-t^{-1})/2} = e^{xt/2} e^{-xt^{-1}/2}$$

This function of t can be expressed as a series of the form

$$(13.2) \qquad F(t) = \sum_{n=-\infty}^{+\infty} A_n t^n = e^{xt/2} e^{-xt^{-1}/2}$$

This is an infinite series of ascending and descending powers of t and is known in the mathematical literature as a *Laurent series* (see Chap. 19, Sec. 8). In order to obtain the coefficients A_n, we take the product of the following two expansions:

$$(13.3) \qquad \begin{aligned} e^{xt/2} &= 1 + \frac{x}{2}\frac{t}{1!} + \left(\frac{x}{2}\right)^2 \frac{t^2}{2!} + \left(\frac{x}{2}\right)^3 \frac{t^3}{3!} + \cdots \\ e^{-xt^{-1}/2} &= 1 - \frac{x}{2}\frac{t^{-1}}{1!} + \left(\frac{x}{2}\right)^2 \frac{t^{-2}}{2!} - \left(\frac{x}{2}\right)^3 \frac{t^{-3}}{3!} + \cdots \end{aligned}$$

The constant term A_0 of the expansion (13.2) is

$$(13.4) \qquad A_0 = 1 - \frac{(x/2)^2}{(1!)^2} + \frac{(x/2)^4}{(2!)^2} - \cdots = J_0(x)$$

The term A_n is

(13.5)

$$A_n = \frac{(x/2)^n}{n!} \left[1 - \frac{(x/2)^2}{1 \times (n+1)} + \frac{(x/2)^4}{1 \times 2(n+1)(n+2)} - \cdots \right] = J_n(x)$$

Similarly the coefficient A_{-n} is

$$(13.6) \quad A_{-n} = \frac{(-x/2)^n}{n!} \left[1 - \frac{(x/2)^2}{1 \times (n+1)} \right. $$
$$\left. + \frac{(x/2)^4}{1 \times 2(n+1)(n+2)} - \cdots \right] = J_{-n}(x)$$

Accordingly we have

$$(13.7) \quad e^{x(t-t^{-1})/2} = \sum_{n=-\infty}^{+\infty} J_n(x)t^n$$

$$= J_0(x) + J_1(x)(t - t^{-1}) + J_2(x)(t^2 + t^{-2}) + \cdots$$

If we place $t = e^{j\theta}$, $j = (-1)^{\frac{1}{2}}$ in the result (13.7), we obtain the following series:

$$(13.8) \quad e^{jx \sin \theta} = J_0(x) + 2J_2(x) \cos 2\theta + 2J_4(x) \cos 4\theta + \cdots$$
$$+ 2j[J_1(x) \sin \theta + J_3(x) \sin 3\theta + \cdots]$$

Since $e^{jx \sin \theta} = \cos (x \sin \theta) + j \sin (x \sin \theta)$, if the real and imaginary parts of (13.8) are separated, the results are

$$(13.9) \quad \cos (x \sin \theta) = J_0(x) + 2J_2(x) \cos 2\theta + 2J_4(x) \cos 4\theta + \cdots$$

and

$$(13.10) \quad \sin (x \sin \theta) = 2[J_1(x) \sin \theta + J_3(x) \sin 3\theta + \cdots]$$

If in (13.9) and (13.10) θ is replaced by its complement, $\pi/2 - \theta$, the following equations are obtained:

$$(13.11) \quad \cos (x \cos \theta) = J_0(x) - 2J_2(x) \cos 2\theta + 2J_4(x) \cos 4\theta - \cdots$$
$$(13.12) \quad \sin (x \cos \theta) = 2[J_1(x) \cos \theta - J_3(x) \cos 3\theta + \cdots]$$

These series are usually called *Jacobi series* in the mathematical literature. Each of these series may be regarded as a Fourier series. If we multiply all terms of (13.9) by $\cos n\theta \, d\theta$ and all terms of (13.10) by $\sin n\theta \, d\theta$ and integrate between 0 and π, the following results are obtained as a consequence of the orthogonality relations of the sines and cosines:

$$(13.13) \quad \frac{1}{\pi} \int_0^\pi \cos (x \sin \theta) \cos n\theta \, d\theta = \begin{cases} J_n(x) & n \text{ even or zero} \\ 0 & n \text{ odd} \end{cases}$$

and

$$(13.14) \quad \frac{1}{\pi} \int_0^\pi \sin (x \sin \theta) \sin n\theta \, d\theta = \begin{cases} J_n(x) & n \text{ odd} \\ 0 & n \text{ even} \end{cases}$$

From this it can be deduced that

$$(13.15) \quad J_n(x) = \frac{1}{\pi} \int_0^\pi [\cos (x \sin \theta) \cos n\theta + \sin (x \sin \theta) \sin n\theta] \, d\theta$$

whether n is an odd or even integer. Therefore

$$(13.16) \quad J_n(x) = \frac{1}{\pi} \int_0^\pi \cos (n\theta - x \sin \theta) \, d\theta \qquad n \text{ any integer}$$

These integrals are originally due to Bessel. The integral (13.16) occurred in an astronomy problem involving what is known as the *eccentric anomaly*.

PROBLEMS

1. Prove that

$$\frac{d}{dx}\left[x^n J_n(ax)\right] = ax^n J_{n-1}(ax)$$

2. Show that the differential equation

$$\frac{x\, d^2 y}{dx^2} + (1 + n)\frac{dy}{dx} + y = 0$$

is satisfied by $y = x^{-n^2} J_n(2x^{\frac{1}{2}})$.

3. Show that

$$J_{\frac{5}{2}}(x) = \left(\frac{2}{\pi x}\right)^{\frac{1}{2}}\left[(3 - x^2)\frac{\sin x}{x^2} - \frac{3\cos x}{x}\right]$$

4. Show that

$$J_n(x + y) = \sum_{k = -\infty}^{k = +\infty} J_k(x)J_{n-k}(y)$$

for integral values of n.

5. By multiplying the expansions for $e^{x(t - t^{-1})/2}$ and $e^{-x(t - t^{-1})/2}$ show that

$$[J_0(x)]^2 + 2[J_1(x)]^2 + 2[J_2(x)]^2 + \cdots = 1$$

6. Show that

$$\int_0^\infty e^{-pt} J_0(at)\, dt = (p^2 + a^2)^{-\frac{1}{2}} \qquad p > 0$$

7. Obtain the recurrence formulas of Sec. 6 by differentiating the relation

$$e^{x(t - t^{-1})/2} = \sum_{n = -\infty}^{n = +\infty} J_n(x)t^n$$

with respect to x, or to t, and comparing the coefficients of corresponding powers of t.

8. By modifying the variables in the above relation prove that

$$e^{x(t + t^{-1})/2} = \sum_{n = -\infty}^{+\infty} I_n(x)t^n$$

Replace t by t^{-1} and deduce that $I_n(x) = I_{-n}(x)$.

9. Prove that

(*a*) $\cos(x\cosh\theta) = J_0(x) - 2J_2(x)\cosh 2\theta + 2J_4(x)\cosh 4\theta - \cdots$.

(*b*) $\sin(x\cosh\theta) = 2[J_1(x)\cosh\theta - J_3(x)\cosh 3\theta + \cdots]$.

10. Show that

(*a*) $\sinh(x\cosh\theta) = 2[I_1(x)\cosh\theta + I_3(x)\cosh 3\theta + \cdots]$.

(*b*) $\cosh(x\cosh\theta) = I_0(x) + 2[I_2(x)\cosh 2\theta + I_4(x)\cosh 4\theta + \cdots]$.

11. Show that $e^{x\cos\theta} = I_0(x) + 2I_1(x)\cos\theta + 2I_2(x)\cos\theta + \cdots$.

12. From the Jacobi series deduce that

$$1 = J_0(x) + 2J_2(x) + 2J_4(x) + \cdots$$
$$\cos x = J_0(x) - 2J_2(x) + 2J_4(x) - \cdots$$

13. A simple pendulum is performing small oscillations about the vertical while the length of the pendulum is increasing at a constant rate. Obtain the equation of motion of this pendulum, and express the solution in terms of Bessel functions.

14. A variable mass $m(t)$ is attached to a spring of constant spring constant k. One end of the spring is fixed, and the mass is performing oscillations on a smooth horizontal plane. Discuss the oscillations of the mass if its magnitude is $m = (a + bt)^{-1}$, where a and b are positive constants and t is the time.

15. A nonlinear electrical circuit has a potential $E \cos wt$ impressed upon it. The current produced by this potential can be expressed in the form $i = Ae^{bE \cos wt}$, where A and b are positive constants. Prove that the mean value of the current is $AI_0(bE)$ and that the root-mean-square current is $A[I_0(2bE)]^{\frac{1}{2}}$. I_0 is the modified Bessel function of zeroth order.

16. Prove that $\displaystyle\int_0^\infty J_0(bx)\,dx = 1/b$.

17. Find the complete solution of the differential equation $d^2y/dx^2 + x^{-\frac{1}{2}}y = 0$.

18. Show that $x/2 = J_1(x) + 3J_3(x) + 5J_5(x) + \cdots$.

19. Show that $x \sin x/2 = 2^2 J_2(x) - 4^2 J_4(x) + 6^2 J_6(x) - \cdots$.

20. Show that $x \cos x/2 = 1^2 J_1(x) - 3^2 J_3(x) + 5^2 J_5(x) - \cdots$.

21. Find the general solution of the equation $d^2y/dx^2 + (1/x)\,dy/dx - k^2y = a$, where k and a are constants.

REFERENCES

1. McLachlan, N. W.: "Bessel Functions for Engineers," Oxford University Press New York, 1934.
2. Watson, G. N.: "Theory of Bessel Functions," Cambridge University Press, New York, 1922.
3. Gray, A., G. B. Mathews, and T. M. Macrobert: "A Treatise on Bessel Functions," The Macmillan Company, New York, 1931.
4. Relton, F. E.: "Applied Bessel Functions," Blackie & Son, Ltd., Glasgow, 1946.
5. Bickley, W. G.: "Bessel Functions and Formulae," Cambridge University Press, New York, 1953.
6. Whittaker, E. J., and G. N. Watson: "A Course in Modern Analysis," 4th ed., Cambridge University Press, New York, 1927.

CHAPTER 14

LEGENDRE'S DIFFERENTIAL EQUATION
AND LEGENDRE POLYNOMIALS

1. Introduction. In the last chapter we discussed the solutions of Bessel's differential equation or Bessel functions. Another differential equation that arises very frequently in various branches of applied mathematics is Legendre's differential equation. This equation occurs in the process of obtaining solutions of Laplace's equation in spherical coordinates and hence is of great importance in mathematical applications to physics and engineering. This chapter is devoted to the study of the solutions of Legendre's differential equation and to a discussion of their most important properties.

2. Legendre's Differential Equation. The differential equation

$$(2.1) \qquad (1 - x^2) \frac{d^2y}{dx^2} - 2x \frac{dy}{dx} + n(n + 1)y = 0$$

is known in the literature as *Legendre's differential equation of degree n.* We shall consider here only the important special case in which the parameter n is zero or a positive integer. As in the case of Bessel's differential equation let us assume an infinite-series solution of this differential equation in the form

$$(2.2) \qquad y = x^m \sum_{r=0}^{r=\infty} a_r x^r = \sum_{r=0}^{r=\infty} a_r x^{m+r}$$

For (2.2) to be a solution of (2.1), it is necessary that when (2.2) is substituted into (2.1) the coefficient of every power of x vanish. Equating the coefficient of the power x^{m+r-2} to zero, we obtain

$$(2.3) \quad (m + r)(m + r - 1)a_r$$
$$+ (n - m - r + 2)(n + m + r - 1)a_{r-2} = 0$$

Since the leading coefficient in the series (2.2) is a_0, we have

$$(2.4) \qquad a_{-1} = 0 \qquad a_{-2} = 0$$

in (2.3).

With this stipulation, placing $r = 0$ in (2.3), we have

$$(2.5) \qquad\qquad m(m - 1)a_0 = 0$$

Placing $r = 1$ in (2.3), we obtain

$$(2.6) \qquad\qquad (m + 1)ma_1 = 0$$

Equation (2.5) gives $m = 0$ or $m = 1$, with a_0 arbitrary in any case. Let us take $m = 0$; then a_1 is arbitrary. Placing this value of m in (2.3), we have

$$(2.7) \qquad\qquad a_r = - \frac{(n - r + 2)(n + r - 1)}{r(r - 1)} a_{r-2}$$

This enables us to determine any coefficient from the one which precedes it by two terms. We therefore have

$$(2.8) \quad y = a_0 \left[1 - \frac{n(n + 1)}{2!} x^2 + \frac{n(n - 2)(n + 1)(n + 3)}{4!} x^4 - \cdots \right]$$
$$+ a_1 \left[x - \frac{(n - 1)(n + 2)}{3!} x^3 \right.$$
$$\left. + \frac{(n - 1)(n - 3)(n + 2)(n + 4)}{5!} x^5 - \cdots \right]$$

It may be shown by the ratio test that each of these series converges in the interval $(-1, +1)$. Had we taken the possibility $m = -1$ in (2.6), we would not have obtained anything new but only the second series in (2.8).

Since a_0 and a_1 are *arbitrary*, this is the general solution of Legendre's equation. We notice that the first series reduces to a polynomial when n is an even integer and the second series reduces to a polynomial when n is an odd integer. Now if we give the arbitrary coefficients a_0 or a_1, as the case may be, such a numerical value that the polynomial becomes equal to unity when x is unity, we obtain the following system of polynomials:

$$(2.9) \quad \begin{aligned} &P_0(x) = 1 & &P_4(x) = \tfrac{1}{8}(35x^4 - 30x^2 + 3) \\ &P_1(x) = x & &P_5(x) = \tfrac{1}{8}(63x^5 - 70x^3 + 15x) \\ &P_2(x) = \tfrac{1}{2}(3x^2 - 1) & &P_6(x) = \tfrac{1}{16}(231x^6 - 315x^4 + 105x^2 - 5) \\ &P_3(x) = \tfrac{1}{2}(5x^3 - 3x) & & \end{aligned}$$

These are called *Legendre polynomials*. Each satisfies a Legendre differential equation in which n has the value indicated by the subscript.

The general polynomial $P_n(x)$ is given by the series

$$(2.10) \qquad P_n(x) = \sum_{r=0}^{N} (-1)^r \frac{(2n - 2r)!}{2^n r!(n - r)!(n - 2r)!} x^{n-2r}$$

where $N = n/2$ for n even and $N = (n - 1)/2$ for n odd.

It is thus seen that the Legendre polynomial $P_n(x)$ is even or odd according as its degree n is even or odd.   Since

$$(2.11) \qquad\qquad P_n(1) = 1$$

we therefore conclude that

$$(2.12) \qquad\qquad P_n(-1) = (-1)^n$$

3. Rodrigues' Formula for the Legendre Polynomials.   An important formula for $P_n(x)$ may be deduced directly from Legendre's differential equation.   Let

$$(3.1) \qquad\qquad v = (x^2 - 1)^n$$

Then

$$(3.2) \qquad\qquad \frac{dv}{dx} = 2nx(x^2 - 1)^{n-1}$$

Hence

$$(3.3) \qquad\qquad (1 - x^2)\frac{dv}{dx} + 2nxv = 0$$

If we differentiate (3.3) with respect to x, we obtain

$$(3.4) \qquad\qquad (1 - x^2)\frac{d^2v}{dx^2} + 2(n - 1)x\frac{dv}{dx} + 2nv = 0$$

If we now differentiate this equation r times in succession, we have

$$(3.5) \quad (1 - x^2)\frac{d^2v_r}{dx^2} + 2(n - r - 1)x\frac{dv_r}{dx} + (r + 1)(2n - r)v_r = 0$$

where

$$(3.6) \qquad\qquad v_r = \frac{d^r v}{dx^r}$$

In particular, if $r = n$, (3.5) reduces to

$$(3.7) \qquad\qquad (1 - x^2)\frac{d^2v_n}{dx^2} - 2x\frac{dv_n}{dx} + (n + 1)nv_n = 0$$

This is Legendre's equation (2.1).   Hence v_n satisfies Legendre's equation.   But since v_n is

$$(3.8) \qquad\qquad v_n = \frac{d^n v}{dx^n} = \frac{d^n}{dx^n}(x^2 - 1)^n$$

v_n is a polynomial of degree n, and since Legendre's equation has one and only one distinct solution of that form, $P_n(x)$, it follows that $P_n(x)$ is a constant multiple of v_n.   Hence we have

$$(3.9) \qquad\qquad P_n(x) = C\frac{d^n}{dx^n}(x^2 - 1)^n$$

To determine the constant C we merely consider the highest power of x on each side of the equation, that is,

$$(3.10) \qquad \frac{(2n)!}{2^n(n!)^2} x^n = C \frac{d^n}{dx^n} x^{2n}$$

$$= C \frac{(2n)!}{n!} x^n$$

Hence

$$(3.11) \qquad C = \frac{1}{2^n n!}$$

Substituting this value of C into (3.9), we obtain

$$(3.12) \qquad P_n(x) = \frac{1}{2^n n!} \frac{d^n}{dx^n} (x^2 - 1)^n$$

This is *Rodrigues' formula* for the Legendre polynomials.

4. Legendre's Function of the Second Kind. The *general* solution of Legendre's equation may be written in the form

$$(4.1) \qquad Y = A P_n(x) + B Q_n(x)$$

where A and B are arbitrary constants and $Q_n(x)$ is called *Legendre's function of the second kind*. This function is obtained by methods that are beyond the scope of this discussion. It is defined by the following series when $|x| < 1$:

$$(4.2) \quad Q_n(x) = b_1 \left[x - \frac{(n-1)(n+2)}{3!} x^3 \right.$$

$$\left. + \frac{(n-1)(n-3)(n+2)(n+4)}{5!} x^5 - \cdots \right]$$

if n is even and

$$(4.3) \quad Q_n(x) = b_0 \left[1 - \frac{n(n+1)}{2!} x^2 \right.$$

$$\left. + \frac{n(n-2)(n+1)(n+3)}{4!} x^4 - \cdots \right]$$

if n is odd, where

$$b_1 = (-1)^{n/2} \frac{2^n [(n/2)!]^2}{n!}$$

$$(4.4)$$

$$b_0 = (-1)^{(n+1)/2} \frac{2^{n-1} \left[\left(\frac{n-1}{2} \right)! \right]^2}{n!}$$

If, however, $|x| > 1$, the above series do not converge. In this case the following series in descending powers of x is taken as the definition of $Q_n(x)$:

$$(4.5) \qquad Q_n(x) = \sum_{r=0}^{r=\infty} \frac{2^n(n+r)!(n+2r)!}{r!(2n+2r+1)!} x^{-n-2r-1}$$

Both $P_n(x)$ and $Q_n(x)$ are special cases of a function known as the *hypergeometric function*. The function $P_n(x)$ is the more important and occurs more frequently in the literature of applied mathematics.

5. The Generating Function for $P_n(x)$. The Legendre polynomial $P_n(x)$ is the coefficient of Z^n in the expansion of

$$(5.1) \qquad \begin{aligned} \phi &= (1 - 2xZ + Z^2)^{-\frac{1}{2}} \\ &= (1 + Z^2 - 2xZ)^{-\frac{1}{2}} \end{aligned}$$

in ascending powers of Z. This may be verified for the lower powers of n by expanding (5.1) by the binomial theorem. To prove it for the general term, we write

$$(5.2) \qquad \phi = \sum_{n=0}^{n=\infty} A_n Z^n$$

Now it is obvious from the nature of the binomial expansion that A_n is a polynomial in x of degree n. Also, if we place $x = 1$ in (5.1), we obtain

$$(5.3) \qquad \begin{aligned} \phi &= (1 - 2Z + Z^2)^{-\frac{1}{2}} = \frac{1}{1 - Z} \\ &= 1 + Z + Z^2 + Z^3 + \cdots + Z^n + \cdots \end{aligned}$$

Hence A_n is equal to 1, when $x = 1$. Now, if we can show that A_n satisfies Legendre's equation, it will be identical with $P_n(x)$ as the A_n's are the only polynomials of degree n that satisfy the equation and have the value 1 when $x = 1$. From (5.1) we obtain by differentiation

$$(5.4) \qquad (1 - 2Zx + Z^2)\frac{\partial \phi}{\partial Z} = (x - Z)\phi$$

and

$$(5.5) \qquad Z\frac{\partial \phi}{\partial Z} = (x - Z)\frac{\partial \phi}{\partial x}$$

If we now substitute from (5.2) into (5.4) and equate the coefficients of Z^{n-1} on both sides of the equation, we obtain

$$(5.6) \qquad nA_n - (2n - 1)xA_{n-1} + (n - 1)A_{n-2} = 0$$

Substituting into (5.5) from (5.2) and equating the coefficients of the power Z^{n-1} on both sides, we obtain

$$(5.7) \qquad x\frac{dA_{n-1}}{dx} - \frac{dA_{n-2}}{dx} = (n - 1)A_{n-1}$$

If in (5.7) we replace n by $n + 1$, we obtain

$$(5.8) \qquad x \frac{dA_n}{dx} - \frac{dA_{n-1}}{dx} = nA_n$$

Now if we differentiate (5.6) with respect to x and eliminate dA_{n-2}/dx by (5.7), we have

$$(5.9) \qquad \frac{dA_n}{dx} - x \frac{dA_{n-1}}{dx} = nA_{n-1}$$

We now multiply (5.8) by $-x$ and add it to (5.9) and obtain

$$(5.10) \qquad (1 - x^2) \frac{dA_n}{dx} = n(A_{n-1} - xA_n)$$

Differentiating (5.10) with respect to x and simplifying the result by means of (5.8), we finally obtain

$$(5.11) \qquad (1 - x^2) \frac{d^2 A_n}{dx^2} - 2x \frac{dA_n}{dx} + n(n + 1)A_n = 0$$

This shows that A_n is a solution of Legendre's equation. Hence, for the reasons stated above, it is the same as $P_n(x)$. We therefore have

$$(5.12) \qquad A_n = P_n(x)$$

The above formulas for the A_n's are therefore valid for $P_n(x)$ and give important relations connecting Legendre polynomials of different orders. From (5.1) and (5.2) we have the important relation

$$(5.13) \qquad \phi = \frac{1}{\sqrt{1 - 2xZ + Z^2}} = \sum_{n=0}^{n=\infty} P_n(x)Z^n$$

This equation is valid in the ranges

$$(5.14) \qquad -1 \leq x \leq 1 \quad \text{and} \quad |Z| < 1$$

because of the region of convergence of the binomial expansion (5.2). The function ϕ is called the *generating function* for $P_n(x)$. This result is of great importance in potential theory.

6. The Legendre Coefficients. If we let

$$(6.1) \qquad x = \cos\theta = \frac{e^{j\theta} + e^{-j\theta}}{2} \qquad j = \sqrt{-1}$$

and substitute this into (5.13), we have

$$(6.2) \qquad [1 - Z(e^{j\theta} + e^{-j\theta}) + Z^2]^{-\frac{1}{2}} = \sum_{n=0}^{n=\infty} P_n(\cos\theta)Z^n$$

Now we have

(6.3) $[1 - Z(e^{i\theta} + e^{-i\theta}) + Z^2]^{-\frac{1}{2}} = (1 - Ze^{i\theta})^{-\frac{1}{2}}(1 - Ze^{-i\theta})^{-\frac{1}{2}}$

By the binomial theorem we obtain

(6.4) $(1 - Ze^{i\theta})^{-\frac{1}{2}} = 1 + \dfrac{Ze^{i\theta}}{2} + \dfrac{1 \times 3}{2 \times 4} Z^2 e^{2i\theta} + \cdots$

$$+ \frac{1 \times 3 \times \cdots \times (2n - 1)}{2 \times 4 \times \cdots \times 2n} Z^n e^{in\theta} + \cdots$$

and

(6.5) $(1 - Ze^{-i\theta})^{-\frac{1}{2}} = 1 + \dfrac{Ze^{-i\theta}}{2} + \dfrac{1 \times 3}{2 \times 4} Z^2 e^{-2i\theta} + \cdots$

$$+ \frac{1 \times 3 \times \cdots \times 2(n - 1)Z^n e^{-in\theta}}{2 \times 4 \times \cdots \times 2n} + \cdots$$

Multiplying (6.4) and (6.5) and picking out the coefficient of Z^n, we have

(6.6) $P_n(\cos \theta) = \dfrac{1 \times 3 \times \cdots \times (2n - 1)}{2 \times 4 \times \cdots \times 2n} 2 \cos n\theta$

$$+ \frac{1 \times 1 \times 3 \times \cdots \times (2n - 3)}{2 \times 2 \times 4 \times \cdots \times (2n - 2)} 2 \cos (n - 2)\theta + \cdots$$

Every coefficient is positive so that P_n is numerically greatest when each cosine is equal to unity, that is, when $\theta = 0$.   But since

(6.7) $P_n(\cos 0) = P_n(1) = 1$

it follows that

(6.8) $|P_n(\cos \theta)| \leq 1$ $n = 0, 1, 2, \ldots$

The first few functions $P_n(\cos \theta)$ are

(6.9)
$$\begin{aligned}
P_0(\cos \theta) &= 1 \\
P_1(\cos \theta) &= \cos \theta \\
P_2(\cos \theta) &= \tfrac{1}{4}(3 \cos 2\theta + 1) \\
P_3(\cos \theta) &= \tfrac{1}{8}(5 \cos 3\theta + 3 \cos \theta) \\
P_4(\cos \theta) &= \tfrac{1}{64}(35 \cos 4\theta + 20 \cos 2\theta + 9)
\end{aligned}$$

7. The Orthogonality of $P_n(x)$.   Like the trigonometric functions $\cos mx$ and $\sin mx$, the Legendre polynomials $P_n(x)$ are orthogonal functions.   Because of this property it is possible to expand an arbitrary function in a series of Legendre polynomials.

We shall now establish the orthogonality property

(7.1) $\displaystyle\int_{-1}^{+1} P_m(x)P_n(x) \, dx = 0$ if $m \neq n$

To do this, recall that $P_n(x)$ satisfies the Legendre differential equation (2.1). This equation may be written in the form

$$(7.2) \qquad \frac{d}{dx}[(1-x^2)P_n'(x)] + n(n+1)P_n(x) = 0$$

If we now multiply this by $P_m(x)$ and integrate between the limits -1 and $+1$, we obtain

$$(7.3) \qquad \int_{-1}^{+1} P_m(x) \frac{d}{dx}[(1-x^2)P_n'(x)]\,dx$$
$$+ n(n+1) \int_{-1}^{+1} P_m(x)P_n(x)\,dx = 0$$

Now we may integrate the first term by parts in the form

$$(7.4) \qquad \int_{-1}^{+1} P_m(x) \frac{d}{dx}[(1-x^2)P_n'(x)]\,dx = \{P_m(x)[(1-x^2)P_n'(x)]\}_{-1}^{+1}$$
$$- \int_{-1}^{+1} (1-x^2)P_n'(x)P_m'(x)\,dx$$

The first term of (7.4) vanishes at both limits because of the factor $1-x^2$; hence (7.3) reduces to

$$(7.5) \qquad -\int_{-1}^{+1}(1-x^2)P_n'(x)P_m'(x)\,dx + n(n+1)\int_{-1}^{+1}P_m(x)P_n(x)\,dx = 0$$

If in (7.5) we interchange n and m, we obtain

$$(7.6) \qquad -\int_{-1}^{+1}(1-x^2)P_m'(x)P_n'(x)\,dx + m(m+1)\int_{-1}^{+1}P_n(x)P_m(x)\,dx = 0$$

Subtracting (7.6) from (7.5), we get

$$(7.7) \qquad (n-m)(n+m+1)\int_{-1}^{+1}P_m(x)P_n(x)\,dx = 0$$

This establishes (7.1).

If $n = m$, Eq. (7.1) fails to hold. We shall now show that

$$(7.8) \qquad \int_{-1}^{+1}[P_n(x)]^2\,dx = \frac{2}{2n+1} \qquad n = 0, 1, 2, \ldots$$

To do this, we square both sides of (5.13) and obtain

$$(7.9) \qquad (1-2xZ+Z^2)^{-1} = \left[\sum_{n=0}^{\infty} P_n(x)Z^n\right]^2$$

We now integrate both sides of this equation with respect to x over the interval $(-1,1)$ and observe that the product terms on the right vanish in view of the orthogonality property (7.1).

We thus obtain

$$(7.10) \qquad \int_{-1}^{+1} \frac{dx}{1 - 2xZ + Z^2} = \sum_{n=0}^{n=\infty} Z^{2n} \int_{-1}^{+1} [P_n(x)]^2 \, dx$$

if $|Z| < 1$.

But the integral on the left has the value

$$(7.11) \qquad \int_{-1}^{+1} \frac{dx}{1 - 2xZ + Z^2} = \frac{1}{2} \ln \frac{1 + Z}{1 - Z}$$

$$= 2 \left(1 + \frac{Z^2}{3} + \frac{Z^4}{5} + \cdots + \frac{Z^{2n}}{2n + 1} + \cdots \right)$$

$$= \sum_{n=0}^{\infty} Z^{2n} \int_{-1}^{+1} [P_n(x)]^2 \, dx \qquad |Z| < 1$$

Equating the coefficient of the power Z^{2n} on both sides of (7.11), we have

$$(7.12) \qquad \int_{-1}^{+1} [P_n(x)]^2 \, dx = \frac{2}{2n + 1} \qquad n = 0, 1, 2, \ldots$$

8. Expansion of an Arbitrary Function in a Series of Legendre Polynomials. If $F(x)$ is sectionally continuous in the interval $(-1,1)$ and if its derivative $F(x)$ is sectionally continuous in every interval interior to $(-1,1)$, it may be shown that $F(x)$ may be expanded in a series of the form

$$(8.1) \qquad F(x) = \sum_{n=0}^{n=\infty} a_n P_n(x)$$

To obtain the general coefficient a_m, we multiply both sides of (8.1) by $P_m(x)$ and integrate over the interval $(-1,1)$. We then obtain

$$(8.2) \qquad \int_{-1}^{1} F(x)P_m(x) \, dx = a_m \int_{-1}^{1} [P_m(x)]^2 \, dx$$

$$= \frac{2a_m}{2m + 1}$$

in view of (7.1) and (7.8). The general coefficient of the expansion (8.1) is given by

$$(8.3) \qquad a_n = \frac{2n + 1}{2} \int_{-1}^{+1} F(x)P_n(x) \, dx$$

The expansion (8.1) is similar to an expansion of an arbitrary function into a Fourier series.

9. Associated Legendre Polynomials. In the solution of some potential problems it is convenient to use certain polynomials closely related to the Legendre polynomials. We shall discuss them briefly in this section.

If we differentiate Legendre's equation

$$(9.1) \qquad (1 - x^2) \frac{d^2y}{dx^2} - 2x \frac{dy}{dx} + n(n + 1)y = 0$$

m times with respect to x and write

$$(9.2) \qquad v = \frac{d^m y}{dx^m}$$

we obtain

$$(9.3) \quad (1 - x^2) \frac{d^2v}{dx^2} - 2x(m + 1) \frac{dv}{dx} + (n - m)(n + m + 1)v = 0$$

Since P_n is a solution of Legendre's equation (9.1), this equation is satisfied by

$$(9.4) \qquad v = \frac{d^m}{dx^m} P_n(x)$$

If now in (9.3) we let

$$(9.5) \qquad w = v(1 - x^2)^{m/2}$$

we obtain

$$(9.6) \qquad (1 - x^2) \frac{d^2w}{dx^2} - 2x \frac{dw}{dx} + \left[n(n + 1) - \frac{m^2}{1 - x^2} \right] w = 0$$

This equation differs from Legendre's equation in an added term involving m. It is called the *associated Legendre equation*. By Eq. (9.5) we see that it is satisfied by

$$(9.7) \qquad w = (1 - x^2)^{m/2} \frac{d^m}{dx^m} P_n(x)$$

This value of w is the *associated Legendre polynomial*, and it is denoted by $P_n^m(x)$. We therefore have

$$(9.8) \qquad P_n^m(x) = (1 - x^2)^{m/2} \frac{d^m}{dx^m} P_n(x)$$

We notice that, if $m > n$, we have

$$(9.9) \qquad P_n^m(x) = 0$$

PROBLEMS

1. Show that

$$\int_{-1}^{1} P_n(x)\, dx = 0 \qquad n = 1, 2, 3, \ldots$$

2. Establish the orthogonality property of the Legendre polynomials (7.1) by using Rodrigues' formula for $P_n(x)$ and successive integration by parts.

3. Show that

$$x^2 = \tfrac{2}{3} P_2(x) + \tfrac{1}{3} P_0(x)$$
$$x^3 = \tfrac{2}{5} P_3(x) + \tfrac{3}{5} P_1(x)$$

4. Show that

$$\int_{-1}^{1} x P_n(x) P_{n-1}(x) \, dx = \frac{2n}{4n^2 - 1}$$

5. Prove that

$$\frac{dP_{n+1}}{dx} - \frac{dP_{n-1}}{dx} = (2n + 1)P_n$$

6. Using Rodrigues' formula, integrate by parts to show that

$$\int_{-1}^{1} x^m P_n(x) \, dx = 0 \qquad \text{if } m < n$$

7. Show that, if $R_m(x)$ is a polynomial of degree m less than n, we have

$$\int_{-1}^{+1} P_n(x) R_m(x) \, dx = 0$$

REFERENCES

1. Byerly, W. E.: "Fourier's Series and Spherical Harmonics," Ginn & Company, Boston, 1893.
2. Churchill, R. V.: "Fourier Series and Boundary Value Problems," McGraw-Hill Book Company, Inc., New York, 1941.
3. Jeans, J. H.: "The Mathematical Theory of Electricity and Magnetism," Cambridge University Press, New York, 1927.
4. Smythe, W. R.: "Static and Dynamic Electricity," 1st ed., McGraw-Hill Book Company, Inc., New York, 1939.
5. Whittaker, E. T., and G. N. Watson: "A Course in Modern Analysis," Cambridge University Press, New York, 1927.

CHAPTER 15

VECTOR ANALYSIS

1. Introduction. The equations of applied mathematics express relations between quantities that are capable of measurement in terms of certain defined units. The simplest types of physical quantities are completely defined by a certain simple number. Examples of such quantities are mass, temperature, length. Such quantities are called *scalars*.

There are, however, other physical quantities that are not scalars. Such quantities as the displacement of a point, the velocity of a particle, a mechanical force require three numbers to specify them completely. The three numbers that are required to specify the quantities are scalars and could be, for example, the components of the displacement of the particle with respect to an arbitrary cartesian coordinate reference frame.

We could carry out the various mathematical operations with these scalar quantities, but we would be neglecting the fact that from a physical point of view a displacement, for example, is one entity, and also we are introducing a foreign element into the question, that is, the coordinate system. Accordingly it has been found convenient to introduce a mathematical discipline that enables us to study quantities of this type without recourse to a definite coordinate system.

It is only when we come to evaluate formulas numerically that it will be necessary to introduce a definite coordinate system. The mathematical technique that enables us to do this is *vector analysis*.

2. The Concept of a Vector. A physical quantity possessing both magnitude and direction is called a *vector*. Typical examples are force, velocity, acceleration, momentum. It is customary to represent vectors by letters in boldface type and scalars in lightface italics.

A vector may be indicated graphically by an arrow drawn between two points. It is thus evident that rectilinear displacements of a point and all physical quantities that can be represented by such displacements in the same manner that a scalar can be represented by the points of a straight line are vectors.

3. Addition and Subtraction of Vectors. Multiplication of a Vector by a Scalar. A vector having been defined as an entity that behaves in the same manner as the rectilinear displacement of a point, vector addition is reduced to a composition of linear displacements.

Consider two vectors **A** and **B** as shown in Fig. 3.1.

The vector **C**, which is obtained by moving a point along **A** and then along **B**, is called the resultant, or sum, of the vectors **A** and **B**, and we write

(3.1) $\mathbf{C} = \mathbf{A} + \mathbf{B}$

From the nature of the definition of vector addition it is apparent that

(3.2) $\mathbf{B} + \mathbf{A} = \mathbf{A} + \mathbf{B}$

Fig. 3.1

and that therefore vector addition is commutative. If the vectors **A** and **B** are situated as shown in Fig. 3.2, then the resultant vector **C** is obtained by completing the parallelogram formed by the two vectors.

In general, the sum of the vectors **A** and **B** is obtained by placing the origin of **B** at the terminus of **A**. Then the vector **C** extending from the origin of **A** to the terminus of **B** is defined as the sum, or resultant, of **A** and **B**.

Fig. 3.2

To add several vectors **A**, **B**, and **C**, first find the sum of **A** and **B** and the sum of **A** + **B** and **C**. It is seen that the result is the same as finding the sum of **B** and **C** first and then the sum of **A** and **B** + **C**. Thus vector addition is associative.

$$\mathbf{A} + (\mathbf{B} + \mathbf{C}) = (\mathbf{A} + \mathbf{B}) + \mathbf{C}$$

To subtract **B** from **A**, add −**B** to **A** as shown in Fig. 3.3.

Equality of Vectors. Two vectors are said to be equal if they have the same magnitude and the same direction.

Multiplication of a Vector by a Scalar. By the product of a vector **a** by a scalar n we understand a vector whose magnitude is equal to the magnitude of the product of the magnitudes of **a** and n and has the same direction as **a** or the opposite direction, depending on whether the scalar n is positive or negative. We thus write

Fig. 3.3

(3.3) $\mathbf{A} = n\mathbf{a}$

to denote this new vector.

Unit Vectors. A vector having unit magnitude is called a *unit vector.* The most common unit vectors are those which have the directions of a right-handed cartesian coordinate system as shown in Fig. 3.4. The vector *i* is a unit vector having the x direction of the coordinate system;

the unit vector j has the y direction; and the unit vector k has the z direction.

The Components of a Vector. The components of a vector **A** are any vectors whose sum is **A**. The components most frequently used are those parallel to the axes x, y, and z. These are called the *rectangular components* of the vector. If A_x, A_y, and A_z are the projections of **A** on the axes x, y, z, respectively, we may write

(3.4) $$\mathbf{A} = iA_x + jA_y + kA_z$$

If a vector **A** is given in magnitude and direction, then its components along the three axes of a cartesian reference frame are given by

FIG. 3.4

(3.5) $$A_x = |\mathbf{A}| \cos (\mathbf{A},x)$$
$$A_y = |\mathbf{A}| \cos (\mathbf{A},y)$$
$$A_z = |\mathbf{A}| \cos (\mathbf{A},z)$$

where $|\mathbf{A}|$ denotes the magnitude of the vector. If, conversely, the three components of the vector are assigned, the vector **A** is uniquely specified as the diagonal of the rectangular parallelepiped whose edges are the vectors iA_x, jA_y, and kA_z. Its magnitude is

(3.6) $$|\mathbf{A}| = \sqrt{A_x^2 + A_y^2 + A_z^2}$$

and its direction is given by the three cosines which can be found from (3.5) and (3.6).

4. The Scalar Product of Two Vectors. The scalar, or dot, product of two vectors is defined as a scalar quantity equal in magnitude to the product of the magnitudes of the two given vectors and the cosine of the angle between them. The scalar product of the two vectors **A** and **B** is thus given by the equation

(4.1) $$\mathbf{A} \cdot \mathbf{B} = |\mathbf{A}|\,|\mathbf{B}| \cos (\mathbf{A},\mathbf{B})$$

FIG. 4.1

The cosine of the angle between the directions of the two vectors becomes $+1$ when the directions are the same, -1 when they are opposite, and 0 when they are perpendicular.

It is clear from the definition of the dot product that the commutative law of multiplication holds, that is,

(4.2) $$\mathbf{A} \cdot \mathbf{B} = \mathbf{B} \cdot \mathbf{A}$$

The fact that the distributive law of multiplication holds can be seen with the aid of Fig. 4.1.

We have from the figure

(4.3) $\mathbf{P} \cdot \mathbf{R} + \mathbf{Q} \cdot \mathbf{R} = (OA)\mathbf{R} + (AB)\mathbf{R}$
$$= (OB)\mathbf{R} = (\mathbf{P} + \mathbf{Q}) \cdot \mathbf{R}$$

From the fundamental unit vectors we can form the following scalar products:

(4.4) $\begin{aligned} \boldsymbol{i} \cdot \boldsymbol{i} &= \boldsymbol{j} \cdot \boldsymbol{j} = \boldsymbol{k} \cdot \boldsymbol{k} = 1 \\ \boldsymbol{i} \cdot \boldsymbol{j} &= \boldsymbol{j} \cdot \boldsymbol{k} = \boldsymbol{k} \cdot \boldsymbol{i} = 0 \end{aligned}$

As a consequence of these results, we obtain

(4.5) $\mathbf{A} \cdot \mathbf{B} = (\boldsymbol{i}A_x + \boldsymbol{j}A_y + \boldsymbol{k}A_z) \cdot (\boldsymbol{i}B_x + \boldsymbol{j}B_y + \boldsymbol{k}B_z)$
$$= A_x B_x + A_y B_y + A_z B_z$$

We may also write

(4.6) $A^2 = \mathbf{A} \cdot \mathbf{A} = A_x^2 + A_y^2 + A_z^2 = |A|^2$

5. The Vector Product of Two Vectors. The vector, or cross, product of two vectors is defined to be a vector perpendicular to the plane of the two given vectors in the sense of advance of a right-handed screw rotated from the first to the second of the given vectors through the smaller angle between their positive directions.

The meaning of this definition is made clear in Fig. 5.1.

The magnitude of this vector is equal to the product of the magnitudes of the two given vectors times the sine of the angle between them.

The vector, or cross, product is denoted by $\mathbf{A} \times \mathbf{B}$. As is clear from the definition and the figure, the commutative law does not hold for this type of multiplication; instead we have

Fig. 5.1

(5.1) $\mathbf{A} \times \mathbf{B} = -\mathbf{B} \times \mathbf{A}$

Also we have

(5.2) $\mathbf{A} \times \mathbf{A} = 0$

Fig. 5.2

It follows from the definition that if the vector product of two vectors vanishes the vectors are parallel provided neither vector is zero.

Vector Representation of Surfaces. Let us consider a plane surface such as shown in Fig. 5.2.

Since this surface has a magnitude represented by its area and a direction specified by its normal, it is a vector quantity. A certain ambiguity exists as to the positive sense of the normal. In order to remove this ambiguity, the following conventions are adopted:

If the surface is part of a closed surface, the outward-drawn normal is taken as positive.

If the surface is not part of a closed surface, the positive sense in describing the periphery is connected with the positive direction of the normal by the rule that a right-handed screw rotated in the plane of the surface in the positive sense of describing the periphery advances along the positive normal. For example, in Fig. 5.2, if the periphery of the surface is described in the sense ABC, the positive sense of the normal, and therefore the direction of the vector S representing the surface, is upward.

If a surface is not plane, it may be divided into a number of elementary surfaces each of which is plane to any desired degree of approximation. In this case the vector representative of the entire surface is the sum of the vectors representing its elements. Two surfaces, considered as vectors, are equal if the representative vectors are equal. Therefore two plane surfaces are equal if they have equal areas and are normal in the same direction even if they have different shapes.

FIG. 5.3

A curved surface may be replaced by a plane surface perpendicular to its representative vector having an area equal to the magnitude of this vector. The vector representing a closed surface is zero because the projection of the entire surface on any plane is zero; since as much of the projected area is negative as positive, it therefore follows that the vector representing the entire surface has zero components along the three axes x, y, z, and consequently it equals zero.

The Distributive Law of Vector Multiplication. To prove that the distributive law of multiplication holds for the vector product, consider the prism of Fig. 5.3. The edges of this prism are the vectors P, Q, $P + Q$, and R.

The vectors representing the faces of the closed prism are

$$\overline{ABED} = R \times P$$
$$\overline{BCFE} = R \times Q$$
$$\overline{ACFD} = (P + Q) \times R$$
$$\overline{ABC} = \tfrac{1}{2}(Q \times P)$$
$$\overline{DEF} = \tfrac{1}{2}(P \times Q)$$

Therefore the representative vector for the entire polyhedral surface is

(5.3) $R \times P + R \times Q + (P + Q) \times R + \tfrac{1}{2}(Q \times P) + \tfrac{1}{2}(P \times Q) = 0$

or

(5.4) $(P + Q) \times R = P \times R + Q \times R$

By the definition of the vector product we have the following relations for the unit vectors:

(5.5) $i \times j = k \quad j \times k = i \quad k \times i = j$
$$i \times i = j \times j = k \times k = 0$$

If we write the vectors P and Q in terms of their rectangular components,

(5.6)
$$P = iP_x + jP_y + kP_z$$
$$Q = iQ_x + jQ_y + kQ_z$$

and realize that the distributive law holds for a vector product, we obtain

(5.7) $P \times Q = (iP_x + jP_y + kP_z) \times (iQ_x + jQ_y + kQ_z)$
$$= i(P_yQ_z - P_zQ_y) + j(P_zQ_x - P_xQ_z) + k(P_xQ_y - P_yQ_x)$$

in view of the properties of the unit vectors expressed by (5.5).

This expression can be represented in a compact fashion by the determinant

(5.8) $P \times Q = \begin{vmatrix} i & j & k \\ P_x & P_y & P_z \\ Q_x & Q_y & Q_z \end{vmatrix}$

6. Multiple Products.   There are several types of multiple products used in vector analysis, and in this section the most important types will be considered.

a. The Product of a Vector and the Scalar Product of Two Other Vectors, $A(B \cdot C)$.   Here $B \cdot C$ is a scalar so that $A(B \cdot C)$ is a vector parallel to A and is of course an entirely different vector from $(A \cdot B)C$.

b. Scalar Product of a Vector and the Vector Product of Two Other Vectors.   Consider $A \cdot B \times C$.   In this case we have the important relation

(6.1) $A \cdot (B \times C) = B \cdot (C \times A) = C \cdot (A \times B)$

The proof of this relation follows from the fact that each of these expressions represents the volume of the parallelepiped whose edges are A, B, C.   Furthermore, all three expressions give this volume with the positive sign provided the vectors A, B, C, in that order, form a right-handed system.

c. Vector Product of a Vector and the Vector Product of Two Other Vectors.   Consider the product

(6.2) $q = a \times (b \times c)$

By the definition of a cross product $\mathbf{q}$ is perpendicular to the vector $\mathbf{a}$ and also to the vector $\mathbf{b} \times \mathbf{c}$. Accordingly the vector $\mathbf{q}$ lies in the plane of $\mathbf{b}$ and $\mathbf{c}$ and may be expressed in the form

$$(6.3) \qquad \mathbf{q} = u\mathbf{b} + v\mathbf{c}$$

where u and v are scalar multipliers.

Now we have

$$(6.4) \qquad \mathbf{q} \cdot \mathbf{a} = u(\mathbf{b} \cdot \mathbf{a}) + v(\mathbf{c} \cdot \mathbf{a}) = 0$$

or

$$(6.5) \qquad v = -\frac{u(\mathbf{b} \cdot \mathbf{a})}{\mathbf{c} \cdot \mathbf{a}}$$

Hence

$$(6.6) \qquad \mathbf{q} = u\mathbf{b} - \frac{u(\mathbf{b} \cdot \mathbf{a})\mathbf{c}}{\mathbf{c} \cdot \mathbf{a}}$$

$$= \frac{u}{\mathbf{c} \cdot \mathbf{a}} [\mathbf{b}(\mathbf{a} \cdot \mathbf{c}) - \mathbf{c}(\mathbf{a} \cdot \mathbf{b})]$$

Now let

$$(6.7) \qquad n = \frac{u}{\mathbf{c} \cdot \mathbf{a}}$$

where n is some scalar. To find the magnitude of n, consider a set of cartesian coordinate axes oriented so that the vectors $\mathbf{a}$, $\mathbf{b}$, and $\mathbf{c}$ have the following components in terms of these axes:

$$(6.8) \qquad \begin{aligned} \mathbf{a} &= ia_x + ja_y + ka_z \\ \mathbf{b} &= ib_x \\ \mathbf{c} &= ic_x + jc_y \end{aligned}$$

In this case we have

$$(6.9) \qquad \mathbf{b} \times \mathbf{c} = kb_xc_y$$

$$\begin{aligned} (6.10) \quad \mathbf{a} \times (\mathbf{b} \times \mathbf{c}) &= (ia_x + ja_y + ka_z) \times (kb_xc_y) \\ &= -j(a_xb_xc_y) + i(a_yb_xc_y) \\ &= ib_x(a_yc_y) + ib_xa_xc_x - ib_xa_xc_x - j(a_xb_xc_y) \\ &= ib_x(a_xc_x + a_yc_y) - (ic_x + jc_y)(a_xb_x) \\ &= \mathbf{b}(\mathbf{a} \cdot \mathbf{c}) - \mathbf{c}(\mathbf{a} \cdot \mathbf{b}) \end{aligned}$$

Hence, comparing (6.9) and (6.10), it is seen that the constant n is equal to 1.

7. Differentiation of a Vector with Respect to Time. The differential coefficient or derivative of a vector $\mathbf{A}$ with respect to a scalar variable t, say, the time, is defined as a limit by the equation

$$(7.1) \qquad \frac{d\mathbf{A}}{dt} = \lim_{\Delta t \to 0} \frac{\mathbf{A}(t + \Delta t) - \mathbf{A}(t)}{\Delta t}$$

Since division by a scalar does not alter vectorial properties, the derivative of a vector with respect to a scalar variable is itself a vector.

As an example of differentiation of a vector with respect to a scalar, consider a particle p moving along a curve c as shown in Fig. 7.1.

Let the position of the particle with respect to the origin of a cartesian reference frame be denoted by $\mathbf{r}$. In that case the velocity of the particle is given by

(7.2) $$\mathbf{v} = \frac{d\mathbf{r}}{dt} = \frac{d\mathbf{r}}{ds}\frac{ds}{dt}$$

FIG. 7.1

where ds is a differential of arc measured along the curve as shown in Fig. 7.2. Now

(7.3) $$\frac{d\mathbf{r}}{ds} = \lim_{\Delta s \to 0} \frac{\Delta \mathbf{r}}{\Delta s} = t$$

where t is a unit vector tangent to the curve defining the path of the particle. Hence we have

FIG. 7.2

(7.4) $$\mathbf{v} = \frac{d\mathbf{r}}{ds} = t\frac{ds}{dt}$$

The quantity ds/dt is the speed of the particle. The acceleration of the particle is defined as the time derivative of the velocity. We thus have

(7.5) $$\mathbf{a} = \frac{d\mathbf{v}}{dt} = \frac{d}{dt}t\frac{ds}{dt} = \frac{dt}{dt}\frac{ds}{dt} + t\frac{d^2s}{dt^2}$$

Now

(7.6) $$\frac{dt}{dt} = \frac{dt}{ds}\frac{ds}{dt}$$

Consider Fig. 7.3.

We may write

(7.7) $$\frac{dt}{ds} = \frac{dt}{d\phi}\frac{d\phi}{ds}$$

(7.8) $$\frac{dt}{d\phi} = n = \text{unit inward normal to the curve}$$

(7.9) $$\frac{d\phi}{ds} = \frac{1}{\rho} = \frac{1}{\text{radius of curvature of path}}$$

Substituting these expressions into (7.6), we obtain

(7.10) $$\frac{dt}{dt} = \frac{n}{\rho}\frac{ds}{dt}$$

Substituting this into (7.5), we finally obtain

$$(7.11) \qquad \mathbf{a} = t\frac{d^2s}{dt^2} + \frac{\mathbf{n}}{\rho}\left(\frac{ds}{dt}\right)^2$$

We thus see that the acceleration of the particle consists of two terms. The first term depends upon the rate of change of speed of the particle and is directed along the tangent to the particle; the second term is the centripetal acceleration of the particle and depends on the radius of curvature ρ of the particle and the square of the speed. This acceleration is directed in a direction normal to the curve and toward the center of curvature.

Fig. 7.3

Since the derivatives of vectors with respect to a scalar variable are deduced by a limiting process from subtraction of vectors and division by scalars, which are operations subject to the rules of ordinary algebra, it follows that the rules of the differential calculus can be extended at once to the differentiation of a sum of vectors,

$$(7.12) \qquad \frac{d}{dt}(\mathbf{A} + \mathbf{B}) = \frac{d\mathbf{A}}{dt} + \frac{d\mathbf{B}}{dt}$$

or the product of a scalar and a vector,

$$(7.13) \qquad \frac{d}{dt}(u\mathbf{a}) = \mathbf{a}\frac{du}{dt} + u\frac{d\mathbf{a}}{dt}$$

And, similarly,

$$(7.14) \qquad \frac{d}{dt}(\mathbf{A} \cdot \mathbf{B}) = \mathbf{B} \cdot \frac{d\mathbf{A}}{dt} + \mathbf{A} \cdot \frac{d\mathbf{B}}{dt}$$

$$(7.15) \qquad \frac{d}{dt}(\mathbf{A} \times \mathbf{B}) = \frac{d\mathbf{A}}{dt} \times \mathbf{B} + \mathbf{A} \times \frac{d\mathbf{B}}{dt}$$

Application to Mechanics—Coriolis' Acceleration. An interesting application of vector differentiation of importance to mechanics will now be discussed. Consider a small insect on a rotating plane sheet of cardboard. The cardboard will be assumed to be rotating about a fixed point O with a uniform angular velocity w. It will be supposed that the insect may move with respect to the cardboard. In order to describe the velocity and acceleration of the moving insect, let a cartesian coordinate system x, y be drawn on the rotating cardboard with the center of rotation as the origin.   Let the position vector of the insect be

(7.16) $$\mathbf{r} = \mathbf{i}x + \mathbf{j}y$$

where $\mathbf{i}$ and $\mathbf{j}$ are unit vectors in the x and y directions that rotate with the cardboard.

The velocity of the insect $\mathbf{v}$ relative to fixed space is

(7.17) $$\mathbf{v} = \frac{d\mathbf{r}}{dt} = \frac{d}{dt}(\mathbf{i}x + \mathbf{j}y) = \mathbf{i}\frac{dx}{dt} + \mathbf{j}\frac{dy}{dt} + x\frac{d\mathbf{i}}{dt} + y\frac{d\mathbf{i}}{dt}$$

Now, since $\mathbf{i}$ and $\mathbf{j}$ are *unit* vectors rotating with angular velocity w, it is easy to show by the reasoning of Eqs. (7.6) and (7.10) that

(7.18) $$\frac{d\mathbf{i}}{dt} = w\mathbf{j} \qquad \frac{d\mathbf{i}}{dt} = -w\mathbf{i}$$

Hence (7.17) may be written in the form

(7.19) $$\mathbf{v} = (\dot{x} - wy)\mathbf{i} + (\dot{y} + wx)\mathbf{j}$$

where the dots indicate differentiation with respect to the time in the usual manner.   The acceleration $\mathbf{a}$ of the insect is given by

(7.20) $$\mathbf{a} = \frac{d\mathbf{v}}{dt} = (\ddot{x} - w\dot{y})\mathbf{i} + (\ddot{y} + w\dot{x})\mathbf{j} + (\dot{x} - wy)\frac{d\mathbf{i}}{dt} + (\dot{y} + wx)\frac{d\mathbf{i}}{dt}$$
$$= (\ddot{x} - 2w\dot{y} - w^2x)\mathbf{i} + (\ddot{y} + 2w\dot{x} - w^2y)\mathbf{j}$$

Equation (7.20) indicates that the acceleration of the insect consists of three separate terms of the form

(7.21) $$\mathbf{a} = \mathbf{a}_1 + \mathbf{a}_2 + \mathbf{a}_3$$

where

(7.22) $$\mathbf{a}_1 = \ddot{x}\mathbf{i} + \ddot{y}\mathbf{j}$$
$$\mathbf{a}_2 = 2w(-\dot{y}\mathbf{i} + \dot{x}\mathbf{j})$$
$$\mathbf{a}_3 = -w^2(x\mathbf{i} + y\mathbf{j}) = -w^2\mathbf{r}$$

$\mathbf{a}_1$ is the acceleration of the insect with respect to the rotating coordinate system.   If the angular velocity w were zero and the card were stationary, this would be the only acceleration. $\mathbf{a}_2$ is the so-called *Coriolis' acceleration*.   It depends on the angular velocity w of the rotating card and on the *velocity* of the particle *relative to* the rotating coordinate axis.   This relative velocity $\mathbf{v}_r$ is given by

(7.23) $$\mathbf{v}_r = \dot{x}\mathbf{i} + \dot{y}\mathbf{j}$$

If the scalar product of the relative velocity $\mathbf{v}_r$ and the Coriolis' acceleration $\mathbf{a}_2$ is taken, the following result is obtained:

(7.24) $$\mathbf{a}_2 \cdot \mathbf{v}_r = 0$$

This indicates that the Coriolis' acceleration is perpendicular to the relative velocity.

The acceleration $\mathbf{a}_3$ is the centripetal acceleration. Its magnitude is proportional to the square of the angular velocity w of the frame of reference and to the distance of the particle from the center of rotation. It is directed radially toward the center of rotation. Equation (7.20) may be generalized, and the acceleration of a particle in a rotating reference plane such as the earth can be computed. The Coriolis' acceleration causes deviation of falling bodies and projectiles and explains the motion of Foucault's pendulum.*

8. The Gradient. Let $\phi(x,y,z)$ be a scalar function of position in space, that is, of the coordinates x, y, z. If the coordinates x, y, z are increased by dx, dy, dz, respectively, we have

$$(8.1) \qquad d\phi = \frac{\partial \phi}{\partial x}\, dx + \frac{\partial \phi}{\partial y}\, dy + \frac{\partial \phi}{\partial z}\, dz$$

If we denote by $d\mathbf{r}$ the vector representing the displacement specified by dx, dy, dz, then

$$(8.2) \qquad d\mathbf{r} = i\, dx + j\, dy + k\, dz$$

In vector analysis a certain vector differential operator ∇ (read "del") defined by

$$(8.3) \qquad \nabla = i\frac{\partial}{\partial x} + j\frac{\partial}{\partial y} + k\frac{\partial}{\partial z}$$

plays a very prominent role. The gradient of a scalar function $\phi(x,y,z)$ is defined by

$$(8.4) \qquad \text{grad } \phi = i\frac{\partial \phi}{\partial x} + j\frac{\partial \phi}{\partial y} + k\frac{\partial \phi}{\partial z}$$

Operating with ∇ on the scalar function $\phi(x,y,z)$, we get

$$(8.5) \qquad \nabla\phi = i\frac{\partial \phi}{\partial x} + j\frac{\partial \phi}{\partial y} + k\frac{\partial \phi}{\partial z} = \text{a vector}$$

This is just the expression (8.4) defined as the gradient of ϕ.

Now, from (8.1) and (8.2), we have

$$(8.6) \qquad d\phi = \left(i\frac{\partial \phi}{\partial x} + j\frac{\partial \phi}{\partial y} + k\frac{\partial \phi}{\partial z}\right) \cdot (i\, dx + j\, dy + k\, dz)$$
$$= (\nabla\phi) \cdot d\mathbf{r}$$

The equation

$$(8.7) \qquad \phi(x,y,z) = \text{const}$$

---

* See J. L. Synge and B. A. Griffith, "Principles of Mechanics," 1st ed., chap. 13, McGraw-Hill Book Company, Inc., New York, 1942.

represents a certain surface, and as we change the value of the constant, we obtain a family of surfaces.

Consider the surfaces of Fig. 8.1.

If dn denotes the distance along the normal from the point p to the surface S_2, we may write

$$(8.8) \qquad\qquad dn = \mathbf{n} \cdot d\mathbf{r}$$

where $\mathbf{n}$ is the unit normal to the surface S_1 at p.

We have

$$(8.9) \qquad d\phi = \frac{\partial \phi}{\partial n}\, dn = \frac{\partial \phi}{\partial n}\, \mathbf{n} \cdot d\mathbf{r} = (\nabla \phi) \cdot d\mathbf{r}$$

and, in particular, if $d\mathbf{r}$ lies in the surface S_1, we have

$$(8.10) \qquad\qquad d\phi = (\nabla \phi) \cdot d\mathbf{r} = 0$$

showing that the vector $\nabla \phi$ is normal to the surface $\phi = \text{const.}$ Since the vector $d\mathbf{r}$ is arbitrary, we have from (8.9)

$$(8.11) \qquad\qquad \nabla \phi = \left(\frac{\partial \phi}{\partial n}\right) \mathbf{n}$$

FIG. 8.1

Hence $\nabla \phi$ is a vector whose magnitude is equal to the maximum rate of change of ϕ with respect to the space variables and has the direction of that change.

9. The Divergence and Gauss's Theorem. The scalar product of the vector operator ∇ and a vector $\mathbf{A}$ gives a scalar that is called the divergence of $\mathbf{A}$; that is,

$$(9.1) \qquad \nabla \cdot \mathbf{A} = \frac{\partial A_x}{\partial x} + \frac{\partial A_y}{\partial y} + \frac{\partial A_z}{\partial z} = \text{div } \mathbf{A}$$

This quantity has an important application in hydrodynamics. Consider a fluid of density $\rho(x,y,z,t)$ and velocity $\mathbf{v} = \mathbf{v}(x,y,z,t)$, and let

$$(9.2) \qquad\qquad \mathbf{V} = \mathbf{v}\rho$$

If $\mathbf{S}$ is the representative vector of the area of a plane surface, then $\mathbf{V} \cdot \mathbf{S}$ is the mass of fluid flowing through the surface S in a unit time.

Consider a small fixed rectangular parallelepiped of dimensions dx, dy, dz as shown in Fig. 9.1.

The mass of fluid flowing in through face F_1 per unit time is

$$(9.3) \qquad\qquad V_y\, dx\, dz = (\rho v)_y\, dx\, dz$$

and that flowing out through face F_2 is

$$(9.4) \qquad V_{y+dy}\, dx\, dz = \left(V_y + \frac{\partial V_y}{\partial y}\, dy\right) dx\, dz$$

Hence the net increase of mass of fluid inside the parallelepiped per unit time is

$$(9.5) \qquad V_y \, dx \, dz - \left(V_y + \frac{\partial V_y}{\partial y} \, dy \right) dx \, dz = - \frac{\partial V_y}{\partial y} \, dx \, dz \, dy$$

Considering the net increase of mass of fluid per unit time entering through the other two pairs of faces, we obtain

$$(9.6) \qquad - \left(\frac{\partial V_x}{\partial x} + \frac{\partial V_y}{\partial y} + \frac{\partial V_z}{\partial z} \right) dx \, dy \, dz = -(\nabla \cdot \mathbf{V}) \, dx \, dy \, dz$$

as the total increase in mass in the parallelepiped per unit time.

FIG. 9.1

But by the principle of conservation of matter, this must be equal to the time rate of increase of density multiplied by the volume of the parallelepiped.   Hence

$$(9.7) \qquad -(\nabla \cdot \mathbf{V}) \, dx \, dy \, dz = \left(\frac{\partial \rho}{\partial t} \right) dx \, dy \, dz$$

or

$$(9.8) \qquad \nabla \cdot \mathbf{V} = - \frac{\partial \rho}{\partial t}$$

This is known in hydrodynamics as the *equation of continuity*.   If the fluid is incompressible, then

$$(9.9) \qquad \nabla \cdot \mathbf{V} = - \frac{\partial \rho}{\partial t} = 0$$

The name *divergence* originated in this interpretation of $\nabla \cdot \mathbf{V}$.   For since $-\nabla \cdot \mathbf{V}$ represents the excess of the inward over the outward flow, or the convergence of the fluid, so $\nabla \cdot \mathbf{V}$ represents the excess of the outward over the inward flow, or the divergence of the fluid.

Surface Integral.   Consider a surface s as shown in Fig. 9.2.

Divide the surface into the representative vectors $d\mathbf{s}_1, d\mathbf{s}_2, \ldots$, etc. Let $\mathbf{V}_1$ be the value of the vector function of position $\mathbf{V}_i(x,y,z)$ at $d\mathbf{s}_i$.

Then

(9.10)
$$\lim_{\substack{\Delta s_i \to 0 \\ n \to \infty}} \sum_{i=1}^{n} \mathbf{V}_i \cdot d\mathbf{s}_i = \int_s\!\!\int \mathbf{V} \cdot d\mathbf{s}$$

is known as the *surface integral* of $\mathbf{V}$ over the surface s. The sign of the integral depends on which face of the surface is taken as positive. If the surface is closed, the outward normal is taken as positive.

Since

(9.11)
$$d\mathbf{s} = \mathbf{i}\, ds_x + \mathbf{j}\, ds_y + \mathbf{k}\, ds_z$$

we have

(9.12)
$$\int_s\!\!\int \mathbf{V} \cdot d\mathbf{s} = \int\!\!\int (V_x\, ds_x + V_y\, ds_y + V_z\, ds_z)$$

The surface integral of a vector $\mathbf{V}$ is called the flux of $\mathbf{V}$ throughout the surface.

Gauss's Theorem. This is one of the most important theorems of vector analysis. It states that the volume integral of the divergence of a vector

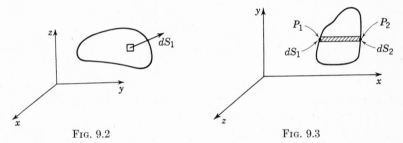

Fig. 9.2 Fig. 9.3

field $\mathbf{A}$ taken over any volume V is equal to the surface integral of $\mathbf{A}$ taken over the closed surface surrounding the volume V; that is,

(9.13)
$$\iiint_v (\nabla \cdot \mathbf{A})\, dv = \int_s\!\!\int \mathbf{A} \cdot d\mathbf{s}$$

To prove Gauss's theorem, let us expand the left-hand side of Eq. (9.13). We then have

(9.14)
$$\iiint (\nabla \cdot \mathbf{A})\, dv = \iiint_v \left(\frac{\partial A_x}{\partial x} + \frac{\partial A_y}{\partial y} + \frac{\partial A_z}{\partial z} \right) dx\, dy\, dz$$
$$= \iiint_v \frac{\partial A_x}{\partial x} dx\, dy\, dz + \iiint_v \frac{\partial A_y}{\partial y} dx\, dy\, dz + \iiint_v \frac{\partial A_z}{\partial z} dx\, dy\, dz$$

Let us consider the first integral on the right. Integrate with respect to x, that is, along a strip of cross section $dy\, dz$ extending from P_1 to P_2 of Fig. 9.3. We thus obtain

(9.15)
$$\iiint_v \frac{\partial A_x}{\partial x} dx\, dy\, dz = \int\!\!\int [A_x(x_2,y,z) - A_x(x_1,y,z)]\, dy\, dz$$

Here (x_1, y, z) are the coordinates of P_1, and (x_2, y, z) are the coordinates of P_2. Now at P_1 we have

$$(9.16) \qquad\qquad dy\, dz = -ds_x$$

At P_2 we have

$$(9.17) \qquad\qquad dy\, dz = ds_x$$

Therefore

$$(9.18) \qquad\qquad \iiint_v \frac{\partial A_x}{\partial x}\, dx\, dy\, dz = \iint_s A_x\, ds_x$$

where the surface integral on the right is evaluated over the entire surface. In the same manner we obtain

$$(9.19) \qquad\qquad \iiint_v \frac{\partial A_y}{\partial y}\, dx\, dy\, dz = \iint_s A_y\, ds_y$$

$$(9.20) \qquad\qquad \iiint_v \frac{\partial A_z}{\partial z}\, dx\, dy\, dz = \iint_s A_z\, ds_z$$

If we now add (9.18), (9.19), and (9.20), we obtain Gauss's theorem:

$$(9.21) \qquad \iiint_v (\nabla \cdot \mathbf{A})\, dv = \iint_s (A_x\, ds_x + A_y\, ds_y + A_z\, ds_z)$$
$$= \iint_s \mathbf{A} \cdot d\mathbf{s}$$

Green's Theorem. By the use of Gauss's theorem we are able to make some important transformations. Consider

$$(9.22) \qquad\qquad \mathbf{A} = u\, \nabla w$$

that is, let the vector field $\mathbf{A}$ be the product of a scalar function u and the gradient of another scalar function w. Consider

$$(9.23) \quad \nabla \cdot \mathbf{A} = \frac{\partial A_x}{\partial x} + \frac{\partial A_y}{\partial y} + \frac{\partial A_z}{\partial z} = \frac{\partial}{\partial x}\left(u\,\frac{\partial w}{\partial x}\right) + \frac{\partial}{\partial y}\left(u\,\frac{\partial w}{\partial y}\right)$$
$$+ \frac{\partial}{\partial z}\left(u\,\frac{\partial w}{\partial z}\right)$$
$$= u\left(\frac{\partial^2 w}{\partial x^2} + \frac{\partial^2 w}{\partial y^2} + \frac{\partial^2 w}{\partial z^2}\right) + \frac{\partial u}{\partial x}\frac{\partial w}{\partial x} + \frac{\partial u}{\partial y}\frac{\partial w}{\partial y} + \frac{\partial u}{\partial z}\frac{\partial w}{\partial z}$$
$$= u\, \nabla^2 w + \nabla u \cdot \nabla w$$

If we place this value of $\nabla \cdot \mathbf{A}$ in the left-hand side of Gauss's theorem (9.21), we obtain

$$(9.24) \qquad \iiint_v (u\, \nabla^2 w + \nabla u \cdot \nabla w)\, dv = \iint_s (u\, \nabla w) \cdot d\mathbf{s}$$

This transformation is referred to as the *first form of Green's theorem.*

In (9.24) if we interchange the functions u and w, we obtain

$$(9.25) \qquad \iiint_v (w \, \nabla^2 u + \nabla u \cdot \nabla w) \, dv = \iint_s (w \, \nabla u) \cdot d\mathbf{s}$$

If we now subtract Eq. (9.25) from Eq. (9.24), we obtain

$$(9.26) \qquad \iiint_v (u \, \nabla^2 w - w \, \nabla^2 u) \, dv = \iint_s (u \, \nabla w - w \, \nabla u) \cdot d\mathbf{s}$$

This transformation is referred to as the *second form of Green's theorem.* The transformations (9.24) and (9.26) are of extreme importance in the fields of electrodynamics and ~~hydrodynamics~~.

FIG. 10.1

10. The Curl of a Vector Field and Stokes's Theorem. *The Line Integral.* Let $\mathbf{A}$ be a vector field in space and AB (Fig. 10.1) a curve described in the sense A to B. Let the continuous curve AB be subdivided into infinitesimal vector elements $d\mathbf{l}_1, d\mathbf{l}_2, \ldots, d\mathbf{l}_n$. Take the scalar products $\mathbf{A}_1 \cdot d\mathbf{l}_1, \mathbf{A}_2 \cdot d\mathbf{l}_2, \ldots, \mathbf{A}_n \cdot d\mathbf{l}_n$, where $\mathbf{A}_1, \mathbf{A}_2, \ldots, \mathbf{A}_n$ are the values that the vector field $\mathbf{A}$ takes at the junction points of the vectors $d\mathbf{l}_1, d\mathbf{l}_2, \ldots, d\mathbf{l}_n$. The sum of these scalar products, that is,

$$(10.1) \qquad \sum_A^B \mathbf{A}_r \cdot d\mathbf{l}_r = \int_A^B \mathbf{A} \cdot d\mathbf{l}$$

summed up along the entire length of the curve, is known as the *line integral* of $\mathbf{A}$ along the curve AB. It is obvious that the line integral from B to A is the negative of that from A to B.

In terms of cartesian components we can write

$$(10.2) \qquad \int_A^B \mathbf{A} \cdot d\mathbf{l} = \int_A^B (A_x \, dx + A_y \, dy + A_z \, dz)$$

If $\mathbf{F}$ represents the force on a moving particle, then the line integral of $\mathbf{F}$ over the path described by the particle is the work done by the force.

Let $\mathbf{A}$ be the gradient $\nabla\phi$ of a scalar function of position; that is,

$$(10.3) \qquad \mathbf{A} = \nabla\phi$$

Then

$$(10.4) \qquad \int_A^B \mathbf{A} \cdot d\mathbf{l} = \int_A^B (\nabla\phi) \cdot d\mathbf{l} = \int_A^B \left(\frac{\partial\phi}{\partial x} \, dx + \frac{\partial\phi}{\partial y} \, dy + \frac{\partial\phi}{\partial z} \, dz \right)$$

But we have

$$(10.5) \qquad \frac{\partial\phi}{\partial x} \, dx + \frac{\partial\phi}{\partial y} \, dy + \frac{\partial\phi}{\partial z} \, dz = d\phi$$

the total differential of ϕ. We thus have

(10.6) $$\int_A^B \mathbf{A} \cdot d\mathbf{l} = \int_A^B d\phi = \phi_B - \phi_A$$

where ϕ_B and ϕ_A are the values of ϕ at the points B and A, respectively. It follows from this that the line integral of the gradient of any scalar function of position ϕ around a closed curve vanishes, because if the curve is closed, the points A and B are coincident and the line integral is equal to $\phi_A - \phi_A$, which is zero. The line integral around a closed curve is denoted by an integral sign with a circle around it, as follows:

FIG. 10.2

$$\oint \mathbf{A} \cdot d\mathbf{l}$$

Let us suppose that the line integral of $\mathbf{A}$ vanishes about *every* closed path in space. If we denote the path of integration by a subscript under the integral sign (Fig. 10.2),

(10.7) $$\int_{ACB} \mathbf{A} \cdot d\mathbf{l} - \int_{ADB} \mathbf{A} \cdot d\mathbf{l} = \int_{ACB} \mathbf{A} \cdot d\mathbf{l} + \int_{BDA} \mathbf{A} \cdot d\mathbf{l} = 0$$

and therefore

(10.8) $$\int_{ACB} \mathbf{A} \cdot d\mathbf{l} = \int_{ADB} \mathbf{A} \cdot d\mathbf{l}$$

This shows that the line integral of $\mathbf{A}$ from A to B is independent of the path followed. It is apparent, therefore, that it can depend only upon the initial point A and the final point B of the path, that is,

(10.9) $$\int_A^B \mathbf{A} \cdot d\mathbf{l} = \phi_B - \phi_A$$

Now if we take the two points A and B very close together, we have

(10.10) $$\mathbf{A} \cdot d\mathbf{l} = d\phi = (\nabla \phi) \cdot d\mathbf{l}$$

or

(10.11) $$(A - \nabla \phi) \cdot d\mathbf{l} = 0$$

As this is true for all directions, the vector $\mathbf{A} - \nabla \phi$ can have no component in any direction, and hence it must vanish. Therefore

(10.12) $$\mathbf{A} = \nabla \phi$$

That is, if the line integral of $\mathbf{A}$ vanishes about every closed path, $\mathbf{A}$ must be the gradient of some scalar function ϕ.

The Curl of a Vector Field. If $\mathbf{A}$ is a vector field, the curl, or rotation, of $\mathbf{A}$ is defined as the vector function of space obtained by taking the vector product of the operator ∇ and $\mathbf{A}$. That is,

(10.13)   curl $\mathbf{A} = \nabla \times \mathbf{A}$

$$= i\left(\frac{\partial A_z}{\partial y} - \frac{\partial A_y}{\partial z}\right) + j\left(\frac{\partial A_x}{\partial z} - \frac{\partial A_z}{\partial x}\right) + k\left(\frac{\partial A_y}{\partial x} - \frac{\partial A_x}{\partial y}\right)$$

This may be written conveniently in the following determinantal form:

(10.14)
$$\nabla \times \mathbf{A} = \begin{vmatrix} i & j & k \\ \dfrac{\partial}{\partial x} & \dfrac{\partial}{\partial y} & \dfrac{\partial}{\partial z} \\ A_x & A_y & A_z \end{vmatrix}$$

If $\mathbf{A} = \nabla\phi$,

(10.15) $\nabla \times \mathbf{A} = \nabla \times (\nabla\phi) = i\left(\dfrac{\partial^2\phi}{\partial y\,\partial z} - \dfrac{\partial^2\phi}{\partial z\,\partial y}\right)$

$$+ j\left(\frac{\partial^2\phi}{\partial z\,\partial x} - \frac{\partial^2\phi}{\partial x\,\partial z}\right) + k\left(\frac{\partial^2\phi}{\partial x\,\partial y} - \frac{\partial^2\phi}{\partial y\,\partial x}\right) = 0$$

It thus follows that if $\mathbf{A}$ is the gradient of a scalar the curl of $\mathbf{A}$ vanishes.

Line Integral in a Plane.   To show the connection between the line integral and the curl of a vector field, let us compute the line integral of a vector field $\mathbf{A}$ around an infinitesimal rectangle of side Δx and Δy lying in the xy plane as shown in Fig. 10.3.   That is, we shall compute

Fig. 10.3

$\oint \mathbf{A} \cdot d\mathbf{l}$ around this rectangle.   We may write down the various contributions to this integral as follows:

Along AB: $A_x\,\Delta x$

Along BC: $\left(A_y + \dfrac{\partial A_y}{\partial x}\,\Delta x\right)\Delta y$

Along CD: $-\left(A_x + \dfrac{\partial A_x}{\partial y}\,\Delta y\right)\Delta x$

Along DA: $-A_y\,\Delta y$

where we have made use of the fact that Δx and Δy are infinitesimals. Adding the various contributions, we obtain

(10.16) $\displaystyle\oint_{ABCD} \mathbf{A} \cdot d\mathbf{l} = \left(\frac{\partial A_y}{\partial x} - \frac{\partial A_x}{\partial y}\right)\Delta x\,\Delta y$

In view of (10.13), this may be written in the form

(10.17) $\displaystyle\oint_{ABCD} \mathbf{A} \cdot d\mathbf{l} = (\nabla \times \mathbf{A})_z\, ds_{xy}$

where $\nabla \times \mathbf{A}_z$ is the z component of the curl of $\mathbf{A}$ and ds_{xy} is the area of the rectangle $ABCD$.

Consider now a closed curve in the xy plane as shown in Fig. 10.4.

Divide the space inside C by a network of lines joining a network of infinitesimal rectangles.

If we take the sum of the line integrals around the various meshes, we obtain

FIG. 10.4

$$(10.18) \qquad \sum_{r=1}^{\infty} \oint_r \mathbf{A} \cdot d\mathbf{l} = \sum_{r=1}^{\infty} (\nabla \times \mathbf{A})_z \, ds_{xy}$$

Now it is easily seen that the contributions to the line integrals of adjoining meshes neutralize each other because they are traversed in opposite directions; the only contributions which are not neutralized are those on the periphery of the surface. Hence

$$(10.19) \qquad \sum_{r=1}^{\infty} \oint_r \mathbf{A} \cdot d\mathbf{l} = \oint_C \mathbf{A} \cdot d\mathbf{l}$$

where the line integral on the right is taken along the boundary curve C in the positive sense.

Now the sum on the right of (10.18) reduces to the following integral:

$$(10.20) \qquad \sum (\nabla \times \mathbf{A})_z \, ds_{xy} = \int_s \int (\nabla \times \mathbf{A})_z \, ds_{xy}$$

Hence, substituting this into (10.18), we obtain

$$(10.21) \qquad \oint_C \mathbf{A} \cdot d\mathbf{l} = \int_s \int (\nabla \times \mathbf{A})_z \, ds_{xy}$$

FIG. 10.5

That is, the line integral of a vector field $\mathbf{A}$ about the contour C of a plane surface S is equal to the surface integral of the normal component of the curl of $\mathbf{A}$ to the surface throughout the surface s.

Consider now the triangular surface of Fig. 10.5.

It is easy to see that

$$(10.22) \qquad \oint_{ABC} \mathbf{A} \cdot d\mathbf{l} = \oint_{OBC} \mathbf{A} \cdot d\mathbf{l} + \oint_{OCA} \mathbf{A} \cdot d\mathbf{l} + \oint_{OAB} \mathbf{A} \cdot d\mathbf{l}$$

since the contribution along the lines OA, OB, and OC cancel each other. However, as a consequence of (10.21), we have

$$(10.23) \qquad \begin{aligned} \int_{OBC} \mathbf{A} \cdot d\mathbf{l} &= \int_{OBC} \int (\nabla \times \mathbf{A})_x \, dy \, dz \\ \int_{OCA} \mathbf{A} \cdot d\mathbf{l} &= \int_{OCA} \int (\nabla \times \mathbf{A})_y \, dz \, dx \\ \int_{OAB} \mathbf{A} \cdot d\mathbf{l} &= \int_{OAB} \int (\nabla \times \mathbf{A})_z \, dx \, dy \end{aligned}$$

If we add these equations and make use of (10.22), we obtain

$$(10.24) \quad \oint_{ABC} \mathbf{A} \cdot d\mathbf{l} = \int_{OBC}\!\!\int (\nabla \times \mathbf{A})_x \, dy \, dz$$
$$+ \int_{OCA}\!\!\int (\nabla \times \mathbf{A})_y \, dz \, dx + \int_{OAB}\!\!\int (\nabla \times \mathbf{A})_z \, dx \, dy$$

Now we may write

$$(10.25) \qquad ds = \mathbf{i} \, ds_x + \mathbf{j} \, ds_y + \mathbf{k} \, ds_z$$
$$= \mathbf{i} \, dy \, dz + \mathbf{j} \, dx \, dz + \mathbf{k} \, dx \, dy$$

for the projections of the representative surface vector **s** of the plane ABC to the yz, xz, and xy planes.

Using this notation, (10.24) becomes

$$(10.26) \qquad \oint_{ABC} \mathbf{A} \cdot d\mathbf{l} = \int_{ABC}\!\!\int (\nabla \times \mathbf{A}) \cdot ds$$

Consider now the open surface of Fig. 10.6.

We can regard the surface s of this open surface as being made up of an infinite number of elementary triangular surfaces. If we label r the typical triangle, we have from (10.26)

$$(10.27) \quad \sum_r \oint_r \mathbf{A} \cdot d\mathbf{l} = \sum_r \int_r\!\!\int (\nabla \times \mathbf{A}) \cdot ds$$

Now the sum of the line integrals of the ele-
mentary triangles reduces to a line integration about the periphery C of the closed surface S since

Fig. 10.6

the line integrations along adjacent triangles are described in opposite senses and hence cancel. We therefore have

$$(10.28) \qquad \sum_r \oint_r \mathbf{A} \cdot d\mathbf{l} = \int_s\!\!\int \mathbf{A} \cdot d\mathbf{l}$$

In the limit the summation on the right of (10.27) reduces to an integral, and we have

$$(10.29) \qquad \sum_r \oint_r (\nabla \times \mathbf{A}) \cdot ds = \int_s\!\!\int (\nabla \times \mathbf{A}) \cdot ds$$

As a consequence of (10.19), we then have

$$(10.30) \qquad \oint_C \mathbf{A} \cdot d\mathbf{l} = \int_s\!\!\int (\nabla \times \mathbf{A}) \cdot ds$$

This relation is known as *Stokes's theorem*. It states that the surface integral of the curl of a vector field **A** taken over any surface S is equal to the line integral of **A** around the periphery of the surface.

If the surface to which Stokes's theorem is applied is a closed surface, the length of the periphery is zero and then

(10.31)
$$\oint_s (\nabla \times \mathbf{A}) \cdot d\mathbf{s} = 0$$

By the use of Stokes's theorem we see that, if $\nabla \times \mathbf{A} = 0$ everywhere, $\mathbf{A}$ is the gradient of a scalar function, because if $\nabla \times \mathbf{A} = 0$, then the line integral of $\mathbf{A}$ around any closed curve vanishes. This is just the condition that $\mathbf{A}$ should be the gradient of a scalar function.

11. Successive Applications of the Operator ∇. It frequently happens in various applications of vector analysis that we must operate successively with the operator ∇. For example, since the curl of a vector field $\mathbf{A}$, $\nabla \times \mathbf{A}$, is a vector field $\mathbf{B}$, it is possible to take the curl of $\mathbf{B}$, that is,

(11.1)
$$\nabla \times \mathbf{B} = \nabla \times (\nabla \times \mathbf{A})$$

If we expand this equation in terms of the cartesian coordinates of $\mathbf{A}$, we obtain

(11.2)
$$\nabla \times (\nabla \times \mathbf{A}) = i\left[\frac{\partial}{\partial x}\left(\frac{\partial A_y}{\partial y} - \frac{\partial A_x}{\partial y} \right) - \frac{\partial}{\partial z}\left(\frac{\partial A_x}{\partial z} - \frac{\partial A_z}{\partial x} \right) \right] +, \text{etc.}$$

$$= i\left(\frac{\partial^2 A_y}{\partial y\,\partial x} + \frac{\partial^2 A_z}{\partial z\,\partial x} - \frac{\partial^2 A_x}{\partial y^2} - \frac{\partial^2 A_x}{\partial z^2} \right) +, \text{etc.}$$

$$= i\left[\frac{\partial}{\partial x}\left(\frac{\partial A_x}{\partial x} + \frac{\partial A_y}{\partial y} + \frac{\partial A_z}{\partial z} \right) \right.$$
$$\left. - \left(\frac{\partial^2}{\partial x^2} + \frac{\partial^2}{\partial y^2} + \frac{\partial^2}{\partial y^2} \right) A_x \right] +, \text{etc.}$$

$$= \nabla(\nabla \cdot \mathbf{A}) - \nabla^2 \mathbf{A}$$

In the same manner the following vector identities may be established by expanding ∇ and the other vectors concerned in terms of their components:

(11.3) $\nabla \cdot (u\mathbf{A}) = u(\nabla \cdot \mathbf{A}) + \mathbf{A} \cdot (\nabla u)$

(11.4) $\nabla \times (u\mathbf{A}) = u(\nabla \times \mathbf{A}) + (\nabla u) \times \mathbf{A}$

(11.5) $\nabla \cdot (\mathbf{A} \times \mathbf{B}) = \mathbf{B} \cdot (\nabla \times \mathbf{A}) - \mathbf{A} \cdot (\nabla \times \mathbf{B})$

(11.6) $\nabla(\mathbf{A} \cdot \mathbf{B}) = \mathbf{A} \times (\nabla \times \mathbf{B}) + (\mathbf{A} \cdot \nabla)\mathbf{B} + \mathbf{B} \times (\nabla \times \mathbf{A}) + (\mathbf{B} \cdot \nabla)\mathbf{A}$

(11.7) $\nabla \times (\mathbf{A} \times \mathbf{B}) = (\mathbf{B} \cdot \nabla)\mathbf{A} - (\mathbf{A} \cdot \nabla)\mathbf{B} - \mathbf{B}(\nabla \cdot \mathbf{A}) + \mathbf{A}(\nabla \cdot \mathbf{B})$

(11.8) $\nabla \times (\nabla u) = 0$

(11.9) $\nabla \cdot (\nabla \times \mathbf{A}) = 0$

In the above set of equations the symbol $(\mathbf{A} \cdot \nabla)\mathbf{B}$ stands for the vector

(11.10)
$$(\mathbf{A} \cdot \nabla)\mathbf{B} = i\left(A_x \frac{\partial B_x}{\partial x} + A_y \frac{\partial B_x}{\partial y} + A_z \frac{\partial B_x}{\partial z} \right)$$
$$+ j\left(A_x \frac{\partial B_y}{\partial x} + A_y \frac{\partial B_y}{\partial y} + A_z \frac{\partial B_y}{\partial z} \right)$$
$$+ k\left(A_x \frac{\partial B_z}{\partial x} + A_y \frac{\partial y}{\partial B_z} + A_z \frac{\partial B_z}{\partial z} \right)$$

The above formulas are very useful in applications of vector analysis to various branches of engineering and physics.

12. Orthogonal Curvilinear Coordinates. Many calculations in applied mathematics can be simplified by choosing instead of a cartesian coordinate system another kind of system that takes advantage of the relations of symmetry involved in the particular problem under consideration.

Let these new coordinates be denoted by u_1, u_2, u_3. These are defined by specifying the cartesian coordinates x, y, z as functions of u_1, u_2, u_3, as follows:

(12.1)
$$x = x(u_1, u_2, u_3)$$
$$y = y(u_1, u_2, u_3)$$
$$z = z(u_1, u_2, u_3)$$

We shall confine ourselves to the case when the three families of surfaces $u_1 = $ const, $u_2 = $ const, $u_3 = $ const are orthogonal to one another. In this case the line element ds is given by

(12.2) $$ds^2 = h_1^2\, du_1^2 + h_2^2\, du_2^2 + h_3^2\, du_3^2$$

where h_1, h_2, h_3 may be functions of u_1, u_2, u_3. We shall also adopt the convention that the new coordinate system shall be right-handed like the old.

Consider now the infinitesimal parallelepiped whose diagonal is the line element ds and whose faces coincide with the planes u_1 or u_2 or $u_3 = $ const (see Fig. 12.1).

FIG. 12.1

The lengths of its edges are $h_1\, du_1$, $h_2\, du_2$, $h_3\, du_3$, and its volume is $h_1 h_2 h_3\, du_1\, du_2\, du_3$. Furthermore let $\phi(u_1, u_2, u_3)$ be a scalar function and $\mathbf{A}$ be a vector field with components A_1, A_2, A_3 in the three directions in which the coordinates u_1, u_2, u_3 increase. The u_1 component of the gradient of ϕ we can compute at once since by definition

(12.3)
$$(\text{grad } \phi)_1 = \lim_{du_1 \to 0} \frac{\phi(A) - \phi(O)}{h_1\, du_1}$$
$$= \frac{1}{h_1} \frac{\partial \phi}{\partial u_1}$$

We also have similar relations for the directions 2 and 3.

In order to calculate the divergence of a vector field $\mathbf{A}$, we use Gauss's theorem,

(12.4) $$\iiint (\nabla \cdot \mathbf{A})\, dV = \int_s \int \mathbf{A} \cdot d\mathbf{s}$$

The contribution to the integral $\iint \mathbf{A} \cdot d\mathbf{s}$ through the area $OBHC$, taken in the direction of the outward normal, is $-A_1 h_2 h_3 \, du_2 \, du_3$, while that through the area $AFGJ$ is

$$A_1 h_2 h_3 \, du_2 \, du_3 + \frac{\partial}{\partial u_1} (A_1 h_2 h_3) \, du_1 \, du_2 \, du_3$$

From these and the corresponding expressions for the other two pairs of surfaces, we have by (12.4)

$$(12.5) \qquad \lim_{V \to 0} \iiint (\nabla \cdot \mathbf{A}) \, dv = (\nabla \cdot \mathbf{A}) h_1 h_2 h_3 \, du_1 \, du_2 \, du_3$$

$$= \iint \mathbf{A} \cdot d\mathbf{s}$$

We thus obtain

$$(12.6) \quad \nabla \cdot \mathbf{A} = \frac{1}{h_1 h_2 h_3} \left[\frac{\partial}{\partial u_1} (h_2 h_3 A_1) + \frac{\partial}{\partial u_2} (h_3 h_1 A_2) + \frac{\partial}{\partial u_3} (h_1 h_2 A_3) \right]$$

If $\mathbf{A} = \nabla \phi$,

$$(12.7) \quad \nabla^2 \phi = \frac{1}{h_1 h_2 h_3} \left[\frac{\partial}{\partial u_1} \left(\frac{h_2 h_3}{h_1} \frac{\partial \phi}{\partial u_1} \right) + \frac{\partial}{\partial u_2} \left(\frac{h_3 h_1}{h_2} \frac{\partial \phi}{\partial u_2} \right) + \frac{\partial}{\partial u_3} \left(\frac{h_1 h_2}{h_3} \frac{\partial \phi}{\partial u_3} \right) \right]$$

The components of the curl of $\mathbf{A}$ may be found by Stokes's theorem,

$$(12.8) \qquad \int_s \int (\nabla \times \mathbf{A}) \cdot d\mathbf{s} = \oint \mathbf{A} \cdot d\mathbf{l}$$

For example, the component 1 of the curl of $\mathbf{A}$ is obtained by applying Stokes's theorem to the surface $OBHC$. We calculate

$$(12.9) \quad \oint_{OBHC} \mathbf{A} \cdot d\mathbf{l} = \int_O^B \mathbf{A} \cdot d\mathbf{l} + \int_B^H \mathbf{A} \cdot d\mathbf{l} + \int_H^C \mathbf{A} \cdot d\mathbf{l} + \int_C^O \mathbf{A} \cdot d\mathbf{l}$$

$$= A_2 h_2 \, du_2 + A_3 h_3 \, du_3 + \frac{\partial}{\partial u_2} (A_3 h_3) \, du_3 \, du_2$$

$$- \left[A_2 h_2 \, du_2 + \frac{\partial}{\partial u_3} (A_2 h_2) \, du_2 \, du_3 \right] - A_3 h_3 \, du_3$$

$$= \left[\frac{\partial}{\partial u_2} (A_3 h_3) - \frac{\partial}{\partial u_3} (A_2 h_2) \right] du_2 \, du_3$$

By Stokes's theorem this equals the 1 component of the curl of $\mathbf{A}$, $(\nabla \times \mathbf{A})_1$, multiplied by the area of the face $OBHC$. That is,

$$(12.10) \quad (\nabla \times \mathbf{A})_1 h_2 h_3 \, du_2 \, du_3 = \left[\frac{\partial}{\partial u_2} (A_3 h_3) - \frac{\partial}{\partial u_3} (A_2 h_2) \right] du_2 \, du_3$$

Hence

$$(12.11) \qquad (\nabla \times \mathbf{A})_1 = \frac{1}{h_2 h_3} \left[\frac{\partial}{\partial u_2} (A_3 h_3) - \frac{\partial}{\partial u_3} (A_2 h_2) \right]$$

By a cyclic change of the indices we obtain

$$(12.12) \qquad (\nabla \times \mathbf{A})_2 = \frac{1}{h_3 h_1} \left[\frac{\partial}{\partial u_3} (h_1 A_1) - \frac{\partial}{\partial u_1} (h_3 A_3) \right]$$

$$(12.13) \qquad (\nabla \times \mathbf{A})_3 = \frac{1}{h_1 h_2} \left[\frac{\partial}{\partial u_1} (h_2 A_2) - \frac{\partial}{\partial u_2} (h_1 A_1) \right]$$

If we introduce unit vectors i_1, i_2, i_3 along the directions 1, 2, and 3, we may write symbolically

$$(12.14) \qquad \nabla \times \mathbf{A} = \frac{1}{h_1 h_2 h_3} \begin{vmatrix} h_1 i_1 & h_2 i_2 & h_3 i_3 \\ \dfrac{\partial}{\partial u_1} & \dfrac{\partial}{\partial u_2} & \dfrac{\partial}{\partial u_3} \\ h_1 A_1 & h_2 A_2 & h_3 A_3 \end{vmatrix}$$

FIG. 12.2

In the case of cartesian coordinates we have $u_1 = x$, $u_2 = y$, $u_3 = z$, $h_1 = h_2 = h_3 = 1$, and $i_1 = i$, $i_2 = j$, $i_3 = k$. In this case (12.14) reduces to (10.14).

We shall now apply these general formulas to two special cases that are particularly important in applications.

a. Cylindrical Coordinates. The position of a point in space may be determined by the cylindrical coordinate system of Fig. 12.2.

In this case we have

$$(12.15) \qquad \begin{aligned} x &= r \cos \theta \\ y &= r \sin \theta \\ z &= z \end{aligned}$$

$$(12.16) \qquad ds^2 = dr^2 + r^2 \, d\theta^2 + dz^2$$

We have, therefore, in this case,

$$(12.17) \qquad \begin{aligned} u_1 &= r \\ u_2 &= \theta \\ u_3 &= z \end{aligned} \quad \text{and} \quad \begin{aligned} h_1 &= 1 \\ h_2 &= r \\ h_3 &= 1 \end{aligned}$$

By (12.3) we obtain

$$(12.18) \qquad \operatorname{grad}_r \phi = \frac{\partial \phi}{\partial r} \qquad \operatorname{grad}_\theta \phi = \frac{1}{r} \frac{\partial \phi}{\partial \theta} \qquad \operatorname{grad}_z \phi = \frac{\partial \phi}{\partial z}$$

By (12.6) we have

$$(12.19) \qquad \nabla \cdot \mathbf{A} = \frac{1}{r} \frac{\partial}{\partial r} (r A_r) + \frac{1}{r} \frac{\partial A_\theta}{\partial \theta} + \frac{\partial A_z}{\partial z}$$

The Laplacian operator as given by (12.7) gives

$$(12.20) \qquad \nabla^2 \phi = \frac{1}{r} \frac{\partial}{\partial r} \left(r \frac{\partial \phi}{\partial r} \right) + \frac{1}{r^2} \frac{\partial^2 \phi}{\partial \theta^2} + \frac{\partial^2 \phi}{\partial z^2}$$

We obtain the components of the curl of **A** by (12.11), (12.12), and (12.13):

FIG. 12.3

$$(12.21) \quad (\nabla \times \mathbf{A})_r = \frac{1}{r}\frac{\partial A_z}{\partial \theta} - \frac{\partial A_\theta}{\partial z}$$

$$(12.22) \quad (\nabla \times \mathbf{A})_\theta = \frac{\partial A_r}{\partial z} - \frac{\partial A_z}{\partial r}$$

$$(12.23) \quad (\nabla \times \mathbf{A})_z = \frac{1}{r}\left[\frac{\partial}{\partial r}(rA_\theta) - \frac{\partial A_r}{\partial \theta}\right]$$

b. Spherical Polar Coordinates. Another very important coordinate system is that of spherical polar coordinates as shown in Fig. 12.3.

In this case we have

$$(12.24) \quad \begin{aligned} x &= r\sin\theta\cos\phi \\ y &= r\sin\theta\sin\phi \\ z &= r\cos\theta \\ ds^2 &= dr^2 + r^2\sin^2\theta\,d\phi^2 + r^2\,d\theta^2 \end{aligned}$$

We have therefore

$$(12.25) \quad \begin{aligned} u_1 &= r \\ u_2 &= \theta \\ u_3 &= \phi \end{aligned} \quad \text{and} \quad \begin{aligned} h_1 &= 1 \\ h_2 &= r \\ h_3 &= r\sin\theta \end{aligned}$$

$$(12.26) \quad (\text{grad } V)_r = \frac{\partial V}{\partial r} \quad (\text{grad } V)_\theta = \frac{1}{r}\frac{\partial V}{\partial \theta} \quad (\text{grad } V)_\phi = \frac{1}{r\sin\theta}\frac{\partial V}{\partial \phi}$$

$$(12.27) \quad \nabla \cdot \mathbf{A} = \frac{1}{r^2}\frac{\partial}{\partial r}(r^2 A_r) + \frac{1}{r\sin\theta}\frac{\partial}{\partial \theta}(\sin\theta A_\theta) + \frac{1}{r\sin\theta}\frac{\partial A_\phi}{\partial \phi}$$

$$(12.28) \quad \nabla^2 V = \frac{1}{r^2}\frac{\partial}{\partial r}\left(r^2\frac{\partial V}{\partial r}\right) + \frac{1}{r^2\sin\theta}\frac{\partial}{\partial \theta}\left(\sin\theta\frac{\partial V}{\partial \theta}\right) + \frac{1}{r^2\sin^2\theta}\frac{\partial^2 V}{\partial \phi^2}$$

$$(12.29) \quad \begin{aligned} (\nabla \times \mathbf{A})_r &= \frac{1}{r\sin\theta}\left[\frac{\partial}{\partial \theta}(\sin\theta A_\phi) - \frac{\partial A_\theta}{\partial \phi}\right] \\ (\nabla \times \mathbf{A})_\theta &= \frac{1}{r}\left[\frac{1}{\sin\theta}\frac{\partial A_r}{\partial \phi} - \frac{\partial(rA_\phi)}{\partial r}\right] \\ (\nabla \times \mathbf{A})_\phi &= \frac{1}{r}\left[\frac{\partial}{\partial r}(rA_\theta) - \frac{\partial A_r}{\partial \theta}\right] \end{aligned}$$

13. Application to Hydrodynamics. Consider a region of space containing a fluid of density $\rho(x,y,z,t)$. Let V be the volume inside an arbitrary closed surface s located in this region. Let $Q(t)$ be the mass of fluid inside the volume V at any instant. Then

$$(13.1) \qquad Q(t) = \iiint_V \rho\,dV$$

If v denotes the velocity of a typical particle of the fluid, the rate at which the mass of fluid inside V is *increasing* is

$$(13.2) \qquad \frac{dQ}{dt} = - \iint_s (\rho \mathbf{v}) \cdot d\mathbf{s}$$

Now, if we differentiate (13.1) with respect to time and equate the result to (13.2), we have

$$(13.3) \qquad \frac{dQ}{dt} = \iiint_v \left(\frac{\partial \rho}{\partial t} \right) dV = - \iint_s (\rho \mathbf{v}) \cdot d\mathbf{s}$$

But, by Gauss's theorem, we have

$$(13.4) \qquad \iint (\rho \mathbf{v}) \cdot d\mathbf{s} = \iiint_v \nabla \cdot (\rho \mathbf{v}) \, dV$$

Substituting this into (13.3) and transposing, we obtain

$$(13.5) \qquad \iiint_V \left[\frac{\partial \rho}{\partial t} + \nabla \cdot (\rho \mathbf{v}) \right] dV = 0$$

Now since the integrand is continuous and the volume V is arbitrary, we conclude that

$$(13.6) \qquad \frac{\partial \rho}{\partial t} + \nabla \cdot (\rho \mathbf{v}) = 0$$

This is the basic equation of hydrodynamics and is known as the *equation of continuity*.

If the fluid is incompressible, then ρ is a constant and we have

$$(13.7) \qquad \frac{\partial \rho}{\partial t} = 0 = \rho (\nabla \cdot \mathbf{v})$$

If the flow is irrotational, then we have

$$(13.8) \qquad \nabla \times \mathbf{v} = 0$$

and we know from Sec. 10 that there exists a scalar function ϕ such that

$$(13.9) \qquad \mathbf{v} = \nabla \phi$$

If the fluid is incompressible, then from (13.7) we have

$$(13.10) \qquad \nabla \cdot \mathbf{v} = 0$$

and hence ϕ, called the *velocity potential*, satisfies the equation

$$(13.11) \qquad \nabla \cdot (\nabla \phi) = \nabla^2 \phi = 0$$

On a fixed boundary of the fluid, the velocity has no normal component, and if $\partial / \partial n$ denotes differentiation with respect to the normal direction of the boundary, we must have

$$(13.12) \qquad \frac{\partial \phi}{\partial n} = 0$$

as a consequence of (13.9).

Let us denote any general property of a particle of the fluid, such as its pressure, density, etc., by the function $H(x,y,z,t)$. Then by $\partial H/\partial t$ is meant the variation of H at a *particular point* in *space* as a function of the time t. If we take the total differential of $H(x,y,z,t)$, we obtain

$$(13.13) \qquad dH = \frac{\partial H}{\partial x} \, dx + \frac{\partial H}{\partial y} \, dy + \frac{\partial H}{\partial z} \, dz + \frac{\partial H}{\partial t} \, dt$$

$$(13.14) \qquad \frac{dH}{dt} = \frac{\partial H}{\partial x} \frac{dx}{dt} + \frac{\partial H}{\partial y} \frac{dy}{dt} + \frac{\partial H}{\partial z} \frac{dz}{dt} + \frac{\partial H}{\partial t}$$

The quantity dH/dt is the variation of H when we fix our attention *on the same particle of fluid.*

The velocity of the particle is given by

$$(13.15) \qquad \mathbf{v} = \mathbf{i} \frac{dx}{dt} + \mathbf{j} \frac{dy}{dt} + \mathbf{k} \frac{dz}{dt}$$

By definition we have

$$(13.16) \qquad \nabla H = \mathbf{i} \frac{\partial H}{\partial x} + \mathbf{j} \frac{\partial H}{\partial y} + \mathbf{k} \frac{\partial H}{\partial z}$$

Hence

$$(13.17) \qquad \mathbf{v} \cdot \nabla H = \frac{\partial H}{\partial x} \frac{dx}{dt} + \frac{\partial H}{\partial y} \frac{dy}{dt} + \frac{\partial H}{\partial z} \frac{dz}{dt}$$

$$(13.18) \qquad \frac{dH}{dt} = \frac{\partial H}{\partial t} + \mathbf{v} \cdot \nabla H$$

Euler's Equation of Motion. To obtain the equation of motion of a frictionless fluid, we consider the forces acting on an element of fluid whose volume is $dx \, dy \, dz$ and whose mass is $\rho \, dx \, dy \, dz$. As a consequence of the pressure of the fluid, p, there will be a force in the x direction on the element of fluid under consideration, of magnitude

$$(13.19) \qquad p \, dy \, dz - \left(p + \frac{\partial p}{\partial x} \, dx \right) dy \, dz = - \frac{\partial p}{\partial x} \, dx \, dy \, dz$$

Let us also consider the action of an external force $\mathbf{F}$ acting on unit *mass* of fluid. The external force acting on the element under consideration in the x direction is $F_x \rho \, dx \, dy \, dz$.

The acceleration of the element in the x direction is dv_x/dt. Hence, by Newton's second law of motion, we have

$$(13.20) \qquad F_x \rho \, dx \, dy \, dz - \frac{\partial p}{\partial x} \, dx \, dy \, dz = \frac{dv_x}{dt} \rho \, dx \, dy \, dz$$

By this reasoning, and considering the y and z directions, we obtain Euler's equations of motion,

(13.21)
$$\frac{dv_x}{dt} = F_x - \frac{1}{\rho}\frac{\partial p}{\partial x}$$
$$\frac{dv_y}{dt} = F_y - \frac{1}{\rho}\frac{\partial p}{\partial y}$$
$$\frac{dv_z}{dt} = F_z - \frac{1}{\rho}\frac{\partial p}{\partial z}$$

These three scalar equations may be combined into the single vector equation

(13.22)
$$\frac{d\mathbf{v}}{dt} = \mathbf{F} - \frac{1}{\rho}\nabla p$$

As a consequence of Eq. (13.18), we have

(13.23)
$$\frac{d\mathbf{v}}{dt} = \frac{\partial \mathbf{v}}{\partial t} + (\mathbf{v}\cdot\nabla)\mathbf{v}$$

Now by the vector identity (11.6), we have

(13.24)
$$(\mathbf{v}\cdot\nabla)\mathbf{v} = \tfrac{1}{2}\nabla v^2 + (\nabla\times\mathbf{v})\times\mathbf{v}$$

Hence, by the use of the two equations above, we may write Euler's equation of motion in the following form:

(13.25)
$$\frac{\partial \mathbf{v}}{\partial t} + \tfrac{1}{2}\nabla v^2 + (\nabla\times\mathbf{v})\times\mathbf{v} = \mathbf{F} - \frac{1}{\rho}\nabla p$$

If the external force is *conservative*, it has a potential V and we have

(13.26)
$$F = -\nabla V$$

If the motion of the fluid is *irrotational*, $\nabla\times\mathbf{v} = 0$ and $v = \nabla\phi$. In this case Eq. (13.25) becomes

(13.27)
$$\nabla\left(\frac{\partial\phi}{\partial t}\right) + \tfrac{1}{2}\nabla v^2 + \nabla V + \frac{1}{\rho}\nabla p = 0$$

or

(13.28)
$$\nabla w = 0$$

where

(13.29)
$$w = \frac{\partial\phi}{\partial t} + \frac{v^2}{2} + V + \frac{p}{\rho}$$

Now if $d\mathbf{r}$ denotes an *arbitrary* path in the fluid at any instant, we have

(13.30)
$$d\mathbf{r} = \mathbf{i}\,dx + \mathbf{j}\,dy + \mathbf{k}\,dz$$

Let us form the scalar product of ∇w and $d\mathbf{r}$. We then obtain

$$(13.30a) \quad \nabla w \cdot d\mathbf{r} = \left(\mathbf{i}\frac{\partial w}{\partial x} + \mathbf{j}\frac{\partial w}{\partial y} + \mathbf{k}\frac{\partial w}{\partial z} \right) (\mathbf{i}\, dx + \mathbf{j}\, dy + \mathbf{k}\, dz)$$

$$= \frac{\partial w}{\partial x}\, dx + \frac{\partial w}{\partial y}\, dy + \frac{\partial w}{\partial z}\, dz = dw = 0$$

as a consequence of Eq. (13.28).

Hence

$$(13.31) \qquad\qquad w = \beta(t)$$

where $\beta(t)$ is an arbitrary function of *time*, since we have integrated along an arbitrary path in the fluid at any instant. That is, we have

$$(13.32) \qquad\qquad w = \frac{\partial \phi}{\partial t} + \frac{v^2}{2} + \int \frac{dp}{\rho} = \beta(t)$$

Equation (13.32) is known as *Bernoulli's* equation.

In the special case where ρ is constant and the motion is steady so that $\partial \phi / \partial t = 0$, this equation takes the form

$$(13.33) \qquad\qquad \frac{v^2}{2} + V + \frac{p}{\rho} = \beta$$

where β is now a constant. This equation states that, *per unit mass* of fluid, the sum of the kinetic energy, the potential energy V, and the pressure energy p/ρ has a constant value β for all points of the fluid.

Usually in aerodynamics the variations in V are so small that they can be neglected so that we can write

$$(13.34) \qquad\qquad \frac{\rho v^2}{2} + p = p_0$$

where p_0 is the pressure when the fluid is at rest. It can be seen from this that in this case the pressure diminishes as the velocity increases in the form

$$(13.35) \qquad\qquad p = p_0 - \frac{\rho v^2}{2}$$

Airplanes are equipped with instruments for measuring p and p_0 so that the velocity of the machine relative to the air can be determined by the equation

$$(13.36) \qquad\qquad v = \sqrt{\frac{2(p_0 - p)}{\rho}}$$

14. The Equation of Heat Flow in Solids. Consider a region inside a solid body such as a large block of metal. Let a closed surface s be situated inside this region. Let the volume inside the surface s be denoted by V.

In suitable units the amount of heat H inside the volume V of this body is given by

$$(14.1) \qquad\qquad H = \iiint_V (uc\rho)\, dV$$

where $u = u(x,y,z,t)$ = temperature of body
c = specific heat of body
ρ = density of body

It is an empirical fact that the rate of flow of heat *into* the volume V may be expressed in the following form:

$$(14.2) \qquad\qquad \frac{dH}{dt} = \iint_s \left(k\, \frac{\partial u}{\partial n}\right) ds$$

where k is a constant known as the *thermal conductivity* and $\partial u/\partial n$ is the derivative of the temperature with respect to the outward drawn normal to the surface s.

If we differentiate (14.1) with respect to t and equate the result to (14.2), we obtain

$$(14.3) \qquad \frac{dH}{dt} = \iiint_V \left(c\rho\, \frac{\partial u}{\partial t}\right) dV = \iint_s \left(k\, \frac{\partial u}{\partial n}\right) ds$$

If $d\mathbf{n}$ is a vector drawn in the direction of the outward drawn normal to the surface s, we have

$$(14.4) \qquad\qquad du = \nabla u \cdot d\mathbf{n}$$

where du is the total derivative of the temperature and represents the change in temperature as one moves through the distance $d\mathbf{n}$. If we divide both sides of (14.4) by the differential dn, we obtain

$$(14.5) \qquad\qquad \frac{\partial u}{\partial n} = \nabla u \cdot \mathbf{n}$$

where $\mathbf{n}$ represents a unit vector in the normal direction. We then have

$$(14.6) \qquad \iint_s \left(k\, \frac{\partial u}{\partial n}\right) ds = \iint_s k(\nabla u) \cdot \mathbf{n}\, ds = \iint_s (k\, \nabla u) \cdot d\mathbf{s}$$

If we let

$$(14.7) \qquad\qquad \mathbf{q} = k\, \nabla u$$

we have, in view of (14.3) and (14.6),

$$(14.8) \qquad \iiint_V \left(c\rho\, \frac{\partial u}{\partial t}\right) dV = \iint_s \mathbf{q} \cdot d\mathbf{s} = \iiint_V (\nabla \cdot \mathbf{q})\, dV$$

where we have used Gauss's theorem to transform the last integral.

Transposing, we may write

$$(14.9) \qquad \iiint_V \left(c\rho \frac{\partial u}{\partial t} - \Delta \cdot \mathbf{q} \right) dV = 0$$

Since the integral is continuous and the volume V is arbitrary, the integrand must vanish and we obtain

$$(14.10) \qquad \nabla \cdot \mathbf{q} = c\rho \frac{\partial u}{\partial t}$$

or

$$(14.11) \qquad \nabla \cdot (k\,\nabla u) = c\rho \frac{\partial u}{\partial t}$$

If k is a constant, we have

$$(14.12) \qquad \nabla \cdot (k\,\nabla u) = k\,\nabla^2 u = c\rho \frac{\partial u}{\partial t}$$

or

$$(14.13) \qquad \frac{\partial u}{\partial t} = \frac{k}{c\rho}\,\nabla^2 u = h^2\,\nabla^2 u$$

where

$$(14.14) \qquad h^2 = \frac{k}{c\rho}$$

Equation (14.13) was derived by Fourier in 1822 and is sometimes called the *heat-flow*, or *diffusion*, *equation*.

15. The Gravitational Potential. Consider two particles at Q and P of masses m_1 and m_2, respectively. Then, according to the Newtonian law of gravitation, there is a force of attraction between them given in magnitude by the equation

FIG. 15.1

$$(15.1) \qquad F = k\,\frac{m_1 m_2}{r^2}$$

where k is a constant depending upon the units and r is the distance between the particles as shown in Fig. 15.1.

If we choose the unit of mass as that of a particle which, placed at a unit distance from one of equal mass, attracts it with unit force, Eq. (15.1) becomes

$$(15.2) \qquad F = \frac{m_1 m_2}{r^2}$$

If we denote the vector QP by $\mathbf{r}$, we may express the force per unit mass at P due to the attracting particle at Q by

$$(15.3) \qquad \mathbf{F} = -\frac{m\mathbf{r}}{r^3} = \nabla \frac{m}{r}$$

F is called the *intensity* of force or the *gravitational field* of force at the point P, and we note that it may be expressed as the gradient of the scalar m/r. It follows therefore that $\mathbf{F}$ satisfies the equation

$$(15.4) \qquad \nabla \times \mathbf{F} = \nabla \times \nabla \frac{m}{r} = 0$$

and is therefore a conservative field of force.

Let us suppose that the particle m is stationary at Q and that another of unit mass moves under the attraction of the former from infinity up to P along any path. The work done by the force of attraction during an infinitesimal displacement $d\mathbf{r}$ of the unit mass is $\mathbf{F} \cdot d\mathbf{r}$. The total work done by the force while the unit particle moves from infinity up to P is

$$(15.5) \qquad \int_\infty^r \mathbf{F} \cdot d\mathbf{r} = \int_\infty^r \nabla \frac{m}{r} \cdot d\mathbf{r} = \frac{m}{r} \Big|_\infty^r = \frac{m}{r}$$

This is independent of the path by which the particle comes to P and is called the *potential* at P due to the particle of mass at Q. Let us denote it by V. We then have

$$(15.6) \qquad V = \frac{m}{r}$$

while the intensity of force at P due to it is

$$(15.7) \qquad \mathbf{F} = \nabla \frac{m}{r} = \nabla V$$

That is, the intensity at any point is equal to the gradient of the potential.

If we now suppose that there are n particles of masses $m_1, m_2, \ldots, m_n$, relative to which P has position vectors $\mathbf{r}_1, \ldots, \mathbf{r}_n$, respectively, then the force of attraction per unit mass at P due to the system is the vector sum of the intensities due to each, that is,

$$(15.8) \qquad \mathbf{F} = \nabla \frac{m_1}{r_1} + \nabla \frac{m_2}{r_2} + \cdots + \nabla \frac{m_n}{r_n} = \nabla \sum_{s=1}^n \frac{m_s}{r_s}$$

Now, by the same argument as before, the work done by the attracting forces on a particle of unit mass while it moves from infinity up to P is

$$(15.9) \qquad \int_\infty^P \mathbf{F} \cdot d\mathbf{r} = \sum_{s=1}^n \frac{m_s}{r_s} = V$$

Therefore the potential at P due to a system of particles is the sum of the potentials due to each. The potential V is a scalar function of position and, except at the points Q_s where the masses are situated, it satisfies

$$(15.10) \qquad \nabla^2 V = \nabla^2 \sum_{s=1}^{n} \frac{m_s}{r_s} = \sum_{s=1}^{n} \nabla^2 \frac{m_s}{r_s} = 0$$

which is Laplace's equation. Since $\mathbf{F} = \nabla V$, this means that at points excluding matter we must have

$$(15.11) \qquad \nabla \cdot \mathbf{F} = 0$$

Continuous Distribution of Matter. Let us now suppose that the attracting matter forms a continuous body filling the space bounded by the closed surface s. We divide the body into an infinite number of elements of mass $\rho\, dV$, where ρ is the density of the body and dV is the element of volume of the body, as shown in Fig. 15.2.

If P is *outside* the body, the sum in Eq. (15.9) passes into the integral

$$(15.12) \qquad V_P = \iiint \frac{\rho\, dV}{r}$$

Fig. 15.2

where r is the distance from the element of volume dV to the point P. This gives the potential at P due to the entire body.

If the point P is *inside* the body, the integrand (15.12) becomes infinite. In this case we define the potential in the following manner: Surround the point P by a closed spherical surface s_0, and consider the potential due to the matter in the space between s_0 and s. The integrand is finite everywhere, since P is outside the region. Now let the surface s_0 decrease indefinitely, converging to the point P as a limit.

We then consider

$$(15.13) \qquad V_P = \lim_{s_0 \to 0} \iiint_{s_0}^{s} \frac{\rho\, dv}{r}$$

Since the volume of s_0 is of the same order as r^3, where r is the radius of the sphere s_0, while the integrand becomes infinite like $1/r$ if ρ is finite, the value of the above integral tends to a definite limit, which is called the *potential at P due to the whole body*.

Poisson's Equation. We have seen that the potential function satisfies $\nabla^2 V = 0$, or Laplace's equation, in the region outside matter. Let us now consider the equation satisfied by the potential in a region inside matter.

Consider a point P inside a body of density ρ. Surround the point P by a sphere s_0 of radius a as shown in Fig. 15.3.

The gravitational field at the point P is the vector sum of the gravitational field $\mathbf{F}_o$ produced by the matter outside s_0 and $\mathbf{F}_i$ produced by the matter inside s_0. That is, we write

(15.14) $$\mathbf{F}_P = \mathbf{F}_o + \mathbf{F}_i$$

Now let us calculate $\nabla \cdot \mathbf{F}_P$, that is,

(15.15) $$\nabla \cdot \mathbf{F}_P = \nabla \cdot \mathbf{F}_o + \nabla \cdot \mathbf{F}_i$$

Fig. 15.3

But since $\mathbf{F}_o$ is produced by matter outside s_0, we have from (15.11)

(15.16) $$\nabla \cdot \mathbf{F}_o = 0$$

Hence we have

(15.17) $$\nabla \cdot \mathbf{F}_P = \nabla \cdot \mathbf{F}_i$$

Consider the sphere of radius a; its mass is therefore equal to

(15.18) $$m = \tfrac{4}{3}\pi\rho a^3$$

Now as a tends to zero, the intensity at the surface of this sphere is equal to

(15.19) $$F_s = \frac{m}{a^2} = \frac{4}{3}\pi\rho a$$

in magnitude and in the direction of the inwardly drawn normal to the surface.

By Gauss's theorem we then have

(15.20) $$\lim_{a\to 0} \iiint (\nabla \cdot \mathbf{F}_i)\, dV = \lim_{a\to 0} (\nabla \cdot \mathbf{F})\tfrac{4}{3}\pi a^3$$
$$= \lim_{a\to 0} \iint \mathbf{F}_s \cdot d\mathbf{s} = \lim_{a\to 0} (-\tfrac{4}{3}\pi\rho a \times 4\pi a^2)$$

Hence

(15.21) $$\nabla \cdot \mathbf{F}_P = \nabla \cdot \mathbf{F}_i = -4\pi\rho$$

But $$\mathbf{F}_P = \nabla V_P$$

Hence by (15.21) the equation satisfied by the potential in a region containing matter is

(15.22) $$\nabla^2 V = -4\pi\rho = \nabla \cdot \mathbf{F}$$

This relation is known as *Poisson's equation*. In view of (15.13) we see that we may take

(15.23)
$$V = \iiint \frac{\rho \, dv}{r}$$

as a solution of Poisson's equation.*

Gauss's Law of Gravitation. As a consequence of Poisson's equation we may prove that the surface integral of the gravitational force **F** over a closed surface s drawn in the field is equal to -4π times the total mass enclosed by the surface.

To establish this, apply Gauss's theorem to Eq. (15.22); we then have

(15.24)
$$\int_s \int \mathbf{F} \cdot d\mathbf{s} = \iiint_v (\nabla \cdot \mathbf{F}) \, dv = -4\pi \iiint_v \rho \, dv$$

But $\iiint \rho \, dv$ is the total mass enclosed by the surface s. This theorem has many applications in potential theory and in the theory of electrostatics.

16. Maxwell's Equations. The study of electrodynamics affords one of the most important applications of vector analysis. According to the modern point of view, by an *electromagnetic field* is understood the domain of the five vectors **E**, **B**, **D**, **H**, and **J**. These vectors satisfy the differential equations

(16.1)
$$\nabla \times \mathbf{E} = -\frac{\partial \mathbf{B}}{\partial t}$$

(16.2)
$$\nabla \times \mathbf{H} = \mathbf{J} + \frac{\partial \mathbf{D}}{\partial t}$$

(16.3)
$$\nabla \cdot \mathbf{B} = 0$$

(16.4)
$$\nabla \cdot \mathbf{D} = \rho$$

and in a homogeneous isotropic medium we have the additional relations

(16.5) $\mathbf{D} = K\mathbf{E}$

(16.6) $\mathbf{B} = \mu\mathbf{H}$

(16.7) $\mathbf{J} = \sigma\mathbf{E}$

The above set of differential equations are the fundamental equations of Maxwell written in a rationalized mks system of units. In this system of units we have

> $\mathbf{E}$ = electric intensity, volts per m
> $\mathbf{B}$ = magnetic induction, webers per m
> $\mathbf{D}$ = electric displacement, coulombs per m²
> $\mathbf{H}$ = magnetic intensity, amp per m
> $\mathbf{J}$ = current density, amp per m²

* For a more rigorous derivation of Poisson's integral, refer to O. D. Kellogg, "Foundations of Potential Theory," Springer-Verlag OHG, Berlin, 1929.

σ = electric conductivity, 1/ohm-m

$K = K_r K_0$ = electric inductive capacity of medium

$\mu = \mu_r \mu_0$ = magnetic inductive capacity of medium

K_r = dielectric constant

μ_r = permeability

$K_0 = 8.854 \times 10^{-12}$ farad per m

$\mu_0 = 4\pi \times 10^{-7} = 1.257 \times 10^{-6}$ henry per m

ρ = charge density, coulombs per m^3

$c = 1/\sqrt{K_0 \mu_0} = 2.998 \times 10^8$ m per sec

The solution of electrodynamic problems depends on the solution of these equations in special cases. For example, we may discuss briefly the following special cases.

Electrostatics and Magnetostatics. In the case that the field vectors are independent of the time and in a region where $\mathbf{J} = 0$, we see that all the terms involving partial derivatives with respect to time vanish and the electric vectors and magnetic vectors become independent of each other. We then have

(16.8) $$\nabla \times \mathbf{E} = 0$$
(16.9) $$\nabla \cdot \mathbf{D} = \rho$$
(16.10) $$\mathbf{D} = K\mathbf{E}$$

and

(16.11) $$\nabla \times \mathbf{H} = 0$$
(16.12) $$\nabla \cdot \mathbf{B} = 0$$

Since the curls of $\mathbf{E}$ and $\mathbf{H}$ vanish, we see that both these fields may be derived from potential functions. It is conventional to write

(16.13) $$\mathbf{E} = -\nabla V_E$$
(16.14) $$\mathbf{H} = -\nabla V_M$$

where V_E and V_M are the electric and magnetic scalar potentials, respectively.

In view of (16.9) and (16.12) we see that these potentials satisfy the equations

(16.15) $$\nabla^2 V_E = -\frac{\rho}{K}$$

and

(16.16) $$\nabla^2 V_M = 0$$

That is, the electric potential satisfies Poisson's equation, and the magnetic potential satisfies Laplace's equation. If the charge density ρ vanishes, then both V_E and V_M satisfy Laplace's equation and the solution of electrostatic and magnetostatic problems reduces to the solution of this equation subject to the proper boundary conditions.

17. The Wave Equation. Let us eliminate the magnetic-intensity vector **H** from the Maxwell field equations. To do this, let us take the curl of both sides of Eq. (16.1); we then have

$$(17.1) \qquad \nabla \times (\nabla \times \mathbf{E}) = -\mu \frac{\partial}{\partial t} (\nabla \times \mathbf{H})$$

in view of the fact that $\mathbf{B} = \mu\mathbf{H}$ and that the operators $\nabla \times$ and $\partial/\partial t$ commute.

Equation (16.2) may be written in the form

$$(17.2) \qquad \nabla \times \mathbf{H} = \sigma\mathbf{E} + K \frac{\partial \mathbf{E}}{\partial t}$$

Substituting this into (17.1) and making use of the identity

$$(17.3) \qquad \nabla \times (\nabla \times \mathbf{E}) = \nabla(\nabla \cdot \mathbf{E}) - \nabla^2\mathbf{E}$$

we obtain

$$(17.4) \qquad \nabla(\nabla \cdot \mathbf{E}) - \nabla^2\mathbf{E} = -\mu K \frac{\partial^2 \mathbf{E}}{\partial t^2} - \mu\sigma \frac{\partial \mathbf{E}}{\partial t}$$

Now, in view of (16.4), we have

$$(17.5) \qquad \nabla \cdot \mathbf{E} = \frac{\rho}{K}$$

and it may be shown that in free space or in a conducting medium ρ is independent of the field distribution and may be taken to be equal to zero. Accordingly, Eq. (17.4) becomes

$$(17.6) \qquad \nabla^2\mathbf{E} = \mu K \frac{\partial^2 \mathbf{E}}{\partial t^2} + \mu\sigma \frac{\partial \mathbf{E}}{\partial t}$$

As a consequence of (16.7) we also have

$$(17.7) \qquad \nabla^2\mathbf{J} = \mu K \frac{\partial^2 \mathbf{J}}{\partial t^2} + \mu\sigma \frac{\partial \mathbf{J}}{\partial t}$$

Eliminating **E** from the Maxwell equations, we also obtain

$$(17.8) \qquad \nabla^2\mathbf{H} = \mu K \frac{\partial^2 \mathbf{H}}{\partial t^2} + \mu\sigma \frac{\partial \mathbf{H}}{\partial t}$$

It is thus seen that the three vectors **H**, **E**, and **J** satisfy equations of the same form.

In free space we have the conductivity $\sigma = 0$ and $\mu_r = K_r = 1$; we then obtain

$$(17.9) \qquad \nabla^2\mathbf{E} = \mu_0 K_0 \frac{\partial^2 \mathbf{E}}{\partial t^2}$$

and

(17.10)
$$\nabla^2 H = \mu_0 K_0 \frac{\partial^2 H}{\partial t^2}$$

If we let

(17.11)
$$c = \frac{1}{\sqrt{\mu_0 K_0}}$$

We may write (17.9) in the form

(17.12)
$$\nabla^2 E = \frac{1}{c^2} \frac{\partial^2 E}{\partial t^2}$$

This equation is the general wave equation in vector form and is discussed in Chap. 16. It is there shown that this equation governs the propagation of various entities, such as electric waves, displacements of tightly stretched strings, deflections of membranes, etc. It will be shown that such disturbances are propagated with a velocity equal to c.

Equations (17.9) and (17.10) are taken as the starting point in the theory of electromagnetic waves. In this case, c is the velocity of light in free space and is approximately 3×10^8 m per sec.

18. The Skin-effect, or Diffusion, Equation. In metals σ is of the order of $10^7(1/\text{ohm-m})$ and $\epsilon_r \approx 1$, and it may be seen that the term involving the second derivative in (17.7) may be neglected for frequencies of the order of 10^{10} cycles per sec and lower. In such a case this equation reduces to

(18.1)
$$\nabla^2 J = \mu\sigma \frac{\partial J}{\partial t}$$

We thus see that the current density in metals satisfies an equation of the same form as is satisfied by the equation of heat flow in solids as given in Sec. 14. In the electrical-engineering literature this equation is called the *skin-effect equation*. The solution of this equation in various special cases is considered in Chap. 18.

19. Tensors (Qualitative Introduction). In many physical problems vector notation is not sufficiently general to express the relations between the quantities involved. For example, in electrostatics, if a dielectric medium is isotropic, the relation between the electric-displacement vector D and the electric-intensity vector E is given by the vector equation

(19.1)
$$D = KE$$

where the scalar K is the electric inductive capacity of the medium (see Sec. 16). If, however, the dielectric medium is *not* isotropic, the electric-displacement vector D does not have the same direction as the vector E, so that the scalar K must be replaced by a more general quantity to effect the required change in direction and magnitude. Such a quantity is called a *tensor*.

A similar situation arises in the formulation of elastic problems. If $\mathbf{F}$ is the stress vector in an isotropic medium and $\mathbf{X}$ is the strain vector, then the relation

$$(19.2) \qquad\qquad \mathbf{F} = k\mathbf{X}$$

where k is a scalar, exists. If the medium is *not* isotropic, $\mathbf{F}$ and $\mathbf{X}$ are no longer in the same direction and Eq. (19.2) takes on a more general form in which k is a tensor.

After this qualitative introduction, the simpler analytical properties of tensors will be discussed in the following sections.

20. Coordinate Transformations. The fundamental definitions involved in the calculus of tensors or tensor analysis are intimately connected with the subject of coordinate transformations. In this section some of the fundamental properties of these transformations will be discussed.

Linear Transformations and the Summation Convention. Consider a set of variables (u^1, u^2, u^3) related to another set of variables (w^1, w^2, w^3). (The superscripts denote *different* variables and *not* the powers of the variables involved.) Let the relation between the two sets of variables be of the form

$$(20.1) \qquad \begin{aligned} w^1 &= c_1^1 u^1 + c_2^1 u^2 + c_3^1 u^3 \\ w^2 &= c_1^2 u^1 + c_2^2 u^2 + c_3^2 u^3 \\ w^3 &= c_1^3 u^1 + c_2^3 u^2 + c_3^3 u^3 \end{aligned}$$

where the coefficients c_j^i are constants. In this case the variables (u^1, u^2, u^3) are related to the variables (w^1, w^2, w^3) by a *linear* transformation. This transformation may be expressed by the equation

$$(20.2) \qquad\qquad w^r = \sum_{n=1}^{n=3} c_n^r u^n \qquad r = 1, 2, 3$$

For convenience, in tensor analysis, the following *summation convention* has been adopted:

The repetition of an index in a term once as a subscript and once as a superscript will denote a summation with respect to that index over its range. In (20.2) the range of n is from 1 to 3, so that, by the above summation convention, (20.2) may be written in the form

$$(20.3) \qquad\qquad w^r = c_n^r u^n \qquad r = 1, 2, 3$$

The determinant $C = |c_s^r|$ is the determinant of the linear transformation (20.1). If $C \neq 0$, the transformation will have an inverse. Let b_r^s be the *cofactor* of c_s^r, in the determinant C, divided by C. Then, by

Chap. 4, Eq. (4.8), we have

$$(20.4) \qquad c_m^r b_s^m = b_m^r c_s^m = \delta_s^r = \begin{cases} 0 & \text{if } r \neq s \\ 1 & \text{if } r = s \end{cases}$$

The symbol δ_s^r is called a *Kronecker delta* and has the values indicated in (20.4). In order to solve the system of Eqs. (20.1), multiply both sides by b_r^i and obtain

$$(20.5) \qquad b_r^i w^r = b_r^i c_n^r u^n = \delta_n^i u^n = u^i$$

Therefore the solution of the system (20.3) is

$$(20.6) \qquad u^i = b_r^i w^r$$

and therefore the transformation (20.1) is *reversible*.

Successive Linear Transformations.   Consider the two linear transformations

$$(20.7) \qquad y^r = b_s^r x^s$$

and

$$(20.8) \qquad z^r = a_k^r y^k$$

where all the indices range from 1 to n. If (20.7) is substituted into (20.8), the result is

$$(20.9) \qquad z^r = a_k^r b_s^k x^s = c_s^r x^s$$

where

$$(20.10) \qquad c_s^r = a_k^r b_s^k$$

is the transformation matrix of the linear transformation (20.9). These linear transformations may also be expressed by means of the matrix notation of Chap. 4 in the following form:

$$(20.11) \qquad (y) = [b](x) \qquad (z) = [a](y)$$

Therefore

$$(20.12) \qquad (z) = [a][b](x) \qquad [c] = [a][b]$$

where the matrices (x), (y), (z) are column matrices of order n and the matrices $[a]$, $[b]$, and $[c]$ are square matrices of order n.

Functional Transformations, Curvilinear Coordinates.   Consider a three-dimensional Euclidean space. The position of a point P in this space can be specified by its coordinates referred to an orthogonal cartesian system of axes. Let (y^1, y^2, y^3) denote such a system of coordinates. Let

$$(20.13) \qquad x^r = F^r(y^1, y^2, y^3) \qquad r = 1, 2, 3$$

be a transformation of coordinates from the rectangular cartesian coordinates (y^1, y^2, y^3) to some general coordinates (x^1, x^2, x^3), not necessarily rectangular cartesian coordinates. For example, (x^1, x^2, x^3) may be spherical coordinates. The inverse of the transformation of coordinates (20.13) is the transformation that takes one from the coordinates (x^1, x^2, x^3) to the rectangular cartesian coordinates (y^1, y^2, y^3). Let

$$(20.14) \qquad y^r = G^r(x^1, x^2, x^3)$$

be the inverse of the coordinate transformation (20.13). When this transformation exists, it is seen that to each set of values y^r there is a unique set of values of x^r, and vice versa. Hence the variables x^r determine a point in space uniquely and they are called *curvilinear coordinates*.

Spherical Polar Coordinates. The spherical polar coordinates of Sec. 12

FIG. 20.1. Spherical polar coordinates.

may be taken as a special example of the general transformations (20.13) and (20.14). In this notation, consider the spherical polar coordinates of Fig. 20.1. In this figure y^1, y^2, y^3 are the cartesian coordinates of a point P, and x^1, x^2, x^3 are the spherical polar coordinates of P. x^1 is the radius vector from the origin to the point P, and x^2 and x^3 are the angles shown in Fig. 20.1. In this special case the transformation (20.13) takes the form

$$(20.15) \qquad \begin{aligned} x^1 &= [(y^1)^2 + (y^2)^2 + (y^3)^2]^{\frac{1}{2}} \\ x^2 &= \cos^{-1} \frac{y^3}{[(y^1)^2 + (y^2)^2 + (y^3)^2]^{\frac{1}{2}}} \\ x^3 &= \tan^{-1} \left(\frac{y^2}{y^1} \right) \end{aligned}$$

The inverse transformation (20.14) in this case takes the following form:

$$(20.16) \qquad \begin{aligned} y^1 &= x^1 \sin x^2 \cos x^3 \\ y^2 &= x^1 \sin x^2 \sin x^3 \\ y^3 &= x^1 \cos x^2 \end{aligned}$$

21. Scalars, Contravariant Vectors, Covariant Vectors. The fundamental types of tensors will now be defined with respect to functional transformations from one set of curvilinear coordinates to another. The discussion of tensors with respect to general functional transformations follows the same fundamental principles and may be carried out by considering a space of n dimensions.

a. Scalars. Let a Euclidean space be specified by the curvilinear coordinates (x^1, x^2, x^3). Let new curvilinear coordinates $(\bar{x}^1, \bar{x}^2, \bar{x}^3)$ be introduced by the transformation

$$(21.1) \qquad \bar{x}^r = F^r(x^1, x^2, x^3) = \bar{x}^r(x^1, x^2, x^3) \qquad r = 1, 2, 3$$

Let a quantity have the value N in the *old* variables x^r and the value $\bar{N}$ in the *new* variables $\bar{x}^r$. Then, if the quantity has the *same* value in both sets of variables so that

$$(21.2) \qquad\qquad\qquad \bar{N} = N$$

the quantity N is called a scalar, or an *invariant*, or a tensor of order zero.

b. Contravariant Vectors. Let three quantities have the values (A^1, A^2, A^3) when expressed in terms of the coordinates (x^1, x^2, x^3), and let these quantities have the values $(\bar{A}^1, \bar{A}^2, \bar{A}^3)$ when expressed in the coordinates $(\bar{x}^1, \bar{x}^2, \bar{x}^3)$. If

$$(21.3) \qquad \bar{A}^m = \frac{\partial \bar{x}^m}{\partial x^i} A^i \qquad m = 1, 2, 3 \qquad i = 1, 2, 3$$

then the quantities (A^1, A^2, A^3) are said to be the components of a *contravariant vector* or a *contravariant tensor of the first rank* with respect to the transformation (21.1).

Taking differentials on both sides of (21.1),

$$(21.4) \qquad\qquad\qquad dx^r = \frac{\partial \bar{x}^r}{\partial x^s} dx^s$$

Since the components of an ordinary vector in three-dimensional space transform as the differentials of the coordinates, it is seen that the components of an ordinary vector are actually the components of a *contravariant* tensor of rank 1.

If three quantities have the values (A_1, A_2, A_3) in the system of coordinates (x_1, x_2, x_3) and the values $(\bar{A}_1, \bar{A}_2, \bar{A}_3)$ in the system of coordinates $(\bar{x}_1, \bar{x}_2, \bar{x}_3)$, and if

$$(21.5) \qquad\qquad\qquad \bar{A}_m = \frac{\partial x^i}{\partial \bar{x}^m} A_i$$

then (A_1, A_2, A_3) are the components of a *covariant vector* or a covariant tensor of rank 1.

Tensors of Higher Ranks. In the above three classes of quantities, scalars or invariants, contravariant and covariant vectors, there exist components in any two coordinate systems, and the components in any two coordinate systems are related by the defining laws of transformation. There are other quantities whose components in any two coordinate systems are related by characteristic laws of transformation.

These laws of transformation are involved in the definitions of tensors of higher ranks. There are three varieties of second-rank tensors:

$$(21.6) \quad \bar{A}^{mn} = \frac{\partial \bar{x}^m}{\partial x^i} \frac{\partial \bar{x}^n}{\partial x^j} A^{ij} \qquad \text{contravariant tensor of second rank}$$

$$(21.7) \quad \bar{A}_{mn} = \frac{\partial x^i}{\partial \bar{x}^m} \frac{\partial x^j}{\partial \bar{x}^n} A_{ij} \qquad \text{covariant tensor of second rank}$$

$$(21.8) \quad \bar{A}_n^m = \frac{\partial \bar{x}^m}{\partial x^j} \frac{\partial x^j}{\partial \bar{x}^n} A_j^i \qquad \text{mixed tensor of second rank}$$

The A's with the bars denote components in the coordinates $(\bar{x}_1, \bar{x}_2, \bar{x}_3)$, and those without the bars denote components in the coordinates (x_1, x_2, x_3).

Tensors of higher rank are defined by similar laws; for example, a mixed tensor of rank 4 is

$$(21.9) \qquad \bar{A}_{npq}^m = \frac{\partial \bar{x}^m}{\partial x^i} \frac{\partial x^j}{\partial \bar{x}^n} \frac{\partial x^k}{\partial \bar{x}^p} \frac{\partial x^h}{\partial \bar{x}^q} A_{jhk}^i$$

A very useful mixed tensor of the second rank is the Kronecker delta δ_n^m. This is defined by the equation

$$(21.10) \qquad \delta_n^m = \begin{cases} 1 & \text{if } m = n \\ 0 & \text{if } m \neq n \end{cases}$$

To determine whether δ_n^m is a mixed tensor of the second rank, we investigate whether it satisfies the definition (21.8).

$$(21.11) \qquad \bar{\delta}_n^m = \frac{\partial \bar{x}^m}{\partial x^i} \frac{\partial x^j}{\partial \bar{x}^n} \delta_j^i = \frac{\partial \bar{x}^m}{\partial x^i} \frac{\partial x^i}{\partial \bar{x}^n} = \frac{\partial \bar{x}^m}{\partial \bar{x}^n}$$

But

$$(21.12) \qquad \frac{\partial \bar{x}^m}{\partial \bar{x}^n} = \begin{cases} 1 & \text{if } m = n \\ 0 & \text{if } m \neq n \end{cases}$$

since $\bar{x}^m$ and $\bar{x}^n$ are *independent* variables. Hence

$$(21.13) \qquad \bar{\delta}_n^m = \delta_n^m \qquad \text{an invariant}$$

We thus see that δ_n^m has the same components in all coordinate systems. The relation

$$(21.14) \qquad \frac{\partial \bar{x}^m}{\partial x^i} \frac{\partial x^i}{\partial \bar{x}^n} = \delta_n^m$$

is a very useful one.

22. Addition, Multiplication, and Contraction of Tensors. *a. Addition.* It can be easily shown that the sum or difference of two or more tensors of the same rank and type is a tensor of the same rank and type.

For example, if

$$(22.1) \qquad\qquad A^{mn} + B^{mn} = C^{mn}$$

it follows from (22.1) that C^{mn} is a contravariant tensor of the second rank.

b. The Outer Product.   If the contravariant tensor A^m is multiplied by the covariant tensor B_n, the product is the following mixed tensor of the second rank:

$$(22.2) \qquad\qquad C_n^m = A^m B_n$$

It is easy to see that C_n^m transforms like (21.8).   The product (22.2) is called the *outer product*.   It may be obtained with tensors of any rank or type.   For example, the tensor A_n^m may be multiplied by the tensor B_{pq} to obtain the following outer product:

$$(22.3) \qquad\qquad C_{npq}^m = A_n^m B_{pq}$$

c. Contraction.   Consider the mixed tensor A_n^m, and let the index m be set equal to n so that $m = n$.   The law of transformation (21.8) now gives the result

$$(22.4) \qquad\qquad \bar{A}_n^m = \frac{\partial \bar{x}^m}{\partial x^i} \frac{\partial x^j}{\partial \bar{x}^m} A_j^i = A_i^i = A_m^m$$

and hence A_n^m is a scalar.   This process of summing over a pair of contravariant and covariant indices is called *contraction*.   As another example, consider the mixed tensor A_{npq}^m, and let $m = q$.   Let $B_{np} = A_{npm}^m$.   The law of transformation now gives

$$(22.5) \qquad \bar{B}_{np} = \bar{A}_{npm}^m = \frac{\partial \bar{x}^m}{\partial x^i} \frac{\partial x^j}{\partial \bar{x}^n} \frac{\partial x^k}{\partial \bar{x}^p} \frac{\partial x^h}{\partial \bar{x}^m} A_{jkh}^i$$

$$= \frac{\partial x^i}{\partial \bar{x}^n} \frac{\partial x^k}{\partial \bar{x}^p} \delta_i^h = \frac{\partial x^j}{\partial \bar{x}^n} \frac{\partial x^k}{\partial \bar{x}^p} A_{jki}^i$$

Therefore A_{npm}^m is a covariant tensor of rank 2.   The process of contraction always reduces the rank of a mixed tensor by 2.

d. The Inner Product.   If two tensors are multiplied together and then contracted, the result is called the *inner product*.   For example, the inner product is

$$(22.6) \qquad\qquad A^m B_m = C \qquad \text{a scalar}$$

The inner product of A^{mn} and B_{rpq} is

$$(22.6a) \qquad\qquad A^{mn} B_{npq} = C_{pq}^m$$

The product $A^m B_m$ is equivalent to the scalar product of two vectors in rectangular coordinates.   In tensor analysis the length L of the tensor A^m or A_m is defined by the equation

$$(22.7) \qquad\qquad L^2 = A^m A_m = |A|^2$$

The scalar product of the two vectors $\mathbf{A}_m$ and $\mathbf{B}_m$ is

$$(22.8) \qquad A_m B^m = |A||B| \cos \theta = (A_m A^m)^{\frac{1}{2}} (B_m B^m)^{\frac{1}{2}} \cos \theta$$

where θ is the angle between the vectors $\mathbf{A}_m$ and $\mathbf{B}_m$. Hence

$$(22.9) \qquad \cos \theta = \frac{A_m B^m}{[(A_m A^m)(B_m B^m)]^{\frac{1}{2}}}$$

If $\mathbf{A}_m$ and $\mathbf{B}_m$ are orthogonal, then

$$(22.10) \qquad A_m B^m = 0$$

23. Associated Tensors. *a. The Quotient Law of Tensors.* It can be shown by applying the law of transformation of tensors that, if the following relation exists,

$$(23.1) \qquad A(r,s,t) B^{st} = C^r$$

where C^r is known to be a tensor and B^{st} is a known arbitrary tensor, then $A(r,s,t)$ is a tensor of the rank

$$(23.2) \qquad A(r,s,t) = A^r_{st}$$

This law is of importance in recognizing tensors.

b. The Metric Tensor. Let the cartesian coordinates of the point P be y^r. The element of length dS of such a coordinate system is given by

$$(23.3) \qquad \overline{dS}^2 = (dy^1)^2 + (dy^2)^2 + (dy^3)^2 = dy^i\, dy^i$$

Since the cartesian coordinates are related to the general coordinates x^i by the functional relations

$$(23.4) \qquad y^i = y^i(x^1,x^2,x^3)$$

we have

$$(23.5) \qquad dy^i = \frac{\partial y^i}{\partial x^m}\, dx^m$$

It therefore can be seen that

$$(23.6) \qquad \overline{dS}^2 = g_{mn}\, dx^m\, dx^n$$

where

$$(23.7) \qquad g_{mn} = \sum_{i=1}^{3} \frac{\partial y^i}{\partial x^m} \frac{\partial y^i}{\partial x^n} = \frac{\partial y^i}{\partial x^m} \frac{\partial y^i}{\partial x^n}$$

This equation shows that g_{mn} is *symmetric*, and since dS is an *invariant* for arbitrary values of the contravariant vector dx^m, it follows from the *quotient law* that g_{mn} is a double covariant tensor. The tensor g_{mn} is called the *fundamental*, or *metric, tensor*. Let g denote the *determinant*

$|g_{mn}|$ and G^{mn} denote the *cofactor* of g_{mn} in g.   We now define the quantity g^{mn} by the equation

(23.8) $$g^{mn} = \frac{G^{mn}}{g}$$

Now, from the theory of determinants [see Chap. 4] we have

(23.9) $$g_{mn}g^{mr} = \delta_n^r$$

Hence by the *quotient law* it can be seen that g^{mn} is a double contravariant tensor of rank 2.

Two vectors related by the following equations,

(23.10) $$A^m = g^{mn}A_n$$

and

(23.11) $$A_m = g_{mn}A^n$$

are called *associated vectors*.   In the literature of tensor analysis it is sometimes said that A^m and A_m are the same vector, A^m being the *contravariant* components and A_m the *covariant* ones.   Besides the fundamental, or metric, tensor g_{mn} and the second fundamental tensor g^{mn} there is the third associated tensor, g_s^r, defined by the equation

(23.12) $$g_s^r = g_{sm}g^{rm} = \delta_s^r$$

This relation follows from (23.9).   Associated tensors of any rank may be obtained in the same manner as (23.10) and (23.11).   For example,

(23.13) $$A^{mn} = g^{mp}g^{nq}A_{pq}$$

If we are given a contravariant vector A^r, we can form an invariant A by means of the equation

(23.14) $$A = (g_{mn}A^mA^n)^{\frac{1}{2}}$$

A is called the *magnitude* of the vector **A**.   In the same manner the magnitude B of the covariant vector B_m is defined by the equation

(23.15) $$B = (g^{mn}B_mB_n)^{\frac{1}{2}}$$

A unit vector is one whose magnitude is unity.   If (23.6) is divided by $\overline{dS}^2$, we have

(23.16) $$g_{mn}\frac{dx^m}{dS}\frac{dx^n}{dS} = 1$$

From this it can be concluded that dx^m/dS is a *unit vector*.   By the use of (22.9) and (23.11) it can be shown that the angle θ between the vectors A^m and B^m may be expressed in the form

(23.17) $$\cos\theta = \frac{g_{mn}\mathbf{A}^m\mathbf{B}^n}{AB}$$

24. Differentiation of an Invariant. Let ϕ be an *invariant* function of a parameter t; then, in the new variables $\bar{x}^r$, we have $\bar{\phi} = \phi$, and it can be shown that

$$(24.1) \qquad \frac{d\bar{\phi}}{dt} = \frac{d\phi}{dt}$$

so that $d\phi/dt$ is also an *invariant*. If ϕ is an invariant function of x^r, we have

$$(24.2) \qquad \frac{\partial \bar{\phi}}{\partial \bar{x}^r} = \frac{\partial \phi}{\partial x^m} \frac{\partial x^m}{\partial \bar{x}^r}$$

This shows that $\partial\phi/\partial x^r$ is a *covariant vector* since it transforms like one.

25. Differentiation of Tensors: The Christoffel Symbols. In Sec. 24 it has been shown that the derivative of a scalar point function is a *covariant vector*. However, the derivative of a covariant vector is *not* a tensor, for if

$$(25.1) \qquad \bar{A}_m = \frac{\partial x^h}{\partial \bar{x}^m} A_h$$

the derivative of $\bar{A}_m$ with respect to $\bar{x}^n$ is

$$(25.2) \qquad \frac{\partial \bar{A}_m}{\partial \bar{x}^n} = \frac{\partial^2 x^h}{\partial \bar{x}^n \, \partial \bar{x}^m} A_h + \frac{\partial x^h}{\partial \bar{x}^m} \frac{\partial A_h}{\partial \bar{x}^n}$$

The presence of the second derivative shows that $\partial A_m/\partial x^n$ does *not* transform like a tensor.

In order to define "derivatives" of tensors that preserve the proper tensor character, it is necessary to introduce the following notation:[*]

$$(25.3) \qquad [mn,p] = \frac{1}{2}\left(\frac{\partial g_{np}}{\partial x^m} + \frac{\partial g_{pm}}{\partial x^n} - \frac{\partial g_{mn}}{\partial x^p} \right)$$

and

$$(25.4) \qquad \left\{ \begin{matrix} r \\ mn \end{matrix} \right\} = g^{rp}[mn,p]$$

The quantity $[mn,p]$ is called the *Christoffel symbol of the first kind*, and $\left\{ \begin{matrix} r \\ mn \end{matrix} \right\}$ is called the *Christoffel symbol of the second kind*.

a. The Intrinsic Derivative of a Vector. It can be shown that the quantity

$$(25.5) \qquad \frac{\delta A^r}{\delta t} = \frac{dA^r}{dt} + \left\{ \begin{matrix} r \\ mn \end{matrix} \right\} A^m \frac{dx^n}{dt}$$

is a *contravariant vector*. This vector is defined to be the *intrinsic derivative* of the vector A^r with respect to the parameter t.

---

[*] See A. J. McConnel, "Applications of the Absolute Differential Calculus," pp. 143–150, Blackie & Son, Ltd., Glasgow, 1931.

The quantity

$$(25.6) \qquad \frac{\delta A_r}{\delta t} = \frac{dA_r}{dt} - \begin{Bmatrix} m \\ rn \end{Bmatrix} A_m \frac{dx^n}{dt}$$

can be shown to be a covariant vector and is defined to be the *intrinsic derivative* of A_r with respect to the parameter t.

b. *The Covariant Derivative of a Vector.* The *covariant derivative* of the contravariant vector A^r with respect to the coordinate x^s is defined by the equation

$$(25.7) \qquad A_s^r = \frac{\partial A^r}{\partial x^s} + \begin{Bmatrix} r \\ ms \end{Bmatrix} A^m$$

This quantity can be shown to be a mixed tensor contravariant in r and covariant in s. The *covariant derivative* of the covariant vector A_r with respect to the coordinate x^s is defined by the equation

$$(25.8) \qquad A_{r,s} = \frac{\partial A_r}{\partial x^s} - \begin{Bmatrix} m \\ rs \end{Bmatrix} A_m$$

This quantity can be shown to be a tensor covariant in both r and s.

26. Intrinsic and Covariant Derivatives of Tensors of Higher Order. The intrinsic derivative of the tensor A^r_{sp} with respect to the parameter t is defined by the equation

$$(26.1) \qquad \frac{\delta A^r}{\delta t^{sp}} = \frac{dA^r}{dt^{sp}} + \begin{Bmatrix} r \\ mn \end{Bmatrix} A^m_{sp} \frac{dx^n}{dt} - \begin{Bmatrix} m \\ sn \end{Bmatrix} A^r_{mp} \frac{dx^n}{dt} - \begin{Bmatrix} m \\ np \end{Bmatrix} A^r_{sm} \frac{dx^n}{dt}$$

It can be shown that this quantity is a tensor of the type A^r_{sp}.

The *covariant derivative* of the tensor A^r_{st} with respect to the variable x^n is defined by the equation

$$(26.2) \qquad A^r_{st,n} = \frac{\partial A^r_{st}}{\partial x^n} + \begin{Bmatrix} r \\ mn \end{Bmatrix} A^m_{st} - \begin{Bmatrix} m \\ sn \end{Bmatrix} A^r_{mt} - \begin{Bmatrix} m \\ tn \end{Bmatrix} A^r_{sm}$$

This is a tensor with one covariant index more than A^r_{st}. The definitions of the intrinsic and covariant derivatives are quite general. Terms of the form (25.5) and (25.7) appear in the derivatives of a mixed tensor for each contravariant index, and terms of the form (25.6) and (25.8) appear in the derivatives of mixed tensors for each covariant index.

If the coordinate system is a rectangular cartesian one, the g_{mn} quantities are all constants and the Christoffel systems are identically zero. In such case the *intrinsic* derivatives are identical to the ordinary derivatives, and the *covariant* derivatives are ordinary partial derivatives.

The fundamental, or metric, tensor g_{rs} has components that are constants in cartesian systems, and therefore

$$(26.3) \qquad g_{rs} = 0$$

in such a system.   Since g_{rs} is a tensor, it follows that, in *every* coordinate system, the following equation must be satisfied:

$$(26.4) \qquad\qquad g_{rs,m} = 0$$

Therefore the covariant derivative of the metric tensor g_{rs} is zero.   It can also be shown that the covariant derivative of the associated tensor g^{rs} is zero.

27. Application of Tensor Analysis to the Dynamics of a Particle.   In the brief introduction to the basic ideas and definitions of tensor analysis given in this chapter, space does not permit the discussion of numerous applications to applied mathematics.   These applications will be found in the treatises on tensor analysis listed in the references at the end of this chapter.   For purposes of illustration, however, a brief discussion of the application of tensor analysis to the dynamics of a particle will be given in this section.

Consider a particle of mass M that is moving in space.   Let the position of this particle be given by a system of curvilinear coordinates x^r.   As the time t varies, the particle will describe a certain curve in space, called the *trajectory* of the particle.   The equations of this curve may be written in the form

$$(27.1) \qquad\qquad x^r = x^r(t) \qquad r = 1, 2, 3$$

If we transform to another curvilinear coordinate system, $\bar{x}^r$, in accordance with the transformation

$$(27.2) \qquad\qquad \bar{x}^r = \bar{x}^r(x^1, x^2, x^3)$$

then the trajectory of the particle may be obtained in terms of t by substituting (27.1) into (27.2).

Consider the quantity

$$(27.3) \qquad\qquad v^r = \frac{dx^r}{dt}$$

In the new coordinates $\bar{x}^r$ the corresponding quantities are

$$(27.4) \qquad\qquad \bar{v}^r = \frac{d\bar{x}^r}{dt} = \frac{\partial \bar{x}^r}{\partial x^s} \frac{dx^s}{dt} = \frac{\partial \bar{x}^r}{\partial x^s} v^s$$

This equation expresses the fact that the v^r are the components of a *contravariant vector*.   In dynamics this vector is called the *velocity* of the particle.   The velocity vector v^r is a function of the time t.   If the *intrinsic derivative* with respect to t is taken, the following result is obtained,

$$(27.5) \qquad\qquad a^r = \frac{\delta v^r}{\delta t} = \frac{d^2 x^r}{dt^2} + \begin{Bmatrix} r \\ mn \end{Bmatrix} \frac{dx^m}{dt} \frac{dx^n}{dt}$$

where $\begin{Bmatrix} r \\ mn \end{Bmatrix}$ are the Christoffel symbols of the coordinate system x^r. If the coordinates are rectangular cartesian, the Christoffel symbols are identical to zero and the vector a^r becomes

$$(27.6) \qquad a^r = \frac{d^2 x^r}{dt^2}$$

These are the components of acceleration along the three coordinate axes; (27.5) is called the *acceleration vector* of the particle. If the mass of the particle M remains constant, it is obviously a quantity independent of the coordinate system and the time and is, therefore, an *invariant*.

Newton's second law of motion may be expressed in the form

$$(27.7) \qquad F^r = M a^r$$

where the contravariant vector F^r is called the *force vector*. This vector completely specifies the magnitude and direction of the force acting upon the particle. In cartesian coordinates (27.7) takes the well-known form

$$(27.8) \qquad F^r = M \frac{d^2 x^r}{dt^2}$$

and F^1, F^2, F^3 are the components of the force along the three axes of coordinates. In curvilinear coordinates this equation takes the form

$$(27.9) \qquad F^r = M \frac{d^2 x^r}{dt^2} + M \begin{Bmatrix} r \\ mn \end{Bmatrix} \frac{dx^m}{dt} \frac{dx^n}{dt}$$

Work and Energy. Lagrange's Equations. If the axes $\bar{x}^r$ are rectangular cartesian, a force whose components in these coordinates are $\bar{F}^r$ and whose point of application is moved through a small displacement $\delta \bar{x}^r$ does an amount of work given by

$$(27.10) \qquad \delta W = \bar{F}^1 \, \delta \bar{x}^1 + \bar{F}^2 \, \delta \bar{x}^2 + \bar{F}^3 \, \delta \bar{x}^3$$

In orthogonal cartesian coordinates the associated vector $\bar{F}_r$ has exactly the same components as $\bar{F}^r$, and the expression for δW becomes

$$(27.11) \qquad \delta W = \bar{F}_r \, \delta \bar{x}^r$$

From the relation connecting $\bar{x}^r$ and x^r it can be seen that δW can also be written in the form

$$(27.12) \qquad \partial W = F_r \, \delta x^r$$

Since δW is an *invariant*, it can be concluded from the above equation that the F_r are the components of a covariant vector. Since the components of F_r in an orthogonal cartesian coordinate system are those of the force vector, it follows that F_r is the *covariant force vector* in the coordinates x^r. The covariant and contravariant components of this vector are related to each other by the following formulas:

$$(27.13) \qquad F_r = g_{rs}F^s \qquad F^r = g^{rs}F_s$$

If the expression $F_r \, dx^r$ is a *perfect differential*, then the force is said to be *conservative* and a function V may be defined by the equation

$$(27.14) \qquad V = -\int F_r \, dx^r$$

The function V is called the *force potential*. From (27.14) it follows that

$$(27.15) \qquad F_r = -\frac{\partial V}{\partial x^r}$$

The *kinetic energy* T of a particle is defined as $\frac{1}{2}Mv^2$, where v is the magnitude of the velocity. Therefore

$$(27.16) \qquad T = \tfrac{1}{2}Mv^2 = \tfrac{1}{2}Mg_{mn}v^m v^n = \tfrac{1}{2}Mg_{mn}\dot{x}^m \dot{x}^n$$

where g_{mn} is the metric tensor of the curvilinear coordinates x^m.

Lagrange's Equations. If T is differentiated partially with respect to $\dot{x}^r$, the result is

$$(27.17) \qquad \frac{\partial T}{\partial \dot{x}^r} = Mg_{rm}\dot{x}^m$$

Therefore

$$(27.18) \qquad \frac{d}{dt}\left(\frac{\partial T}{\partial \dot{x}^n}\right) = M\left(g_{rm}x^m + \frac{\partial g_{rm}}{\partial x^n}\dot{x}^m\dot{x}^n\right)$$

Also, if T is differentiated partially with respect to x^r, the result is

$$(27.19) \qquad \frac{\partial T}{\partial x^r} = \tfrac{1}{2}M\frac{\partial g_{mn}}{\partial x^r}\dot{x}^m\dot{x}^n \qquad \backslash$$

From (27.18) and (27.19) it can be deduced that

$$(27.20) \quad \frac{d}{dt}\left(\frac{\partial T}{\partial \dot{x}^r}\right) - \frac{\partial T}{\partial x^r} = M\left[g_{rm}x^m + \frac{1}{2}\left(\frac{\partial g_{rm}}{\partial x^n} + \frac{\partial g_{rn}}{\partial x^m} - \frac{\partial g_{mn}}{\partial x^r}\right)\dot{x}^m\dot{x}^n\right]$$
$$= M(g_{rm}x^m + [mn,r]\dot{x}^m\dot{x}^n)$$

where $[mn,r]$ is the first Christoffel symbol. Therefore

$$(27.21) \qquad \frac{d}{dt}\left(\frac{\partial T}{\partial \dot{x}^r}\right) - \frac{\partial T}{\partial x^r} = Mg_{rx}\left(\ddot{x}^s + \begin{Bmatrix} s \\ mn \end{Bmatrix}\dot{x}^m\dot{x}^n\right)$$

As a consequence of (27.5) it can be seen that the right-hand member of (27.21) is equal to $Mg_{rs}a^s = Ma_r$. Therefore (27.21) may be written in the form

$$(27.22) \qquad \frac{d}{dt}\left(\frac{\partial T}{\partial \dot{x}^r}\right) - \frac{\partial T}{\partial x^r} = Ma_r = F_r$$

These are Lagrange's equations. If the force system is conservative, these equations may be written in the form

$$(27.23) \qquad \frac{d}{dt}\left(\frac{\partial T}{\partial \dot{x}^r}\right) - \frac{\partial T}{\partial x^r} + \frac{\partial V}{\partial x^r} = 0$$

PROBLEMS

1. The point of application of a force $\mathbf{F} = 5, 10, 15$ lb is displaced from the point $(1,0,3)$ to the point $(3,-1,-6)$. Find the work done by the force.

2. Find the scalar product of two diagonals of a unit cube. What is the angle between them?

3. A force $\mathbf{F}$ acts at a distance $\mathbf{r}$ from the origin. Show that the torque L about any axis through the origin is $L = (\mathbf{r} \times \mathbf{F}) \cdot \mathbf{a}$ when $\mathbf{a}$ is a unit vector in the direction of the axis.

4. Show that the lines joining the mid-points of the opposite sides of a quadrilateral bisect each other.

5. Show that the bisectors of the angles of a triangle meet at a point.

6. What is the cosine of the angle between the vectors $\mathbf{A} = 4\mathbf{i} + 6\mathbf{j} + 2\mathbf{k}$ and $\mathbf{B} = \mathbf{i} - 2\mathbf{j} + 3\mathbf{k}$?

7. Let $\mathbf{r}$ be the radius vector from the origin to any point and $\mathbf{a}$ a constant vector. Find the gradient of the scalar product of $\mathbf{a}$ and $\mathbf{r}$.

8. A plane central field $\mathbf{A}$ is defined by $\mathbf{A} = \mathbf{r}F(r)$. Determine $F(r)$ so that the field may be irrotational and solenoidal.

9. A central field $\mathbf{A}$ in space is defined by $\mathbf{A} = \mathbf{r}F(r)$. Determine $F(r)$ so that the field may be irrotational and solenoidal.

10. If $\mathbf{r}$ is a unit vector of variable direction, the position vector of a moving point may be written $\mathbf{r} = r\mathbf{r}$. Find by vector methods the components of the acceleration $\mathbf{F}$ parallel and perpendicular to the radius vector of a particle moving in the xy plane.

11. Prove that the vector $\nabla\phi$ is perpendicular to the surface $\phi(x,y,z) = \text{const.}$

12. Find ∇u if $u = \ln(x^2 + y^2 + z^2)$.

13. Show that if $\mathbf{r}$ is the position vector of any point of a closed surface s, then

$$\int_s \int (\mathbf{r} \cdot d\mathbf{s}) = 3V,$$ where V is the volume bounded by s.

14. Show that a vector field $\mathbf{A}$ is uniquely determined within a region V bounded by a surface S when its divergence and curl are given throughout V and the normal component of the curl is given on S.

15. With every point of a curve in space there is associated a unit vector t the direction of which is that of the velocity of a point describing the curve. This vector therefore has the direction of the tangent. Prove that $t \cdot dt/ds = 0$, where s is the length of the arc of the curve measured from a fixed point on it. What is the geometrical meaning of $d\vec{t}/ds$?

16. The expression for $(ds)^2$ is $(ds)^2 = (u^2 + v^2)[(du)^2 + (dv)^2] + u^2v^2(d\phi)^2$ in parabolic coordinates. What is the form assumed by Laplace's equation in these coordinates?

17. Write the heat-flow equation in cylindrical and spherical coordinates.

18. What form does the general wave equation take in cylindrical coordinates?

19. Write Maxwell's equations in cylindrical coordinates.

20. Show that the potential due to a solid sphere of mass M and uniform density at an *external* point at a distance r from the center is M/r and, hence, that the gravitational intensity is M/r^2 toward the center.

21. Show that the gravitational field inside a homogeneous spherical shell is zero.

22. Find the potential inside a solid uniform sphere and the gravitational force inside the sphere.

23. Find the covariant components of the acceleration vector in spherical coordinates.

24. Show that the velocity vector is given by $(1/M)g^{rs}(\partial T/\partial \dot{x}s)$.

25. If ϕ is an invariant function of x^r and $\dot{x}^r$, show that the partial derivative of ϕ with respect to $\dot{x}^r$ is a covariant vector.

26. If a particle is moving with uniform velocity in a straight line prove that $\delta v^r/\delta t = 0$.

27. Find the contravariant components of the acceleration vector in cylindrical coordinates.

REFERENCES

1. Coffin, Joseph George: "Vector Analysis," John Wiley & Sons, Inc., New York, 1911.
2. Weatherburn, C. E.: "Elementary Vector Analysis with Applications to Geometry and Physics," George Bell & Sons, Ltd., London, 1928.
3. Weatherburn, C. E.: "Advanced Vector Analysis with Application to Mathematical Physics," George Bell & Sons, Ltd., London, 1928.
4. Wills, A. P.: "Vector Analysis with an Introduction to Tensor Analysis," Prentice-Hall, Inc., Englewood Cliffs, N.J., 1931.
5. Gibbs, J. Willard, and Edwin Bidwell Wilson: "Vector Analysis," Yale University Press, New Haven, Conn., 1901.
6. Gans, Richard: "Vector Analysis with Applications to Physics," Blackie & Son, Ltd., Glasgow, 1932.
7. McConnel, A. J.: "Applications of the Absolute Differential Calculus," Blackie & Son, Ltd., Glasgow, 1931.
8. Brillouin, L.: "Les Tenseurs en mécanique et en élasticité," Dover Publications, New York, 1946.
9. Sokolnikoff, I. S.: "Tensor Analysis," John Wiley & Sons, Inc., New York, 1951.

CHAPTER 16

THE WAVE EQUATION

1. Introduction. In this chapter solutions of the so-called "wave equation" in simple cases will be considered. One of the most fundamental and common phenomena that occur in nature is the phenomenon of wave motion. When a stone is dropped into a pond, the surface of the water is disturbed and waves of displacement travel radially outward; when a tuning fork or a bell is struck, sound waves are propagated from the source of sound. The electrical oscillations of a radio antenna generate electromagnetic waves that are propagated through space. These various physical phenomena have something in common. Energy is propagated with a finite velocity to distant points, and the wave disturbance travels through the medium that supports it without giving the medium any permanent displacement. We shall find in this chapter that whatever the nature of the wave phenomenon, whether it be the displacement of a tightly stretched string, the deflection of a stretched membrane, the propagation of currents and potentials along an electrical transmission line, or the propagation of electromagnetic waves in free space, these entities are governed by a certain differential equation, the wave equation. This equation has the form

$$(1.1) \qquad \nabla^2 u = \frac{\partial^2 u}{\partial x^2} + \frac{\partial^2 u}{\partial y^2} + \frac{\partial^2 u}{\partial z^2} = \frac{1}{c^2} \frac{\partial^2 u}{\partial t^2}$$

where c is a constant having dimensions of velocity, t is the time, x, y, and z are the coordinates of a cartesian reference frame, and u is the entity under consideration, whether it be a mechanical displacement, or the field components of an electromagnetic wave, or the currents or potentials of an electrical transmission line.

2. The Transverse Vibrations of a Stretched String. The study of the oscillations of a tightly stretched string is a fundamental problem in the theory of wave motion. Consider a perfectly flexible string that is stretched between two points by a constant tension T so great that gravity may be neglected in comparison with it. Let the string be uniform and have a mass per unit length equal to m. Let us take the undisturbed position of the string to be the x axis and suppose that the

427

motion is confined to the xy plane.   Consider the motion of an element PQ of length ds as shown in Fig. 2.1.

The net force in the y direction, F_y, is given by

(2.1) $F_y = T \sin \theta_2 - T \sin \theta_1$

Now, for small oscillations, we may write

(2.2) $\sin \theta_2 \doteq \tan \theta_2 = \left(\dfrac{\partial y}{\partial x} \right)_{x+dx}$

(2.3) $\sin \theta_1 \doteq \tan \theta_1 = \left(\dfrac{\partial y}{\partial x} \right)_x$

Hence we have

(2.4) $F_y = \left(T \dfrac{\partial y}{\partial x} \right)_{x+dx} - \left(T \dfrac{\partial y}{\partial x} \right)_x$

By Taylor's expansion we have

(2.5) $\left(T \dfrac{\partial y}{\partial x} \right)_{x+dx} \doteq \left(T \dfrac{\partial y}{\partial x} \right)_x + \dfrac{\partial}{\partial x} \left(T \dfrac{\partial y}{\partial x} \right)_x dx$

where we have neglected terms of order dx^2 and higher.   Substituting this into (2.4), we get

(2.6) $F_y = \dfrac{\partial}{\partial x} \left(T \dfrac{\partial y}{\partial x} \right) dx$

By Newton's law of motion we have

(2.7) $Fy = \dfrac{\partial}{\partial x} \left(T \dfrac{\partial y}{\partial x} \right) dx = m \, dx \left(\dfrac{\partial^2 y}{\partial t^2} \right)$

where $m \, dx$ represents the mass of the section of string under consideration and where we have written dx for ds since the displacement is small. $\partial^2 y / \partial t^2$ is the acceleration of the section of string in the y direction.   We thus have

FIG. 2.1

(2.8) $\dfrac{\partial}{\partial x} \left(T \dfrac{\partial y}{\partial x} \right) = m \dfrac{\partial^2 y}{\partial t^2}$

as the equation governing the small oscillations of a flexible string.   If the stretching force is constant throughout the string, we may write

(2.9) $\dfrac{\partial}{\partial x} \left(T \dfrac{\partial y}{\partial x} \right) = T \dfrac{\partial^2 y}{\partial x^2} = m \dfrac{\partial^2 y}{\partial t^2}$

or

(2.10) $\dfrac{\partial^2 y}{\partial x^2} = \dfrac{1}{c^2} \dfrac{\partial^2 y}{\partial t^2}$

This is a special case of the general wave equation (1.1), where in this case we have

(2.11) $$c = \sqrt{\frac{T}{m}}$$

It is easy to show that the constant c has dimensions of length/time and hence the same dimensions as a velocity.

3. D'Alembert's Solution; Waves on Strings.

We may obtain a general solution of (2.10) by a symbolic method in the following manner: If we write

(3.1) $$D_x = \frac{\partial}{\partial x} \qquad D_x^2 = \frac{\partial^2}{\partial x^2}$$

then Eq. (2.10) may be written symbolically in the form

(3.2) $$\frac{\partial^2 y}{\partial t^2} = c^2 \frac{\partial^2 y}{\partial x^2} = (cD_x)^2 y$$

Let us now treat Eq. (3.2) as an ordinary differential equation with constant coefficients of the form

(3.3) $$\frac{d^2 y}{dt^2} = a^2 y$$

where

(3.4) $$a = cD_x$$

The solution of (3.3) if a were a constant would be of the form

(3.5) $$y = A_1 e^{at} + A_2 e^{-at}$$

where A_1 and A_2 are arbitrary constants. Thus Eq. (3.3) is formally satisfied by

(3.6) $$y = e^{cD_x t} F_1(x) + e^{-cD_x t} F_2(x)$$

where, since the integration has been performed with respect to t, instead of the arbitrary constants A_1 and A_2 we have the arbitrary functions of x, $F_1(x)$ and $F_2(x)$. To interpret the solution, we use the symbolic form of Taylor's expansion as written in Chap. 1:

(3.7) $$e^{hD_x} F(x) = F(x + h)$$

If we let

(3.8) $$h = ct$$

we have

(3.9) $$e^{cD_x t} F_1(x) = F_1(x + ct)$$

If we let

(3.10) $$h = -ct$$

we have

(3.11)
$$e^{-cD_x t}F_2(x) = F_2(x - ct)$$

Hence, by (3.6), the general solution of the one-dimensional wave equation (2.10) is given by

(3.12)
$$y(x,t) = F_1(x + ct) + F_2(x - ct)$$

Now if $F_1(x + ct)$ is plotted as a function of x, it is exactly the same as $F_1(x)$ in shape, but every point on it is displaced a distance ct to the left of the corresponding point in $F_1(x)$. The function $F_1(x + ct)$ thus represents a wave of displacement of arbitrary shape traveling toward the left along the string with a velocity equal to c. In the same manner it may be seen that $F_2(x - ct)$ represents a wave of displacement traveling with a velocity c to the right along the string. The general solution is the sum of these two waves.

Consider a string having one end fixed at the origin, and let the other end be a great distance away at $x = s$. Suppose that a wave of arbitrary shape given by

(3.13)
$$y = F(ct + x)$$

is approaching the origin. At the origin the displacement must be zero for all time t; hence the reflected wave must have the form

(3.14)
$$y = -F(ct - x)$$

since the sum of this and the original expression is zero at $x = 0$ for all values of t. This shows that the transverse waves in a stretched string are inverted by reflection from a fixed end.

4. Harmonic Waves. Consider the expression

(4.1)
$$y = A \cos \frac{2\pi}{T}\left(t - \frac{x}{c}\right) = A \cos 2\pi\left(\frac{t}{T} - \frac{x}{\lambda}\right)$$

By plotting the expression as a function of x for successive values of t it may be shown to represent an infinite train of progressive harmonic waves. It is seen that, as t increases, the whole wave profile moves forward in the positive x direction with a velocity equal to c. The *wavelength*, that is, the distance between two successive crests at any time, is given by

(4.2)
$$\lambda = cT$$

The time that it takes a complete wave to pass a fixed point is called the *period* and is given by T. The *frequency* of the wave is denoted by f and is given by

(4.3)
$$f = \frac{1}{T}$$

The *wave number*, the number of waves that lie in a distance of 2π units, is denoted by k and is given by the equation

$$(4.4) \qquad k = \frac{2\pi}{\lambda}$$

5. Fourier-series Solution. The general solution of the wave equation for the vibrating string shows clearly the wave nature of the phenomenon but is not very well suited for certain types of physical investigations. Consider a string fastened at $x = 0$ and $x = s$ to fixed supports, and let us suppose that at $t = 0$ we are given the displacement and velocity of every point of the string. That is, we stipulate that

$$(5.1) \qquad \left. \begin{array}{l} y(x,t) = y_0(x) \\ \dfrac{\partial y}{\partial t} = v_0(x) \end{array} \right\} \qquad \text{at } t = 0$$

where $y_0(x)$ and $v_0(x)$ are the initial displacement and velocity of the string, respectively. We then wish to determine the subsequent behavior of the string. To do this, let us assume a solution of the form

$$(5.2) \qquad y(x,t) = e^{j\omega t}v(x) \qquad j = \sqrt{-1}$$

where $v(x)$ is a function of x alone and ω is to be determined. We thus have

$$(5.3) \qquad \frac{\partial^2 y}{\partial t^2} = -\omega^2 e^{j\omega t}v$$

$$(5.4) \qquad \frac{\partial^2 y}{dx^2} = e^{j\omega t}\frac{d^2v}{\partial x^2}$$

On substituting these expressions into the wave equation

$$(5.5) \qquad \frac{\partial^2 y}{\partial x^2} = \frac{1}{c^2}\frac{\partial^2 y}{\partial t^2}$$

it becomes, after some reductions,

$$(5.6) \qquad \frac{d^2v}{dx^2} + \left(\frac{\omega}{c}\right)^2 v = 0$$

This ordinary differential equation has the solution

$$(5.7) \qquad v = A \sin\frac{\omega}{c}x + B \cos\frac{\omega}{c}x$$

However, since the string is fastened at $x = 0$ and at $x = s$, we have the boundary conditions

$$(5.8) \qquad v = 0 \qquad \left\{ \begin{array}{l} \text{at } x = 0 \\ \text{at } x = s \end{array} \right.$$

The first condition leads to

(5.9) $$B = 0$$

The second condition gives

(5.10) $$0 = A \sin \frac{\omega s}{c}$$

Since we are looking for a nontrivial solution, $A \neq 0$; therefore

(5.11) $$\sin \frac{\omega s}{c} = 0$$

This transcendental equation leads to the possible values of ω. Therefore we have

(5.12) $$\frac{\omega s}{c} = k\pi \qquad k = 0, 1, 2, \ldots$$

or

(5.13) $$\omega_k = \frac{k\pi c}{s} \qquad k = 0, 1, 2, \ldots$$

where we have labeled ω_k the value corresponding to the particular value of k. For each value of k we may write in view of (5.7) and (5.9) the equation

(5.14) $$v_k = A_k \sin \frac{k\pi x}{s}$$

As a consequence of (5.2) we have for every value of k the solution

(5.15) $$y_k = e^{j\omega_k t} A_k \sin \frac{k\pi x}{s} \qquad A_k \text{ arbitrary}$$

This expression satisfies the wave equation (5.5) and the boundary conditions (5.8). Since the real and imaginary parts of (5.15) satisfy the wave equation and the equation is linear, we may write

(5.16) $$y_k = \left(C_k \cos \frac{k\pi ct}{s} + D_k \sin \frac{k\pi ct}{s} \right) \sin \frac{k\pi x}{s}$$

where C_k and D_k are arbitrary constants.

By summing over all the values of k we can construct a general solution of the form

(5.17) $$y = \sum_{k=1}^{\infty} y_k = \sum_{k=1}^{k=\infty} \left(C_k \cos \frac{k\pi ct}{s} + D_k \sin \frac{k\pi ct}{s} \right) \sin \frac{k\pi x}{s}$$

The arbitrary constants C_k and D_k must now be determined from the initial conditions (5.1).

We thus have at $t = 0$

$$(5.18) \qquad y_0(x) = \sum_{k=1}^{k=\infty} C_k \sin \frac{k\pi x}{s}$$

This requires the expansion of an arbitrary function, $y_0(x)$, the initial displacement into a series of sines. To obtain the typical coefficient C_r, we multiply both sides of (5.18) by the expression

$$(5.19) \qquad \sin \frac{r\pi x}{s}$$

and integrate with respect to x from $x = 0$ to $x = s$.

We then have

$$(5.20) \qquad \int_0^s y_0(x) \sin \frac{r\pi x}{s} \, dx = \sum_{k=1}^{k=\infty} C_k \int_0^s \sin \frac{k\pi x}{s} \sin \frac{r\pi x}{s} \, dx$$

If we now make use of the result

$$(5.21) \qquad \int_0^s \sin \frac{k\pi x}{s} \sin \frac{r\pi x}{s} \, dx = \begin{cases} 0 & \text{if } k \neq r \\ \dfrac{s}{2} & \text{if } k = r \end{cases}$$

then (5.20) reduces to

$$(5.22) \qquad \int_0^s y_0(x) \sin \frac{r\pi x}{s} \, dx = \frac{s}{2} C_r$$

or

$$(5.23) \qquad C_r = \frac{2}{s} \int_0^s y_0(x) \sin \frac{r\pi x}{s} \, dx \qquad r = 1, 2, 3, \ldots$$

This determines the arbitrary constants C_k in the general solution (5.17). To determine the arbitrary constants D_k, we make use of the second initial condition (5.1). We then have, on computing $\partial y / \partial t$ from (5.17) and putting $t = 0$,

$$(5.24) \qquad v_0(x) = \sum_{k=1}^{k=\infty} \frac{k\pi c}{s} D_k \sin \frac{k\pi x}{s}$$

Proceeding in the same manner as before, we obtain

$$(5.25) \qquad D_r = \frac{2}{r\pi c} \int_0^s v_0(x) \sin \frac{r\pi x}{s} \, dx \qquad r = 1, 2, \ldots$$

for the D_k coefficients.

From (5.23) and (5.25) we see that if the string has no initial velocity the D_k constants are all zero, while if the string has no initial displacement all the C_k coefficients are zero.

Each term of (5.17) represents a stationary wave; the wavelengths are given by $2s/n$, where n is any integer.   The frequency, or number of periods per second, of the fundamental note is given by

$$(5.26) \qquad\qquad F_1 = \frac{1}{2s}\sqrt{\frac{T}{m}}$$

and the frequency of the *harmonics*, as the other terms are called, is given by

$$(5.27) \quad F_n = \frac{n}{2s}\sqrt{\frac{T}{m}} \qquad n = 2, 3, \ldots$$

FIG. 5.1

As an example of the application of Eqs. (5.23) and (5.25), let us consider the case of a string that is plucked at its mid-point as shown in Fig. 5.1.

In this case, we have the initial condition

$$(5.28) \qquad\qquad v_0(x) = 0$$

Hence by (5.25) we have

$$(5.29) \qquad\qquad D_r = 0 \qquad r = 1, 2, 3, \ldots$$

The initial displacement $y_0(x)$ is given by

$$(5.30) \qquad
\begin{aligned}
y_0(x) &= \frac{2hx}{s} & 0 &\le x \le \frac{s}{2} \\[2mm]
y_0(x) &= \frac{2h}{s}(s - x) & \frac{s}{2} &\le x \le s
\end{aligned}$$

Substituting the analytical expression for the initial displacement into Eq. (5.22), we obtain

$$(5.31) \quad C_r = \frac{2}{s}\left[\int_0^s \frac{2hx}{s}\sin\frac{r\pi x}{s}\,dx + \int_{s/2}^s \frac{2h}{s}(s - x)\sin\frac{r\pi x}{s}\,dx\right]$$

On carrying out the integrations, we obtain

$$(5.32) \qquad
\begin{aligned}
C_r &= \frac{8h}{\pi^2 r^2}\sin\frac{\pi r}{2} & &\text{if } r \text{ is odd} \\[2mm]
C_r &= 0 & &\text{if } r \text{ is even}
\end{aligned}$$

Substituting these results into (5.17), we obtain the following expression for the displacement of the string on being released from the initial position given by Fig. 5.1:

$$(5.33) \quad y = \frac{8h}{\pi^2}\left(\sin\frac{\pi x}{s}\cos\frac{\pi ct}{s} - \frac{1}{9}\sin\frac{3\pi x}{s}\cos\frac{3\pi ct}{s} + \cdots\right)$$

It is thus seen that no even harmonics are excited and that the second harmonic has one-ninth the amplitude of the fundamental. It is shown in treatises on sound that the energy emitted by an oscillating string as sound is proportional to the square of the amplitude of the oscillation. It is thus evident that in this case the fundamental tone will appear much louder than the harmonic tone.

6. Orthogonal Functions. In the last section a general solution of the wave equation of the vibrating string was constructed by assuming a solution of the form

(6.1) $$y(x,t) = e^{j\omega t}v(x)$$

This assumption, on substitution into the one-dimensional wave equation, led to the ordinary differential equation

(6.2) $$\frac{d^2v}{dx^2} + k^2v = 0$$

where k is given by

(6.3) $$k = \frac{\omega}{c}$$

The general solution of (6.2) may be written in the form

(6.4) $$v = A \sin kx + B \cos kx$$

Every solution of this form is perfectly acceptable as far as the differential equation is concerned, but it does not describe the behavior of the string. This solution permits the ends of the string to vibrate, whereas the physical condition of the problem requires these to be fixed. It is thus necessary to impose the following boundary conditions upon the solution (6.4):

(6.5) $$v(0) = 0 \qquad v(s) = 0$$

The boundary conditions may, of course, be satisfied by placing $A = 0$ and $B = 0$, but this would lead to the trivial and unwanted solution $y = 0$ everywhere. Hence there is left only the arbitrary constant B for adjustment. It must be taken to be zero in order to satisfy the first condition of (6.5). However, the function

(6.6) $$v = A \sin kx$$

will not satisfy the second condition of (6.5). The problem can be solved only if we are willing to prescribe only certain values to the undetermined constant k. If $\sin ks$ must be zero, then k must be 0, or π/s, $2\pi/s$, . . . , $n\pi/s$. The value $k = 0$ is rejected because it leads to the trivial solution $y = 0$.

The permissible values of k,

$$(6.7) \qquad k = \frac{n\pi}{s} \qquad n = 1, 2, 3, \ldots$$

are called *eigenvalues* in the modern literature of mathematical physics. To each eigenvalue there corresponds an *eigenfunction*

$$(6.8) \qquad v_n = A_n \sin \frac{n\pi x}{s}$$

The eigenfunctions under consideration have two important properties: they are (1) orthogonality and (2) completeness.

Orthogonality is defined as

$$(6.9) \qquad \int_0^s v_n(x)v_m(x)\, dx = 0 \qquad \text{if } n \neq m$$

The word comes originally from vector analysis, where two vectors **A** and **B** are said to be orthogonal if

$$(6.10) \qquad \mathbf{A} \cdot \mathbf{B} = A_x B_x + A_y B_y + A_z B_z = 0$$

In the same manner vectors in n dimensions having components A_i, B_i $(i = 1, 2, \ldots, n)$ are said to be orthogonal when

$$(6.11) \qquad \sum_{i=1}^{i=n} A_i B_i = 0$$

Imagine now a vector space of an infinite number of dimensions in which the components A_i and B_i become continuously distributed. Then i is no longer a denumerable index but a continuous variable x and the scalar product of (6.11) turns into

$$(6.12) \qquad \int_0^s A(x)B(x)\, dx = 0$$

In this case the functions A and B are said to be orthogonal. The idea of orthogonality is indefinite unless reference is made to a specific range of integration, which in the present case is from 0 to s. The fact that the eigenfunctions (6.8) are orthogonal may be verified at once since we have

$$(6.13) \qquad \int_0^s v_n(x)v_m(x)\, dx = A_n A_m \int_0^s \sin \frac{n\pi x}{s} \sin \frac{m\pi x}{s}\, dx = 0 \qquad \text{if } n \neq m$$

If $n = m$, we have

$$(6.14) \qquad \int_0^s v_n^2(x)\, dx = A_n^2 \int_0^s \sin^2 \frac{n\pi x}{s}\, dx = \frac{s}{2} A_n^2$$

We now turn to the notion of *completeness*. A set of functions is said to be complete if an arbitrary function $f(x)$ satisfying the same boundary conditions as the functions of the set can be expanded as follows,

$$(6.15) \qquad f(x) = \sum_{n=1}^{n=\infty} A_n v_n(x)$$

where the quantities A_n are constant coefficients. In the present discussion, Eq. (6.15) is equivalent to the theorem of Fourier discussed in Chap. 3.

7. The Oscillations of a Hanging Chain. Let us consider the small coplanar oscillations of a uniform flexible string or chain hanging from a support under the action of gravity as shown in Fig. 7.1. We consider only small deviations y from the equilibrium position; x is measured from the free end of the chain. Let it be required to determine the position of the chain

$$(7.1) \qquad y = y(x,t)$$

FIG. 7.1

where at $t = 0$ we give the chain an arbitrary displacement

$$(7.2) \qquad y = y_0(x)$$

In this case the tension T of the chain is variable, and hence Eq. (2.8) governs the displacement of the chain at any instant. Accordingly we have

$$(7.3) \qquad \frac{\partial}{\partial x}\left(T\,\frac{\partial y}{\partial x} \right) = m\,\frac{\partial^2 y}{\partial t^2}$$

where m is the mass per unit length of the chain. In this case the tension T is given by

$$(7.4) \qquad T = mgx$$

Hence we have

$$(7.5) \qquad \frac{\partial}{\partial x}\left(mgx\,\frac{\partial y}{\partial x} \right) = m\,\frac{\partial^2 y}{\partial t^2}$$

Or, differentiating and dividing both members by the common factor m, we have

$$(7.6) \qquad x\,\frac{\partial^2 y}{\partial x^2} + \frac{\partial y}{\partial x} = \frac{1}{g}\,\frac{\partial^2 y}{\partial t^2}$$

As in the case of the tightly stretched string, let us assume

$$(7.7) \qquad y(x,t) = e^{i\omega t}v(x)$$

Substituting this into (7.6), we obtain

$$(7.8) \qquad x \frac{d^2v}{dx^2} + \frac{dv}{dx} + \frac{\omega^2}{g} v = 0$$

This equation resembles Bessel's differential equation [Chap. 13, Eq. (9.6)]. The change in variable,

$$(7.9) \qquad Z^2 = \frac{4\omega^2 x}{g}$$

reduces (7.8) to

$$(7.10) \qquad Z^2 \frac{d^2v}{dZ^2} + Z \frac{dv}{dZ} + Z^2v = 0$$

whose general solution is

$$(7.11) \qquad v = AJ_0(Z) + BY_0(Z)$$

In order to satisfy the condition that the displacement of the string y remain finite when $x = 0$, we must place

$$(7.12) \qquad B = 0$$

Accordingly, in terms of the original variable x, we have the solution

$$(7.13) \qquad v = AJ_0\left(2\omega \sqrt{\frac{x}{g}}\right)$$

for the function v.

So far, the value of ω is undetermined. In order to determine it, we make use of the boundary condition

$$(7.14) \qquad v = 0 \qquad \text{at } x = s$$

This leads to the equation

$$(7.15) \qquad 0 = AJ_0\left(2\omega \sqrt{\frac{s}{g}}\right)$$

Now, for a nontrivial solution, A cannot be equal to zero, and hence we have

$$(7.16) \qquad J_0\left(2\omega \sqrt{\frac{s}{g}}\right) = 0$$

If we let

$$(7.17) \qquad u = 2\omega \sqrt{\frac{s}{g}}$$

we must find the roots of the equation

$$(7.18) \qquad J_0(u) = 0$$

If we consult a table of Bessel functions,* we find that the zeros of the

* See, for example, N. W. McLachlan, "Bessel Functions for Engineers," Oxford University Press, New York, 1934.

Bessel function $J_0(u)$ are given by the values

$$2.405, \ 5.52, \ 8.654, \ 11.792, \ \text{etc.}$$

Accordingly the various possible values of ω are given by

$$(7.19) \quad \omega_1 = \frac{2.405}{2} \sqrt{\frac{g}{s}} \qquad \omega_2 = \frac{5.52}{2} \sqrt{\frac{g}{s}} \qquad \omega_3 = \frac{8.654}{2} \sqrt{\frac{g}{s}} \qquad \text{etc.}$$

To each value of ω we associate a characteristic function or eigenfunction v_n of the form

$$(7.20) \qquad v_n = A_n J_0 \left(2\omega_n \sqrt{\frac{x}{g}} \right)$$

Since the real and imaginary parts of the assumed solution (7.7) are solutions of the original differential equation, we can construct a general solution of (7.6) satisfying the boundary conditions by summing the particular solutions corresponding to the various possible values of n in the manner

$$(7.21) \qquad y(x,t) = \sum_{n=1}^{n=\infty} J_0 \left(2\omega_n \sqrt{\frac{x}{g}} \right) (A_n \cos \omega_n t + B_n \sin \omega_n t)$$

where the quantities A_n and B_n are arbitrary constants to be determined from the boundary conditions of the problem. In the case under consideration there is no initial velocity imparted to the chain; hence

$$(7.22) \qquad \left(\frac{\partial y}{\partial t} \right)_{t=0} = 0$$

This leads to the condition

$$(7.23) \qquad B_n = 0$$

At $t = 0$ we have

$$(7.24) \qquad y_0(x) = \sum_{n=1}^{n=\infty} A_n J_0 \left(2\omega_n \sqrt{\frac{x}{g}} \right)$$

That is, we must expand the arbitrary displacement $y_0(x)$ into a series of Bessel functions of zeroth order. To do this, we can make use of the results (12.17) and (12.20) of Chap. 13. It is there shown that an arbitrary function of $F(x)$ may be expanded in a series of the form

$$(7.25) \qquad F(z) = \sum_{n=1}^{n=\infty} A_n J_0 (u_n z)$$

where the quantities u_n are successive positive roots of the equation

$$(7.26) \qquad J_n(u) = 0$$

The coefficients A_n are then given by the equation

$$(7.27) \qquad A_n = \frac{2}{J_1^2(u_n)} \int_0^1 zJ_0(u_n z)F(z) \, dz$$

To make use of this result to obtain the coefficients of the expansion (7.24), it is necessary only to introduce the variable

$$(7.28) \qquad z = \sqrt{\frac{x}{s}}$$

In view of (7.17) and (7.18), Eq. (7.24) becomes

$$(7.29) \qquad y_0(x) = y_0(sz^2) = F(z) = \sum_{n=1}^{n=\infty} A_n J_0(u_n z)$$

This is in the form (7.25), and the arbitrary constants are determined by (7.27).

The determination of the possible frequencies and modes of oscillation of a hanging chain is of historical interest. It appears to have been the first instance where the various normal modes of a continuous system were determined by Daniel Bernoulli (1732).

8. The Vibrations of a Rectangular Membrane.   As another example leading to the solution of the wave equation, let us consider the oscil-

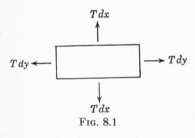

FIG. 8.1

lations of a flexible membrane. Let us suppose that the membrane has a density of m g per cm² and that it is pulled evenly around its edge with a tension of T dynes per cm length of edge. If the membrane is perfectly flexible, this tension will be distributed evenly throughout its area, that is, the material on opposite sides of any line segment dx is pulled apart with a force of $T \, dx$ dynes.

Let us call u the displacement of the membrane from its equilibrium position. It is a function of time and of the position on the membrane of the point in question. If we use rectangular coordinates to locate the point, u will be a function of x, y, and t. Let us consider an element $dx \, dy$ of the membrane shown in Fig. 8.1.

If we refer to the analogous argument of Sec. 2 for the string, we see that the net force normal to the surface of the membrane due to the pair of tensions $T \, dy$ is given by

$$(8.1) \qquad T \, dy \left[\left(\frac{\partial u}{\partial x} \right)_{x+dx} - \left(\frac{\partial u}{\partial x} \right)_x \right] = T \frac{\partial^2 u}{\partial x^2} \, dx \, dy$$

The net normal force due to the pair $T\,dx$ by the same reasoning is

$$(8.2) \qquad T\,dx\left[\left(\frac{\partial u}{\partial y}\right)_{y+dy} - \left(\frac{\partial u}{\partial y}\right)_{y}\right] = T\,\frac{\partial^2 u}{\partial y^2}\,dx\,dy$$

The sum of these forces is the net force on the element and is equal to the mass of the element times its acceleration. That is, we have

$$(8.3) \qquad T\left(\frac{\partial^2 u}{\partial x^2} + \frac{\partial^2 u}{\partial y^2}\right)dx\,dy = m\,\frac{\partial^2 y}{\partial t^2}\,dx\,dy$$

Dividing out the common factors of both sides of this equation, we obtain

$$(8.4) \qquad \frac{\partial^2 u}{\partial x^2} + \frac{\partial^2 u}{\partial y^2} = \frac{1}{c^2}\,\frac{\partial^2 u}{\partial t^2}$$

where

$$(8.5) \qquad c = \sqrt{\frac{T}{m}}$$

FIG. 8.2

Equation (8.4) is the wave equation for the membrane.   Let us consider the oscillations of the rectangular membrane of Fig. 8.2.

Let us assume that

$$(8.6) \qquad u = v(x,y)e^{j\omega t}$$

On substituting this assumption into (8.4) and canceling common factors, we obtain

$$(8.7) \qquad \frac{\partial^2 v}{\partial x^2} + \frac{\partial^2 v}{\partial y^2} + k^2 v = 0$$

where

$$(8.8) \qquad k^2 = \left(\frac{\omega}{c}\right)^2$$

Let us now assume

$$(8.9) \qquad v(x,y) = F_1(x)F_2(y)$$

that is, that v is the product of two functions, a function only of x and the other one only of y.   If we substitute this into (8.7), we obtain

$$(8.10) \qquad F_2\,\frac{d^2 F_1}{dx^2} + F_1\,\frac{d^2 F_2}{dy^2} + k^2 F_1 F_2 = 0$$

This equation may be written in the form

$$(8.11) \qquad \frac{1}{F_1}\,\frac{d^2 F_1}{dx^2} = -\frac{1}{F_2}\,\frac{d^2 F_2}{dy^2} - k^2$$

Now the first member of Eq. (8.11) is a function of x only, while the second member is a function of y only. Now a function of y cannot equal a function of x for all values of x and y if both functions really vary with x and y. Thus the only possible way for the equation to be true for both sides to be independent of both x and y is for it to be a constant. Let us call this constant $-m^2$; we then have

$$(8.12) \qquad \frac{1}{F_1}\frac{d^2F_1}{dx^2} = -\frac{1}{F_2}\frac{d^2F_2}{dy^2} - k^2 = -m^2$$

We thus obtain the two equations

$$(8.13) \qquad \frac{d^2F_1}{dx^2} + m^2F_1 = 0$$

and

$$(8.14) \qquad \frac{d^2F_2}{dy^2} + q^2F_2 = 0$$

where

$$(8.15) \qquad q^2 = k^2 - m^2$$

Now since the membrane is fastened at the edges $x = 0$, $x = a$, $y = 0$, $y = b$, the solution of Eq. (8.13) must vanish at $x = 0$ and $x = a$, while the solution of Eq. (8.14) must vanish at $y = 0$, $y = b$. A solution of (8.13) that vanishes at 0 is

$$(8.16) \qquad F_1 = A_1 \sin mx$$

In order for this to vanish at $x = a$, we must have

$$(8.17) \qquad ma = n\pi \qquad n = 1, 2, 3, \ldots$$

or

$$(8.18) \qquad m = \frac{n\pi}{a}$$

A solution of Eq. (8.14) that vanishes at $y = 0$ is

$$(8.19) \qquad F_2 = A_2 \sin qy$$

In order for this solution to vanish at

$$(8.20) \qquad y = b$$

we must have

$$(8.21) \qquad qb = r\pi \qquad r = 1, 2, 3, \ldots$$

Hence

$$(8.22) \qquad q = \frac{r\pi}{b}$$

Now from (8.15) we have

$$(8.23) \qquad k^2 = m^2 + q^2 = \pi^2 \left(\frac{n^2}{a^2} + \frac{r^2}{b^2} \right)$$

Hence the possible angular frequencies are given by

$$(8.24) \qquad \omega_{nr} = c\pi \sqrt{\frac{n^2}{a^2} + \frac{r^2}{b^2}} \qquad \begin{cases} n = 1, 2, 3, \ldots \\ r = 1, 2, 3, \ldots \end{cases}$$

Substituting (8.16) and (8.19) into (8.9), we obtain

$$(8.25) \qquad v(x,y) = A_1 A_2 \sin \frac{n\pi x}{a} \sin \frac{r\pi y}{b}$$

Since the indices r and n may take positive integral values and A_1 and A_2 are arbitrary, we may write instead of (8.25) the functions $v(x,y)$ in the form

$$(8.26) \qquad v_{nr} = A_{nr} \sin \frac{n\pi x}{a} \sin \frac{r\pi y}{b}$$

If the membrane is excited from rest with an initial displacement $u_0(x,y)$ and with *no* initial velocity, we retain the real part of (8.6) and construct a general solution by summing over all possible values of n and r. We thus obtain

$$(8.27) \qquad u = \sum_{n=1}^{\infty} \sum_{r=1}^{\infty} A_{nr} \cos \omega_{nr} t \sin \frac{n\pi x}{a} \sin \frac{r\pi y}{b}$$

We are now confronted with the question of expanding the function $u_0(x,y)$ into the series

$$(8.28) \qquad u_0(x,y) = \sum_{n=1}^{\infty} \sum_{r=1}^{\infty} A_{nr} \sin \frac{n\pi x}{a} \sin \frac{r\pi y}{b}$$

Let us first regard y as a constant. In that case $u_0(x,y)$ can be expanded in the form

$$(8.29) \qquad u_0(x,y)_{y=\text{const}} = \sum_{n=1}^{\infty} A_n \sin \frac{n\pi x}{a}$$

where we have

$$(8.30) \qquad A_n = \frac{2}{a} \int_0^a u_0(x,y) \sin \frac{n\pi x}{a} \, dx$$

After the integration with respect to x is performed and the limits substituted, regard A_n as a function of y and let it be expanded in terms of

$\sin (r\pi y/b)$ by the series

$$(8.31) \qquad A_n = \sum_{r=1}^{r=\infty} A_{nr} \sin \frac{r\pi y}{b}$$

where

$$(8.32) \qquad A_{nr} = \frac{4}{ab} \int_0^b dy \int_0^a u_0(x,y) \sin \frac{n\pi x}{a} \sin \frac{r\pi y}{b} \, dx$$

This determines the arbitrary constants A_{nr}, and the subsequent motion is given by (8.27).

From (8.24) and (8.27) it is evident that if any mode is excited for which n or r is greater than unity we have nodal lines parallel to the edges. It also appears that, if the ratio a^2/b^2 is not equal to that of two integers, the frequencies are all distinct. However, if a^2/b^2 is commensurable, some of the periods coincide. The nodal lines may then assume a great variety of forms. The simplest example is the square membrane; in this case we have

$$(8.33) \qquad \omega_{nr}^2 = \frac{c^2\pi^2}{a^2} (n^2 + r^2)$$

for the squares of the angular frequencies.

9. The Vibrations of a Circular Membrane. In the case of the circular membrane we naturally have recourse to polar coordinates with the origin at the center. In this case the equation of motion deduced in Sec. 8 must be transformed from cartesian to polar coordinates. We may write the basic equation of motion of the membrane in the form

$$(9.1) \qquad \nabla^2 u = \frac{1}{c^2} \frac{\partial^2 u}{\partial t^2}$$

where in this case ∇^2 is the Laplacian operator in two dimensions. To write this equation in polar coordinates, it is necessary only to write the invariant quantity $\nabla^2 u$ in polar coordinates. Using Eq. (12.20) of Chap. 15, we have

$$(9.2) \qquad \nabla^2 u = \frac{1}{r} \frac{\partial}{\partial r} \left(r \frac{\partial u}{\partial r} \right) + \frac{1}{r^2} \frac{\partial^2 u}{\partial \theta^2}$$

Accordingly the wave equation for the membrane becomes in this case

$$(9.3) \qquad \frac{1}{r} \frac{\partial}{\partial r} \left(r \frac{\partial u}{\partial r} \right) + \frac{1}{r^2} \frac{\partial^2 u}{\partial \theta^2} = \frac{1}{c^2} \frac{\partial^2 u}{\partial t^2}$$

Let us consider the symmetrical case where the motion is started in a symmetrical manner about the origin so that the displacement u is a function only of r and t and independent of the angle θ. This is the case of symmetrical oscillations about the origin.   Since in this case we have

(9.4) $u = u(r,t)$

Eq. (9.3) becomes

(9.5) $$\frac{1}{r}\frac{\partial}{\partial r}\left(r\,\frac{\partial u}{\partial r}\right) = \frac{1}{c^2}\frac{\partial^2 u}{\partial t^2}$$

Let us now study the symmetrical oscillations of a circular membrane of radius a that is given an initial displacement $u_0(r)$ at $t = 0$.   In this case we have to find a solution of (9.5) that vanishes at $r = a$ and has the initial value $u_0(r)$ at $t = 0$.   As in the above examples, let us assume a solution of the form

(9.6) $u = v(r)e^{j\omega t}$

Substituting this assumed form of the solution in (9.5), we obtain, on dividing out the factor $e^{j\omega t}$,

(9.7) $$\frac{1}{r}\frac{d}{dr}\left(r\,\frac{dv}{dr}\right) + \left(\frac{\omega}{c}\right)^2 v = 0$$

On carrying out the differentiation we have

(9.8) $$r\,\frac{d^2 v}{dr^2} + \frac{dv}{dr} + \left(\frac{\omega}{c}\right)^2 vr = 0$$

or

(9.9) $$\frac{d^2 v}{dr^2} + \frac{1}{r}\frac{dv}{dr} + k^2 v = 0$$

where

(9.10) $$k = \frac{\omega}{c}$$

Equation (9.9) is an equation of the form discussed in Chap. 13, Sec. 9. Its general solution is

(9.11) $v = AJ_0(kr) + BY_0(kr)$

where A and B are arbitrary constants and J_0 and Y_0 are the Bessel functions of the zeroth order and of the first and second kind, respectively.

Since the amplitude of the oscillation is finite at the origin, we must have

(9.12) $B = 0$

We must now satisfy the condition that the amplitude of the oscillation must vanish at $r = a$.   Hence we must have

(9.13) $0 = AJ_0(ka)$

For nontrivial solutions A cannot be equal to zero; hence we must have

(9.14) $0 = J_0(ka)$

From a table of Bessel functions, we find that Eq. (9.14) is satisfied if ka has values 2.404, 5.520, 8.653, 11.791, 14.93, etc. Accordingly the fundamental angular frequency is given by

$$(9.15) \qquad \omega_1 = \frac{2.404c}{a}$$

The other possible angular frequencies are given by the above numbers multiplied by c/a. It is thus seen that there are an infinite number of natural frequencies possible, but these frequencies are *not* multiples of each other as is the case of the vibrating string. By summing over all the possible values of ω we may construct a general solution of (9.5) that satisfies the boundary condition at the periphery of the membrane and the initial condition that at $t = 0$ the membrane has no initial velocity and an arbitrary initial displacement $u_0(r)$. We thus obtain

$$(9.16) \qquad u = \sum_{n=1}^{n=\infty} A_n J_0 \left(\frac{\omega_n}{c} r \right) \cos \omega_n t$$

Now, at $t = 0$, we have

$$(9.17) \qquad u = u_0(r)$$

Accordingly we must expand an arbitrary function $u_0(r)$ in a series of the form

$$(9.18) \qquad u_0(r) = \sum_{n=1}^{n=\infty} A_n J_0 \left(\frac{\omega_n r}{c} \right)$$

To determine the arbitrary constants A_n, we may use Eq. (12.20) of Chap. 13. We thus obtain

$$(9.19) \qquad A_n = \frac{2}{a^2 J_1^2[(\omega_n/c)a]} \int_0^a r J_0 \left(\omega_n \frac{r}{c} \right) u_0(r) \, dr$$

When these values of the constants A_n are substituted into (9.16), we obtain the subsequent displacement of the membrane.

10. The Telegraphist's, or Transmission-line, Equations. In this section we shall consider the flow of electricity in a pair of linear conductors such as telephone wires or an electrical transmission line.

FIG. 10.1

Consider a long, imperfectly insulated transmission line as shown in Fig. 10.1.

Let us consider that an electric current is flowing from the source A to the receiving end B in the direction shown in the figure. Let the distance measured along the length of the cable be denoted by x; then both the current i and the potential difference e between the two wires are functions of x and t. Denote the resistance per unit length of the wires by R, the conductance per unit length between the two wires by G, the capacitance per unit length of the two wires by C, and the inductance per unit length by L.

Now consider an element of the transmission line of length Δx. If the electromotive force at the point x is $e(x,t)$, then, if we compute the potential drop along an element of length Δx, we have

$$(10.1) \qquad e(x,t) = iR\,\Delta x + L\,\Delta x\,\frac{\partial i}{\partial t} + e(x + \Delta x, t)$$

However, by Taylor's expansion, we have

$$(10.2) \qquad e(x + \Delta x, t) = e(x,t) + \frac{\partial e}{\partial x}\,\Delta x + \cdots$$

where we neglect terms of higher order. Substituting this into (10.1), we have

$$(10.3) \qquad -\frac{\partial e}{\partial x} = iR + L\,\frac{\partial i}{\partial t}$$

If we denote by $i(x,t)$ the current entering a section of length Δx and by $i(x + \Delta x, t)$ the current leaving this element, we have

$$(10.4) \qquad i(x,t) = eG\,\Delta x + \frac{\partial e}{\partial t}\,C\,\Delta x + i(x + \Delta x, t)$$

where $eG\,\Delta x$ is the current that leaks through the insulation and $(\partial e/\partial t)C\,\Delta x$ is the current involved in charging the capacitor formed by the proximity of the two conductors forming the transmission line. By Taylor's expansion we have

$$(10.5) \qquad i(x + \Delta x, t) = i(x,t) + \frac{\partial i}{\partial x}\,\Delta x + \cdots$$

where we neglect higher-order terms. Substituting this into (10.4), we obtain

$$(10.6) \qquad -\frac{\partial i}{\partial x} = eG + C\,\frac{\partial e}{\partial t}$$

Equations (10.3) and (10.6) are simultaneous partial differential equations for the potential difference and the current of the transmission line. To eliminate the potential difference, we take the partial derivative of (10.6) with respect to x. We then obtain

$$(10.7) \qquad -\frac{\partial^2 i}{\partial x^2} = G\,\frac{\partial e}{\partial x} + C\,\frac{\partial}{\partial t}\left(\frac{\partial e}{\partial x}\right)$$

We then substitute the value of $\partial e/\partial x$ given by (10.3) into (10.7) and thus obtain

$$(10.8) \qquad \frac{\partial^2 i}{\partial x^2} = LC \frac{\partial^2 i}{\partial t^2} + (LG + RC) \frac{\partial i}{\partial t} + RGi$$

In the same manner we have, on eliminating the current,

$$(10.9) \qquad \frac{\partial^2 e}{\partial x^2} = LC \frac{\partial^2 e}{\partial t^2} + (LG + RC) \frac{\partial e}{\partial t} + RGe$$

Equations (10.8) and (10.9) are sometimes known as the *telephone equations* since they are used in discussing telephonic transmission.

In many applications to telegraph signaling the leakage G is small and the term for the effect of inductance L is negligible, so that we may place

$$(10.10) \qquad\qquad G = L = 0$$

The equations then take the simplified form

$$(10.11) \qquad\qquad \frac{\partial^2 i}{\partial x^2} = RC \frac{\partial i}{\partial t}$$

and

$$(10.12) \qquad\qquad \frac{\partial^2 e}{\partial x^2} = RC \frac{\partial e}{\partial t}$$

These are known as the *telegraph*, or *cable, equations*.

For high frequencies the terms in the time derivatives are large, and some qualitative properties of the solution may be found by neglecting the terms for the effect of leakage and resistance in comparison with them. On placing

$$(10.13) \qquad\qquad G = R = 0$$

the equations become

$$(10.14) \qquad\qquad \frac{\partial^2 i}{\partial x^2} = LC \frac{\partial^2 i}{\partial t^2}$$

$$(10.15) \qquad\qquad \frac{\partial^2 e}{\partial x^2} = LC \frac{\partial^2 e}{\partial t^2}$$

If we let

$$(10.16) \qquad\qquad v = \frac{1}{\sqrt{LC}}$$

then we see that in this case both the current and the potential difference between the lines satisfy the one-dimensional wave equation

$$(10.17) \qquad\qquad \frac{\partial^2 u}{\partial x^2} = \frac{1}{v^2} \frac{\partial^2 u}{\partial t^2}$$

This equation has the same form as that governing the displacement of the tightly stretched oscillating string. We thus see that a transmission line with negligible resistance and leakage propagates waves of current and potential with a velocity equal to $1/\sqrt{LC}$. The study of Eqs. (10.3) and (10.6) is fundamental in the theory of electrical power transmission and telephony.

The Distortionless Transmission Line. A very interesting special case occurs when the parameters of the transmission line satisfy the relation

$$(10.18) \qquad \frac{R}{L} = \frac{G}{C}$$

The amount of leakage indicated by this equation is reduced by increasing the inductance parameter L. A line having this relation between its parameters is called a *distortionless line*. This type of line is of considerable importance in telephony and telegraphy. To analyze this special case, let

$$(10.19) \qquad a^2 = RG$$

Now we have

$$(10.20) \qquad RC = LG$$

Hence

$$(10.21) \qquad R^2C^2 = (LG)(RC) = (RG)(LC)$$
$$= \frac{a^2}{v^2}$$

But

$$(10.22) \qquad LG + RC = 2RC = \frac{2a}{v}$$

Hence Eq. (10.9) in this case becomes

$$(10.23) \qquad \frac{\partial^2 e}{\partial x^2} = \frac{1}{v^2}\frac{\partial^2 e}{\partial t^2} + \frac{2a}{v}\frac{\partial e}{\partial t} + a^2 e$$

Let us now introduce the variable $y(x,t)$ defined by the equation

$$(10.24) \qquad e(x,t) = e^{-avt}y(x,t)$$

If we perform the indicated differentiation and substitute the results into (10.23), we obtain after some reductions

$$(10.25) \qquad \frac{\partial^2 y}{\partial x^2} = \frac{1}{v^2}\frac{\partial^2 y}{\partial t^2}$$

This is a one-dimensional wave equation in y, and its general solution is

$$(10.26) \qquad y = F(x - vt) + G(x + vt)$$

where F and G denote arbitrary functions of the arguments $x - vt$ and $x + vt$, respectively. Now

$$(10.27) \qquad av = (RC)v^2 = \frac{R}{L}$$

Hence in view of (10.24) we have

$$(10.28) \qquad e(x,t) = e^{-Rt/L}[F(x - vt) + G(x + vt)]$$

We thus see that the general solution of (10.9) in this case is given by the superposition of two arbitrary waves that travel without distortion to the left and to the right along the line with velocity of v but with an attenuation given by the factor $e^{-Rt/L}$.

Line without Leakage. In most practical power-transmission lines the insulation between the line wires is so good that the leakage conductance coefficient G may be taken equal to zero. In such a case the equations for the potential and current of the transmission line become

$$(10.29) \qquad \frac{\partial^2 e}{\partial x^2} = LC \frac{\partial^2 e}{\partial t^2} + RC \frac{\partial e}{\partial t}$$

$$(10.30) \qquad \frac{\partial^2 i}{\partial x^2} = LC \frac{\partial^2 i}{\partial t^2} + RC \frac{\partial i}{\partial t}$$

To solve (10.30), we let

$$(10.31) \qquad i = ye^{-Rt/2L}$$

Making this substitution in (10.30), we obtain after some reductions

$$(10.32) \qquad \frac{\partial^2 y}{\partial x^2} = \frac{1}{v^2} \frac{\partial^2 y}{\partial t^2} - \frac{a^2}{v^2} y \qquad a = \frac{R}{2L}$$

Now let

$$(10.33) \qquad z = a \sqrt{t^2 - \frac{x^2}{v^2}}$$

We have

$$(10.34) \qquad \frac{\partial^2 y}{\partial x^2} = \frac{d^2 y}{dz^2} \left(\frac{\partial z}{\partial x} \right)^2 + \frac{dy}{dz} \frac{\partial^2 z}{\partial x^2}$$

$$(10.35) \qquad \frac{\partial^2 y}{\partial t^2} = \frac{d^2 y}{dz^2} \left(\frac{\partial z}{\partial t} \right)^2 + \frac{dy}{dz} \frac{\partial^2 z}{\partial t^2}$$

On substituting these expressions for $\partial^2 y/\partial x^2$ and $\partial^2 y/\partial t^2$ in (10.32), we obtain after some reductions

$$(10.36) \qquad \frac{d^2 y}{dz^2} + \frac{1}{z} \frac{dy}{dz} - y = 0$$

This equation is the modified Bessel differential equation of the zeroth order discussed in Chap. 13, Sec. 10. Its general solution is

$$(10.37) \qquad y = AI_0(z) + BK_0(z)$$

where $I_0(z)$ and $K_0(z)$ are modified Bessel functions of the zeroth order of the first and second kind and A and B are arbitrary constants. Since the function $K_0(z)$ does not remain finite at $z = 0$, we must have $B = 0$. Hence the solution for the current is

$$(10.38) \qquad i = e^{-Rt/2L} A I_0(z)$$

The constant A must be determined from a knowledge of the initial conditions of the transmission line.

The Steady-state Solution. Let us consider the transmission line shown in Fig. 10.2. In this case we consider the effect of impressing a harmonic potential difference of the form $E_g \cos \omega t$ at one end of the line. This case is of great importance in power transmission and in communication networks.

In this case we impress on the line at $x = 0$ a potential difference of the form

FIG. 10.2

$$(10.39) \quad E_g \cos \omega t = \text{Re} \, (E_g e^{j\omega t})$$

where Re denotes the "real part of." To solve Eqs. (10.3) and (10.6) in this case, we assume a solution of the form

$$(10.40) \qquad \begin{aligned} e(x,t) &= \text{Re} \, [E(x)e^{j\omega t}] \\ i(x,t) &= \text{Re} \, [I(x)e^{j\omega t}] \end{aligned}$$

We now substitute these assumed forms of the solution in (10.3) and (10.6) and drop the Re sign, remembering that to get the instantaneous potential difference $e(x,t)$ and the instantaneous current $i(x,t)$ we must use Eqs. (10.40). On substituting the above assumed form of the solution into (10.3) and (10.6) and dividing out the common factor $e^{j\omega t}$ we obtain

$$(10.41) \qquad \begin{aligned} \frac{dE}{dx} + (R + j\omega L)I &= 0 \\ \frac{dI}{dx} + (G + j\omega C)E &= 0 \end{aligned}$$

It is convenient to introduce the notation

$$(10.42) \qquad \begin{aligned} Z &= R + j\omega L \\ Y &= G + j\omega C \end{aligned}$$

Then Eqs. (10.41) become

$$(10.43) \qquad \begin{aligned} \frac{dE}{dx} + ZI &= 0 \\ \frac{dI}{dx} + YE &= 0 \end{aligned}$$

We may eliminate E and I by differentiating each equation with respect to x and substituting either dE/dx or dI/dx from the other.   We thus obtain

(10.44)
$$\frac{d^2E}{dx^2} = a^2E$$
$$\frac{d^2I}{dx^2} = a^2I$$

where

(10.45)
$$a^2 = ZY$$

These equations are linear differential equations of the second order with constant coefficients, and their solutions are

(10.46)
$$E(x) = A_1e^{-ax} + A_2e^{ax}$$
$$I(x) = B_1e^{-ax} + B_2e^{ax}$$

The evaluation of the arbitrary constants A_1, A_2, B_1, B_2 requires a knowledge of the terminal conditions of the transmission line.   The

FIG. 10.3

evaluation of these arbitrary constants in the case of general terminal conditions is straightforward but rather tedious.*

To illustrate the general procedure, let us consider the case of a line short-circuited at $x = s$, as shown in Fig. 10.3.

In this case, we have the boundary conditions

(10.47)
$$E(0) = E_g$$
$$E(s) = 0$$

These boundary conditions lead to the two simultaneous equations in the arbitrary constants A_1 and A_2,

(10.48)
$$A_1 + A_2 = E_g$$
$$A_1e^{-as} + A_2e^{as} = 0$$

Solving for A_1 and A_2 and substituting the results into (10.46), we obtain

(10.49)
$$E(x) = \frac{E_g}{e^{as} - e^{-as}} (e^{a(s-x)} - e^{-a(s-x)})$$

This result may be written more concisely in terms of hyperbolic func-

* See, for example, E. A. Guillemin, "Communication Networks," chap. II, John Wiley & Sons, Inc., New York, 1935.

tions in the form

$$(10.50) \qquad E(x) = \frac{E_g \sinh a(s - x)}{\sinh as}$$

We may obtain $I(x)$ directly from (10.43) in the form

$$(10.51) \qquad I(x) = -\frac{1}{Z}\frac{dE}{dx}$$

$$= \frac{E_g a}{Z}\frac{\cosh a(s - x)}{\sinh as}$$

If we introduce the notation

$$(10.52) \qquad Z_0 = \sqrt{\frac{Z}{Y}}$$

then (10.51) may be written in the form

$$(10.53) \qquad I(x) = \frac{E_g}{Z_0}\frac{\cosh a(s - x)}{\sinh as}$$

Since a is in general complex, we see that $E(x)$ and $I(x)$ are complex functions of x. To obtain the instantaneous potential $e(x,t)$ and current $i(x,t)$, we must use Eqs. (10.40). An interesting physical significance of the solution may be obtained by considering an indefinitely long line. Since in general a is a complex number, we may write

$$(10.54) \qquad a = a_1 + ja_2$$

In this case the arbitrary constant A_2 in (10.46) must be equal to zero, since if it were not, the absolute value of $E(x)$ would increase indefinitely. Hence in this case we have

$$(10.55) \qquad E(x) = E_g e^{-ax} = E_g e^{-a_1 x} e^{-ja_2 x}$$

since $\qquad\qquad\quad E(0) = E_g$

The instantaneous potential is then given by (10.40) in the form

$$(10.56) \qquad e(x,t) = \mathrm{Re}\,(E_g e^{-ax} e^{j\omega t})$$

$$= E_g e^{-a_1 x} \cos(\omega t - a_2 x)$$

That is, as we travel along the infinite line, the potential is diminished by the factor e^{-ax} and a phase difference $a_2 x$ is introduced. In this case we have

$$(10.57) \qquad I(x) = \frac{E_g}{Z_0} e^{-ax}$$

and the instantaneous current is given by (10.40). If there is no dissipation of energy along the line, then $R = 0$, $G = 0$; hence

$$(10.58) \qquad a = j\omega\sqrt{LC}$$

or

(10.59) $$a_1 = 0 \qquad a_2 = \omega \sqrt{LC}$$

In this case there is no attenuation of potential or current along the line, but we have

(10.60) $$e(x,t) = E_g \cos \omega(t - x \sqrt{LC})$$

This represents a harmonic wave having a phase velocity of $1/\sqrt{LC}$. The current in this case is given by

(10.61) $$i(x,t) = E_g \sqrt{\frac{C}{L}} \cos \omega(t - x \sqrt{LC})$$

The study of more complicated boundary conditions may be undertaken in the same manner, beginning from Eqs. (10.46). An excellent discussion of the general solution will be found in the above-mentioned reference.

11. Tidal Waves in a Canal. Let us consider an incompressible liquid of uniform depth h. The waves which occur on the surface of a liquid may be divided into the following two types:

FIG. 11.1

1. Ripples. These are waves whose wavelength is small, being of the order of $\frac{2}{3}$ in. These waves owe their propagation to the surface tension in the liquid-air surface and to gravity.

2. Tidal waves. These waves are characterized by having such a long wavelength that the effect of surface tension can be neglected. In the case of these waves the vertical displacement of the surface is small in comparison with the wavelength.

In this section the theory of tidal waves will be discussed. Consider Fig. 11.1.

Let the bottom of the liquid be given by the plane $y = 0$. Let y be measured so that the y axis points upward. Let the free surface in the xy plane be given by

(11.1) $$y_s = h + u$$

where h is the depth of the liquid in the undisturbed state and u is the height of the wave above the undisturbed surface of the liquid.

Let the liquid be bounded in the z direction by fixed planes parallel to the xy plane. It will be assumed that these planes are smooth and the liquid slips along them without any frictional resistance.

As a consequence of this assumption the distance between these planes is of no consequence. However, for simplicity, it will be assumed that they are a unit distance apart; that is, the liquid is constrained to move in a uniform canal of unit width and depth h.

Let us use the following notation:

(11.2) p_0 = pressure at surface of liquid

(11.3) ρ = density of liquid

(11.4) g = gravitational constant

If we neglect the vertical acceleration of the particles of the liquid, we may write the following expression for the pressure at the point x, y:

(11.5)
$$p(x,y) = p_0 + g\rho(y_s - y)$$
$$= p_0 + g\rho(h + u - y)$$

as a consequence of (11.1).

Now let us consider the vertical strip which is bounded by the planes x and $x + dx$ before the wave motion begins. The volume of this strip is $h\,dx$. An instant after the motion is started, let the elevation of the surface of the strip be $y_s = h + u$, and let the planes bounding it have moved to $x + v$ and $x + dx + v + (\partial v/\partial x)\,dx$. The volume of the strip is then $(h + u)[dx + (\partial v/\partial x)\,dx]$. Since the liquid is assumed incompressible, the volume of the strip does not vary with the time. Hence we have

(11.6)
$$h\,dx = (h + u)\left(dx + \frac{\partial v}{\partial x}\,dx\right)$$

or

(11.7)
$$u + h\frac{\partial v}{\partial x} = 0$$

where the second term has been neglected since it is a quantity of higher order.

The Resultant Force on the Strip. Let the strip under consideration be divided into elements parallel to the bottom. Consider one of these elements of height dy. The force on this element is given by

(11.8)
$$p\,dy - \left(p + \frac{\partial p}{\partial x}\,dx\right)dy = -\frac{\partial p}{\partial x}\,dx\,dy$$

But from Eq. (11.5) we have

(11.9)
$$\frac{\partial p}{\partial x} = g\rho\frac{\partial u}{\partial x}$$

since u is the only function of x in (11.5). Hence the force on the element is given by

(11.10)
$$-\frac{\partial p}{\partial x}\,dx\,dy = -g\rho\frac{\partial u}{\partial x}\,dx\,dy$$

The force F_x on the whole strip is obtained by integrating the force on the element of height dy, and we have

$$(11.11) \qquad F_x = -g\rho \frac{\partial u}{\partial x} dx \int_0^h dy = -g\rho h \frac{\partial u}{\partial x} dx$$

This is the rate of increase in momentum by Newton's second law of motion:

$$(11.12) \qquad F_x = h\rho \, dx \frac{\partial^2 v}{\partial t^2} = -g\rho h \frac{\partial u}{\partial x} dx$$

However, differentiating (11.7), we have

$$(11.13) \qquad \frac{\partial u}{\partial x} = -h \frac{\partial^2 v}{\partial x^2}$$

Substituting this into (11.12) and dividing by the common factor, we obtain

$$(11.14) \qquad \frac{\partial^2 v}{\partial x^2} = \frac{1}{gh} \frac{\partial^2 v}{\partial t^2}$$

This is the one-dimensional wave equation discussed in Sec. 3. The velocity of propagation of long waves is therefore

$$(11.15) \qquad c = \sqrt{gh}$$

Equation (11.14) may be used to study the pattern of long water waves in a rectangular trough whose length is much greater than its breadth and depth. The conditions at the ends of the trough are $v = 0$ at $x = 0$ and $v = 0$ at $x = s$, where s is the length of the trough.

This analysis is similar to that of the vibrating string of length s considered in Sec. 5. The *period* of the fundamental oscillation is $2s/\sqrt{gh}$.

If the restriction that the long waves move only in one dimension is removed, then a similar analysis shows that the quantity v above satisfies the two-dimensional wave equation.

$$(11.16) \qquad \frac{\partial^2 v}{\partial x^2} + \frac{\partial^2 v}{\partial y^2} = \frac{1}{c^2} \frac{\partial^2 v}{\partial t^2} \qquad \text{where } c = \sqrt{gh}$$

12. Sound Waves in a Gas. An important class of problems involving wave propagation is that of waves in a *compressible* fluid such as a gas. The case of sound waves is a particular example of this type of wave motion.

To derive the equation for the propagation of sound in a compressible gas we recall (see Chap. 15) that the general equation of continuity for a fluid is

$$(12.1) \qquad \frac{\partial \rho}{\partial t} + \nabla \cdot (\rho \mathbf{v}) = 0$$

where ρ is the density of the fluid and $\mathbf{v}$ the vector velocity of the fluid defined by

$$(12.2) \qquad \mathbf{v} = i v_x + j v_y + k v_z$$

where v_x, v_y, and v_z are the components of the velocity of the fluid in a cartesian frame of reference.

The Euler equation of motion in vector form is

$$(12.3) \qquad \frac{\partial \mathbf{v}}{\partial t} + (\mathbf{v} \cdot \nabla) \mathbf{v} = \mathbf{F} - \frac{1}{\rho} \nabla p$$

where p is the pressure of the fluid and $\mathbf{F}$ is the "body" force per unit mass.

These fundamental equations will now be applied to the case of wave motion in a perfect gas. The following assumptions will be made:

1. The motion is *irrotational* so that there exists a velocity potential ϕ defined by the equation

$$(12.4) \qquad v = -\nabla \phi$$

2. The velocities are so small that their squares and products can be neglected.

3. The body force $\mathbf{F}$ can be neglected.

Let us write

$$(12.4a) \qquad \rho = \rho_0 (1 + s)$$

where ρ_0 is the initial value of the density. The quantity s is called the *condensation*. Since the changes in density in a sound wave are small, the condensation s is small. It will be assumed that as a consequence of this the term $\nabla \cdot s$ can be neglected in the continuity equation.

Substituting (12.4) into (12.1), we obtain

$$(12.5) \qquad \frac{\partial}{\partial t} [\rho_0 (1 + s)] + \nabla \cdot [\rho_0 (1 + s) \mathbf{v}] = 0$$

By the assumption that s is small this equation becomes

$$(12.6) \qquad \frac{\partial s}{\partial t} = -\nabla \cdot \mathbf{v}$$

In terms of the velocity potential of Eq. (12.4) this becomes

$$(12.7) \qquad \frac{\partial s}{\partial t} = \nabla^2 \phi$$

Neglecting the squares and products of the velocities in Eq. (12.3) and writing the resulting vector equation in scalar form, we obtain

$$\frac{\partial}{\partial t}\frac{\partial \phi}{\partial x} = \frac{1}{\rho}\frac{\partial p}{\partial x}$$

(12.8)
$$\frac{\partial}{\partial t}\frac{\partial \phi}{\partial y} = \frac{1}{\rho}\frac{\partial p}{\partial y}$$

$$\frac{\partial}{\partial t}\frac{\partial \phi}{\partial z} = \frac{1}{\rho}\frac{\partial p}{\partial z}$$

If the first equation is multiplied by dx, the second one by dy, the third by dz and the results are added, we obtain

(12.9) $\quad \dfrac{\partial}{\partial t}\left(\dfrac{\partial \phi}{\partial x}\,dx + \dfrac{\partial \phi}{\partial y}\,dy + \dfrac{\partial \phi}{\partial z}\,dz\right) = \dfrac{1}{\rho}\left(\dfrac{\partial p}{\partial x}\,dx + \dfrac{\partial p}{\partial y}\,dy + \dfrac{\partial p}{\partial z}\,dz\right)$

or

(12.10) $$\frac{\partial}{\partial t}(d\phi) = \frac{dp}{\rho}$$

Integrating, we obtain

(12.11) $$\frac{\partial \phi}{\partial t} = \int \frac{dp}{\rho} = \text{const}$$

The Isothermal Assumption (Newton's Equation). Isaac Newton assumed that the condensation and rarefaction process involved in the propagation of sound waves takes place in such a manner that the *temperature* of each element of mass is constant. In this case we may assume that Boyle's law holds, and we have

(12.12) $$p = c\rho$$

where ρ is the density, p the pressure, and c a constant. Then we have

(12.13) $$dp = c\,d\rho = c\rho_0\,ds$$

by Eq. (12.4).

Consequently we have

(12.14) $$\int \frac{dp}{\rho} = \int \frac{c\,ds}{1 + s} = c\ln(1 + s)$$

Substituting this into (12.11), we have

(12.15) $$\frac{\partial \phi}{\partial t} = c\ln(1 + s) = \text{const}$$

Differentiating with respect to t, we obtain

(12.16) $$\frac{\partial^2 \phi}{\partial t^2} = \frac{c}{1 + s}\frac{\partial s}{\partial t} = c\frac{\partial s}{\partial t}$$

since $s \ll 1$.

Eliminating $\partial s / \partial t$ between (12.16) and (12.7), we have

$$(12.17) \qquad \nabla^2 \phi = \frac{1}{c} \frac{\partial^2 \phi}{\partial t^2}$$

This isothermal assumption gives the general wave equation (12.17). The velocity of propagation v_0 is

$$(12.18) \qquad v_0 = \sqrt{c} = \sqrt{\frac{p}{\rho}}$$

This is the well-known expression derived by Newton for the velocity of sound in a gas. However, it does not agree with experiment since its value is too small.

The Adiabatic Assumption of Laplace. Laplace showed that, in the case of sound waves, the condensation and rarefaction take place so rapidly that the heat produced has not time to disappear by conduction. Hence the *temperature* of each element of mass will not be constant, but its quantity of heat will remain constant. This process is not an isothermal one but an adiabatic one.

In this case, instead of Boyle's law, (12.12), we have the adiabatic relation

$$(12.19) \qquad p = c \rho^k$$

where c and k are constants. The constant k is given by the following relation:

$$(12.20) \qquad k = \frac{\text{specific heat at constant pressure}}{\text{specific heat at constant volume}}$$

k is of the order of 1.41 for air, oxygen, hydrogen, and nitrogen. As a consequence of Eqs. (12.19) and (12.4), we have

$$(12.21) \qquad dp = c k \rho^{k-1} \, d\rho = c \rho_0^k k (1 + s)^{k-1} \, ds$$

We also have

$$(12.22) \qquad \int \frac{dp}{\rho} = c k \rho_0^{k-1} \int (1 + s)^{k-2} \, ds = \frac{c k \rho_0^{k-1}}{k - 1} (1 + s)^{k-1}$$

Hence by Eq. (12.11)

$$(12.23) \qquad \frac{\partial^2 \phi}{\partial t^2} = \frac{\partial}{\partial t} \int \frac{dp}{\rho} = c k \rho_0^{k-1} (1 + s)^{k-2} \frac{\partial s}{\partial t}$$

Since s is small, $(1 + s)^{k-2} \approx 1$ and

$$(12.24) \qquad c \rho_0^{k-1} = \frac{p_0}{\rho_0}$$

as a consequence of (12.19).

Equation (12.23) then may be written in the form

$$(12.25) \qquad \frac{\partial^2 \phi}{\partial t^2} = \frac{k p_0}{\rho_0} \frac{\partial s}{\partial t}$$

Using (12.7) to eliminate $\partial s / \partial t$, we obtain

$$(12.26) \qquad \nabla^2 \phi = \frac{\rho_0}{k p_0} \frac{\partial^2 \phi}{\partial t^2}$$

and the velocity of propagation of the wave is

$$(12.27) \qquad v_0 = \sqrt{\frac{k p_0}{\rho_0}}$$

This result agrees well with experiment. The velocity of sound in air at standard conditions (20°C, 760 mm Hg) is 34,400 cm per sec.

13. The Magnetic Vector Potential. In this section a very important method of integrating the equations of electrodynamics will be discussed. This method of integration leads to an equation known in the literature as the *homogeneous wave equation*. The integration of this equation is discussed in Sec. 14.

The general equations of electrodynamics, or Maxwell's equations, are formulated in Chap. 15, Sec. 16. They are

$$(13.1) \qquad \nabla \times E = - \frac{\partial B}{\partial t}$$

$$(13.2) \qquad \nabla \times H = J + \frac{\partial D}{\partial t}$$

$$(13.3) \qquad \nabla \cdot B = 0$$
$$(13.4) \qquad \nabla \cdot D = \rho$$

The significance of the various symbols is discussed in Chap. 15.

In certain problems of electrodynamics the current-density distribution J and the charge density ρ are specified as given functions of space and time. It is then required to determine the electric intensity E and the magnetic intensity H.

In addition to the above equations we have the following relations in a homogeneous isotropic medium:

$$(13.5) \qquad D = KE$$
$$(13.6) \qquad B = \mu H$$
$$(13.7) \qquad J = \sigma E$$

In order to integrate the Maxwell equations, let us introduce a vector **A**, defined by the following relation:

$$(13.8) \qquad B = \nabla \times A$$

The vector **A** is called the *magnetic vector potential*.

Substitute (13.8) into (13.1) and obtain

$$(13.9) \qquad \nabla \times \mathbf{E} = -\frac{\partial}{\partial t} (\nabla \times \mathbf{A}) = -\nabla \times \frac{\partial \mathbf{A}}{\partial t}$$

since the order of time differentiation and space differentiation may be interchanged.

Equation (13.9) may be written in the form

$$(13.10) \qquad \nabla \times \left(\mathbf{E} + \frac{\partial \mathbf{A}}{\partial t} \right) = 0$$

This shows that the vector $\mathbf{E} + \partial \mathbf{A}/\partial t$ is irrotational and may therefore be expressed as the gradient of a scalar point function in the form

$$(13.11) \qquad \mathbf{E} + \frac{\partial \mathbf{A}}{\partial t} = -\nabla \phi$$

(ϕ is called the *scalar potential*) or

$$(13.12) \qquad \mathbf{E} = -\frac{\partial \mathbf{A}}{\partial t} - \nabla \phi$$

If we multiply Eq. (13.2) by μ, we obtain

$$(13.13) \qquad \nabla \times \mathbf{B} = \mu \mathbf{J} + \mu \frac{\partial \mathbf{D}}{\partial t}$$

in view of Eq. (13.6).   Now

$$(13.14) \qquad \nabla \times \mathbf{B} = \nabla \times (\nabla \times \mathbf{A}) = \nabla(\nabla \cdot \mathbf{A}) - \nabla^2 \mathbf{A}$$

by Chap. 15, Eq. (11.2).   If this result is substituted into (13.13), we have

$$(13.15) \qquad \nabla(\nabla \cdot \mathbf{A}) - \nabla^2 \mathbf{A} = \mu \mathbf{J} + \mu K \frac{\partial \mathbf{E}}{\partial t}$$

Equation (13.12) may be differentiated with respect to t, and the result is

$$(13.16) \qquad \frac{\partial \mathbf{E}}{\partial t} = -\frac{\partial^2 \mathbf{A}}{\partial t^2} - \nabla \frac{\partial \phi}{\partial t}$$

The quantity $\partial \mathbf{E}/\partial t$ may now be eliminated between Eqs. (13.16) and (13.15), and the resulting equation is

$$(13.17) \qquad \nabla(\nabla \cdot \mathbf{A}) - \nabla^2 \mathbf{A} = \mu \mathbf{J} + \mu K \left(-\frac{\partial^2 \mathbf{A}}{\partial t^2} - \nabla \frac{\partial \phi}{\partial t} \right)$$

or

$$(13.18) \qquad -\nabla^2 \mathbf{A} = \mu \mathbf{J} - \mu K \frac{\partial^2 \mathbf{A}}{\partial t^2} - \nabla \left(\nabla \cdot \mathbf{A} + \mu K \frac{\partial \phi}{\partial t} \right)$$

Now the curl of the magnetic vector potential **A** is specified by Eq. (13.8).   The divergence of **A** has not been specified.

In order to determine the vector **A** uniquely, both its curl and its divergence must be specified.   Let

$$(13.19) \qquad \nabla \cdot \mathbf{A} = -\mu K \frac{\partial \phi}{\partial t}$$

Then Eq. (13.18) may be written in the following form:

$$(13.20) \qquad \nabla^2 \mathbf{A} - \mu K \frac{\partial^2 \mathbf{A}}{\partial t^2} = -\mu \mathbf{J}$$

Equation (13.4) may be written in the form

$$(13.21) \qquad \nabla \cdot \mathbf{E} = \frac{\rho}{K}$$

However, **E** is given in terms of **A** and ϕ by Eq. (13.12).   Hence, if we substitute this value of **E** in (13.21), we obtain

$$(13.22) \qquad \nabla \cdot \left(-\frac{\partial \mathbf{A}}{\partial t} - \nabla \phi \right) = \frac{\rho}{K}$$

or

$$(13.23) \qquad -\frac{\partial}{\partial t} (\nabla \cdot \mathbf{A}) - \nabla^2 \phi = \frac{\rho}{K}$$

Eliminate $\nabla \cdot \mathbf{A}$ between Eqs. (13.19) and (13.23), and we have

$$(13.24) \qquad \nabla^2 \phi - \mu K \frac{\partial^2 \phi}{\partial t^2} = -\frac{\rho}{K}$$

Let

$$(13.25) \qquad c = \frac{1}{\sqrt{\mu K}}$$

Then Eqs. (13.20) and (13.24) may be written in the form

$$(13.26) \qquad \nabla^2 \mathbf{A} - \frac{1}{c^2} \frac{\partial^2 \mathbf{A}}{\partial t^2} = -\mu \mathbf{J}$$

and

$$(13.27) \qquad \nabla^2 \phi - \frac{1}{c^2} \frac{\partial^2 \phi}{\partial t^2} = -\frac{\rho}{K}$$

These two equations have the same form.   In the literature of electrodynamics they are known as the *inhomogeneous wave equations*, or Lorenz's equations.   The quantity c is the velocity of propagation of electromagnetic waves.   If the variation of the current density **J** and the charge density ρ is given in space and time, then Eqs. (13.26) and (13.27) may be solved for **A** and ϕ and the field vectors **B** and **E** determined by Eqs.

(13.8) and (13.12).   The solution of Eqs. (13.26) and (13.27) is discussed in the next section.

14. The Inhomogeneous Wave Equation.   In the last section it was demonstrated that both the magnetic vector potential **A** and the scalar potential ϕ are propagated in accordance with equations of the type

$$(14.1) \qquad \nabla_u^2 - \frac{1}{c^2}\frac{\partial^2 u}{\partial t^2} = -f(x,y,z,t)$$

This is the *inhomogeneous wave equation,* or Lorenz's equation. $f(x,y,z,t)$ is a given function of the space variables and the time t.

Let it be required to solve this equation subject to the *initial conditions*

$$(14.2) \qquad \left.\begin{matrix} u = 0 \\ \dfrac{\partial u}{\partial t} = 0 \end{matrix}\right\} \qquad \text{at } t = 0$$

In order to solve this equation, the method of the Laplace transform described in Chap. 6 may be used.   Let us introduce the following two transforms,

$$(14.3) \qquad Lu(x,y,z,t) = U(x,y,z,p)$$

and

$$(14.4) \qquad Lf(x,y,z,t) = F(x,y,z,p)$$

That is, we introduce a Laplace transform with respect to the time variable.   By Theorem (III) of Chap. 6, we have, using (14.2),

$$(14.5) \qquad L\frac{\partial^2 u}{\partial t^2} = p^2 U$$

Hence, by the Laplace transformation, Eq. (14.1) is transformed to

$$(14.6) \qquad \nabla^2 U - \frac{p^2}{c^2} U = -F$$

Let

$$(14.7) \qquad k^2 = -\frac{p^2}{c^2} \qquad k = \pm j\frac{p}{c}$$

Then Eq. (14.6) may be written in the form

$$(14.8) \qquad \nabla^2 U + k^2 U + F = 0$$

This equation is known in the literature as *Helmholtz's equation.*
   Consider the equation

$$(14.9) \qquad \nabla^2 U_0 + k^2 U_0 = 0$$

A‑particular solution of this equation is

$$(14.10) \qquad U_0 = \frac{e^{\pm jkr}}{r}$$

where r is the distance from the point where U_0 is calculated to another point. By the use of this particular solution the solution of the more general equation (14.8) may be constructed. It is

$$(14.11) \qquad U(x,y,z,p) = \frac{1}{4\pi} \iiint \frac{F(x_1,y_1,z_1)e^{\pm jkr}}{r}\, dv$$

where x, y, z are the variables of integration and

$$(14.12) \quad r = \sqrt{(x - x_1)^2 + (y - y_1)^2 + (z - z_1)^2} \qquad dv = dx_1\, dy_1\, dz_1$$

The fact that (14.11) satisfies (14.8) may be easily verified by differentiation. Let us substitute the value of k given by (14.7) into (14.11). We then obtain

$$(14.13) \qquad U(x,y,z,p) = \frac{1}{4\pi} \iiint \frac{F(x_1,y_1,z_1,p)e^{\pm(p/c)r}\, dv}{r}$$

In order to obtain u, the solution of the inhomogeneous wave equation, we must take the inverse transform of $U(x,y,z,p)$ and obtain

$$(14.14) \qquad u(x,y,z,t) = L^{-1}U(x,y,z,p)$$

To do this, we use Theorem (VII) of Chap. 6. This theorem states that, if $Lh(t) = g(p)$, then

$$(14.15) \qquad L^{-1}e^{-ap}g(p) = \begin{cases} 0 & t < a \\ h(t - a) & t > a \end{cases}$$

a is a constant. Applying this theorem to (14.13), we obtain

$$(14.16) \qquad u(x,y,z,t) = \frac{1}{4\pi} \iiint \frac{F(x,y,z,t^{-r/c})\, dv}{r}$$

This indicates that the effects in the variation of $F(x_1,y_1,z_1,t)$ do not reach the point x, y, z until a retarded time $t - r/c$. If the plus sign in the exponential term of (14.13) were used, the inverse transform would lead to an anticipated term of the form $t + r/c$. These anticipated terms are of little importance in physical applications.

A more complete discussion of the solution of the inhomogeneous wave equation, taking into account more general initial conditions, is given by Pipes.*

* L. A. Pipes, Operational Solution of the Wave Equation, *Philosophical Magazine*, ser. 7, vol. 26, pp. 333–340, September, 1938.

Let us return now to the equations governing the propagation of the magnetic vector potential **A** and the scalar potential ϕ:

(14.17)
$$\nabla^2 A - \frac{1}{c^2}\frac{\partial^2 \mathbf{A}}{\partial t^2} = -\mu \mathbf{J}$$

and

(14.18)
$$\nabla^2 \phi - \frac{1}{c^2}\frac{\partial^2 \phi}{\partial t^2} = -\frac{\rho}{k}$$

Comparing these equations with (14.1), we see that they have solutions of the form

(14.19)
$$\mathbf{A} = \frac{\mu}{4\pi} \iiint \frac{\mathbf{J}(x_1, y_1, z_1, t - r/c)\,dv}{r}$$

and

(14.20)
$$\phi = \frac{1}{4\pi k} \iiint \frac{\rho(x_1, y_1, z_1, t - r/c)\,dv}{r}$$

If the space and time distribution of the current density **J** and the charge density ρ is known in space and time, then the potentials **A** and ϕ may be computed. These potentials are called the *retarded potentials* of electrodynamics. They are of fundamental importance in the theory of electromagnetic waves.

15. The Theory of Waveguides. In this section the propagation of electromagnetic waves traveling in the longitudinal direction in a homogeneous isotropic medium that fills the interior of a metal tube of infinite length will be considered. The tube under consideration will be assumed to have a uniform cross section and will be assumed to be straight in the x direction.

It will be assumed that the conductivity of the metal of the tube is infinite. The equations governing the propagation of electromagnetic waves in the interior of tubes are of great importance in the field of communication engineering.*

Let us write the fundamental Maxwell equations in the form

(15.1)
$$\nabla \times \mathbf{E}_0 = -\mu \frac{\partial \mathbf{H}_0}{\partial t}$$

(15.2)
$$\nabla \times \mathbf{H}_0 = \sigma \mathbf{E}_0 + k \frac{\partial \mathbf{E}_0}{\partial t}$$

(15.3)　　　　　　$\nabla \cdot \mathbf{E}_0 = 0$

(15.4)　　　　　　$\nabla \cdot \mathbf{H}_0 = 0$

(See Chap. 15, Sec. 16.)

---

* See L. J. Chu and W. L. Barrow, Electromagnetic Waves in Hollow Metal Tubes of Rectangular Cross Section, *Proceedings of the Institute of Radio Engineers*, vol. 26, p. 1520, 1938.

These equations govern the distribution of the electric intensity $\mathbf{E}_0$ and the magnetic intensity $\mathbf{H}_0$ in a medium of conductivity σ, electric inductive capacity K, and magnetic inductive capacity μ. It is assumed that the medium is devoid of free charges.

In order to discuss the possible oscillations that may be propagated inside the waveguide, let us assume that the time dependence of the electric and magnetic fields $\mathbf{E}_0$ and $\mathbf{H}_0$ is of the form $e^{j\omega t}$. Let us take the y and z axes of a cartesian reference frame in the plane of the cross section of the waveguide, and let the x axis be taken in the longitudinal direction along the waveguide.

Let it be assumed that the fields $\mathbf{E}_0$ and $\mathbf{H}_0$ are of the form

$$(15.5) \qquad \mathbf{E}_0 = \mathbf{E}e^{j(\omega t - ax)}$$

$$(15.6) \qquad \mathbf{H}_0 = \mathbf{H}e^{j(\omega t - ax)} \qquad j = \sqrt{-1}$$

The frequency of the oscillations F is $f = \omega/2\pi$. a is called the *propagation constant*. $\mathbf{E}$ and $\mathbf{H}$ are vectors of the form

$$(15.7) \qquad \mathbf{E} = iE_x + jE_y + kE_z$$

and

$$(15.8) \qquad \mathbf{H} = iH_x + jH_y + kH_z$$

If we substitute Eqs. (15.5) and (15.6) into (15.1) and (15.2) and expand the resulting vector equations into cartesian components, we obtain

$$(15.9) \qquad \begin{aligned} \frac{\partial E_z}{\partial y} - \frac{\partial E_y}{\partial z} &= -j\omega\mu H_x \\ \frac{\partial E_x}{\partial z} + aE_z &= -j\omega\mu H_y \\ aE_y + \frac{\partial E_x}{\partial y} &= j\omega\mu H_z \end{aligned}$$

$$(15.10) \qquad \begin{aligned} \frac{\partial H_z}{\partial y} - \frac{\partial H_y}{\partial z} &= (\sigma + j\omega k)E_x \\ \frac{\partial H_x}{\partial z} + aH_z &= (\sigma + j\omega k)E_y \\ -aH_y - \frac{\partial H_x}{\partial y} &= (\sigma + j\omega k)E_z \end{aligned}$$

It will now be shown that there are two types of waves which satisfy these equations and which may exist independently. In the literature these waves are known as the TM, or E, waves and the TE, or H, waves.

a. Transverse Electric (TE), or H, Waves. These waves are characterized by the fact that

$$(15.11) \qquad E_x = 0 \qquad \text{and} \qquad H_x \neq 0$$

That is, the *electric* field has no component in the direction of propagation, and the *magnetic* field has a component in the direction of propagation.

With the restriction that $E_x = 0$, Eqs. (15.9) and (15.10) become

(15.12)
$$\frac{\partial E_z}{\partial y} - \frac{\partial E_y}{\partial z} = -j\omega\mu H_x$$
$$aE_z = -j\omega\mu H_y$$
$$aE_y = j\omega\mu H_z$$

and

(15.13)
$$\frac{\partial H_z}{\partial y} - \frac{\partial H_y}{\partial z} = 0$$
$$\frac{\partial H_x}{\partial z} + aH_z = (\sigma + j\omega k)E_y$$
$$-aH_y - \frac{\partial H_x}{\partial y} = (\sigma + j\omega k)E_z$$

It will be left as an exercise for the reader to show that, if H_y, H_z, E_y, and E_z are eliminated between Eqs. (15.12) and (15.13), the following equation for H_x is obtained:

(15.14)
$$\frac{\partial^2 H_x}{\partial z^2} + \frac{\partial^2 H_x}{\partial y^2} = -[a^2 - (\sigma + j\omega k)j\omega\mu]H_x$$

In the dielectric region inside the waveguide we have

(15.15)
$$\sigma \ll \omega k$$

Hence (15.14) reduces to

(15.16)
$$\frac{\partial^2 H_x}{\partial z^2} + \frac{\partial^2 H_x}{\partial y^2} = -(a^2 + \omega^2\mu k)H_x$$
$$= -k^2 H_x$$

where

(15.17)
$$k^2 = a^2 + \omega^2\mu K$$

Equation (15.16) determines the magnetic intensity H_x subject to the boundary conditions. It may be shown by the use of (15.12) and (15.13) that

(15.18)
$$H_y = -\frac{a}{k^2}\frac{\partial H_x}{\partial y}$$

(15.19)
$$H_z = -\frac{a}{k^2}\frac{\partial H_x}{\partial z}$$

(15.20)
$$E_y = \frac{j\omega\mu}{a}H_z$$

(15.21)
$$E_z = -\frac{j\omega\mu}{a}H_y$$

This shows that, when H_x is known, then the vector **E** and the vector **H** are fully determined.

THE BOUNDARY CONDITIONS. If the surface of the metallic waveguide is a perfect conductor, then the tangential component of the **E** vector must vanish. In the case of a rectangular waveguide whose sides are parallel to the y and z axes we must have E_y and E_z equal to zero at the surface of the waveguide. From Eqs. (15.18) and (15.19) this means that $\partial H_x / \partial y$ and $\partial H_x / \partial z$ must vanish at the surface.

In the general case the fact that the electric lines of force must enter the perfectly conducting surface $\sigma = \infty$ normally implies that

$$(15.21a) \qquad \frac{\partial H_x}{\partial n} = 0 \qquad \text{at surface of waveguide}$$

n is the normal to the surface. In general coordinates, Eq. (15.16) may be written in the form

$$(15.22) \qquad \nabla^2_{y,z} H_x + k^2 H_x = 0 \qquad \nabla^2_{y,z} = \frac{\partial^2}{\partial y^2} + \frac{\partial^2}{\partial z^2}$$

subject to the boundary condition (15.21). It will be noted that this equation has the same form as Eq. (8.7) for the vibrations of a membrane. However, the boundary condition is different.

The solution of Eq. (15.22) subject to the boundary condition (15.21) determines the possible values of k. For given frequencies, therefore, the values of the propagation constant a are found from the equation

$$(15.23) \qquad a = \sqrt{k^2 - \omega^2 \mu k}$$

Only imaginary values of a lead to possible wave propagation along the waveguide. If a is real, then the waves are rapidly attenuated as they move along the x direction of the waveguide.

b. Transverse Magnetic (TM), or E, Waves. These TM, or E, waves are characterized by the fact that

$$(15.24) \qquad H_x = 0 \qquad \text{and} \qquad E_x \neq 0$$

If we place the restriction that $H_x = 0$ in Eqs. (15.9) and (15.10), we obtain

$$\frac{\partial E_z}{\partial y} - \frac{\partial E_y}{\partial z} = 0$$

$$(15.25) \qquad \frac{\partial E_x}{\partial z} + a E_z = -j\omega\mu H_y$$

$$a E_y + \frac{\partial E_x}{\partial y} = j\omega\mu H_z$$

and

$$\frac{\partial H_z}{\partial y} - \frac{\partial H_y}{\partial z} = (\sigma + j\omega k)E_x$$

$$(15.26) \qquad a H_z = (\sigma + j\omega k)E_y$$

$$-a H_y = (\sigma + j\omega k)E_z$$

It is possible to eliminate E_z, E_y, H_y, and H_z by the use of these equations and obtain the equation

$$(15.27) \qquad \frac{\partial^2 E_x}{\partial y^2} + \frac{\partial^2 E_x}{\partial z^2} = -(a^2 + \omega^2 \mu k)E_x$$

$$= -k^2 E_x \qquad \text{in the dielectric}$$

In the general case, this may be written in the form

$$(15.28) \qquad \nabla^2_{yz} E_x + k^2 E_x = 0$$

The field **E** can have no tangential component at the surface of the perfectly conducting waveguide. Hence we have the boundary condition

$$(15.29) \qquad E_x = 0 \qquad \text{at surface of waveguide}$$

Equation (15.28) and the boundary condition (15.29) are precisely the same as the equation and the boundary condition of the vibrating membrane of Sec. 8. This is the well-known analogy first noticed by Lord Rayleigh.*

The calculation of the possible values of k leads to the possible values of the propagation constant a.

The quantities E_z, E_y, H_y, and H_z are determined from E_x by the use of Eqs. (15.25) and (15.26).

PROBLEMS

1. Find the form at time t of a vibrating string of length s, whose ends are fixed and which is initially displaced into an isosceles triangle. The string is vibrating transversely, is under constant stretching force, and starts from rest.

2. A transversely vibrating string of length s is stretched between two points A and B. The initial displacement of each point of the string is zero, and the initial velocity at a distance x from A is $kx(s - x)$. Find the form of the string at any subsequent time.

3. The differential equation governing the displacement of a viscously damped string is

$$\frac{\partial^2 y}{\partial t^2} = c^2 \frac{\partial^2 y}{\partial x^2} - 2k \frac{\partial y}{\partial t}$$

Find the general solution of this equation when the string has an initial displacement $y = y_0(x)$ and an initial velocity $\partial y / \partial t = v_0(x)$ at $t = 0$.

4. A square membrane is made of material of density m g per cm^2 and is under a tension of T dynes per cm. What must be the length of one side of the membrane in order that the fundamental frequency be F_0? What will be the frequencies of the two lowest overtones?

5. A rectangular membrane is struck at its center, starting from rest, in such a way that at $t = 0$ a small rectangular region about the center may be considered to have a velocity v_0 and the rest has no velocity. Find the amplitudes of the various overtones.

6. Write the differential equation governing the displacement of the *general* oscillations of a circular membrane. Show that the allowed angular frequencies are deter-

* See Lord Rayleigh, *Philosophical Magazine*, ser. 5, no. 43, p. 125, 1897.

mined by the equation

$$J_n \left(a \sqrt{\frac{m\omega^2}{T}} \right) = 0 \qquad n = 0, 1, 2, 3, \ldots$$

where J_n is the Bessel function of the first kind and nth order, a is the radius of the circular membrane, m the mass per unit area of the membrane, and T the tension per unit length.

7. Show that the general solution of the differential equations governing the propagation of current and potential along a dissipationless transmission line $R = 0$, $G = 0$ is

$$e = f \left(x - \frac{t}{\sqrt{LC}} \right) + g \left(x + \frac{t}{\sqrt{LC}} \right)$$

$$i = \sqrt{\frac{C}{L}} f \left(x - \frac{t}{\sqrt{LC}} \right) - \sqrt{\frac{C}{L}} g \left(x + \frac{t}{\sqrt{LC}} \right)$$

where f and g are arbitrary functions.

These solutions may be interpreted as a combination of two waves, one moving to the left and one moving to the right each with velocity $1/\sqrt{LC}$.

8. Show that, if we place $G = 0$ and $L = 0$ in the transmission-line equations, we obtain an equation of the form

$$\frac{\partial^2 u}{\partial x^2} = h^2 \frac{\partial u}{\partial t}$$

This is the differential equation governing the distribution of temperature in the theory of one-dimensional heat conduction. Discuss the analogy between the transmission line in this case and the one-dimensional heat flow.

9. Show that the small longitudinal oscillations of a long rod satisfy the equation

$$\frac{\partial^2 u}{\partial t^2} = \frac{E}{m} \frac{\partial^2 u}{\partial x^2}$$

where u is the displacement of a point originally at a distance x from the end of the rod, E is the modulus of elasticity of the rod, and m is the density.

10. Find the natural frequencies of vibration of a long prismatic rod of length s, density m, and elastic modulus E, which is fixed at $x = 0$ and free at $x = s$.

11. Find the equation that determines the natural frequencies of vibration of the rod described above if the end $x = 0$ is fixed and the end $x = s$ is fastened to a mass M.

12. Starting with the differential equations of the dissipationless transmission line ($R = 0$, $G = 0$) and that governing the oscillations of a long prismatic bar, show that there exists a close analogy between the electrical and mechanical systems. What is the electrical analogue of a long rod oscillating freely whose end at $x = 0$ is fixed and whose other end at $x = s$ is free?

REFERENCES

1. Coulson, C. A.: "Waves," Interscience Publishers, Inc., New York, 1943.
2. Morse, P. M.: "Vibration and Sound," 1st ed., McGraw-Hill Book Company, Inc., New York, 1936.
3. Guillemin, E. A.: "Communication Networks," vol. II, John Wiley & Sons, Inc., New York, 1935.
4. Timoshenko, S.: "Vibration Problems in Engineering," D. Van Nostrand Company, Inc., Princeton, N.J., 1937.

CHAPTER 17

SIMPLE SOLUTIONS OF LAPLACE'S
DIFFERENTIAL EQUATION

1. Introduction. Perhaps the most important partial differential equation of applied mathematics is the equation of Laplace,

$$(1.1) \qquad \nabla^2 v = \frac{\partial^2 v}{\partial x^2} + \frac{\partial^2 v}{\partial y^2} + \frac{\partial^2 v}{\partial z^2} = 0$$

As was shown in Chap. 15, if (x,y,z) are the rectangular coordinates of any point in space, this equation is satisfied by the following functions, which occur in various branches of applied mathematics:

1. The gravitational potential in regions not occupied by attracting matter

2. The electrostatic potential in a uniform dielectric, in the theory of electrostatics

3. The magnetic potential in free space, in the theory of magnetostatics

4. The electric potential, in the theory of the steady flow of electric currents in solid conductors

5. The temperature, in the theory of thermal equilibrium of solids

6. The velocity potential at points of a homogeneous liquid moving irrotationally, in hydrodynamical problems

In spite of the physical differences of the above subjects the mathematical investigations are much the same for all of them. For example, the problem of determining the temperature in a solid when its surface is maintained at a given temperature is mathematically identical with the problem of determining the electric intensity in a region when the points of its boundary are maintained at given potentials. In this chapter we shall discuss the solution of Laplace's equation by the method of separation of variables. The method of conjugate functions will be discussed in Chap. 20.

2. Laplace's Equation in Cartesian, Cylindrical, and Spherical Coordinate Systems. In Chap. 15, Sec. 12, the Laplace operator ∇^2 was expressed in general orthogonal curvilinear coordinates. From the results of that chapter we have the following forms of Laplace's equation:

a. Cartesian Coordinates

$$(2.1) \qquad \nabla^2 v = \frac{\partial^2 v}{\partial x^2} + \frac{\partial^2 v}{\partial y^2} + \frac{\partial^2 v}{\partial z^2} = 0$$

b. Cylindrical Coordinates. Expressed in terms of the cylindrical coordinates of Fig. 2.1, Laplace's equation is

$$(2.2) \qquad \nabla^2 v = \frac{1}{r} \frac{\partial}{\partial r} \left(r \frac{\partial v}{\partial r} \right) + \frac{1}{r^2} \frac{\partial^2 v}{\partial \theta^2} + \frac{\partial^2 v}{\partial z^2} = 0$$

c. Spherical Coordinates. Laplace's equation expressed in the spherical coordinates of Fig. 2.2 is

$$(2.3) \quad \nabla^2 v = \frac{1}{r^2} \frac{\partial}{\partial r} \left(r^2 \frac{\partial v}{\partial r} \right) + \frac{1}{r^2 \sin \theta} \frac{\partial}{\partial \theta} \left(\sin \theta \frac{\partial v}{\partial \theta} \right) + \frac{1}{r^2 \sin^2 \theta} \frac{\partial^2 v}{\partial \phi^2} = 0$$

These are the most common coordinates usually encountered in practice.

FIG. 2.1   FIG. 2.2

3. Two-dimensional Steady Flow of Heat. To illustrate the solution of Laplace's equation in a simple two-dimensional case, let us consider the following problem:

Suppose we have a thin plate that is bounded by the lines $x = 0$,

FIG. 3.1

$x = s$, $y = 0$, and $y = \infty$ (Fig. 3.1). Let the temperature of the edge $y = 0$ be constant with time and be given by $F(x)$. Let the temperature on the other edges be always zero. We shall suppose that heat cannot escape from either surface of the plate and that the effect of initial conditions has passed away. We assume that the temperature is everywhere independent of time. We wish to determine the temperature within the plate.

The problem is one of steady two-dimensional heat flow. In Chap. 15, Sec. 14, we found that the temperature distribution v inside a homogeneous solid satisfies the equation

$$(3.1) \qquad \frac{\partial v}{\partial t} = h^2 \nabla^2 v$$

where h^2 is the diffusivity of the substance and is a constant.

In the case under consideration we have

(3.2)
$$\frac{\partial v}{\partial t} = 0$$

since, by hypothesis, the temperature v does not depend on the time t. Equation (3.1) therefore reduces to

(3.3)
$$\nabla^2 v = \frac{\partial^2 v}{\partial x^2} + \frac{\partial^2 v}{\partial y^2} = 0$$

subject to the boundary conditions

(3.4)
$$\begin{array}{cccc} v = 0 & v = 0 & v = 0 & v = F(x) \\ x = 0 & x = s & y = \infty & y = 0 \end{array}$$

In order to solve Eq. (3.3), we try a solution of the form

(3.5)
$$v = F_1(x)F_2(y)$$

where $F_1(x)$ is a function of x only and $F_2(y)$ is a function of y only. On substituting this assumed solution into (3.3) and rearranging, we obtain

(3.6)
$$\frac{1}{F_1(x)}\frac{d^2 F_1}{dx^2} = -\frac{1}{F_2}\frac{d^2 F_2}{dy^2}$$

Now a change in x will not change the right-hand member, and a change in y will not change the left-hand member. Hence each of the expressions of (3.6) must be independent of x and y and must, therefore, be equal to a constant. Let us call this constant $-k^2$. Equation (3.6) then breaks up into two equations:

(3.7)
$$\frac{d^2 F_1}{dx^2} = -k^2 F_1 \quad \text{and} \quad \frac{d^2 F_2}{dy^2} = k^2 F_2$$

The variables are now said to be *separated*. This method of solving the partial differential equation (3.3) is called the *method of separation of variables*. Equations (3.7) are linear differential equations with constant coefficients, and their solutions are

(3.8)
$$\begin{aligned} F_1 &= c_1 \cos kx + c_2 \sin kx \\ F_2 &= c_3 e^{ky} + c_4 e^{-ky} \end{aligned}$$

where the c's are arbitrary constants. Substituting these into (3.5), we have

(3.9)
$$\begin{aligned} v &= (c_1 \cos kx + c_2 \sin kx)(c_3 e^{ky} + c_4 e^{-ky}) \\ &= e^{-ky}(A \cos kx + B \sin kx) + e^{ky}(M \cos kx + N \sin kx) \end{aligned}$$

where A, B, M, and N are *arbitrary constants*. We must now adjust this solution in order to satisfy the boundary conditions (3.4).

In the first place the temperature is zero when y is infinite. Hence we have

$$(3.10) \qquad\qquad M = N = 0$$

Now, since $v = 0$ for $x = 0$, we cannot have a cosine term in the solution; so $A = 0$. At $x = s$, $v = 0$ for all positive values of y. Hence

$$(3.11) \qquad\qquad B \sin ks = 0$$

For a nontrivial solution, $B \neq 0$; hence

$$(3.12) \qquad\qquad \sin ks = 0$$

This equation determines the possible values of k. They are

$$(3.13) \qquad\qquad k = \frac{m\pi}{s} \qquad m = 0, 1, 2, 3, \ldots$$

Hence to each value of m there is a solution

$$(3.14) \qquad\qquad v_m = B_m e^{-m\pi y/s} \sin \frac{m\pi x}{s}$$

where B_m is an arbitrary constant. If we take the sum of all possible solutions of the type (3.14), we construct the solution

$$(3.15) \qquad\qquad v = \sum_{m=1}^{\infty} B_m e^{-m\pi y/s} \sin \frac{m\pi x}{s}$$

We now only have to satisfy the condition $v = F(x)$ at $y = 0$. Placing $y = 0$ in (3.15), we have

$$(3.16) \qquad\qquad F(x) = \sum_{m=1}^{m=\infty} B_m \sin \frac{m\pi x}{s}$$

This is the half-range sine series for v as discussed in Chap. 3. The coefficients B_m are given by

$$(3.17) \qquad B_m = \frac{2}{s} \int_0^s F(x) \sin \frac{m\pi x}{s} \, dx$$

Placing these values of the coefficients B_m in (3.15), we have the solution to the problem.

Temperature Distribution of a Finite Plate. As a simple extension of the above problem,

FIG. 3.2

let us consider the distribution of temperature inside the plate of Fig. 3.2. The boundary conditions are

$$(3.18) \qquad
\begin{array}{cccc}
v = 0 & v = 0 & v = 0 & v = F(x) \\
x = 0 & y = 0 & x = s & y = h
\end{array}$$

Starting with the solution (3.9), we see that we cannot have any cosine terms present, and again the possible values of k are given by (3.13). We thus have

$$(3.19) \qquad v_m = e^{-m\pi y/s} B_m \sin \frac{m\pi x}{s} + e^{m\pi y/s} N_m \sin \frac{m\pi x}{s}$$

$$= (e^{-m\pi y/s} B_m + e^{m\pi y/s} N_m) \sin \frac{m\pi x}{s}$$

Now at $y = 0$, $v = 0$, for $0 \le x \le s$; therefore

$$(3.20) \qquad B_m + N_m = 0 \qquad \text{or} \qquad B_m = -N_m$$

Hence we can write the solution in the form

$$(3.21) \qquad v_m = C_m \sinh \frac{m\pi y}{s} \sin \frac{m\pi x}{s}$$

where C_m is an arbitrary constant.

Summing over all possible values of m, we have

$$(3.22) \qquad v = \sum_{m=1}^{m=\infty} C_m \sinh \frac{m\pi y}{s} \sin \frac{m\pi x}{s}$$

Now, at $y = h$, we have

$$(3.23) \qquad F(x) = \sum_{m=1}^{m=\infty} C_m \sinh \frac{m\pi h}{s} \sin \frac{m\pi x}{s}$$

This is a half-range sine expansion for $F(x)$. Hence

$$(3.24) \qquad C_m \sinh \frac{m\pi h}{s} = \frac{2}{s} \int_0^s F(x) \sin \frac{m\pi x}{s} \, dx$$

or

$$(3.25) \qquad C_m = \frac{2}{s \sinh (m\pi h/s)} \int_0^s F(x) \sin \frac{m\pi x}{s} \, dx$$

If we substitute this value of C_m into (3.22), we have the solution to the problem.

4. Circular Harmonics. In its most general sense the term *harmonic* applies to any solution of Laplace's equation. However, the term harmonic is ordinarily used in a more restricted sense to mean a solution of Laplace's equation in a specified coordinate system. If we write Laplace's equation in cylindrical coordinates and assume that v is independent of the coordinate z, we have from Eq. (2.2)

$$(4.1) \qquad \frac{1}{r} \frac{\partial}{\partial r} \left(r \frac{\partial v}{\partial r} \right) + \frac{1}{r^2} \frac{\partial^2 v}{\partial \theta^2} = 0$$

We now attempt to find a solution of this equation of the form

$$(4.2) \qquad v = F_1(\theta)F_2(r)$$

Substituting this in (4.1), we have

$$(4.3) \qquad \frac{F_1(\theta)}{r} \frac{d}{dr}\left(r \frac{dF_2}{dr}\right) + \frac{F_2(r)}{r^2} \frac{d^2F_1(\theta)}{d\theta^2} = 0$$

Multiplying by r^2 and dividing by $F_1 F_2$, we have

$$(4.4) \qquad \frac{1}{F_2}\left(r^2 \frac{d^2F_2}{dr^2} + r \frac{dF_2}{dr}\right) = -\frac{1}{F_1} \frac{d^2F_1}{d\theta^2} = n^2$$

where, since the left-hand side of the equation is a function of r alone and the right-hand side is a function of θ alone, we conclude that both sides of the equation are equal to the same constant, which we have called n^2. We thus have the two equations

$$(4.5) \qquad \frac{d^2F_1}{d\theta^2} + n^2F_1 = 0$$

and

$$(4.6) \qquad r^2 \frac{d^2F_2}{dr^2} + r \frac{dF_2}{dr} - n^2F_2 = 0$$

The variables are now separated. Equation (4.5) is the well-known equation of simple harmonic motion. Its solution is

$$(4.7) \qquad F_1 = A \cos n\theta + B \sin n\theta \qquad \text{if } n \neq 0$$

It is easily verified that the solution of (4.6) is

$$(4.8) \qquad F_2 = Cr^n + Dr^{-n} \qquad \text{if } n \neq 0$$

If $n = 0$, we have the solutions

$$(4.9) \qquad \begin{aligned} F_1 &= A_0\theta + B_0 \\ F_2 &= C_0 \ln r + D_0 \end{aligned}$$

where the quantities A, B, C, D are arbitrary constants.

The number n is called the *degree of the harmonic*. The solutions of Laplace's equation in cylindrical coordinates when v is independent of the coordinate z are called *circular harmonics*. Circular harmonics are of extreme importance in the solution of two-dimensional problems having cylindrical symmetry.

The circular harmonics are then

$$(4.10) \qquad \begin{aligned} v_0 &= (A_0\theta + B_0)(C_0 \ln r + D_0) \qquad &\text{degree zero} \\ v_n &= (A_n \cos n\theta + B_n \sin n\theta)(C_n r^n + D_n r^{-n}) \qquad &\text{degree } n \end{aligned}$$

In most applications of circular harmonics to physical problems the function v is usually a *single-valued* function of θ. Since if we increase θ by 2π we reach the same point in the xy plane, in order for v_n to be single-valued, we must have

$$(4.11) \qquad v_n(r, \theta + 2\pi) = v_n(r,\theta)$$

It is thus necessary for n to take only integral values. A general single-valued solution of Laplace's equation is obtained by summing the solutions (4.10) over all possible values of n in the form

$$(4.12) \quad v = a_0 \ln r + \sum_{n=1}^{\infty} r^n(a_n \cos n\theta + b_n \sin n\theta)$$

$$+ \sum_{n=1}^{\infty} \frac{1}{r^n} (q_n \cos n\theta + f_n \sin n\theta) + c_0$$

where the quantities a, b, q, f, and c_0 are arbitrary constants.

As a simple illustration of the use of circular harmonics, let us consider the following problem: Suppose a very long circular cylinder is composed of two halves as shown in Fig. 4.1.

FIG. 4.1

The two halves of the cylinder are thermally insulated from each other, and the upper half of the cylinder is kept at temperature v_1, while the lower half is kept at temperature v_2. It is required to find the steady state temperature in the region inside the cylinder. It is assumed that the cylinder is so long in the z direction that the temperature is independent of z.

To solve this problem, we must solve the equation

$$(4.13) \qquad \nabla^2 v = 0$$

in the region inside the cylinder and satisfy the boundary conditions

$$(4.14) \qquad \begin{array}{lll} v = v_1 & \text{at } r = R & 0 < \theta < \pi \\ v = v_2 & \text{at } r = R & \pi < \theta < 2\pi \end{array}$$

We do this by taking the general solution (4.12) and specializing it to the boundary conditions (4.14). In the first place, we notice that the temperature must be finite at the origin $r = 0$. It is necessary, therefore, for the constants a_0, q_n, and f_n to be equal to zero.

There remains the solution

$$(4.15) \qquad v = \sum_{n=1}^{\infty} r^n(a_n \cos n\theta + b_n \sin n\theta) + c_0$$

Before solving the problem under consideration, let us solve the more general problem in which the temperature is specified on the circumference of the cylinder $r = a$ as an arbitrary function of θ, so that

$$(4.16) \qquad v = F(\theta) \qquad \text{at } r = R$$

We then have on placing $r = R$ in (4.15)

$$(4.17) \qquad F(\theta) = \sum_{n=1}^{\infty} R^n(a_n \cos n\theta + b_n \sin n\theta) + c_0$$

The problem of determining the constants a_n, b_n, and c_0 reduces to expanding the function $F(\theta)$ in a Fourier series. We therefore have

FIG. 4.2

$$(4.18) \quad \begin{aligned} a_n &= \frac{1}{R^n\pi} \int_0^{2\pi} F(\theta) \cos n\theta \, d\theta \\ b_n &= \frac{1}{R^n\pi} \int_0^{2\pi} F(\theta) \sin n\theta \, d\theta \\ c_0 &= \frac{1}{2\pi} \int_0^{2\pi} F(\theta) \, d\theta \end{aligned}$$

An interesting special case arises when the temperature of the upper half of the cylinder is kept at v_0 and the lower half is kept at a temperature equal to zero. The function $F(\theta)$ is then given graphically by Fig. 4.2. We then have

$$(4.19) \quad \begin{aligned} a_n &= \frac{v_0}{R^n\pi} \int_0^{\pi} \cos n\theta \, d\theta = 0 \\ b_n &= \frac{v_0}{R^n\pi} \int_0^{\pi} \sin n\theta \, d\theta = \frac{2v_0}{R^n\pi n} \qquad n \text{ odd} \\ c_0 &= \frac{1}{2\pi} \int_0^{\pi} v_0 \, d\theta = \frac{v_0}{2} \end{aligned}$$

Substituting this into (4.15), we obtain

$$(4.20) \qquad v(r,\theta) = \frac{2v_0}{\pi} \sum_{n=1}^{\infty} \left(\frac{r}{R}\right)^n \frac{\sin n\theta}{n} + \frac{v_0}{2} \qquad n \text{ odd}$$

Other two-dimensional problems having circular symmetry may be solved in a similar manner.

5. Conducting Cylinder in a Uniform Field. As another example of the application of circular harmonics, let us consider the following problem:

An infinitely long uncharged conducting cylinder of circular cross section is placed in a uniform electric field $\mathbf{E}_0$, with its axis at right angles to the lines of force.   Denote the radius of the cylinder by a, and take the x axis in the direction of the field as in Fig. 5.1 and the z axis along the axis of the cylinder.   We wish to determine the field induced by the presence of the cylinder.

It is clear from symmetry that the potential v is not a function of z. As explained in Chap. 15, Sec. 16, the electrostatic field E is derived from the potential v by the equation

FIG. 5.1

$$(5.1) \qquad \mathbf{E} = - \operatorname{grad} v = -\nabla v$$

and v satisfies Laplace's equation.

The original potential outside the cylinder is of the form

$$(5.2) \qquad v_0 = -E_0 x = -E_0 r \cos \theta$$

This field will induce charges on the perfectly conducting cylinder, and these induced charges will produce a potential v_i. The total potential due to the external field and the induced separation of charges of the cylinder is given by

$$(5.3) \qquad v = v_0 + v_i = -E_0 r \cos \theta + v_i$$

Since the cylinder is perfectly conducting, it is an equipotential surface and we may take its potential as zero.   We therefore have

$$(5.4) \qquad v = 0 \qquad \text{at } r = a$$

Now, at infinity, the potential produced by the induced charges on the cylinder must vanish, since, by hypothesis, the cylinder is initially uncharged and the external field produces only a separation of charge. Also, by symmetry, the induced potential must be symmetrical about the x axis; hence it must be an even function of θ.

It follows, therefore, that in the general circular harmonic solution of Laplace's equation we must have a_0, a_n, b_n equal to zero so that the potential will remain finite at infinity, and f_n must be equal to zero for a potential that is an even function of θ.   The constant term may be taken equal to zero without loss of generality.   We therefore take v_i in the form

$$(5.5) \qquad v_i = \sum_{n=1}^{\infty} \frac{q_n}{r_n} \cos n\theta$$

The total potential is given by (5.3) in the form

$$(5.6) \qquad v = -E_0 r \cos \theta + \sum_{n=1}^{\infty} \frac{q_n \cos n\theta}{r^n}$$

Now, at $r = a$, we have

$$(5.7) \qquad 0 = -E_0 a \cos \theta + \sum_{n=1}^{\infty} \frac{q_n \cos n\theta}{a^n}$$

or

$$(5.8) \qquad \sum_{n=1}^{\infty} \frac{q_n \cos n\theta}{a^n} = E_0 a \cos \theta$$

To obtain the unknown coefficients q_n, we equate coefficients of like harmonic terms in θ and obtain

$$(5.9) \qquad \begin{aligned} \frac{q_1}{a} &= E_0 a \\ q_n &= 0 \qquad \text{if } n > 1 \end{aligned}$$

Hence

$$(5.10) \qquad q_1 = E_0 a^2$$

The complete potential (5.6) then becomes

$$(5.11) \qquad v = -\left(1 - \frac{a^2}{r^2}\right) E_0 r \cos \theta$$

Since $\mathbf{E} = -\nabla v$, the radial and tangential components of the electric field are obtained by taking the gradient in cylindrical coordinates and we obtain

$$(5.12) \qquad \begin{aligned} E_r &= -\frac{\partial v}{\partial r} = \left(1 + \frac{a^2}{r^2}\right) E_0 \cos \theta \\ E_\theta &= -\frac{\partial v}{r \, \partial \theta} = -\left(1 - \frac{a^2}{r^2}\right) E_0 \sin \theta \end{aligned}$$

6. General Cylindrical Harmonics. We have considered solutions of Laplace's equation in cylindrical coordinates that were independent of the coordinate z. In certain three-dimensional problems it is necessary to obtain solutions of Laplace's equation when v is a function of the three cylindrical coordinates r, θ, and z:

$$(6.1) \qquad \frac{1}{r} \frac{\partial}{\partial r}\left(r \frac{\partial v}{\partial r}\right) + \frac{1}{r^2} \frac{\partial^2 v}{\partial \theta^2} + \frac{\partial^2 v}{\partial z^2} = 0$$

We begin by assuming a solution of the form

$$(6.2) \qquad v = F_1(\theta) F_2(r) F_3(z)$$

where F_1 is a function of θ alone, etc. Substituting this assumed form of solution in (6.1), and after some reductions, we obtain

$$(6.3) \qquad \frac{1}{F_3} \frac{d^2 F_3}{dz^2} = -\frac{1}{F_2} \frac{d^2 F_2}{dr^2} - \frac{1}{r F_2} \frac{d F_2}{dr} - \frac{1}{r^2 F_1} \frac{d^2 F_1}{d\theta^2}$$

Now by hypothesis F_3 is a function of z only, and by (6.3) a change in z does not change the right-hand side since it is not a function of z.   Hence the left-hand side of (6.3) reduces to a constant, and we write

$$(6.4) \qquad \frac{1}{F_3}\frac{d^2F_3}{dz^2} = k^2$$

Hence

$$(6.5) \qquad F_3 = C_1 e^{kz} + C_2 e^{-kz}$$

From (6.3) and (6.4) we have

$$(6.6) \qquad \frac{r^2}{F_2}\frac{d^2F_2}{dr^2} + \frac{r}{F_2}\frac{dF_2}{dr} + k^2 r^2 = -\frac{1}{F_1}\frac{d^2F_1}{d\theta^2}$$

By the same reasoning as above it follows that each member of (6.6) is a constant.   Let us call this constant m^2.   We therefore have

$$(6.7) \qquad \frac{d^2F_1}{d\theta^2} = -m^2 F_1$$

Therefore

$$(6.8) \qquad F_1 = C_3 \cos m\theta + C_4 \sin m\theta$$

and

$$(6.9) \qquad r^2 \frac{d^2F_2}{dr^2} + r\frac{dF_2}{dr} + (k^2 r^2 - m^2)F_2 = 0$$

If we place

$$(6.10) \qquad kr = x$$

in (6.9), we obtain

$$(6.11) \qquad x^2 \frac{d^2F_2}{dx^2} + x\frac{dF_2}{dx} + (x^2 - m^2)F_2 = 0$$

This is Bessel's differential equation discussed in Chap. 13.   Its solution is

$$(6.12) \qquad \begin{aligned} F_2 &= C_5 J_m(x) + C_6 J_{-m}(x) \\ &= C_5 J_m(kr) + C_6 J_{-m}(kr) \end{aligned}$$

if m is fractional or

$$(6.13) \qquad F_2 = C_5 J_m(kr) + C_6 Y_m(kr)$$

if m is integral.

Any of the above values of F_1, F_2, and F_3 substituted in (6.2) gives a solution of Laplace's equation.   If we let k be a fixed constant and if we require v to be a single-valued function of θ, then m must take only integral values and we have the solution

$$(6.14) \quad v = \sum_{m=0}^{m=\infty} [e^{kz}(A_m \cos m\theta + B_m \sin m\theta)$$
$$+ e^{-kz}(C_m \cos m\theta + D_m \sin m\theta)]J_m(kr)$$

This solution remains finite at $r = 0$ and is useful in certain electrical problems and problems of steady heat conduction.

7. Spherical Harmonics. If the boundary conditions of a problem involving the solution of Laplace's equation are simply expressed in spherical polar coordinates, it is useful to have a general solution of Laplace's equation in this system of coordinates.

In this case we must find solutions of Eq. (2.3). This equation may be written in the form

$$(7.1) \quad \frac{\partial}{\partial r}\left(r^2 \frac{\partial v}{\partial r}\right) + \frac{1}{\sin \theta} \frac{\partial}{\partial \theta}\left(\sin \theta \frac{\partial v}{\partial \theta}\right) + \frac{1}{\sin^2 \theta} \frac{\partial^2 v}{\partial \phi^2} = 0$$

We wish to find a solution of the form

$$(7.2) \qquad\qquad v = R\Theta\Phi = RS$$

where R is a function of r only, Θ is a function of θ only, and Φ is a function of ϕ only.

The function

$$(7.3) \qquad\qquad S(\theta,\phi) = \Theta\Phi$$

is called a *surface harmonic*. The function Θ, when ϕ is a constant, is called a *zonal* surface harmonic.

If we substitute (7.2) in (7.1) and divide through by RS, we have

$$(7.4) \quad \frac{1}{R}\frac{d}{dr}\left(r^2 \frac{dR}{dr}\right) + \frac{1}{S \sin \theta}\frac{\partial}{\partial \theta}\sin\theta\frac{\partial S}{\partial \theta} + \frac{1}{S \sin^2 \theta}\frac{\partial^2 S}{\partial \phi^2} = 0$$

The first term is a function of r only, and the other ones involve only the angles. For all values of the coordinates, therefore, the equation can be satisfied only if

$$(7.5) \qquad\qquad \frac{1}{R}\frac{d}{dr}\left(r^2 \frac{dR}{dr}\right) = K$$

and

$$(7.6) \qquad \frac{1}{S \sin \theta}\frac{\partial}{\partial \theta}\left(\sin \theta \frac{\partial S}{\partial \theta}\right) + \frac{1}{S \sin^2 \theta}\frac{\partial^2 S}{\partial \phi^2} = -K$$

If we place

$$(7.7) \qquad\qquad K = n(n + 1)$$

the solution of Eq. (7.5) is easily seen to be

$$(7.8) \qquad R = Ar^n + Br^{-n-1}$$

If we multiply Eq. (7.6) by S, we have

$$(7.9) \qquad \frac{1}{\sin\theta}\frac{\partial}{\partial\theta}\left(\sin\theta\,\frac{\partial S}{\partial\theta}\right) + \frac{1}{\sin^2\theta}\frac{\partial^2 S}{\partial\phi^2} + n(n+1)s = 0$$

Equation (7.2) therefore takes the form

$$(7.10) \qquad v = (Ar^n + Br^{-n-1})S_n$$

The subscript on S_n signifies that the same value of n must be used in both terms of (7.10). Any sum of solutions of the type of (7.10) is also a solution.

A General Property of Surface Harmonics. By the use of Green's theorem (Chap. 15, Sec. 9), which may be written in the form

$$(7.11) \qquad \iiint_v (U\nabla^2 W - W\nabla^2 U)\,dv = \iint_s (U\nabla W - W\nabla U)\cdot ds$$

we may derive an important property of the function S_n. To do this, let

$$(7.12) \qquad U = r^m S_m \qquad W = r^n S_n$$

so that

$$(7.13) \qquad \nabla^2 U = \nabla^2 W = 0$$

and hence the volume integral vanishes. If we take for the surface, in Green's theorem, a unit sphere, we have

$$(7.14) \qquad (\Delta U)_s = \frac{\partial}{\partial r}(r^m S_m) = mr^{m-1}S_m = mS_m \qquad \text{at } r = 1$$

and similarly

$$(7.15) \qquad (\nabla W)_s = nS_n$$

Since both $(\nabla U)_s$ and $(\nabla W)_s$ have the normal direction to the sphere, the dot product in (7.11) is absorbed and we have

$$(7.16) \qquad \iint_s (nS_nS_m - mS_nS_m)\,ds = (n-m)\iint_s S_nS_m\,ds = 0$$

and if $n \neq m$, we obtain the result

$$(7.17) \qquad \iint_s S_nS_m\,ds = 0$$

where the surface integration is taken over a unit sphere.

Surface Zonal Harmonics. A very important special case is the one in which v is independent of ϕ so that Φ is a constant and S_n is a function of

θ only.   In this case, we have

$$(7.18) \qquad\qquad \frac{\partial^2 S}{\partial \phi^2} = 0$$

and Eq. (7.9) reduces to

$$(7.19) \qquad\qquad \frac{1}{\sin \theta} \frac{d}{d\theta}\left(\sin \theta \, \frac{dS_n}{d\theta}\right) + n(n+1)S_n = 0$$

If we write

$$(7.20) \qquad\qquad \mu = \cos \theta$$

and transform Eq. (7.19) from the independent variable θ to the independent variable μ, we obtain

$$(7.21) \qquad\qquad \frac{d}{d\mu}\left[(1 - \mu^2)\,\frac{dS_n}{d\mu}\right] + n(n+1)S_n = 0$$

This we recognize as the Legendre equation of Chap. 14.   If n is a positive integer, a solution of (7.21) is given by the Legendre polynomial

$$(7.22) \qquad\qquad S_n = P_n(\mu) = P_n(\cos \theta)$$

By combining the solutions thus obtained, we have from (7.10) the solution

$$(7.23) \qquad\qquad v = \sum_{n=0}^{n=\infty} \left(A_n r^n + \frac{B_n}{r^{n+1}}\right) P_n(\cos \theta)$$

where A_n and B_n are arbitrary constants.

This solution has many applications to problems in electrostatics, magnetostatics, and potential theory that have spherical symmetry such that the function v is symmetrical about the z axis so that it is independent of the angle ϕ.

8. The Potential of a Ring.   As was shown in Chap. 15, Sec. 15, if a particle of matter of mass m is at a point (a,b,c) of a cartesian reference frame, then the gravitational potential at (x,y,z) due to the mass is

$$(8.1) \qquad\qquad v_m = \frac{m}{\sqrt{(x-a)^2 + (y-b)^2 + (z-c)^2}}$$

It was also shown in that section that the gravitational potential v satisfies Laplace's equation

$$(8.2) \qquad\qquad \nabla^2 v = 0$$

in the region not occupied by matter.

Let us determine the potential at any point due to a uniform circular ring of small cross section lying in the plane of x, y with its center at O as shown in Fig. 8.1.

Evidently the potential v is symmetric about the z axis and is independent of the angle ϕ. We know, therefore, that the potential v is of the form

$$(8.3) \qquad v = \sum_{n=0}^{n=\infty} \left(A_n r^n + \frac{B_n}{r^{n+1}} \right) P_n(\cos \theta)$$

The problem is to determine the unknown coefficients A_n and B_n. We may determine

Fig. 8.1

these coefficients by realizing that any point Q on the z axis is at the same distance

$$\sqrt{a^2 + r^2}$$

from all points of the ring, where $\overline{OQ} = r$ and a is the radius of the ring. The cross section of the ring is assumed negligible. Hence the potential at Q is

$$(8.4) \qquad \frac{M}{\sqrt{a^2 + r^2}}$$

where M is the total mass of the ring.

By the binomial theorem we have

$$(8.5) \qquad \frac{M}{\sqrt{a^2 + r^2}} = \frac{M}{a} \left(1 - \frac{r^2}{2a^2} + \frac{1 \times 3r^4}{2 \times 4a^4} - \cdots \right)$$

when $r < a$, and

$$(8.6) \qquad \frac{M}{\sqrt{a^2 + r^2}} = \frac{M}{a} \left(\frac{a}{r} - \frac{1a^3}{2r^3} + \frac{1 \times 3a^5}{2 \times 4r^5} - \cdots \right)$$

when $r > a$.

The general solution (8.3) must reduce to either (8.5) or (8.6) for a point on z where $\theta = 0$. Now we have from Chap. 14

$$(8.7) \qquad P_n(\cos 0) = P_n(1) = 1$$

Hence for points on the z axis (8.3) becomes

$$(8.8) \qquad v = \sum_{n=0}^{\infty} \left(A_n r^n + \frac{B_n}{r^{n+1}} \right)$$

Comparing this with (8.5) and (8.6), we have $B_n = 0$ if $r < a$ and A_n are the coefficients of (8.5), while $A_n = 0$ if $r > a$ and B_n are the coefficients of (8.6). Hence we have the solution

$$(8.9) \quad v = \frac{M}{a}\left[P_0(\cos\theta) - \frac{1}{2}\frac{a^2}{r^2} P_2(\cos\theta) + \frac{1\times 3}{2\times 4}\frac{r^4}{a^4} P_4(\cos\theta) - \cdots \right]$$

where $r < a$, and

$$(8.10) \quad v = \frac{M}{a}\left[\frac{a}{r} P_0(\cos\theta) - \frac{1}{2}\frac{a^3}{r^3} P_2(\cos\theta)\right.$$

$$\left. + \frac{1\times 3}{2\times 4}\frac{a^5}{r^5} P_4(\cos\theta) - \cdots \right]$$

when $r > a$.

9. The Potential about a Spherical Surface. As another example of the use of the general solution (7.23), let us consider the following problem:

Let a spherical surface be kept at a fixed distribution of electric potential of the form

$$(9.1) \qquad v = F(\theta)$$

on the surface of the sphere of Fig. 9.1.

The space inside and outside the spherical surface is assumed to be free of charges, and it is desired to determine the potential inside and outside the spherical surface.

FIG. 9.1

In this case we have the boundary conditions

$$(9.2) \qquad v = F(\theta) \qquad \text{when } r = a$$

where a is the radius of the sphere, and

$$(9.3) \qquad \lim_{r\to\infty} v = 0$$

that is, the potential vanishes at infinity.

a. The Region outside the Spherical Surface. In the region outside the spherical surface because of the boundary condition (9.3) we cannot have any positive powers of r. In this case the general solution (7.23) has $A_n = 0$, and we have

$$(9.4) \qquad v = \sum_{n=0}^{\infty} \frac{B_n}{r^{n+1}} P_n(\cos\theta) \qquad r > a$$

To determine the unknown constants B_n, we use the boundary condition (9.2). Placing $r = a$ in (9.4), we have

$$(9.5) \qquad F(\theta) = f(\cos\theta) = \sum_{n=0}^{\infty} \frac{B_n}{a^{n+1}} P_n(\cos\theta)$$

If we let

(9.6) $\cos \theta = u$

we have to expand $f(u)$ in a series of Legendre polynomials of the form

(9.7) $$f(u) = \sum_{n=0}^{\infty} \frac{B_n}{a^{n+1}} P_n(u)$$

By the results of Chap. 14 we have

(9.8) $$\frac{B_n}{a^{n+1}} = \frac{2n+1}{2} \int_{-1}^{+1} f(u)P_n(u) \, du$$

$$= \frac{2n+1}{2} \int_{0}^{\pi} F(\theta)P_n(\cos \theta) \sin \theta \, d\theta$$

Hence

(9.9) $$B_n = a^{n+1} \frac{2n+1}{2} \int_{0}^{\pi} F(\theta)P_n(\cos \theta) \sin \theta \, d\theta$$

This determines the coefficients in the solution (9.4).

b. *The Region inside the Spherical Surface.* In the region inside the spherical surface the potential cannot become infinite so that there cannot be any negative powers of r in the general solution (7.23). Hence the coefficients $B_n = 0$, and we have

(9.10) $$v = \sum_{n=0}^{\infty} A_n r^n P_n(\cos \theta) \qquad r < a$$

To determine the unknown coefficients A_n, we place $r = a$, and we have

(9.11) $$F(\theta) = \sum_{n=0}^{\infty} A_n a^n P_n(\cos \theta)$$

Using the formula for the determination of the coefficients of the expansion of an arbitrary function into a series of Legendre polynomials, we obtain

(9.12) $$A_n = \frac{2n+1}{2a^n} \int_{0}^{\pi} F(\theta)P_n(\cos \theta) \sin n\theta \, d\theta$$

These values of A_n when substituted into (9.10) give the solution to the problem.

A discussion of the general case when v is a function of all three spherical coordinates r, θ, and ϕ is beyond the scope of this book. For a detailed account of the theory of spherical harmonics the references at the end of this chapter should be consulted.

10. General Properties of Harmonic Functions.   In this section we shall discuss certain general properties of harmonic functions, that is, functions that satisfy Laplace's differential equation.

Let us suppose that we have a vector field $\mathbf{A}$ such that

$$(10.1) \qquad\qquad \mathbf{A} = \nabla v$$

where v is a scalar point function that satisfies Laplace's equation

$$(10.2) \qquad\qquad \nabla^2 v = 0$$

Now by Gauss's theorem (Chap. 15, Sec. 9), we have

$$(10.3) \qquad\qquad \int_S\!\!\int \mathbf{A} \cdot d\mathbf{s} = \int\!\!\int\!\!\int_V (\nabla \cdot \mathbf{A})\, dv$$

Now, if v satisfies Laplace's equation at every point within the region bounded by the surface S, we have

$$(10.4) \qquad\qquad \nabla \cdot \mathbf{A} = \nabla \cdot (\nabla v) = \nabla^2 v = 0$$

Hence (10.3) becomes

$$(10.5) \qquad\qquad \int_S\!\!\int (\nabla v) \cdot d\mathbf{s} = 0$$

If we take the curl of both sides of (10.1), we have

$$(10.6) \qquad\qquad \nabla \times \mathbf{A} = \nabla \times (\nabla v) = 0$$

Let us now apply Stokes's theorem (Chap. 15, Sec. 10) to the vector field $\mathbf{A}$ and obtain

$$(10.7) \qquad\qquad \oint_C \mathbf{A} \cdot d\mathbf{l} = \int_S\!\!\int (\nabla \times \mathbf{A}) \cdot d\mathbf{s} = 0$$

over the curve C bounding the open surface S.

Substituting (10.1) in (10.7), we have

$$(10.8) \qquad\qquad \oint_C (\nabla v) \cdot d\mathbf{l} = 0$$

From Eqs. (10.5) and (10.8) certain important properties of harmonic functions may be deduced that are similar in the plane and in space.

By an application of Green's theorem

$$(10.9) \quad \int\!\!\int\!\!\int_V (U\nabla^2 W - W\nabla^2 U)\, dv = \int_S\!\!\int (U\nabla W - W\nabla U) \cdot d\mathbf{s}$$

it may be shown that, if $\nabla^2 v = 0$ in the region bounded by a sphere of radius r, the value of v at the center of the sphere v_0 is given by

$$(10.10) \qquad\qquad v_0 = \frac{1}{4\pi r^2} \int_S\!\!\int v\, ds$$

where the integral is taken over the surface of the sphere. The result may be stated as follows:

I. The average value of a harmonic function on the surface of a sphere in which it has no singularities is equal to its value at the center of the sphere.

As a consequence of (10.5) we may deduce the following theorem:

II. A harmonic function without singularities in a given region cannot have a maximum value or a minimum value in the region.

To prove this statement, let us assume that v has a maximum value at the point p. Now, if we draw a small sphere s with p as its center, it is evident that the expression $(\nabla v)\, ds$, which is the normal derivative of v, is everywhere *negative* on s since, by hypothesis, v has a *greater* value at p than at any point in the neighborhood of p. Therefore the integral

$$(10.11) \qquad\qquad \int_s\!\!\int (\nabla v)\cdot d\mathbf{s}$$

is negative.

But by (10.5) this integral must vanish. This contradicts the initial assumption. In the same manner it may be shown that v cannot have a minimum at p, and the proposition is proved.

From the above proposition we deduce the following theorem:

III. A harmonic function with no singularities within a region and constant everywhere on the bounding surface S of the region has the same constant value everywhere inside the region.

To prove this, assume that the function is *not* constant inside the region; it must, therefore, have maximum and minimum values. However, by proposition II, it cannot have any maximum or minimum values in the region, so that these maximum and minimum values must occur on the boundary of the region. However, by hypothesis, the function is *constant* on the boundary, and therefore its maximum and minimum values coincide, and the function is constant. This proves the proposition.

Another very important theorem is the following one:

IV. Two harmonic functions that have identical values upon a closed contour and have no singularities within the contour are identical throughout the region bounded by the contour.

To prove this, let us suppose that we have two harmonic functions v_1 and v_2 which have the same values on the boundary of a closed region. Then $v_1 - v_2$ is a harmonic function which is zero on the boundary and hence, by Theorem III, is zero within the region under consideration. It follows, therefore, that $v_1 = v_2$, and the proposition is proved.

A practical result of this theorem is that if a solution of Laplace's equation has been found so as to take assigned values on a closed boundary no other solution is possible; that is, the solution is unique.

Another important result may be obtained by using the first form of Green's theorem (Chap. 15, Sec. 9) in

$$(10.12) \qquad \int_s\!\!\int (U\nabla W) \cdot d\mathbf{s} = \int\!\!\int\!\!\int_v [U\nabla^2 W + (\nabla U) \cdot (\nabla W)]\, dv$$

If we let

$$(10.13) \qquad\qquad U = W$$

and

$$(10.14) \qquad\qquad \nabla^2 U = 0$$

in the region inside S, Eq. (10.12) reduces to

$$(10.15) \qquad \int_s\!\!\int (U\nabla U) \cdot d\mathbf{s} = \int\!\!\int\!\!\int_v (\nabla U)^2\, dv$$

If the normal derivative of U vanishes on the surface S, we have $(\nabla U)\, ds = 0$ for every point of the surface, and hence the left-hand side of (10.15) vanishes.   We then have

$$(10.16) \qquad\qquad \int\!\!\int\!\!\int_v (\nabla U)^2\, dv = 0$$

Now since the volume v is arbitrary and the integrand $(\nabla U)^2$ is always positive, we must have

$$(10.17) \qquad\qquad \nabla U = 0$$

or hence

$$(10.18) \qquad\qquad U = \text{const}$$

Hence we have the following theorem:

V. If the normal derivative of a harmonic function is zero on a closed surface within which the function has no singularities, the function is a constant.

From this theorem comes the following one:

VI. If two harmonic functions have the same normal derivatives on a closed surface within which they have no singularities, they differ at most by an additive constant.

These theorems are of great importance in the theory of electrostatics, magnetostatics, heat flow, etc.   Applied to heat flow, Theorems IV and VI are physically evident.   Theorem IV states that the temperature within a closed region is fully determined by the temperature on the boundary, and Theorem VI states that except for an additive constant the temperature inside the region is determined by the rate of flow across the boundary.

PROBLEMS

1. A homogeneous spherical shell is made of material of diffusivity h. The inner radius of the shell is a, and the outer radius is b. If the inner shell is kept at a constant temperature v_a and the outer shell is kept at a constant temperature v_b, show that the temperature of the shell is given by

$$v = (v_a - v_b) \frac{ab}{b-a} \frac{1}{r} + \frac{v_b b - v_a a}{b - a}$$

2. Given the temperatures at the boundaries of a rectangular plate as

$$v = 0 \qquad v = 0 \qquad v = \phi(x) \qquad v = F(x)$$
$$x = 0 \qquad x = s \qquad y = 0 \qquad y = h$$

show that the temperature of the region inside the plate is given by $v = U + W$, where

$$U = \sum_{n=1}^{\infty} a_a \frac{\sinh (n\pi y/s)}{\sinh (n\pi h/s)} \sin \frac{n\pi x}{s}$$

where

$$a_n = \frac{2}{s} \int_0^s F(x) \sin \frac{n\pi x}{s} dx$$

and

$$W = \sum_{n=1}^{\infty} b_n \frac{[\sinh \pi n(h - y)]/s}{\sinh (n\pi h/s)} \sin \frac{n\pi x}{s}$$

where

$$b_n = \frac{2}{s} \int_0^s \phi(x) \sin \frac{n\pi x}{s} dx$$

3. An infinitely long plane and uniform plate is bounded by two parallel edges and an end at right angles to these. The breadth is π, and the end is maintained at temperature v_0 at all points and the edge at temperature zero. Show that the steady-state temperature is given by

$$v = \frac{4v_0}{\pi} (e^{-y} \sin x + \tfrac{1}{3}e^{-3y} \sin 3x + \cdots)$$

Show by any method that this is equivalent to

$$v = \frac{2v_0}{\pi} \tan^{-1} \frac{\sin x}{\sinh y}$$

4. Find the temperature for a steady flow of heat in a semicircular plate of radius r. The circumference is kept at a temperature v_0 and the diameter at a temperature zero.

5. A long rectangular plate of width 1 cm with insulated surfaces has its temperature ϕ equal to zero on both the long sides and one of the short sides so that

$$v(0,y) = 0 \qquad v(a,y) = 0 \qquad v(x, \infty) = 0$$
$$v(x,0) = kx$$

Show that the steady-state temperature within the plate is given by

$$v(x,y) = \frac{2ak}{\pi} \sum_{n=1}^{\pi} \frac{(-1)^n}{n} e^{-n\pi y/a} \sin \frac{n\pi x}{a}$$

6. Show that, when the values of a potential function on the boundary of a circle of radius R are given by $v(R,\theta) = F(\theta)$, the potential at any interior point is given by

$$v(r,\theta) = \frac{1}{\pi} \int_{-\pi}^{\pi} \left[\frac{1}{2} + \sum_{n=1}^{\infty} \left(\frac{r}{R} \right)^n \cos n(\theta - u) \right] F(u) \, du$$

7. If the potential is a constant v_0 on the spherical surface of radius R, show that $v = v_0$ at all interior points and $v = v_0 R/r$ at each exterior point.

8. Find the steady temperatures inside a solid sphere of unit radius if one hemisphere of its surface is kept at temperature zero and the other at temperature unity.

9. Find the steady temperature inside a solid sphere of unit radius if the temperature of its surface is given by $U_0 \cos \theta$.

10. Find the gravitational potential due to a uniform circular disk of mass M and unit radius.

11. A square plate has its faces and its edge $y = 0$ insulated. Its edges $x = 0$ and $x = \pi$ are kept at temperature zero, and its edge $y = \pi$ at temperature $F(x)$. Show that its steady temperature is given by

$$v(x,y) = \frac{2}{\pi} \sum_{n=1}^{\infty} \frac{\cosh ny}{\cosh n\pi} \sin nx \int_0^{\pi} F(u) \sin nu \, du$$

12. Show that the steady temperature $v(r,z)$ in a solid cylinder bounded by the surfaces $r = 1$, $z = 0$, and $z = L$, where the first surface is insulated, the second kept at temperature zero, and the last at a temperature $F(r)$, is

$$v(r,z) = \frac{2z}{L} \int_0^1 uF(u) \, du + 2 \sum_{j=2}^{\infty} \frac{J_0(m_j r) \sinh m_j z}{J_0(m_j)^2 \sinh m_j L} \int_0^1 uJ_0(m_j u)F(u) \, du$$

where m_2, m_3, . . . are the positive roots of $J_1(m) = 0$.

13. An infinite uncharged conducting cylinder of radius a is set with its axis perpendicular to a uniform electric field of strength E. Find the potential in the region outside the cylinder.

14. Show that the surface $v = F(x,y,z) = C$ can be equipotential if $\nabla^2 C/(\nabla C)^2$ is a function of C only.

REFERENCES

1. Byerly, W. E.: "Fourier Series and Spherical Harmonics," Ginn & Company, Boston, 1893.
2. Churchill, R. V.: "Fourier Series and Boundary Value Problems," McGraw-Hill Book Company, Inc., New York, 1941.
3. Carslaw, H. S.: "Mathematical Theory of Conduction of Heat in Solids," The Macmillan Company, New York, 1921.
4. MacRobert, T. M.: "Spherical Harmonics," E. P. Dutton & Co., Inc., New York, 1927.
5. McLachlan, N. W.: "Bessel Functions for Engineers," Oxford University Press, New York, 1934.
6. Kellog, O. D.: "Foundations of Potential Theory," Springer-Verlag OHG, Berlin, 1929.
7. MacMillan, W. D.: "The Theory of the Potential," McGraw-Hill Book Company, Inc., New York, 1930.
8. Smythe, W. R.: "Static and Dynamic Electricity," 1st ed., McGraw-Hill Book Company, Inc., New York, 1939.
9. Jeans, J. H.: "The Mathematical Theory of Electricity and Magnetism," Cambridge University Press, New York, 1925.

CHAPTER 18

THE EQUATION OF HEAT CONDUCTION OR DIFFUSION

1. Introduction. Perhaps next in importance to Laplace's equation in applied mathematics is the partial differential equation

$$(1.1) \qquad \frac{\partial V}{\partial t} = h^2 \nabla^2 V$$

where h^2 is a constant and ∇^2 is the Laplacian operator. We have seen in Chap. 15, Sec. 14, that this equation governs the distribution of temperature V in homogeneous solids. In Chap. 15, Sec. 18, it was shown that as a consequence of Maxwell's electromagnetic equations the current-density vector $\mathbf{J}$ satisfies the equation

$$(1.2) \qquad \nabla^2 \mathbf{J} = \mu\sigma \frac{\partial \mathbf{J}}{\partial t}$$

This equation has exactly the same form as Eq. (1.1) and is known in the electrical literature as the *skin-effect* equation. It may also be shown[*] that, if U is the concentration of a certain material in grams per cubic centimeter in a certain homogeneous medium of diffusivity constant K measured in square centimeters per second, U satisfies the equation

$$(1.3) \qquad \nabla^2 U = \frac{1}{K} \frac{\partial U}{\partial t}$$

This equation is also of the form (1.1).

In the theory of the consolidation of soil,[†] it is shown that, if U is the excess hydrostatic pressure at any point at any time t and C_v is the coefficient of consolidation, U satisfies the equation

$$(1.4) \qquad \nabla^2 U = \frac{1}{C_v} \frac{\partial U}{\partial t}$$

This is also of the form of a heat-flow equation.

In Chap. 16, Sec. 10, it was shown that the equations governing the propagation of potential e and current i along an electrical cable having a

---

[*] A. B. Newman, The Drying of Porous Solids; Diffusion Calculation, *Transactions of the American Institute of Chemical Engineers*, vol. 27, p. 310, 1931.

[†] K. Terzaghi, "Erdbaumechanik," Johann Ambrosius Barth, Munich, 1925.

resistance of R ohms per unit length and a capacitance of C farads per unit length are given by

$$(1.5) \qquad \frac{\partial^2 e}{\partial x^2} = RC\,\frac{\partial e}{\partial t}$$

$$(1.6) \qquad \frac{\partial^2 i}{\partial x^2} = RC\,\frac{\partial i}{\partial t}$$

These equations are of the form (1.1) when V is a function of x only so that the Laplacian operator reduces to $\nabla^2 = \partial^2/\partial x^2$.

This chapter will be devoted to a discussion of some of the simpler methods of solution of Eq. (1.1) subject to certain initial and boundary conditions. We have already seen in Chap. 17 that when a steady state with respect to time has been reached the term $\partial V/\partial t$ is absent in Eq. (1.1) and the problem reduces to a solution of Laplace's equation subject to the prescribed boundary conditions of the problem.

2. Variable Linear Flow. Let us suppose that we have a bar of length s and of uniform section, the diameter of which is small in comparison with the radius of curvature. Let us suppose that its surface is impervious to heat so that there is no radiation from the sides.

Let the initial temperature of the bar be given, and let its ends be kept at the constant temperature zero. If we take one end of the bar at the origin and we denote distances along the bar by x, we have

$$(2.1) \qquad \frac{\partial V}{\partial t} = h^2\,\frac{\partial^2 V}{\partial x^2} \qquad h^2 = k$$

as a special case of Eq. (1.1).

The *boundary* conditions are

$$(2.2) \qquad \begin{aligned} v &= 0 & \text{when } x = 0 \\ v &= 0 & \text{when } x = s \end{aligned} \Biggr\} \quad \text{for all values of } t$$

The *initial* condition is

$$(2.3) \qquad v = F(x) \quad \text{for } t = 0 \qquad v \neq \infty \quad \text{for } t = \infty$$

To solve Eq. (2.1), let us try a solution of the form

$$(2.4) \qquad V(x,t) = e^{mt}u(x)$$

where m is a constant and $u(x)$ is a function of x to be determined. On substituting this in (2.1) and dividing out the common factor e^{mt}, we have

$$(2.5) \qquad mu = h^2\,\frac{d^2u}{dx^2}$$

or

$$(2.6) \qquad \frac{d^2u}{dx^2} = \frac{m}{h^2}\,u$$

If we let

$$(2.7) \qquad\qquad a^2 = -\frac{m}{h^2}$$

Eq. (2.6) becomes

$$(2.8) \qquad\qquad \frac{d^2u}{dx^2} + a^2u = 0$$

The general solution of this equation is

$$(2.9) \qquad\qquad u = A \sin ax + B \cos ax$$

Now u must satisfy the boundary conditions (2.2). The first condition, at $x = 0$, gives $B = 0$. In order for u to vanish at $x = s$, we must have

$$(2.10) \qquad\qquad A \sin as = 0$$

or

$$(2.11) \qquad as = r\pi \qquad a = \frac{r\pi}{s} \qquad r = 0, 1, 2, 3, \ldots$$

for a nontrivial solution. To each value of r there corresponds a solution of the differential equation (2.6) of the form

$$(2.12) \qquad\qquad u_r = A_r \sin \frac{r\pi x}{s}$$

where A_r is an arbitrary constant.

The possible values of the constant m are given by Eqs. (2.7) and (2.11) and may be written in the form

$$(2.13) \qquad\qquad m_r = -\left(\frac{hr\pi}{s}\right)^2$$

To each value of r there corresponds a solution of the differential equation (2.1) of the form

$$(2.14) \qquad\qquad v_r = A_r e^{-(hr\pi/s)^2 t} \sin \frac{r\pi x}{s}$$

that satisfies the boundary conditions. By summing over all values of r, we construct the general solution

$$(2.15) \qquad\qquad v = \sum_{r=1}^{\infty} A_r e^{-(hr\pi/s)^2 t} \sin \frac{r\pi x}{s}$$

To evaluate the arbitrary constants A_r, we place $t = 0$ in (2.15) and use the initial conditions (2.3). We thus have

$$(2.16) \qquad\qquad F(x) = \sum_{r=1}^{r=\infty} A_r \sin \frac{r\pi x}{s}$$

We must therefore expand $F(x)$ in a half-range series of sines. We thus obtain

$$(2.17) \qquad A_r = \frac{2}{s} \int_0^s F(x) \sin \frac{r\pi x}{s} \, dx$$

Equation (2.15) with these values of the constants A_r gives the solution of the problem.

If instead of the ends of the bar being kept at temperature zero they are impervious to heat, then the statement of the problem becomes

$$(2.18) \qquad \left. \begin{array}{ll} \dfrac{\partial v}{\partial x} = 0 & \text{at } x = 0 \\[2mm] \dfrac{\partial v}{\partial x} = 0 & \text{at } x = s \end{array} \right\} \quad \text{for all values of } t$$

$$(2.19) \qquad v = F(x) \quad \text{for } t = 0 \quad v \neq \infty \quad \text{at } t = \infty$$

In this case we have from Eq. (2.9)

$$(2.20) \qquad \frac{du}{dx} = aA \cos ax - Ba \sin ax$$

If this is to vanish at $x = 0$ and $x = s$, we must have

$$(2.21) \qquad A = 0 \quad \sin as = 0$$

Again we obtain

$$(2.22) \qquad a = \frac{r\pi}{s} \quad r = 0, 1, 2, \ldots$$

Continuing the same reasoning as before, we obtain the general solution

$$(2.23) \qquad v = B_0 + \sum_{r=1}^{\infty} B_r e^{-(hr\pi/s)^2 t} \cos \frac{r\pi x}{s}$$

We must therefore expand $F(x)$ in a half-range cosine series. We thus obtain

$$(2.24) \qquad B_0 = \frac{1}{s} \int_0^s F(x) \, dx \qquad B_r = \frac{2}{s} \int_0^s F(x) \cos \frac{r\pi x}{s} \, dx$$

It is interesting to note that when $t = \infty$ we have

$$(2.25) \qquad v = B_0 = \frac{1}{s} \int_0^s F(x) \, dx$$

the average initial temperature of the bar. This result might of course have been inferred directly from the fact that no heat leaves the bar.

3. Electrical Analogy of Linear Heat Flow. A very interesting and useful electrical analogy to linear heat flow may be deduced if we employ the following notation.

Consider a uniform bar or rod that is thermally insulated so that no heat escapes from its sides, as shown in Fig. 3.1. Let

$v(x,t)$ = temperature at point a distance x from one end of bar
ϕ = heat flux or quantity of heat passing through cross section s of bar per unit area per unit time
R = thermal or heat resistance per unit length of material, that is, temperature drop per unit length when heat flux is unity ($1/R$ = thermal conductivity)
C = heat capacitance of material = specific heat $\times$ density (number of heat units to raise block of unit area and unit length $1°$ in temperature)

If $v(x + \Delta x, t)$ is the temperature at a point at a distance of $x + \Delta x$ from the end of the bar, we have

$$(3.1) \qquad R\phi\,\Delta x = v(x,t) - v(x + \Delta x, t)$$

Using Taylor's expansion and letting $\Delta x \to 0$ in the limit, we obtain

$$(3.2) \qquad -\frac{\partial v}{\partial x} = R\phi$$

FIG. 3.1

Now the heat flux $\phi(x,t)$ at the point x raises the temperature of a lamina of thickness Δx at the rate $\partial v/\partial t$, and a heat flux of magnitude $\phi(x + \Delta x, t)$ emerges from the lamina of width Δx. We thus have the equation

$$(3.3) \qquad \phi(x,t) = C\,\Delta x\,\frac{\partial v}{\partial t} + \phi(x + \Delta x, t)$$

Again expanding $\phi(x + \Delta x, t)$ by Taylor's expansion and letting $\Delta x \to 0$, we obtain

$$(3.4) \qquad -\frac{\partial \phi}{\partial x} = C\frac{\partial v}{\partial t}$$

Now, in Chap. 16, Sec. 10, it was shown that the flow of current and potential along an electric cable as shown in Fig. 3.2 having a resistance R and a capacitance C per unit length are governed by the equations

FIG. 3.2

$$(3.5) \qquad \begin{aligned} -\frac{\partial i}{\partial x} &= C\frac{\partial e}{\partial t} \\ -\frac{\partial e}{\partial x} &= Ri \end{aligned}$$

Comparing Eqs. (3.2) and (3.4) with (3.5), we see that we have the following set of analogies:

$$\phi \text{ (heat flux)} \rightarrow i \text{ (current along cable)}$$
$$v \text{ (temperature)} \rightarrow e \text{ (electric potential)}$$

$$R \text{ (thermal resistivity)} \rightarrow R \left(\frac{\text{electrical resistance}}{\text{length}} \right)$$

$$C \text{ (heat capacitance)} \rightarrow C \left(\frac{\text{electrical capacitance}}{\text{length}} \right)$$

On eliminating ϕ between Eqs. (3.2) and (3.5), we obtain

(3.6)
$$\frac{\partial^2 v}{\partial x^2} = CR \frac{\partial v}{\partial t}$$

or

(3.7)
$$\frac{\partial v}{\partial t} = \frac{1}{CR} \frac{\partial^2 v}{\partial x^2}$$

The quantity

(3.8)
$$h^2 = \frac{1}{CR} = \frac{\text{thermal conductivity}}{\text{density} \times \text{specific heat}}$$

is called the *diffusivity, diffusion coefficient,* or *thermometric conductivity.*

The above electrical analogy makes it possible to use the methods of electrical-circuit theory to solve problems in one-dimensional heat conduction.

4. Linear Flow in Semi-infinite Solid, Temperature on Face Given as Sinusoidal Function of Time. Let all space on the positive side of the yz plane be filled with a homogeneous solid of diffusivity h^2. Let the temperature on the yz plane be given as a sinusoidal function of the time, and let it be the same for all values of y and z. It is required to find the temperature throughout the solid when the periodic state is established.

It is clear from symmetry that the temperature $v(x,t)$ is independent of y and z, and the conditions to be fulfilled are

(4.1)
$$\frac{\partial v}{\partial t} = h^2 \frac{\partial^2 v}{\partial x^2}$$

(4.2) $v = V_0 \sin \omega t$ for $x = 0$ $v \neq \infty$ at $x = \infty$
$\qquad = \text{Im} \ (V_0 e^{j\omega t})$ $j = \sqrt{-1}$

where Im stands for the "imaginary part of." To solve (4.1), let us assume a solution of the form

(4.3)
$$v(x,t) = \text{Im} \ [u(x)e^{j\omega t}]$$

Discarding the Im symbol and substituting this in (4.1), we obtain

(4.4)
$$j\omega u = h^2 \frac{d^2 u}{dx^2}$$

where the common factor $e^{j\omega t}$ has been divided out.   Equation (4.4) may be written in the form

$$(4.5) \qquad \frac{d^2u}{dx^2} = \frac{j\omega}{h^2} u$$

If we let

$$(4.6) \qquad a^2 = \frac{j\omega}{h^2} = \frac{\omega}{h^2} e^{j(\pi/2 + 2k\pi)} \qquad k = 0, 1, 2, \ldots$$

the solution of (4.5) may be written in the form

$$(4.7) \qquad u = A e^{ax} + B e^{-ax}$$

where A and B are arbitrary constants.   Now since a^2 is given by (4.6), the square root of a^2 is given by

$$(4.8) \qquad a = \sqrt{\frac{\omega}{h^2}} e^{j(\pi/4)}$$

The positive root may be written in the form

$$(4.9) \qquad a = \sqrt{\frac{\omega}{h^2}} e^{j(\pi/4)} = \sqrt{\frac{\omega}{2h^2}} (1 + j)$$

Now, at $x = \infty$, the temperature is finite, and hence we must have the constant A in (4.7) equal to zero.   At $x = 0$ we have

$$(4.10) \qquad u = B = V_0$$

Hence the solution is

$$(4.11) \qquad v(x,t) = \text{Im } (V_0 e^{-ax} e^{j\omega t})$$
$$= \text{Im } (V_0 e^{-\sqrt{\omega/2h^2}\, x} e^{j(\omega t - \sqrt{\omega/2h^2}\, x)})$$
$$= V_0 e^{-\sqrt{\omega/2h^2}\, x} \sin\left(\omega t - \sqrt{\frac{\omega}{2h^2}}\, x\right)$$

The negative root leads to the same solution.

We thus see that the temperature decreases in magnitude and changes in phase as we proceed farther into the solid.   This result explains why the daily variation of the temperature of the earth's surface cannot be traced to a depth of 3 or 4 ft, while the annual variation cannot be traced beyond a depth of 60 or 70 ft.   The greater the frequency of the variation of the surface temperature, the more rapidly is the amplitude of the variation attenuated.   This phenomenon has its counterpart in electromagnetic theory and is known in the electrical literature as the *skin effect*.

5. Two-dimensional Heat Conduction.   To illustrate the solution of the two-dimensional diffusion equation, let us consider the following problem:

A thin rectangular plate (Fig. 5.1) whose surface is impervious to heat flow has at $t = 0$ an arbitrary distribution of temperature. Its four edges are kept at zero temperature. It is required to determine the subsequent temperature of the plate as t increases.

FIG. 5.1

Let the plate extend from $x = 0$ to $x = a$ and from $y = 0$ to $y = b$. Expressing the problem mathematically, we must solve the equation

$$(5.1) \qquad \frac{\partial v}{\partial t} = h^2 \left(\frac{\partial^2 v}{\partial x^2} + \frac{\partial^2 v}{\partial y^2} \right)$$

subject to the boundary conditions

$$(5.2) \qquad \begin{matrix} v = 0 & v = 0 & v = 0 & v = 0 \\ x = 0 & x = a & y = 0 & y = b \\ 0 \le y \le b & 0 \le y \le b & 0 \le x \le a & 0 \le x \le a \end{matrix}$$

for all time t.

The initial conditions are

$$(5.3) \qquad \begin{matrix} v = F(x,y) & \text{for } 0 \le x \le a & 0 \le y \le b & \text{at } t = 0 \\ & v = 0 & \text{at } t = \infty \end{matrix}$$

To solve Eq. (5.1), assume a solution of the form

$$(5.4) \qquad v = e^{-\theta t} F_1(x) F_2(y)$$

where F_1 is a function of x only and F_2 is a function of y only. Substituting (5.4) in (5.1) and dividing out the common term $e^{-\theta t}$, we obtain

$$(5.5) \qquad -\theta F_1 F_2 = h^2 (F_1'' F_2 + F_1 F_2'')$$

If we divide by $h^2 F_1 F_2$, we have

$$(5.6) \qquad \frac{F_1''}{F_1} + \frac{F_2''}{F_2} = -\frac{\theta}{h^2}$$

This may be written in the form

$$(5.7) \qquad \frac{F_1''}{F_1} + \frac{\theta}{h^2} = -\frac{F_2''}{F_2} = k^2$$

We have now succeeded in separating the variables since the left-hand member of (5.7) is a function of x only and the right-hand member of (5.7) is a function of y only, and hence both members of (5.7) are equal to a constant which we have called k^2.

If we let

$$(5.8) \qquad \frac{\theta}{h^2} - k^2 = q^2$$

Eq. (5.7) separates into the two equations

$$(5.9) \qquad \begin{aligned} F_1'' + q^2 F_1 &= 0 \\ F_2'' + k^2 F_2 &= 0 \end{aligned}$$

These equations have the solutions

$$(5.10) \qquad \begin{aligned} F_1 &= A_1 \sin qx + B_1 \cos qx \\ F_2 &= A_2 \sin ky + B_2 \cos ky \end{aligned}$$

where the A's and B's are arbitrary constants. Now, to satisfy the boundary conditions (5.2), it is obvious that there cannot be any cosine terms present so that we must have $B_1 = B_2 = 0$.

Also we must have

$$(5.11) \qquad \begin{aligned} \sin qa &= 0 \\ \sin kb &= 0 \end{aligned}$$

Hence

$$(5.12) \qquad \begin{aligned} q &= \frac{m\pi}{a} \qquad m = 0, 1, 2, \ldots \\ k &= \frac{n\pi}{b} \qquad n = 0, 1, 2, \ldots \end{aligned}$$

From (5.8) we find that

$$(5.13) \qquad \theta_{mn} = h^2 \left[\left(\frac{m\pi}{a} \right)^2 + \left(\frac{n\pi}{b} \right)^2 \right]$$

Hence for each value of m and n we find a particular solution of (5.1) that satisfies the boundary conditions (5.2) of the form

$$(5.14) \qquad v = B_{mn} e^{-\theta_{mn} t} \sin \frac{m\pi x}{a} \sin \frac{n\pi y}{b}$$

If we sum over all possible values of m and n, we construct the general solution

$$(5.15) \qquad v = \sum_{m=1}^{\infty} \sum_{n=1}^{\infty} B_{mn} e^{-\theta_{mn} t} \sin \frac{m\pi x}{a} \sin \frac{n\pi y}{b}$$

where the quantities B_{mn} are *arbitrary* constants that must be determined from the initial conditions (5.3). Placing $t = 0$ in (5.15) we must have

$$(5.16) \qquad F(x,y) = \sum_{m=1}^{m=\infty} \sum_{n=1}^{n=\infty} B_{mn} \sin \frac{m\pi x}{a} \sin \frac{n\pi y}{b}$$

We must therefore expand the initial temperature function $F(x,y)$ into a double sine series.

To do this, let us multiply both sides of (5.16) by

$$\sin \frac{r\pi x}{a} \sin \frac{s\pi y}{b} \, dx \, dy$$

where r and s are integers and integrate from $x = 0$ to $x = a$ and $y = 0$ to $y = b$; because of the orthogonality properties of the sines all the terms in the summation vanish except the term for which $m = r$ and $n = s$, and we obtain the result

$$(5.17) \qquad B_{rs} = \frac{4}{ab} \int_{x=0}^{x=a} \int_{y=0}^{y=b} F(x,y) \sin \frac{r\pi x}{a} \sin \frac{s\pi y}{b} \, dy \, dx$$

This determines the arbitrary constants of the general solution (5.15).

The Cooling of a Hot Brick.   By a simple extension of the above analysis it may be shown that, if we have a rectangular parallelepiped or brick whose sides are kept at zero temperature and whose internal temperature is given arbitrarily at $t = 0$ to be $F(x,y,z)$, then the subsequent temperature is given by

$$(5.18) \qquad v = \sum_{m=1}^{\infty} \sum_{n=1}^{\infty} \sum_{r=1}^{\infty} B_{mnr} e^{-\theta_{mnr} t} \sin \frac{m\pi x}{a} \sin \frac{n\pi y}{b} \sin \frac{r\pi z}{c}$$

where

$$(5.19) \qquad \theta_{mnr} = h^2 \left[\left(\frac{m\pi}{a} \right)^2 + \left(\frac{n\pi}{b} \right)^2 + \left(\frac{r\pi}{c} \right)^2 \right]$$

and

$$(5.20) \quad B_{mnr} = \frac{8}{abc} \int_{x=0}^{a} \int_{y=0}^{b} \int_{z=0}^{c} F(x,y,z) \sin \frac{m\pi x}{a} \sin \frac{n\pi y}{b} \sin \frac{r\pi z}{c} \, dx \, dy \, dz$$

where the brick is oriented with respect to a cartesian coordinate system as shown in Fig. 5.2.

FIG. 5.2

6. Temperatures in an Infinite Bar.   An illustration of the method of solution of the diffusion equation by the use of definite integrals is given by the following example:

Given an infinite bar of small cross section so insulated that there is no transfer of heat at the surface, we take the x axis along the bar. The temperature of the bar at $t = 0$ is given as an arbitrary function $F(x)$ of x.   It is required to find the subsequent temperature.

Stated mathematically, we must solve the equation

$$(6.1) \qquad \frac{\partial v}{\partial t} = h^2 \frac{\partial^2 v}{\partial x^2}$$

subject to the initial condition

(6.2) $$v = F(x) \qquad \text{at } t = 0$$

Let us assume a solution of (6.1) of the form

(6.3) $$v = e^{-a^2t}u(x)$$

Substituting this in (6.1) and dividing out the common factor e^{-a^2t}, we obtain

(6.4) $$-a^2u = h^2\frac{d^2u}{dx^2}$$

or

(6.5) $$\frac{d^2u}{dx^2} + \frac{a^2}{h^2}u = 0$$

If we let

(6.6) $$\frac{a^2}{h^2} = \alpha^2$$

a *particular* solution of (6.5) may be written in the form

(6.7) $$u = \cos \alpha(x - \beta)$$

where β is an arbitrary constant. We thus obtain from (6.3) the following particular solution of Eq. (6.1),

(6.8) $$v_1 = e^{-\alpha^2h^2t} \cos \alpha(x - \beta)$$

where α and β are arbitrary constants.

If we multiply (6.8) by $F(\beta)/\pi$, we obtain

(6.9) $$v_2 = \frac{F(\beta)}{\pi} e^{-\alpha^2h^2t} \cos \alpha(x - \beta)$$

This is still a solution of (6.1). The integral of v_2 with respect to the parameters α and β in the form

(6.10) $$v = \frac{1}{\pi} \int_{\alpha=0}^{\alpha=\infty} \int_{\beta=-\infty}^{\beta=+\infty} F(\beta)e^{-\alpha^2h^2t} \cos \alpha(x - \beta) \, d\alpha \, d\beta$$

is a solution of Eq. (6.1). If we place $t = 0$ in (6.10), we obtain

(6.11) $$v(x,0) = \frac{1}{\pi} \int_{\alpha=0}^{\alpha=\infty} \int_{\beta=-\infty}^{\beta=+\infty} F(\beta) \cos [\alpha(x - \beta)] \, d\alpha \, d\beta$$

But by Chap. 3, Sec. 9, we see that this is the Fourier integral representation of $F(x)$. Hence the solution of the problem is given formally by (6.10). This may be simplified by using the well-known definite integral

(6.12) $$\int_0^\infty e^{-v^2} \cos 2by \, dy = \frac{\sqrt{\pi} \, e^{-b^2}}{2}$$

which is found in most tables of integrals.   Using this integral, we transform (6.10) into

$$(6.13) \qquad v(x,t) = \frac{1}{2h\sqrt{t\pi}} \int_{\beta=-\infty}^{\beta=+\infty} F(\beta)e^{-(x-\beta)^2/4h^2 t}\, d\beta$$

7. Temperatures inside a Circular Plate.

The use of cylindrical coordinates in the solution of a diffusion problem is illustrated by the following:

Consider a thin circular plate whose faces are impervious to heat flow and whose circular edge is kept at zero temperature.   At $t = 0$ the initial temperature of the plate is a function $F(r)$ of the distance from the center of the plate only.   It is required to find the subsequent temperature. Let the radius of the plate be a.

It is obvious because of symmetry that the temperature v must be a function of r and t only.   Using cylindrical coordinates, we know that v must satisfy the equation

$$(7.1) \qquad \frac{\partial v}{\partial t} = h^2 \nabla^2 v$$

$$= h^2 \left(\frac{\partial^2 v}{\partial r^2} + \frac{1}{r}\frac{\partial v}{\partial r} \right) \qquad 0 \le r \le a$$

The boundary condition is

$$(7.2) \qquad\qquad v = 0 \qquad \text{at } r = a$$

The initial condition is

$$(7.3) \qquad\qquad v = F(r) \qquad \text{at } t = 0$$

To solve Eq. (7.1), assume the solution

$$(7.4) \qquad\qquad v = e^{-mt}u(r)$$

where $u(r)$ is a function of r only.   Substituting this into (7.1) and dividing the common factor e^{-mt}, we obtain

$$(7.5) \qquad\qquad -mu = h^2 \left(\frac{d^2 u}{dr^2} + \frac{1}{r}\frac{du}{dr} \right)$$

Dividing by h^2 and multiplying by r, we obtain

$$(7.6) \qquad\qquad r\frac{d^2 u}{dr^2} + \frac{du}{dr} + \frac{m}{h^2}ru = 0$$

If we let

$$(7.7) \qquad\qquad \frac{m}{h^2} = k^2$$

we recognize that Eq. (7.6) has the same form as Eq. (9.1) of Chap. 13, with $n = 0$. Hence the general solution of (7.6) is

$$(7.8) \qquad u = AJ_0(kr) + BY_0(kr)$$

where A and B are arbitrary constants. Since the temperature must remain finite at $r = 0$, the arbitrary constant B in (7.8) must be equal to zero since $Y_0(kr)$ goes to infinity at $r = 0$. We thus have the solution

$$(7.9) \qquad u = AJ_0(kr)$$

However, the boundary of the plate $r = a$ is maintained at zero temperature for all values of time, and hence we must have

$$(7.10) \qquad J_0(ka) = 0$$

Hence only values of k are permissible that satisfy Eq. (7.10). Let these values be k_s ($s = 1, 2, 3, \ldots$). Equation (7.7) gives the following values for m:

$$(7.11) \qquad m_s = (k_s h)^2$$

A particular solution of (7.1) that satisfies the boundary condition is

$$(7.12) \qquad v_s = A_s e^{-k_s^2 h^2 t} J_0(k_s r)$$

If we sum over all possible values of s, we construct the general solution

$$(7.13) \qquad v = \sum_{s=1}^{\infty} A_s e^{-k_s^2 h^2 t} J_0(k_s r)$$

where the arbitrary constants A_s must be determined from the initial condition that, at $t = 0$, $v = F(r)$. Placing $t = 0$ in (7.13), we have

$$(7.14) \qquad F(r) = \sum_{s=1}^{\infty} A_s J_0(k_s r)$$

We must therefore expand the arbitrary function $F(r)$ into a series of Bessel functions. Using the results of Chap. 13, Sec. 12, we have

$$(7.15) \qquad A_s = \frac{2}{a^2 [J_1(k_s a)]^2} \int_{r=0}^{r=a} rF(r) J_0(k_s r)\, dr \qquad s = 1, 2, \ldots$$

This determines the arbitrary constants in the solution (7.13).

8. Skin Effect on a Plane Surface. A very interesting problem in electrodynamics is the one of determining the alternating-current distribution in homogeneous conducting mediums. Perhaps the simplest problem of this type is the following one:

Consider a semi-infinite conducting mass of metal of permeability μ and conductivity σ. Let the equation of the surface of this mass be $z = 0$, and suppose that on this surface the current-density vector $\mathbf{i}$ has only an x component i_x which has the value

$$(8.1) \qquad (i_x)_{z=0} = i_0 \sin \omega t$$

That is, on the surface of the semi-infinite mass we have a sheet of alternating current flowing in the x direction. The problem is to determine the distribution of current density within the conducting mass.

In Chap. 15, Sec. 18, it was shown that the current-density vector $\mathbf{i}$ satisfies the equation

$$(8.2) \qquad \nabla^2 \mathbf{i} = \mu\sigma \frac{\partial \mathbf{i}}{\partial t}$$

in a region of conductivity σ and permeability μ.

This is a vector equation, and in the case we are considering we have

$$(8.3) \qquad \mathbf{i} = (i_x, 0, 0)$$

That is, the current-density vector has only one component, the x component. Accordingly, in the case under consideration, we have

$$(8.4) \qquad \nabla^2 i_x = \mu\sigma \frac{\partial i_x}{\partial t} = \frac{\partial^2 i_x}{\partial z^2}$$

This problem is mathematically identical to the heat-flow problem discussed in Sec. 4. If we let

$$(8.5) \qquad h^2 = \frac{1}{\mu\sigma}$$

and follow the analysis of Sec. 4, writing z instead of x and i_x instead of v_x, etc., we obtain

$$(8.6) \qquad i_x = i_0 e^{-\sqrt{(\omega\mu\sigma/2)}z} \sin\left(\omega t - \sqrt{\frac{\omega\mu\sigma}{2}}\, z\right)$$

for the current density inside the mass of metal. We see that, because of the negative exponential factor, the current amplitude decreases as we penetrate the metal and is greatest at the surface of the mass. This phenomenon is the well-known *skin effect* of electrodynamics.

We may obtain the net current flowing per meter width by integrating

$$(8.7) \qquad \int_0^\infty i_x \, dz = i_0 \int_0^\infty e^{-kz} \sin (\omega t - kz) \, dz$$

where

$$(8.8) \qquad k = 7\sqrt{\frac{\omega\mu\sigma}{2}}$$

Using formulas Nos. 506 and 507 of Peirce's "Tables of Integrals," the integral (8.7) may be evaluated, and we obtain

$$(8.9) \qquad \int_0^\infty i_x \, dz = \frac{i_0}{\sqrt{\omega \mu \sigma}} \sin\left(\omega t - \frac{\pi}{4}\right)$$

It may be noted that this value of current would be increased if all conducting matter below a certain depth were removed since for certain values of z the current is reversed.

The average power $\bar{P}$ converted to heat per square meter of surface is obtained by integrating

$$(8.10) \qquad \bar{P} = \frac{\omega}{2\pi\sigma} \int_{z=0}^{z=\infty} \int_{t=0}^{2\pi/\omega} i_x^2 \, dt \, dz$$

$$= \frac{i_0^2}{2\sigma} \int_0^\infty e^{-2kz} \, dz$$

$$= \frac{i_0^2}{4\sigma k}$$

9. Current Density in a Wire.

A very important problem in electrical engineering is the determination of the current density in a circular wire carrying alternating current.

Let us consider a long cylinder of radius a, oriented along the z axis of a cartesian coordinate system as shown in Fig. 9.1.

Let the material of the cylinder be homogeneous and have a permeability μ and conductivity σ. In this case the current-density vector i has only a z component, and Eq. (8.2) reduces to

$$(9.1) \qquad \nabla^2 i_z = \mu\sigma \frac{\partial i_z}{\partial t}$$

FIG. 9.1

Since we are considering the case of a wire carrying alternating current, the current density has the form

$$(9.2) \qquad i_z = u(r) \cos \omega t$$
$$= \text{Re} \, [u(r)e^{j\omega t}]$$

where the symbol Re denotes the "real part of" and $u(r)$ is a function of r only. Suppressing the Re symbol and substituting this in (9.1), we obtain, on dividing out the common factor $e^{j\omega t}$,

$$(9.3) \qquad \nabla^2 u = j\omega \mu \sigma u$$

Since u is a function of r only, we have (Chap. 15, Sec. 12)

$$(9.4) \qquad \nabla^2 u = \frac{1}{r} \frac{d}{dr} \left(r \frac{du}{dr} \right)$$

Hence Eq. (9.3) becomes

$$(9.5) \qquad \frac{1}{r}\frac{d}{dr}\left(r\frac{du}{dr}\right) = j\omega\mu\sigma u$$

Differentiating, this becomes

$$(9.6) \qquad \frac{d^2u}{dr^2} + \frac{1}{r}\frac{du}{dr} - j\omega\mu\sigma u = 0$$

If we let

$$(9.7) \qquad k^2 = -j\omega ju$$

this may be written in the form

$$(9.8) \qquad \frac{d^2u}{dr^2} + \frac{1}{r}\frac{du}{dr} + k^2 u = 0$$

Equation (9.8) is of the form of Eq. (9.1) of Chap. 13 with $n = 0$. Hence the solution of (9.8) is

$$(9.9) \qquad u = AJ_0(kr) + BY_0(kr)$$

However, since the current density must remain finite at $r = 0$ and the function Y_0 goes to infinity for the zero value of its argument, we must have

$$(9.10) \qquad B = 0$$

The solution (9.9) reduces to

$$(9.11) \qquad u = AJ_0(kr)$$

Now

$$(9.12) \qquad k = \sqrt{-j\omega\mu\sigma} = j\sqrt{j}\sqrt{\omega\mu\sigma}$$
$$= j^{\frac{3}{2}}m$$

where

$$(9.13) \qquad m = \sqrt{\omega\mu\sigma}$$

Hence (9.11) may be written in the form

$$(9.14) \qquad u = AJ_0(j^{\frac{3}{2}}mr)$$

This may be written in terms of the ber and bei functions of Chap. 13, Sec. 11, in the form

$$(9.15) \qquad u = A[\text{ber } (mr) + j\,\text{bei } (mr)]$$

To determine the arbitrary constant A, place $r = 0$ in Eq. (9.14), and let u_0 be the value of the current-density amplitude at the center of the wire. Since $J_0(0) = 1$, we obtain

$$(9.16) \qquad u_0 = AJ_0(0) = A$$

Substituting this in (9.15), we thus have

$$(9.17) \qquad u = u_0[\text{ber } (mr) + j \text{ bei } (mr)]$$

This expression may be written in the polar form

$$(9.18) \qquad u = u_0 M e^{j\theta}$$

where

$$(9.19) \qquad M = \sqrt{\text{ber}^2 (mr) + \text{bei}^2 (mr)}$$

and

$$(9.20) \qquad \tan \theta = \frac{\text{bei } (mr)}{\text{ber } (mr)}$$

We now obtain the instantaneous current density i_z by substituting (9.18) in (9.2). We thus have

$$(9.21) \qquad \begin{aligned} i_z &= \text{Re } (u_0 M e^{j(\omega t + \theta)}) \\ &= u_0 M \cos (\omega t + \theta) \end{aligned}$$

Total Current in Wire. The total current $I(t)$ in the wire may be obtained by integrating the current density i_z throughout the cross section of the wire. We then have

$$(9.22) \qquad \begin{aligned} I(t) &= \int_{r=0}^{r=a} i_z \times 2\pi r \, dr \\ &= \text{Re} \int_{r=0}^{r=a} 2\pi r u \, dr \, e^{j\omega t} \\ &= \text{Re} \left[e^{j\omega t} \int_{r=0}^{r=a} u_0 J_0(j^{\frac{3}{2}} mr) \times 2\pi r \, dr \right] \end{aligned}$$

To integrate this expression, we use expression (6.11) of Chap. 13, for $n = 1$. This equation may be written in the form

$$(9.23) \qquad \int u J_0(u) \, du = u J_1(u)$$

Hence we have

$$(9.24) \qquad \begin{aligned} I(t) &= \text{Re} \left[\frac{2\pi u_0 a J_1(j^{\frac{3}{2}} ma)}{jm \sqrt{j}} e^{j\omega t} \right] \\ &= I_0 \cos (\omega t + \phi) \end{aligned}$$

where

$$(9.25) \qquad I_0 = \left| \frac{2\pi u_0 a J_1(j^{\frac{3}{2}} ma)}{jm \sqrt{j}} \right|$$

If we know the amplitude of the total current in the wire, we may compute u_0 from (9.25) and hence obtain i_z from (9.21).

10. General Theorems. In this section some general theorems useful in the solution of certain heat-flow and diffusion problems will be considered.

THEOREM I.   If $u_1(x,t)$, $u_2(y,t)$, and $u_3(z,t)$ are solutions of the three linear heat-flow equations

$$(10.1) \qquad \frac{\partial u_1}{\partial t} = h^2 \frac{\partial^2 u_1}{\partial x^2}$$

$$(10.2) \qquad \frac{\partial u_2}{\partial t} = h^2 \frac{\partial^2 u_2}{\partial y^2}$$

$$(10.3) \qquad \frac{\partial u_3}{\partial t} = h^2 \frac{\partial^2 u_3}{\partial z^2}$$

then $u = u_1 u_2 u_3$ is necessarily a solution of the three-dimensional heat-flow equation

$$(10.4) \qquad \frac{\partial u}{\partial t} = h^2 \left(\frac{\partial^2 u}{\partial x^2} + \frac{\partial^2 u}{\partial y^2} + \frac{\partial^2 u}{\partial z^2} \right)$$

Proof.   To prove this theorem, substitute the function $u = u_1 u_2 u_3$ in (10.4).   We then have

$$(10.5) \quad \frac{\partial}{\partial t} (u_1 u_2 u_3) = h^2 \left[\frac{\partial^2}{\partial x^2} (u_1 u_2 u_3) + \frac{\partial^2}{\partial y^2} (u_1 u_2 u_3) + \frac{\partial^2}{\partial z^2} (u_1 u_2 u_3) \right]$$

Differentiating, we have

$$(10.6) \quad u_2 u_3 \frac{\partial u_1}{\partial t} + u_1 u_3 \frac{\partial u_2}{\partial t} + u_1 u_2 \frac{\partial u_3}{\partial t}$$

$$= h^2 \left(u_2 u_3 \frac{\partial^2 u_1}{\partial x^2} + u_1 u_3 \frac{\partial^2 u_2}{\partial y^2} + u_1 u_2 \frac{\partial^2 u_3}{\partial z^2} \right)$$

If we now substitute Eqs. (10.1), (10.2), and (10.3) in (10.6), we obtain an identity.   This proves the theorem.

This theorem may be used to facilitate the solution of the "brick" problem of Sec. 5.

THEOREM II.   If $u_1(r,t)$ is a solution of the symmetrical two-dimensional equation

$$(10.7) \qquad \frac{\partial u_1}{\partial t} = h^2 \left(\frac{\partial^2 u_1}{\partial r^2} + \frac{1}{r} \frac{\partial u_1}{\partial r} \right)$$

and $u_2(z,t)$ is a solution of the linear heat-flow equation

$$(10.8) \qquad \frac{\partial u_2}{\partial t} = h^2 \frac{\partial^2 u_2}{\partial z^2}$$

then $u = u_1 u_2$ is necessarily a solution of the three-dimensional heat-flow equation

$$(10.9) \qquad \frac{\partial u}{\partial t} = h^2 \left(\frac{\partial^2 u}{\partial r^2} + \frac{1}{r} \frac{\partial u}{\partial r} + \frac{\partial^2 u}{\partial z^2} \right)$$

This is proved by substituting $u = u_1 u_2$ in Eq. (10.9).   By the use of Eqs. (10.7) and (10.8) we again obtain an identity and this proves the proposition.

PROBLEMS

1. An infinite plate of thickness a and uniform material of permeability μ and conductivity σ carries alternating current of angular frequency ω in one direction.   Show that the current density u_0 at the middle of the plate is related to the current density u_s at the surface of the plate by the equation

$$\frac{u_0}{u_s} = \frac{\sqrt{2}}{\sqrt{\cosh ma + \cos ma}}$$

where $m = \sqrt{\mu\sigma\omega/2}$.

2. An infinite iron plate is bounded by the parallel planes $x = h$ and $x = -h$. Wire is wound uniformly around the plate, and the layers of wire are parallel to the y axis.   An alternating current is sent through the wire.   This current produces a magnetic field $H_0 \cos \omega t$ parallel to the z axis at the surface of the plate.   Show that the magnetic field H inside the plate at a distance of x from the center is given by

$$H = H_0 \left(\frac{\cosh 2mx + \cos 2mx}{\cosh 2mh + \cos 2mh}\right)^{\frac{1}{2}} \cos (\omega t + \phi)$$

where $m = \sqrt{\sigma\omega\mu/2}$ and ϕ is a phase angle. μ and σ are the permeability and the conductivity of the plate, respectively.

HINT: The magnetic field H satisfies the equation $\nabla^2 \mathbf{H} = \mu\sigma(\partial \mathbf{H}/\partial t)$ in the region inside the plate.

3. The rate at which heat is lost from a rod as a consequence of surface radiation into the surrounding air at constant temperature u_0 is proportional to the difference of temperature $u - u_0$ and to the surface area of the element.   Show that this leads to an equation of the form

$$\frac{\partial u}{\partial t} = h^2 \frac{\partial^2 u}{\partial x^2} - k^2(u - u_0)$$

for the temperature of the rod.

4. If u_0 is zero in Prob. 3, show that in the electrical analogy discussed in Sec. 3 we must add a leakage-conductance term to take into account the radiation in the thermal problem.

5. An infinite bar has one end located at $x = 0$, and the other end extends to $x = \infty$. The temperature of the surrounding air is zero, and the end at $x = 0$ is kept at $u = u_0$. Find the steady-state distribution of temperature, taking into account radiation.

6. A thin bar of uniform section is bent into the form of a circular ring of large radius a.   At one point P in the ring, let a steady temperature u_0 be maintained. Let heat be radiated from the ring to the air.   Assume that the air is at zero temperature.   Show that, when a steady state is established, the temperature of the ring is given by

$$u = u_0 \frac{\cosh k(x - \pi a)}{\cosh k\pi a}$$

where k^2 is the radiation coefficient as defined in Prob. 3 and x is a coordinate measured around the ring so that $x = 0$ at P.   This arrangement is known as *Fourier's ring*.

7. It has been proposed to represent the rate of cooling of a surface by the empirical formula $e(v - v_0)^n$, where e is the emissivity of the surface and n has the value 1.2.

Show that on this supposition the equation to be satisfied in a long thin rod cooling laterally is

$$\frac{\partial v}{\partial t} = h^2 \frac{\partial^2 v}{\partial x^2} - \frac{ep}{c\rho\sigma}(v - v_0)^n$$

where v is the temperature at a distance x measured along the rod from one end, v_0 is the temperature of the surrounding medium, h^2 is the diffusivity, ρ the density, p the perimeter, c the specific heat, and σ the area of cross section of the rod.

8. A bar of length s is heated so that its two ends are at temperature zero. If initially the temperature is given by $u = cx(s - x)/s^2$, find the temperature at time t.

9. If in the equation

$$\frac{\partial u}{\partial t} = h^2 \frac{\partial^2 u}{\partial x^2} - k(u - u_0)$$

we introduce the change in variable $u = u_0 + e_v^{-kt}$, show that the equation in v is of the form

$$\frac{\partial v}{\partial t} = a^2 \frac{\partial^2 v}{\partial x^2}$$

10. A rectangular plate bounded by the lines $x = 0$, $y = 0$, $x = a$, $y = b$ has an initial distribution of temperature given by

$$v = A \sin \frac{\pi x}{a} \sin \frac{\pi y}{b}$$

The edges are kept at zero temperature, and the plane faces are impermeable to heat. Find the temperature at any point and time, and show that very close to any corner of the plate the lines of equal temperature and flow of heat are orthogonal systems of rectangular hyperbolas.

Show that the heat lost by the plate across the edges up to time t is

$$\frac{4mAab}{\pi^2}\left(1 - e^{-h^2\left(\frac{1}{a^2} + \frac{1}{b^2}\right)\pi^2 t}\right)$$

where m is the thermal capacity of the plate per unit area.

11. A conducting sphere initially at zero temperature has its surface kept at a constant temperature u_0 for a given time, after which it is kept at zero. Find the temperature at any time in the second stage.

12. A bar of uniform cross section is covered with impermeable varnish and extends from the point $x = 0$ to infinity. The bar being throughout at temperature zero, the extremity is brought at time $t = 0$ to temperature v_0 and kept at this temperature. Find the distribution of temperature in the bar at any subsequent time t, and verify that the solution gives the obvious solution at $t = \infty$.

REFERENCES

1. Carslaw, H. S.: "Mathematical Theory of Conduction of Heat in Solids," Dover Publications, New York, 1945.
2. Byerly, W. E.: "Fourier's Series and Spherical Harmonies," Ginn & Company, Boston, 1893.
3. Churchill, R. V.: "Fourier Series and Boundary Value Problems," McGraw-Hill Book Company, Inc., New York, 1941.
4. Smythe, W. R.: "Static and Dynamic Electricity," 1st ed., McGraw-Hill Book Company, Inc., New York, 1939.

CHAPTER 19

THE ELEMENTS OF THE THEORY
OF THE COMPLEX VARIABLE

1. Introduction. Many of the problems of applied mathematics may be solved particularly simply by the use of the theory of complex functions. Chapter 2 is devoted to an exposition of complex numbers in general, and in Chap. 3 it is demonstrated how periodic phenomena may be simply and concisely expressed in terms of complex exponentials.

In this chapter a brief account of the most useful results of function theory will be given; for a fuller and rigorous exposition of these results the reader should consult the works listed at the end of this chapter. The use of the theory of complex functions in the solution of two-dimensional flow and potential problems is discussed in Chap. 20.

2. General Functions of a Complex Variable. In Chap. 2 the elementary operations involving complex numbers were discussed. It was there shown how the elementary transcendental functions are defined for complex values of their arguments by allowing the variable in the power-series developments of these functions to take on complex values. We have thus seen that the functions of a complex variable obtained by operating on the complex variable

$$(2.1) \qquad z = x + jy \qquad j = \sqrt{-1}$$

with the fundamental laws of algebra or involving the elementary transcendental functions $\sin z$, $\cos z$, e^z, $\sinh z$, etc., are themselves complex numbers of the form $u + jv$, where u and v are *real* functions of x and y.

Let us now assume the expression

$$(2.2) \qquad w(z) = u + jv$$

and determine what conditions it must satisfy in order that it may be a function of z.

If we speak in the broadest sense of the word *function*, then w is always a function of z since if z is given then x and y are determined and it follows that u and v are determined in terms of x and y.

This definition is too broad, and in the theory of functions of a complex variable it is restricted by demanding that the function w shall have a *definite derivative* for a given value of z.

It must be realized that if $w(z)$ is one of the elementary transcendental functions such as z^n, $\sin z$, $\cosh z$, $\ln z$, as discussed in Chap. 2, this condition is certainly met since all the operations used in the calculus of a real variable to obtain the derivatives are still valid for the complex variable and hence the derivative is uniquely determined.   We thus have

$$(2.3) \qquad \frac{d}{dz} \cosh z = \sinh z \qquad \frac{d}{dz} \ln z = \frac{1}{z} \qquad \text{etc.}$$

However, it will now be shown that the uniqueness of the derivative requires the functions u and v to satisfy certain conditions.

3. The Derivative and the Cauchy-Riemann Differential Equations. In the theory of functions of a real variable, if the difference quotient

$$(3.1) \qquad \frac{F(x + h) - F(x)}{h} = F'(x) + \phi(x,h)$$

where $F(x)$ is a real function of the real variable x, can be resolved into two terms in such a way that the first is independent of h and the second one is such that

$$(3.2) \qquad \lim_{h \to 0} \phi(x,h) = 0$$

then by definition it is possible to differentiate $F(x)$, and $F'(x)$ is called the *derivative* of $F(x)$.   Hence

$$(3.3) \qquad F'(x) = \lim_{h \to 0} \frac{F(x + h) - F(x)}{h}$$

This definition is transferred to complex functions as follows:

$$(3.4) \qquad \frac{w(z + q) - w(z)}{q} = w'(z) + \phi(z,q)$$

where

$$(3.5) \qquad \lim_{q \to 0} \phi(z,q) = 0$$

In this case, however, q represents a *vector* in the xy plane of Fig. 3.1. The end point of the vector representing the complex number q can converge toward the origin as $q \to 0$ along any arbitrary curve. The derivative $w'(z)$ is defined by

FIG. 3.1

$$(3.6) \quad w'(z) = \lim_{q \to 0} \frac{w(z + q) - w(z)}{q}$$

and must be independent of the manner in which q approaches zero in order to be unique.

In order to carry out the limiting process (3.6), let

$$(3.7) \qquad q = \Delta z = \Delta x + j\,\Delta y$$

and

(3.8)
$$\Delta w = w(z + \Delta z) - w(z)$$
$$= \Delta u + j\,\Delta v$$

Now, since u and v are functions of x and y, then, if u and v have continuous partial derivatives of the first order, we have

(3.9)
$$\Delta u = \left(\frac{\partial u}{\partial x} + \epsilon_1\right)\Delta x + \left(\frac{\partial u}{\partial y} + \epsilon_2\right)\Delta y$$
$$\Delta v = \left(\frac{\partial v}{\partial x} + \epsilon_3\right)\Delta x + \left(\frac{\partial v}{\partial y} + \epsilon_4\right)\Delta y$$

where

(3.10)
$$\lim_{\substack{\Delta x \to 0 \\ \Delta y \to 0}} \epsilon_r = 0 \qquad r = 1, 2, 3, 4$$

Substituting (3.7), (3.8), and (3.9) in (3.6), we have

(3.11)
$$\frac{dw}{dz} = \lim_{\Delta z \to 0} \frac{\Delta w}{\Delta z} = \frac{\left(\dfrac{\partial u}{\partial x} + j\dfrac{\partial v}{\partial x}\right) + \left(\dfrac{\partial u}{\partial y} + j\dfrac{\partial v}{\partial y}\right)\dfrac{dy}{dx}}{1 + j(dy/dx)}$$
$$= \frac{A + Bm}{1 + mj}$$

where

(3.12)
$$A = \frac{\partial u}{\partial x} + j\,\frac{\partial v}{\partial x}$$
$$B = \frac{\partial u}{\partial y} + j\,\frac{\partial v}{\partial y}$$
$$m = \frac{dy}{dx}$$

Now, if dw/dz is to be unique, it must be independent of the manner in which Δz approaches zero and hence must be independent of $m = dy/dx$. If $dw/dz = w'$ is independent of m, we must have

(3.13)
$$\frac{\partial}{\partial m}(w') = \frac{\partial}{\partial m}\left(\frac{A + Bm}{1 + jm}\right) = 0$$
$$= \frac{(1 + jm)B - (A + Bm)j}{(1 + jm)^2} = 0$$

Hence

(3.14)
$$B = jA$$

or

(3.15)
$$\frac{\partial u}{\partial y} + j\,\frac{\partial v}{\partial y} = j\left(\frac{\partial u}{\partial x} + j\,\frac{\partial v}{\partial x}\right)$$

Equating the coefficients of the real and imaginary terms of (3.15), we obtain

(3.16)
$$\frac{\partial u}{\partial y} = -\frac{\partial v}{\partial x}$$

and

(3.17)
$$\frac{\partial u}{\partial x} = \frac{\partial v}{\partial y}$$

Equations (3.16) and (3.17) are the conditions that the real and imaginary parts of $w(z)$ must satisfy in order that $w(z)$ may have a unique derivative $w'(z)$. Such a function is said to be *analytic* at the point z. These equations are called the *Cauchy-Riemann* differential equations. We thus see that the real and imaginary parts of an analytic function satisfy Cauchy-Riemann differential equations. Conversely, it is easily verified that, if the real and imaginary parts have continuous first partial derivatives satisfying Cauchy-Riemann differential equations, then the function is analytic.

If we differentiate Eq. (3.16) with respect to y and Eq. (3.17) with respect to x and add the results, we obtain

(3.18)
$$\frac{\partial^2 u}{\partial x^2} + \frac{\partial^2 u}{\partial y^2} = 0$$

Differentiating (3.17) with respect to y and (3.16) with respect to x and subtracting the results, we obtain

(3.19)
$$\frac{\partial^2 v}{\partial x^2} + \frac{\partial^2 v}{\partial y^2} = 0$$

We thus see that the real and imaginary parts of an analytic function $w(z)$ of a complex variable are solutions of the Laplace equation in two variables. The functions u and v that satisfy the Cauchy-Riemann equations (3.16) and (3.17) are called *conjugate functions*.

Substituting Eqs. (3.16) and (3.17) in (3.11), we obtain

(3.20)
$$\frac{dw}{dz} = w'(z) = \frac{\partial u}{\partial x} + j\frac{\partial v}{\partial x} = \frac{1}{j}\left(\frac{\partial u}{\partial y} + j\frac{\partial v}{\partial y}\right)$$

The use of these functions in the solution of two-dimensional flow and potential problems will be discussed in Chap. 20.

4. Line Integrals of Complex Functions. The concept of the line integral of a three-dimensional vector field was discussed in Chap. 15, Sec. 10. We shall now consider the definition of the line integral of a complex function along a curve C.

Let $w(z)$ be a complex function of the complex variable z defined in the region B (Fig. 4.1), and let C be a smooth curve in the region B

having end points z_0 and z.   Let z_1, z_2, z_3, . . . , z_{n-1} be an arbitrary number of intermediate points on C and z_n chosen to be the point z.

Let

(4.1) $$\Delta z_r = z_r - z_{r-1} \qquad r = 1, 2, \ldots , n$$

represent chord vectors of the curve C.   Let m_r be a point on the curve C located between z_{r-1} and z_r (this point may also coincide with z_{r-1} or with z_r).   Let the following summation be performed:

(4.2) $$\sum_{r=1}^{r=n} w(m_r)\,\Delta z_r = L_n$$

If the curve C is divided into smaller and smaller parts so that $n \to \infty$, $|\Delta z_r| \to 0$, and if the summation tends to a limit that is independent of the choice of the intermediate points and of the manner in which the division is performed, then the above limit L_n is called the *definite integral* of the complex function $w(z)$ taken along the path C and between the limits $z = z_0$ and $z = z$ and is denoted by

(4.3) $$\lim_{n \to \infty} L_n = \int_C^{z}{}_{z_0} w(\zeta)\,d\zeta$$

Fig. 4.1

As in the case of real quantities, it may be shown that the limit L_n exists if $w(z)$ is continuous along the path of integration.

The value of this integral *in general* depends on $w(z)$ and on the limits of the integral as well as on the form of the path C.

Estimation of the Integral Value.   Let the curve C be a curve of finite length (rectifiable curve); then, if

(4.4) $$|w(z)| \leq M$$

where M represents a fixed real quantity throughout the curve C, the following estimation of the integral along the curve C exists,

(4.5) $$\left| \int_C^{z}{}_{z_0} w(\zeta)\,d\zeta \right| \leq Ms$$

where s is the length of the curve C from z_0 to z.

To prove (4.5), we substitute (4.4) in Eq. (4.2) and obtain

(4.6) $$\left| \int_{z_0}^{z} w(\zeta)\,d\zeta \right| < M \lim_{n \to \infty} \left| \sum_{r=1}^{r=n} \Delta z_r \right|$$

However,

$$(4.7) \qquad \lim_{u \to \infty} \left| \sum_{r=1}^{r=n} \Delta z_r \right| = \left| \int_C^z \bigg|_{z_0}^{z} dz \right| \leqq \int_C^z \bigg|_{z_0}^{z} \sqrt{dx^2 + dy^2} = s$$

This proves Eq. (4.5).

If we decompose $w(z)$ into its real and imaginary parts

$$(4.8) \qquad w(z) = u + jv$$

and write

$$(4.9) \qquad dz = dx + j\, dy$$

we have

$$(4.10) \quad \int_C^z \bigg|_{z_0}^{z} w(z)\, dz = \int_C^{x,y} \bigg|_{x_0, y_0} (u\, dx - v\, dy) + j \int_C^{x,y} \bigg|_{x_0, y_0} (v\, dx + u\, dy)$$

where we now have two real line integrals.

5. Cauchy's Integral Theorem. Let the function $w(z)$ be single-valued and continuous and possess a definite derivative throughout a region R; that is, let $w(z)$ be analytic in R.

Cauchy's integral theorem states that

$$(5.1) \qquad \oint_C w(z)\, dz = 0$$

where the above notation signifies that the line integral is taken along an arbitrary closed path lying inside the region R.

The proof of this theorem can be made to depend on Stokes's theorem of Chap. 15, Sec. 10. Stokes's theorem states that, if we have a vector field **A** whose components possess the continuous partial derivatives involved in the calculation of $\nabla \times \mathbf{A}$, then

$$(5.2) \qquad \oint_C \mathbf{A} \cdot d\mathbf{l} = \int\!\!\int_s (\nabla \times \mathbf{A}) \cdot d\mathbf{s}$$

where the line integral is taken along the curves bounding the open surface s. If **A** is a two-dimensional vector field having the components A_x and A_y above, then (5.2) reduces to

$$(5.3) \qquad \oint_c (A_x\, dx + A_y\, dy) = \int\!\!\int_s \left(\frac{\partial A_y}{\partial x} - \frac{\partial A_x}{\partial y} \right) dx\, dy$$

where c is a closed curve lying in the xy plane and s is the surface bounded by this curve. As a consequence of (4.10) we may write

$$(5.4) \qquad \oint_c w(z)\, dz = \oint_c (u\, dx - v\, dy) + j \oint_c (v\, dx + u\, dy)$$

By means of (5.3) we may transform both the integrals of the right-hand member of (5.4) into surface integrals.

To transform the first one, let

$$A_x = u$$
(5.5)
$$A_y = -v$$

We thus obtain

(5.6)
$$\oint_c (u \, dx - v \, dy) = - \int\int_s \left(\frac{\partial v}{\partial x} + \frac{\partial u}{\partial y} \right) dx \, dy$$

However, as a consequence of the first Cauchy-Riemann equation (3.16), we have

(5.7)
$$\frac{\partial v}{\partial x} + \frac{\partial u}{\partial y} = wF$$

Hence the first integral of the right-hand member of (5.4) vanishes. Using Eq. (5.3) to transform the second integral of the right-hand member of (5.4) and the second Cauchy-Riemann equation (3.16), this integral may be shown to vanish also. Hence Cauchy's integral theorem (5.1) is proved.

As a consequence of this theorem it follows that the path of the line integral, whether closed or between fixed limits, may be deformed without changing the value of the integral provided that in the deformation no point is encountered at which $w(z)$ ceases to be analytic.

Fig. 5.1

Multiply Connected Regions. Cauchy's integral theorem has been deduced under the assumption that the closed curve is the boundary of a *simply connected* region. However, as we shall see, the theorem still holds if the enclosed region is *multiply connected.* Consider the region of Fig. 5.1.

This region requires three curves c_1, c_2, and c_3 to divide it into two separate parts and is therefore a triply connected region. By introducing the crosscuts AB and CD the region may be transformed into a simply connected region. We thus have

(5.8)
$$\oint_s w(z) \, dz = 0$$

where the curve s includes the outer curve c_1 traversed in the mathematically positive direction, the curves c_2 and c_3 traversed in the negative direction, and the crosscuts AB and CD. We thus have

(5.9)
$$\oint_s w(z) \, dz = \oint_{c_1} w(z) \, dz + \oint_{c_2} w(z) \, dz + \oint_{c_3} w(z) \, dz$$
$$+ \int_A^B w(z) \, dz + \int_B^A w(z) \, dz + \int_C^D w(z) \, dz + \int_D^C w(z) \, dz$$

Since the function is analytic along the crosscuts and the integral from A to B is traversed in the opposite direction from the integral B to A, etc., the integrals along the crosscuts cancel out in pairs. Using this fact and transposing, we obtain

$$(5.10) \qquad \oint_{c_1} w(z)\, dz = \oint_{c_2} w(z)\, dz + \oint_{c_3} w(z)\, dz$$

where we have reversed the direction of integration along curves c_2 and c_3.

As an example of the use of Cauchy's integral theorem, let it be required to compute the integral

FIG. 5.2

$$(5.11) \qquad I = \oint_c \frac{dz}{z}$$

where c is a simple closed curve.

The function $w(z) = 1/z$ is analytic for any value of z except for $z = 0$. If, therefore, the simple closed curve c encloses the origin, let us draw an arc c_1 of small radius r with center at the origin as shown in Fig. 5.2.

Since the function $1/z$ is analytic in the region between c_1 and c, we have by Eq. (5.10)

$$(5.12) \qquad \oint_c \frac{dz}{z} = \oint_{c_1} \frac{dz}{z}$$

Now on the circle z_1 we have

$$(5.13) \qquad z = re^{j\theta} \qquad dz = jre^{j\theta}\, d\theta$$

Hence

$$(5.14) \qquad \oint_{c_1} \frac{dz}{z} = \int_{\theta=0}^{\theta=2\pi} j\, d\theta = 2\pi j$$

We thus have the result

$$(5.15) \qquad \oint \frac{dz}{z} = \begin{cases} 0 & \text{if } c \text{ does not surround origin} \\ 2\pi j & \text{if } c \text{ surrounds origin} \end{cases}$$

6. Cauchy's Integral Formula. Let $w(z)$ be analytic in a region including a point $z = a$ and bounded by a curve c. Let us draw a small circle c_1 of radius r and center at a as shown in Fig. 6.1.

Then, in the area bounded by the circle c_1 and the curve c, the function

$$(6.1) \qquad \phi(z) = \frac{w(z)}{z - a}$$

FIG. 6.1

is analytic. Hence, by Cauchy's theorem, we have

$$(6.2) \qquad \oint_c \frac{w(z)\,dz}{z-a} = \oint_{c_1} \frac{w(z)\,dz}{z-a}$$

Now on the circle c_1 we have

$$(6.3) \qquad \begin{aligned} z &= a + re^{j\theta} \qquad dz = jre^{j\theta}\,d\theta \\ w(z) &= w(a) + [w(z) - w(a)] \end{aligned}$$

By continuity of $w(z)$ we may make $|w(z) - w(a)| < \epsilon$, for any given $\epsilon > 0$, by making r sufficiently small. Hence

$$(6.4) \qquad \left| \oint_{c_1} \frac{w(z)\,dz}{z-a} - \int_0^{2\pi} w(a)j\,d\theta \right|$$
$$= \left| \int_0^{2\pi} j[w(z) - w(a)]\,d\theta \right| \le 2\pi\epsilon \qquad \text{by (4.5)}$$

Since by (5.10) the integral on the right may be evaluated on any circle enclosing a and since $w(z)$ is continuous at a, it can be made arbitrarily small in magnitude. In other words,

$$(6.5) \qquad \left| \oint_{c_1} \frac{w(z)\,dz}{z-a} - 2\pi j w(a) \right| = 0$$

Hence, from (6.4) and (6.2), we obtain

$$(6.6) \qquad \oint_c \frac{w(z)\,dz}{z-a} = 2\pi j w(a)$$

or

$$(6.7) \qquad w(a) = \frac{1}{2\pi j} \oint_c \frac{w(z)}{z-a}\,dz$$

This is Cauchy's integral formula; it is remarkable in that it enables one to compute the value of a function $w(z)$ inside a region in which it is analytic from the values of the function on the boundary.

If we apply the formula to a circle with center at a of radius R, we have

$$(6.8) \qquad z = Re^{j\theta} + a \qquad dz = jRe^{j\theta}\,d\theta$$

and we obtain

$$(6.9) \qquad w(a) = \frac{1}{2\pi} \int_{\theta=0}^{\theta=2\pi} w(z)\,d\theta$$

This shows that the value of the function $w(z)$ at the center of a circle is equal to the average value of its boundary values. If M denotes the maximum of the absolute value of $w(z)$ on the boundary of the circle, then

$$(6.10) \qquad \left| \int_{\theta=0}^{\theta=2\pi} w(z)\,dz \right| \le 2\pi M$$

Hence

(6.11) $$|w(a)| \leq M$$

Therefore the maximum of the absolute value of an analytic function cannot be situated inside a circular region.

Another form of Cauchy's integral formula is obtained by replacing a by z and letting $z = t$ in (6.7). We then have

(6.12) $$w(z) = \frac{1}{2\pi j} \oint_c \frac{w(t)}{t - z} \, dt$$

where now z is held fixed in the integration and t traverses the curve c.

Derivatives of an Analytic Function. It may be shown that the integral (6.12) may be differentiated under the integral sign and that the result thus obtained may be differentiated in the same way. This will be assumed. Then we have

(6.13) $$\frac{dw}{dz} = w'(z) = \frac{1}{2\pi j} \oint_c \frac{w(t)}{(t - z)^2} \, dt$$

(6.14) $$w''(z) = \frac{2!}{2\pi j} \oint \frac{w(t)}{(t - z)^3} \, dt$$

(6.15) $$w^{(n)}(z) = \frac{n!}{2\pi j} \oint_c \frac{w(t)}{(t - z)^{n+1}} \, dt \qquad n = 0, 1, 2, 3, \ldots$$

From this it follows that if a function is analytic all its derivatives exist. This is not necessarily true of a function of a real variable.

7. Taylor's Series. In Chap. 1, Sec. 15, the Taylor's-series expansion of a function of a real variable was discussed. By means of Cauchy's integral formula we may discuss the Taylor's-series expansion of an analytic function of a complex variable $w(z)$. If we let

$$z \to z + h$$

in Eq. (6.12), we have

(7.1) $$w(z + h) = \frac{1}{2\pi j} \oint_c \frac{w(t) \, dt}{t - (z + h)}$$

where we assume that $w(z)$ is analytic in a circle R with the boundary c and that the points z and $z + h$ are inside of this circle. Let us now expand $1/[t - (z + h)]$ into a power series in h in the form

(7.2) $$\frac{1}{t - (z + h)} = \frac{1}{(t - z)\left(1 - \dfrac{h}{t - z}\right)}$$

$$= \frac{1}{t - z}\left[1 + \frac{h}{t - z} + \frac{h^2}{(t - z)^2} + \cdots \right.$$

$$\left. + \frac{h^n}{(t - z)^n} + \frac{h^{n+1}}{(t - z)^n(t - z - h)}\right]$$

Hence

$$(7.3) \quad \frac{1}{2\pi j} \oint_c \frac{w(t)\, dt}{t - (z + h)} = \frac{1}{2\pi j} \left[\oint_c \frac{w(t)\, dt}{t - z} + h \oint_c \frac{w(t)\, dt}{(t - z)^2} \right.$$
$$\left. + h^2 \oint_c \frac{w(t)\, dt}{(t - z)^3} + \cdots + h^n \oint_c \frac{w(t)\, dt}{(t - z)^{n+1}} + h^{n+1} \oint_c \frac{w(t)\, dt}{(t - z)^{n+1}(t - z - h)} \right]$$

Using (6.15) and (7.1), we have

$$(7.4) \quad w(z + h) = w(z) + \frac{hw'(z)}{1!} + \frac{h^2 w''(z)}{2!} + \cdots + \frac{h^n}{n!} w^{(n)}(z) + R_{n+1}$$

where R_{n+1} is the remainder after $n + 1$ terms and is given by

$$(7.5) \qquad R_{n+1} = \frac{h^{n+1}}{2\pi j} \oint_c \frac{w(t)\, dt}{(t - z)^{n+1}(t - z - h)}$$

Now, by the estimation formula (4.5), it may be shown that

$$(7.6) \qquad \lim_{n \to \infty} R_{n+1} = 0$$

The series (7.4) converges inside of a circle with z as its center, the radius of the circle being equal to the distance from z to the nearest point $z + H$ at which $w(z + h)$ is no longer analytic. Series (7.4) may also be represented as follows,

$$(7.7) \qquad w(z + h) = \sum_{r=0}^{\infty} a_r h^r$$

where

$$(7.8) \qquad a_r = \frac{1}{2\pi j} \oint \frac{w(t)\, dt}{(t - z)^{r+1}} \qquad r = 0, 1, 2, 3, \ldots$$

Thus the coefficients may be obtained by means of integration.

8. Laurent's Series. Let $w(z)$ be an analytic function in the annular region of Fig. 8.1 including the boundary of the region.

The annular region is formed by two concentric circles c and c_1 whose center is z_0. Let $z_0 + h = z$ be located inside the annular region. If we apply Cauchy's integral theorem to this annular region, we have

FIG. 8.1

$$(8.1) \qquad w(z_0 + h) = \frac{1}{2\pi j} \oint \frac{w(t)\, dt}{t - (z_0 + h)}$$

The integration is carried out over the entire boundary of the annular region composed of the circles c and c_1. We thus have symbolically

$$(8.2) \qquad w(z_0 + h) = \frac{1}{2\pi j} \left(\oint_c - \oint_{c_1} \right)$$

where the integration over both circles must be taken in the positive direction. Each integral is calculated individually. Now, as in Eq. (7.2), we have

$$(8.3) \quad \frac{1}{t - z_0 - h} = \frac{1}{t - z_0} + \frac{h}{(t - z_0)^2} + \frac{h^2}{(t - z_0)^3} + \cdots$$
$$+ \frac{h^n}{(t - z_0)^{n+1}} + \frac{h^{n+1}}{(t - z_0)^{n+1}(t - z_0 - h)}$$

If we interchange $t - z_0$ and h, we have

$$(8.4) \quad - \frac{1}{t - z_0 - h} = \frac{1}{h} + \frac{t - z_0}{h^2} + \frac{(t - z_0)^2}{h^3} + \cdots$$
$$+ \frac{(t - z_0)^n}{h^{n+1}} + \frac{(t - z_0)^{n+1}}{h^{n+1}(t - z_0 - h)}$$

If we now substitute these expansions in Eq. (8.2), we have

$$(8.5) \qquad w(z_0 + h) = \sum_{s = -(n+1)}^{s=n} a_s h^s + R'_n + R''_n$$

where

$$(8.6) \quad a_s = \frac{1}{2\pi j} \oint_c \frac{w(t) \, dt}{(t - z_0)^{s+1}} \qquad s = 0, +1, +2, +3, \ldots$$

$$(8.7) \quad a_s = \frac{1}{2\pi j} \oint_{c_1} \frac{w(t) \, dt}{(t - z_0)^{s+1}} \qquad s = -1, -2, -3, -4, \ldots$$

$$(8.8) \quad R'_n = \frac{1}{2\pi j} \oint_c \frac{h^{n+1} w(t) \, dt}{(t - z_0)^{n+1}(t - z_0 - h)}$$
$$R''_n = \frac{1}{2\pi j} \oint_{c_1} \frac{(t - z_0)^{n+1} w(t) \, d't}{h^{n+1}(t - z_0 - h)}$$

By Cauchy's estimation formula (4.5) it is easy to show that

$$(8.9) \qquad \begin{aligned} \lim_{n \to \infty} R'_n = 0 \\ \lim_{n \to \infty} R''_n = 0 \end{aligned}$$

Hence we obtain the Laurent's series

$$(8.10) \qquad w(z_0 + h) = \sum_{s = -\infty}^{s = +\infty} a_s h^s$$

where the coefficients a_s are given by (8.6) and (8.7). It may be noted that if all the coefficients of negative index have the value zero then (8.10) reduces to Taylor's series.

Examples of Laurent's-series Expansions. Consider the function

$$(8.11) \qquad w(z) = \frac{1}{z(z - 1)}$$

This function is analytic at all points of the z plane except at the points $z = 0$ and $z = 1$. Therefore it is possible to expand this function in a Laurent's series in an annular region about $z = 0$ or $z = 1$.

To expand about $z = 0$, we have

$$(8.12) \quad \frac{1}{z(z-1)} = -\frac{1}{z}(1-z)^{-1}$$
$$= -\frac{1}{z}(1 + z + z^2 + z^3 + \cdots)$$
$$= -\frac{1}{z} - 1 - z - z^2 - z^3 - \cdots \qquad 0 < |z| < 1$$

To expand about $z = 1$, write

$$(8.13) \quad \frac{1}{z(z-1)} = \frac{1}{z-1}\frac{1}{[(z-1)+1]}$$
$$= \frac{1}{z-1}\left[1 - (z-1) + (z-1)^2 - (z-1)^3 + \cdots\right]$$
$$= \frac{1}{z-1} - 1 + (z-1) - (z-1)^2 + \cdots$$
$$0 < |z-1| < 1$$

As another example, consider the function

$$(8.14) \qquad\qquad w(z) = e^{1/z}$$

This function may be expanded in any annular region enclosing the origin in the form

$$(8.15) \quad e^{1/z} = 1 + \frac{1}{z} + \frac{1}{z^2 \times 2!} + \frac{1}{z^3 \times 3!} + \cdots \qquad z \neq 0$$

In this case all the terms of the Laurent's series have a negative index.

9. Residues, Cauchy's Residue Theorem. *Residues.* In the Laurent's series (8.10) let

$$(9.1) \qquad\qquad z = z_0 + h \quad\text{or}\quad h = z - z_0$$

We then obtain

$$(9.2) \qquad\qquad w(z) = \sum_{s=-\infty}^{s=+\infty} a_s(z - z_0)^s$$

The coefficient a_{-1} is given by Eq. (8.7), and it is

$$(9.3) \qquad\qquad a_{-1} = \frac{1}{2\pi j}\oint_{c_1} w(t)\,dt$$

where c_1 is a curve surrounding the point z_0. a_{-1} is in general a complex number and is called the *residue* of $w(z)$ at the point $z = z_0$. It is usually

denoted by

$$(9.4) \qquad a_{-1} = \operatorname{Res} w(z)_{z=z_0}$$

It sometimes happens that the Laurent's series for $w(z)$ is known in the neighborhood of $z = z_0$, or the series is easier to compute than the integral. In this case from a knowledge of a_{-1} we may compute the integral (9.3).

As a very simple example, consider the function $w(z) = 1/z$. In this case the Laurent's series about the origin consists of only one term, and we have

$$(9.5) \qquad a_{-1} = 1$$

Hence

$$(9.6) \qquad \oint \frac{dz}{z} = 2\pi j \times 1 = 2\pi j$$

where the integral is taken about a curve surrounding the origin. In the same manner we have

$$(9.7) \qquad \oint e^{1/z}\, dz = 2\pi j$$

where the path of integration encloses the origin. This follows from the expansion of the function $e^{1/z}$ in the series (8.15). Hence we see that

$$(9.8) \quad a_{-1} = \operatorname{Res} e^{1/z} = 1 \qquad z = 0$$

FIG. 9.1

Cauchy's Residue Theorem. Let $w(z)$ be an analytic function inside a region R at all points except at the points $z_1, z_2, \ldots, z_n$. Let $w(z)$ be analytic at all points on the boundary c of the region R. Let us surround the points $z_1, z_2, \ldots, z_n$ by the closed curves $c_1, c_2, \ldots, c_n$. Then by Cauchy's integral theorem of Sec. 5, we have (see Fig. 9.1)

$$(9.9) \quad \oint_c w(z)\, dz = \oint_{c_1} w(z)\, dz + \oint_{c_2} w(z)\, dz + \cdots + \oint_{c_n} w(z)\, dz$$

However, by (9.3), we have

$$(9.10) \qquad \oint_{c_r} w(z)\, dz = 2\pi j \operatorname{Res} w(z) \qquad z = z_r$$

Hence, substituting this in (9.9), we obtain

$$(9.11) \qquad \oint_c w(z)\, dz = 2\pi j \sum_{r=1}^{r=n} \operatorname{Res} w(z) \qquad z = z_r$$

This is *Cauchy's residue theorem.*   It is of extreme importance in evaluating definite integrals and in the theory of functions in general.   Applications of this theorem to the evaluation of definite integrals will be considered in a later section.

10. Singular Points of an Analytic Function.   All the points of the z plane at which an analytic function does not have a unique derivative are said to be *singular points.*   If we concern ourselves only with single-valued functions of the complex variable $w(z)$, then $w(z)$ may have two types of singularities:

1. *Poles,* or *nonessential singular points*
2. *Essential singular points*

The distinction between these two types of singularities will now be explained.

Let z_0 be a singular point of $w(z)$.   Let us expand $w(z)$ in a Laurent's series in powers of $z - z_0$.   This expansion will contain powers of $z - z_0$ with negative exponents, for otherwise $z = z_0$ would not be a singular point.   Hence we have

$$(10.1) \quad w(z) = \frac{a_{-m}}{(z - z_0)^m} + \frac{a_{-m+1}}{(z - z_0)^{m-1}} + \cdots + \frac{a_{-1}}{z - z_0}$$
$$+ a_0 + a_1(z - z_0) + \cdots$$

There are two possibilities:

a. The expansion (10.1) has only a finite number of powers of $z - z_0$ with negative exponents.

In this case $w(z)$ is said to have a *pole* at $z = z_0$.   If m is the largest of the negative exponents and if the function

$$(10.2) \qquad \phi(z) = (z - z_0)^m w(z) \qquad m \text{ a positive integer}$$

behaves regularly (is analytic) and is not zero at the point z_0, m is called the *order of the pole* z_0 and $w(z)$ is said to have a pole of the mth order at the point z_0.

The sum of the terms with negative exponents

$$(10.3) \qquad \frac{a_{-1}}{z - z_0} + \frac{a_{-2}}{(z - z_0)^2} + \cdots + \frac{a_{-m}}{(z - z_0)^m}$$

is called the *principal part* of the function $w(z)$ at z_0.

b. The other possibility is that the Laurent's expansion of the function $w(z)$ about the point z_0 will have an infinite number of negative powers of $z - z_0$ and is of the form

$$(10.4) \qquad \qquad w(z) = \sum_{r=-\infty}^{r=+\infty} a_r(z - z_0)^r$$

In this case the point $z = z_0$ is said to be an *essential singular point*, and $w(z)$ is said to have an *essential singularity* at $z = z_0$.

As examples of these possibilities, consider the function

$$(10.5) \qquad w(z) = \frac{1}{(z - 2)^2(z - 5)^3(z - 1)}$$

This function has a pole of the second order at $z = 2$, a pole of the third order at $z = 5$, and a pole of the first order at $z = 1$.

The function

$$(10.6) \qquad w(z) = e^{1/z}$$

has the Laurent's series (8.15) in the neighborhood of the origin. Its Laurent's-series expansion contains an infinite number of negative powers of x and has, therefore, an essential singularity at $z = 0$.

Meromorphic Functions. If a function $w(z)$ has poles only in the finite part of the z plane, it is said to be a *meromorphic function*.

11. The Point at Infinity. In the theory of the complex variable it is convenient to regard infinity as a single point. The behavior of $w(z)$ "at infinity" is considered by making the substitution

$$(11.1) \qquad z = \frac{1}{t}$$

and examining $w(1/t)$ at $t = 0$. We then say that $w(z)$ is analytic or has a pole or an essential singularity at infinity according as $w(1/t)$ has the corresponding property at $t = 0$.

It may thus be shown that $1/z^2$ is analytic at infinity, z^3 has a pole of the third order at infinity, and the function

$$(11.2) \qquad \sin z = z - \frac{z^3}{3!} + \frac{z^5}{5!} - \frac{z^7}{7!} + \cdots$$

has an essential singularity at infinity.

The Residue at Infinity. The residue of $w(z)$ at infinity is defined as

$$(11.3) \qquad \frac{1}{2\pi j} \oint_c w(z) \, dz$$

where c is a large circle that encloses all the singularities of $w(z)$ except at $z = \infty$. The integration is taken around c in the *negative* sense, that is, negative with respect to the origin provided that this integral has a definite value.

If we apply the transformation

$$(11.4) \qquad z = \frac{1}{t}$$

to the integral (11.3), it becomes

$$(11.5) \qquad \frac{1}{2\pi j} \oint_s - w\left(\frac{1}{t}\right)\frac{dt}{t^2}$$

where the integration is performed in a positive sense about a small circle whose center is at the origin. It follows that, if

$$(11.6) \qquad \lim_{t \to 0}\left[-w\left(\frac{1}{t}\right)\frac{1}{t}\right] = \lim_{z \to \infty}\ [-zw(z)]$$

has a definite value, then that value is the residue of $w(z)$ at infinity.

For example, the function

$$(11.7) \qquad w(z) = \frac{z}{(z - a)(z - b)}$$

behaves like $1/z$ for large values of z and is therefore analytic at $z = \infty$. However,

$$(11.8) \qquad \lim_{z \to \infty}\ [-zw(z)] = -1$$

Hence the residue of $w(z)$ at infinity is -1. We thus see that a function may be analytic at infinity and still have a residue there.

12. Evaluation of Residues. The calculation of the residues of a function $w(z)$ at its poles may be performed in several ways. By the definition of the residue of the function $w(z)$ at a simple pole $z = z_0$ is meant the coefficient a_{-1} in the Laurent's expansion of $w(z)$ in the form

$$(12.1) \quad w(z) = \frac{a_{-1}}{z - z_0} + a_0 + a_1(z - z_0) + a_2(z - z_0)^2 + \cdots$$

where z_0 is a simple pole. If we now multiply Eq. (12.1) by $z - z_0$ and take the limit $z \to z_0$, we have

$$(12.2) \qquad \lim_{z \to z_0}\ (z - z_0)w(z) = a_{-1}$$
$$= \text{Res}\ w(z) \qquad z = z_0$$

For example, the function

$$(12.3) \qquad w(z) = \frac{e^z}{z^2 + a^2} = \frac{e^z}{(z + ja)(z - ja)}$$

has two simple poles, one at $z = ja$ and another at $z = -ja$. To evaluate the residue at $z = ja$, we form the limit

$$(12.4) \qquad \lim_{z \to ja}\ (z - ja)w(z) = \lim_{z \to ja}\frac{e^z}{z + ja} = \frac{e^{ja}}{2ja}$$

Similarly, the limit at $z = -ja$ is $-e^{-ja}/2ja$.

Residues at Simple Poles of $w(z) = F(z)/G(z)$. Frequently it is required to evaluate residues of a function $w(z)$ that has the form

(12.5) $$w(z) = \frac{F(z)}{G(z)}$$

where $G(z)$ has simple zeros and hence $w(z)$ has simple poles. If $z = z_0$ is a simple pole of $w(z)$, then by (12.2) we have

(12.6) $$\text{Res } w(z)_{z=z_0} = \lim_{z \to z_0} [(z - z_0)w(z)]$$

$$= \lim_{z \to z_0} \left[(z - z_0) \frac{F(z)}{G(z)} \right]$$

Since $z = z_0$ is a simple pole of $w(z)$, we must have

(12.7) $$G(z_0) = 0$$

so that expression (12.6) becomes $0/0$. To evaluate it, we use L'Hospital's rule and obtain

(12.8) $$\text{Res } w(z)_{z=z_0} = \lim_{z \to z_0} \frac{F(z) + (z - z_0)F'(z)}{G'(z)} = \frac{F(z_0)}{G'(z_0)}$$

As an example of the use of this formula, let it be required to compute the residue of $w(z) = e^{jz}/(z^2 + a^2)$ at the simple pole $z = ja$. Using (12.7), we have

(12.9) $$\text{Res } \left(\frac{e^{jz}}{z^2 + a^2} \right)_{z=ja} = \frac{e^{-a}}{2ja}$$

Evaluation of a Residue at a Multiple Pole. If the function $w(z)$ has a multiple pole at $z = z_0$ of order m, then the Laurent's expansion of $w(z)$ is

(12.10) $$w(z) = \frac{a_{-m}}{(z - z_0)^m} + \frac{a_{-m+1}}{(z - z_0)^{m-1}} + \cdots + \frac{a_{-1}}{z - z_0}$$
$$+ a_0 + a_1(z - z_0) + a_2(z - z_0)^2 + \cdots$$

The residue at $z = z_0$ is a_{-1}, and to obtain it we multiply (12.10) by $(z - z_0)^m$ and obtain

(12.11) $$(z - z_0)^m w(z) = a_{-m} + a_{-m+1}(z - z_0) + \cdots + a_{-1}(z - z_0)^{m-1}$$
$$+ (z - z_0)^m a_0 + a_1(z - z_0)^{m+1} + a_2(z - z_0)^{m+2} + \cdots$$

If we differentiate both sides of (12.11), with respect to z, $m - 1$ times and place $z = z_0$, we obtain

(12.12) $$\frac{d^{m-1}}{dz^{m-1}} [(z - z_0)^m w(z)]_{z=z_0} = a_{-1}(m - 1)!$$

Hence the residue a_{-1} at the multiple pole is

(12.13) $$a_{-1} = \frac{1}{(m - 1)!} \frac{d^{m-1}}{dz^{m-1}} [(z - z_0)^m w(z)]_{z=z_0}$$

For example, let it be required to find the residue of

$$(12.14) \qquad w(z) = \frac{ze^z}{(z-a)^3}$$

at the third-order pole $z = a$. Applying (12.13), we have

$$(12.15) \qquad a_{-1} = \frac{1}{2!} \frac{d^2}{dz^2} (ze^z)_{z=a} = e^a \left(1 + \frac{a}{2}\right)$$

13. Liouville's Theorem. A very interesting and useful theorem may be established by the aid of the notion of residues.

Let $w(z)$ be a function that is analytic at all points of the complex z plane and finite at infinity. Then, if a and b are any two distinct points, the only singularities of the function

$$(13.1) \qquad \phi(z) = \frac{w(z)}{(z-a)(z-b)}$$

are a and b and possibly infinity. However, since $w(z)$ is by hypothesis finite at infinity, we have

$$(13.2) \qquad \lim_{z \to \infty} z\phi(z) = 0$$

Hence the residue of $\phi(z)$ is zero at infinity. However, in Sec. 11 we saw that the residue of $\phi(z)$ at infinity is defined by

$$(13.3) \qquad \frac{1}{2\pi j} \oint_c \phi(z) \, dz$$

where c is a large circle that encloses all the singularities of $\phi(z)$ except the one at $z = \infty$ and the integration is performed in the negative sense. However, by Cauchy's residue theorem, we have

$$(13.4) \qquad \frac{1}{2\pi j} \oint_c \phi(z) \, dz = \sum \text{Res inside } c$$

Hence the sum of the residues of $\phi(z)$, including that at infinity, is zero. Now the residue of $\phi(z)$ at $z = a$ is

$$(13.5) \qquad \lim_{z \to a} (z-a) \frac{w(z)}{(z-a)(z-b)} = \frac{w(a)}{a-b}$$

and, similarly, the residue at $z = b$ is $w(b)/(b-a)$. Since the sum of the residues vanishes, we have

$$(13.6) \qquad \frac{w(a)}{a-b} + \frac{w(b)}{b-a} = 0$$

Hence

$$(13.7) \qquad w(a) = w(b)$$

and since a and b are arbitrary points, $w(z)$ is a constant. We have thus proved Liouville's theorem, which states:

A function that is analytic at all points of the z plane and finite at infinity must be a constant.

As a corollary of this theorem, it follows that every function that is not a constant must have at least one singularity.

It also follows that if $w(z)$ is a polynomial in z, the equation

$$(13.8) \qquad\qquad w(z) = 0$$

has a root, because if it had not, the function $1/w(z)$ would be finite and analytic for all values of z and would therefore be a constant; then $w(z)$ would be a constant. This contradicts the original hypothesis. *This is the fundamental theorem of algebra.*

The Integral of a Logarithmic Derivative. A theorem due to Cauchy will now be discussed. This theorem is very useful in determining the number of zeros and poles of a function $W(z)$ within a closed contour by an inspection of the behavior of the function $W(z)$ itself as the point z traverses the given contour. The results of the theorem can be applied to the problem of determining the approximate location of the roots of algebraic equations.

Consider the function $W(z)$ that has both zeros and poles within some prescribed contour C of the z plane and no other singularities. Let

$$(13.9) \qquad\qquad \ln W(z) = A + jB$$

If we differentiate (13.9) with respect to z, we have

$$(13.10) \qquad\qquad \frac{1}{W}\frac{dW}{dz} = \frac{dA}{dz} + j\frac{dB}{dz}$$

Now let z_0 be either a zero of the nth order of $W(z)$ or a pole of the nth order of $1/W$. In such a case we can write

$$(13.11) \qquad\qquad W(z) = (z - z_0)^n g(z)$$

where the function $g(z)$ is analytic and nonzero at $z = z_0$ and n is a positive integer if z_0 is a zero of $W(z)$ or n is a negative integer if z_0 is a pole of $W(z)$.

Let (13.10) be differentiated with respect to z. We then have

$$(13.12) \qquad\qquad \frac{dW}{dz} = n(z - z_0)^{n-1}g(z) + (z - z_0)^n\frac{dg}{dz}$$

Hence

$$(13.13) \qquad\qquad \frac{1}{W}\frac{dW}{dz} = \frac{n}{z - z_0} + \frac{1}{g}\frac{dg}{dz} = \frac{d}{dz}[\ln W(z)]$$

Equation (13.13) shows that the function $\dfrac{1}{W}\dfrac{dW}{dz}$ has a *simple* pole at z_0 and the *residue* at this pole is n. Now consider the closed contour C and the integral (13.13):

$$(13.14) \qquad \oint_C \frac{1}{W}\frac{dW}{dz}\,dz = 2\pi j \sum \text{Res}\,\frac{1}{W}\frac{dW}{dz}\ \text{inside } C$$

It is apparent from (13.12) and (13.13) that

$$(13.15) \qquad \oint_C \frac{1}{W}\frac{dW}{dz}\,dz = 2\pi j(N - P)$$

where N is the *total* number of zeros and P the *total* number of poles of $W(z)$ within the closed contour C, provided multiple zeros and poles are

Fɪɢ. 13.1

weighted according to their multiplicity.   Now

$$(13.16) \qquad \oint_C \frac{1}{W}\frac{dW}{dz}\,dz = \oint_C \frac{d}{dz}\,[\ln W(z)]\,dz = \Delta_C \ln W(z)$$

where $\Delta_C \ln W(z)$ is the change in $\ln W(z)$ as the closed contour C is traversed.   But

$$(13.17) \qquad \ln W(z) = \ln |W(z)| + j\arg W(z) = A + jB$$

by (13.9), where $\arg W(z)$ is the argument of $W(z)$.   But $\ln |W(z)|$ is a single-valued function.   Hence

$$(13.18) \qquad \Delta_C \ln |W(z)| = 0$$

Combining the results of (13.15), (13.16), and (13.18), we get

$$(13.19) \qquad \oint_C \frac{1}{W}\frac{dW}{dz}\,dz = j\Delta_C \arg W(z) = j\Delta_C B = 2\pi j(N - P)$$

or

$$(13.20) \qquad \Delta_C B = 2\pi(N - P)$$

where $\Delta_C B$ indicates the change in B as the closed contour C is traversed. As the point z moves in the z plane and traces the contour C, the point W

moves in the W plane, tracing another contour. B is the angle that the representative vector of the complex variable $W(z)$ makes with the real axis of the complex W plane.

Equation (13.20) states that the number of revolutions that the representative vector in the W plane makes about the origin of the W plane as the point z traverses the contour C in the z plane is equal to $N - P$. This result may be summarized as follows:

If a function $W(z)$ is analytic, except for possible poles within a contour C, then the number of times that the representative point of $W(z)$ encircles the origin in the $W(z)$ plane in the positive direction while the point z traverses the contour C in a positive direction in the z plane equals $N - P$. N is the number of zeros and P the number of poles lying within the contour C. Each zero and pole must be counted in accordance with its multiplicity.

In recent years this theorem has been applied extensively to the study of the stability of electrical and mechanical dynamical systems. In order that these systems shall be stable, it is necessary that their characteristic equations have roots whose real parts are negative (see Chap. 8). The above theorem provides a method of determining whether the roots of characteristic equations have positive real parts without solving the equations. An adaptation of this theorem due to Nyquist in the study of the stability of feedback amplifiers and servomechanisms is called *Nyquist's criterion* in the literature.*

14. Evaluation of Definite Integrals. By the use of Cauchy's residue theorem many definite integrals may be evaluated. It should be observed that a definite integral that can be evaluated by the use of Cauchy's residue theorem may be evaluated by other methods, although not so easily. However, some simple integrals such as $\int_0^\infty e^{-u^2}\, du$ cannot be evaluated by Cauchy's method.

a. Integration around the Unit Circle. An integral of the type

$$(14.1) \qquad \int_0^{2\pi} F(\cos\theta,\, \sin\theta)\, d\theta$$

where the integrand is a rational function of $\cos\theta$ and $\sin\theta$ that is finite in the range of integration, may be evaluated by the transformation

$$(14.2) \qquad e^{i\theta} = z$$

Since

$$(14.3) \qquad \cos\theta = \frac{1}{2}\left(z + \frac{1}{z}\right) \qquad \sin\theta = \frac{1}{2j}\left(z - \frac{1}{z}\right)$$

---

* See H. Nyquist, Regeneration Theory, *Bell System Technical Journal*, p. 126, January, 1932.

the integral takes the form

$$(14.4) \qquad \oint_c S(z)\, dz = 2\pi j \sum \text{Res } S(z) \text{ inside } c$$

where $S(z)$ is a rational function of z finite on the path of integration and c is a circle of unit radius and center at the origin.

As an example of the general procedure, let it be required to prove that if $a > b > 0$

$$(14.5) \qquad I = \int_0^{2\pi} \frac{\sin^2 \theta\, d\theta}{a + b \cos \theta} = \frac{2\pi}{b^2}(a - \sqrt{a^2 - b^2})$$

If we let $e^{i\theta} = z$, this becomes

$$(14.6) \qquad I = \frac{j}{2b} \oint_c \frac{(z^2 - 1)\, dz}{z^2(z - p)(z - q)}$$

where

$$(14.7) \qquad p = \frac{-a + \sqrt{a^2 - b^2}}{b} \qquad q = \frac{-a - \sqrt{a^2 - b^2}}{b}$$

These are the two roots of the quadratic

$$(14.8) \qquad z^2 + \frac{2az}{b} + 1 = 0$$

It is seen that p is the only simple pole of the integrand inside the unit circle c, and the origin is a pole of order 2. We must now compute the residues of

$$(14.9) \qquad S(z) = \frac{(z^2 - 1)^2}{z^2(z - p)(z - q)}$$

at the poles $z = p$ and $z = 0$.

We do this by the methods of Sec. 12. The residue at $z = p$ may be evaluated by formula (12.2). We thus obtain

$$(14.10) \quad \operatorname*{Res}_{z=p} S(z) = \lim_{z \to p} \frac{(z^2 - 1)^2}{z^2(z - q)} = \frac{(p^2 - 1)^2}{p^2(p - q)}$$

$$= \frac{(p - 1/p)^2}{p - q} = \frac{(p - q)^2}{p - q} = p - q = \frac{2\sqrt{a^2 - b^2}}{b}$$

The residue at the double pole $z = 0$ may be evaluated by Eq. (12.12); it is

$$(14.11) \qquad \operatorname*{Res}_{z=0} S(z) = \frac{d}{dz}[z^2 S(z)]_{z=0} = -\frac{2a}{b}$$

Now, by Cauchy's residue theorem (9.11), we have

$$(14.12) \quad I = \frac{j}{2b} \oint_c S(z)\, dz = \frac{j}{2b}\, 2\pi j \left(-\frac{2a}{b} + \frac{2\sqrt{a^2 - b^2}}{b} \right)$$
$$= \frac{2\pi}{b^2}(a - \sqrt{a^2 - b^2})$$

This proves the result.

b. Evaluation of Certain Integrals between the Limits $-\infty$ and $+\infty$.
We shall now consider the evaluation of integrals of the type

$$(14.13) \qquad \int_{-\infty}^{+\infty} Q(x)\, dx = I$$

where $Q(z)$ is a function that satisfies the following restrictions:

1. It is analytic in the upper half plane except at a finite number of poles.

2. It has no poles on the real axis.

3. $zQ(z) \to 0$ uniformly as $|z| \to \infty$ for $0 \le \arg z \le \pi$.

4. When x is real, $xQ(x) \to 0$ as $x \to \pm\infty$ in such a way that $\int_{\infty}^{0} Q(x)\, dx$ and $\int_{-\infty}^{0} Q(x)\, dx$ both converge.   Then

$$(14.14) \qquad \int_{-\infty}^{\infty} Q(x)\, dx = 2\pi j \sum R^+$$

where ΣR^+ denotes the sum of the residues of $Q(z)$ at its poles in the upper half plane.

FIG. 14.1

To prove this, choose as a contour a semicircle c with center at the origin and radius R in the upper half plane as shown in Fig. 14.1. Then, by Cauchy's residue theorem, we have

$$(14.15) \qquad \int_{-R}^{R} Q(x)\, dx + \int_c Q(z)\, dz = 2\pi j \sum R^+$$

Now by condition 3, if R is large enough, we have

$$(14.16) \qquad\qquad |zQ(z)| < \delta$$

for all points on c, and so

$$(14.17) \quad \left| \int_c Q(z)\, dz \right| = \left| \int_0^\pi Q(Re^{j\theta}) j Re^{j\theta}\, d\theta \right| < \delta \int_0^\pi d\theta = \pi\delta$$

Hence as $R \to \infty$, the integral around c tends to zero, and if (4) is satisfied, we have Eq. (14.14).

This theorem is particularly useful in the case when $Q(x)$ is a rational function.   As an example of this theorem, let it be required to prove that if $a > 0$

$$(14.18) \qquad \int_0^\infty \frac{dx}{x^4 + a^4} = \frac{\pi}{2\sqrt{2}\, a^3}$$

Consider

$$(14.19) \qquad Q(z) = \frac{1}{z^4 + a^4}$$

This function has simple poles at $ae^{\pi i/4}$, $ae^{3\pi i/4}$, $ae^{5\pi i/4}$, $ae^{7\pi i/4}$. Only the first two of these poles are in the upper half plane. The function $Q(z)$ clearly satisfies the conditions of the theorem; therefore

$$(14.20) \qquad \int_{-\infty}^{+\infty} \frac{dx}{x^4 + a^4} = 2\pi j \sum \text{Res at } ae^{i\pi/4} \text{ and } ae^{3i\pi/4}$$

By the methods of Sec. 12, we have

$$(14.21) \qquad \operatorname*{Res}_{z=z_0} Q(z) = \lim_{z \to z_0} \frac{1}{4z^3}$$

Hence

$$(14.22) \qquad \operatorname*{Res}_{z=ae^{i\pi/4}} Q(z) = \frac{1}{4a^3} e^{-j3\pi/4}$$

and

$$(14.23) \qquad \operatorname*{Res}_{z=ae^{j3\pi/4}} Q(z) = \frac{1}{4a^3} e^{-j9\pi/4}$$

Therefore

$$(14.24) \qquad \int_{-\infty}^{+\infty} \frac{dx}{x^4 + a^4} = 2\pi j \left(\frac{1}{4a^3} e^{-j3\pi/4} + \frac{1}{4a^3} e^{-j9\pi/4} \right)$$

$$= \frac{\pi}{\sqrt{2}\, a^3}$$

Since the function $Q(x)$ is an even function of x, we have

$$(14.25) \qquad \int_{-\infty}^{+\infty} \frac{dx}{x^4 + a^4} = 2 \int_{0}^{\infty} \frac{dx}{x^4 + a^4}$$

Hence

$$(14.26) \qquad \int_{0}^{\infty} \frac{dx}{x^4 + a^4} = \frac{\pi}{2\sqrt{2}\, a^3}$$

15. Jordan's Lemma. A very useful and important theorem will now be proved. It is usually known as *Jordan's lemma*.

Let $Q(z)$ be a function of the complex variable z that satisfies the following conditions:

1. It is analytic in the upper half plane except at a finite number of poles.

2. $Q(z) \to 0$ uniformly as $|z| \to \infty$ for $0 < \arg z < \pi$.

3. m is a positive number.

Then

$$(15.1) \qquad \lim_{R \to \infty} \int_c e^{jmz} Q(z)\, dz = 0$$

where c is a semicircle with its center at the origin and radius R.

Proof. For all points on c we have

(15.2)
$$z = Re^{j\theta} = R(\cos\theta + j\sin\theta)$$
$$dz = jRe^{j\theta}\,d\theta$$

Now

(15.3)
$$|e^{jmz}| = |e^{jmR(\cos\theta + j\sin\theta)}| = |e^{-mR\sin\theta}|$$

By condition 2, if R is sufficiently large, we have for all points on c

(15.4)
$$|Q(z)| < \delta$$

Hence

(15.5)
$$\left|\int_c Q(z)e^{jmz}\,dz\right| = \left|\int_0^\pi Q(z)e^{jmz}Re^{j\theta}j\,d\theta\right| < \delta\int_0^\pi Re^{-mR\sin\theta}\,d\theta$$
$$= 2R\delta\int_0^{\pi/2} e^{-mR\sin\theta}\,d\theta$$

It can be proved that $\sin\theta/\theta$ decreases steadily from 1 to $2/\pi$ as θ increases from 0 to $\pi/2$.   Hence

(15.6)
$$\frac{\sin\theta}{\theta} \geq \frac{2}{\pi} \qquad \text{when } 0 \leq \theta \leq \frac{\pi}{2}$$

Therefore

(15.7)
$$\left|\int_c Q(z)e^{mjz}\,dz\right| \leq 2R\delta\int_0^{\pi/2} e^{-2m(R\theta/\pi)}\,d\theta = \frac{\pi\delta}{m}(1 - e^{-mR}) < \frac{\pi\delta}{m}$$

from which (15.1) follows.

By the use of Jordan's lemma the following type of integrals may be evaluated: Let

(15.8)
$$Q(z) = \frac{N(z)}{D(z)}$$

where $N(z)$ and $D(z)$ are polynomials and $D(z)$ has no real zeros.   Then if

FIG. 15.1

1. The degree of $D(z)$ exceeds that of $N(z)$ by at least 1, and
2. $m > 0$

we have

(15.9)
$$\int_{-\infty}^{+\infty} Q(x)e^{jmx}\,dx = 2\pi j\sum R^+$$

where ΣR^+ denotes the sum of the residues of $Q(z)e^{jmz}$ at its poles in the upper half plane.   To prove this, integrate $Q(z)e^{jmz}$ around the closed contour of Fig. 15.1.   We then have

(15.10)
$$\int_{-R}^{+R} Q(x)e^{jmx}\,dx + \int_C Q(z)e^{jmz}\,dz = 2\pi j\sum \text{Res inside the contour}$$

Since $Q(z)e^{jmz}$ satisfies the conditions of Jordan's lemma, we have on letting $R \to \infty$ the result (15.9) since the integral around the infinite semicircle vanishes.   Taking the real and imaginary parts of (15.9), we can evaluate integrals of the type

$$(15.11) \qquad \int_{-\infty}^{+\infty} Q(x) \cos mx \, dx \qquad \text{and} \qquad \int_{-\infty}^{+\infty} Q(x) \sin mx \, dx$$

As an example, let it be required to show that

$$(15.12) \qquad \int_{0}^{\infty} \frac{\cos x \, dx}{x^2 + a^2} = \frac{\pi e^{-a}}{2a} \qquad \text{where } a > 0$$

Here we consider the function $e^{jz}/(z^2 + a^2)$, and since it satisfies the above conditions, we have

$$(15.13) \qquad \int_{-\infty}^{+\infty} \frac{e^{jx}}{x^2 + a^2} \, dx = 2\pi j \sum R^{+}$$

The only pole of the integrand in the upper half plane is at ja; the residue there is $e^{-a}/2ja$.   Hence

$$(15.14) \qquad \int_{-\infty}^{+\infty} \frac{e^{jx} \, dx}{x^2 + a^2} = 2\pi j \frac{e^{-a}}{2ja} = \frac{\pi e^{-a}}{a}$$

Therefore, taking the real part of e^{jx}, we have

$$(15.15) \qquad \int_{-\infty}^{+\infty} \frac{\cos dx}{x^2 + a^2} = \frac{\pi e^{-a}}{a} = 2 \int_{0}^{\infty} \frac{\cos dx}{x^2 + a^2}$$

Hence (15.12) follows.

Indenting the Contour.   By an extension of the above theorem it may be proved that

$$(15.16) \qquad \int_{0}^{\infty} \frac{\sin mx}{x} \, dx = \frac{\pi}{2} \qquad \text{if } m > 0$$

To prove this, let us consider the integral

$$(15.17) \qquad \oint_{c} \frac{e^{jmz}}{z} \, dz$$

FIG. 15.2

taken about the contour of Fig. 15.2, where c_1 is a semicircle of radius R and s is a semicircle of radius r.

We notice that the integrand

$$(15.18) \qquad Q(z) = \frac{e^{jmz}}{z}$$

has a simple pole at $z = 0$ and none in the upper half plane.   By Jordan's lemma, we have

$$(15.19) \qquad \lim_{R \to \infty} \left| \int_{c_1} \frac{e^{jmz}}{z} \, dz \right| = 0$$

where c_1 is a semicircle of radius R and center at the origin. Since the contour c does not enclose any singularities of the integrand, we have by Cauchy's residue theorem

$$(15.20) \quad \oint_c \frac{e^{jmz}}{z}\,dz = \int_{-R}^r Q(z)\,dz + \int_s Q(z)\,dz + \int_r^R Q(z)\,dz$$

$$+ \int_{c_1} Q(z)\,dz = 0$$

Now, on the semicircle s, we have

$$(15.21) \qquad\qquad z = re^{j\theta} \qquad \frac{dz}{z} = j\,d\theta$$

and

$$(15.22) \qquad \lim_{r\to 0} \int_s Q(z)\,dz = \lim_{r\to 0} \int_\pi^0 e^{-mr\sin\theta} e^{jmr\cos\theta} j\,d\theta = -j\pi$$

Letting $R \to \infty$ and $r \to 0$ in (15.20), we have

$$(15.23) \qquad\qquad \int_{-\infty}^{+\infty} \frac{e^{jmx}\,dx}{x} = j\pi$$

On equating real and imaginary parts we get

$$(15.24) \quad \int_{-\infty}^{+\infty} \frac{\cos mx\,dx}{x} = 0 \qquad \text{and} \qquad \int_{-\infty}^{+\infty} \frac{\sin mx}{x}\,dx = \pi$$

Hence, since the integrand of the second integral is an even function of x, we have

$$(15.25) \qquad\qquad \int_0^\infty \frac{\sin mx}{x}\,dx = \frac{\pi}{2} \qquad m > 0$$

16. Integrals Involving Multiple-valued Functions. Frequently integrals of the type

$$(16.1) \qquad I = \int_0^\infty x^{a-1} Q(x)\,dx$$

FIG. 16.1

where a is not an integer, are encountered. These integrals can be evaluated by contour integration. However, since z^{a-1} is a multiple-valued function, it is necessary to introduce a barrier or cut in the z plane.

One method of evaluating integrals of this type is to use a contour consisting of a large circle C with center at the origin and radius R. The plane must be cut along the real axis from 0 to ∞ and the branch point $z = 0$ enclosed by a small circle s of radius r, as shown in Fig. 16.1.

Now let $Q(x)$ be a rational function of x with no poles on the positive real axis.   Let us write

$$(16.2) \qquad\qquad w(z) = z^{a-1}Q(z)$$

and let us suppose that

$$(16.3) \qquad\qquad \lim_{|z|\to\infty} zw(z) = 0$$

and

$$(16.4) \qquad\qquad \lim_{|z|\to 0} zw(z) = 0$$

We then get the integral around C tending to zero as $R \to \infty$ and the integral around s tending to zero as $r \to 0$.   Hence, on making $R \to \infty$ and $r \to 0$, we get

$$(16.5) \qquad \int_0^\infty x^{a-1}Q(x)\,dx + \int_\infty^0 x^{a-1}e^{2\pi j(a-1)}Q(x)\,dx = 2\pi j \sum R$$

where ΣR is the sum of the residues of $w(z)$ inside the contour.   It must be noticed that the values of x^{a-1} at points on the upper and lower sides of the cut are not the same.   This may be seen as follows:

If $z = re^{j\theta}$, we have

$$(16.6) \qquad\qquad z^{a-1} = r^{a-1}e^{j\theta(a-1)}$$

and the values on the upper side of the cut correspond to $|z| = x$ and $\theta = 0$, and at the lower side they correspond to $|z| = x$ and $\theta = 2\pi$. Since

$$(16.7) \qquad\qquad e^{2\pi j(a-1)} = e^{2\pi ja}$$

we get

$$(16.8) \qquad\qquad \int_0^\infty x^{a-1}Q(x)\,dx = \frac{2\pi j\Sigma R}{1 - e^{2\pi ja}}$$

As an example of this method of integration, let us evaluate the integral

$$(16.9) \qquad \int_0^\infty \frac{x^{a-1}\,dx}{1+x} = \Gamma(a)\Gamma(1-a) = \frac{\pi}{\sin a\pi} \qquad \text{where } 0 < a < 1$$

This integral is of importance in the theory of gamma functions discussed in Chap. 12, Sec. 7.

In this case we have

$$(16.10) \qquad\qquad w(z) = \frac{z^{a-1}}{1+z}$$

Hence, if $0 < a < 1$, conditions (16.3) and (16.4) are satisfied. $w(z)$ has a pole at $z = -1$. The residue at $z = -1$ is

$$(16.11) \qquad \lim_{z \to -1} \left[(1 + z) \frac{z^{a-1}}{1 + z} \right] = (-1)^{a-1}$$
$$= (e^{j\pi})^{a-1} = e^{j\pi(a-1)}$$
$$= -e^{j\pi a}$$

Hence, by (16.8), we have

$$(16.12) \qquad \int_0^\infty \frac{x^{a-1}\, dx}{1 + x} = \frac{-2\pi j e^{j\pi a}}{1 - e^{2\pi j a}} = -2\pi j \frac{1}{e^{-j\pi a} - e^{j\pi a}} = \frac{\pi}{\sin a\pi}$$

PROBLEMS

1. Show that the function $w(z) = |z|^2$ has a unique derivative at the origin but nowhere else.

2. Show that the real and imaginary parts of $\sin z$ satisfy Laplace's equation in two dimensions.

3. Find the residues of $w(z) = e^z/(z^2 + a^2)$ at its poles.

4. Find the poles of the function $w(z) = e^z/\sin z$.

5. Find the sum of the residues of the function $w(z) = e^z/(z \cosh mz)$ at its poles.

6. Prove that

$$\int_0^\infty \frac{x \sin x\, dx}{x^2 + a^2} = \frac{\pi}{2} e^{-a} \qquad \text{where } a > 0$$

7. Prove that

$$\int_0^\infty \frac{\sinh ax}{\sinh \pi x}\, dx = \frac{1}{2} \tan \frac{a}{2} \qquad \text{where } -\pi < a < \pi$$

HINT: Integrate $e^{az}/\sinh \pi z$ around the rectangle of sides $y = 0$, $y = 1$, $x = \pm R$, indented at the origin and at j.

8. Show that, if m and n are positive integers and $m < n$,

$$\int_0^\infty \frac{x^{2m}}{x^{2n} + 1}\, dx = \frac{\pi}{2n \sin \dfrac{2m + 1}{2n} \pi}$$

9. Show that, if $m > 0$, $a > 0$,

$$\int_0^\infty \frac{x \sin mx}{x^4 + a^4}\, dx = \frac{\pi}{2a^2} e^{-ma/\sqrt{2}} \sin \frac{ma}{\sqrt{2}}$$

10. Show that

$$\int_0^\infty \frac{\cos mx}{x^4 + a^4}\, dx = \frac{\pi}{2a^3} e^{-ma/\sqrt{2}} \sin \left(\frac{ma}{\sqrt{2}} + \frac{\pi}{4} \right)$$

11. Prove that, if $a > 0$,

$$\int_{-\infty}^{+\infty} \frac{a \cos x + x \sin x}{x^2 + a^2}\, dx = 2\pi e^{-a}$$

HINT: Integrate $e^{jz}/(z - ja)$ over a suitable contour.

12. Prove that

$$\int_0^{2\pi} \cos^n \theta \, d\theta = \begin{cases} 0 & \text{if } n \text{ is odd} \\ \dfrac{1 \times 3 \times 5 \times \cdots \times (n-1)}{2 \times 4 \times 6 \times \cdots \times n} \times 2\pi & \text{if } n \text{ is even} \end{cases}$$

13. Show that, if $-\pi < a < \pi$,

$$\int_0^\infty \frac{\cosh ax}{\cosh \pi x} \, dx = \frac{1}{2} \sec \frac{a}{2}$$

HINT: Integrate $e^{az}/\cosh \pi z$ around the rectangle of sides $x = \pm R$, $y = 0$, $y = 1$.

14. Show that

$$\int_0^\infty \frac{x \, dx}{\sinh x} = \frac{\pi^2}{4}$$

15. By integrating e^{jz2}/z around a suitable contour show that

$$\int_0^\infty \frac{\sin x^2 \, dx}{x} = \frac{\pi}{4}$$

16. By integrating $e^{jz}/\sqrt{z}$ along a suitable path show that

$$\int_0^\infty \frac{\cos x \, dx}{\sqrt{x}} = \int_0^\infty \frac{\sin x \, dx}{\sqrt{x}} = \sqrt{\frac{\pi}{2}}$$

17. By taking as a contour a square whose corners are $\pm N$, $\pm N + 2Nj$, where N is an integer, and letting $N \to \infty$, prove that

$$\int_0^\infty \frac{dx}{(1 + x^2) \cosh (\pi x/2)} = \log 2$$

18. Show that

$$\int_0^\infty \frac{x^4 \, dx}{x^6 + 1} = \frac{\pi}{3}$$

19. Show that

$$\int_0^\pi \frac{a \, d\theta}{a^2 + \sin^2 \theta} = \frac{\pi}{\sqrt{1 + a^2}} \qquad a > 0$$

20. Prove that

$$\int_{-\infty}^{+\infty} \frac{\cos x \, dx}{(x^2 + a^2)(x^2 + b^2)} = \frac{\pi}{a^2 - b^2} \left(\frac{e^{-b}}{b} - \frac{e^{-a}}{a} \right) \qquad \text{where } a > b > 0$$

21. Show that

$$\int_{-\infty}^{+\infty} \frac{dx}{(x^2 + b^2)(x^2 + c^2)^2} = \frac{\pi(b + 2c)}{2bc^3(b + c)^2} \qquad b > 0, c > 0$$

REFERENCES

1. Whittaker, E. T., and G. N. Watson: "A Course in Modern Analysis," Cambridge University Press, New York, 1927.
2. MacRobert, T. M.: "Functions of a Complex Variable," The Macmillan Company, New York, 1933.
3. Rothe, R., F. Ollendorf, and K. Pohlhausen: "Theory of Functions as Applied to Engineering Problems," Massachusetts Institute of Technology Press, Cambridge, Mass., 1933.
4. McLachlan, N. W.: "Complex Variable and Operational Calculus," Cambridge University Press, New York, 1939.

CHAPTER 20

THE SOLUTION OF TWO-DIMENSIONAL POTENTIAL
PROBLEMS BY THE METHOD OF CONJUGATE FUNCTIONS

1. Introduction. Many problems of applied mathematics involve the determination of two-dimensional vector fields that are *irrotational* and *solenoidal*. If we let **A** be such a vector field, then we have seen in Chap. 15, Sec. 10, that if

$$(1.1) \qquad \nabla \times \mathbf{A} = 0$$

then

$$(1.2) \qquad \mathbf{A} = \nabla V$$

That is, an irrotational field may be obtained by taking the gradient of a certain scalar function V.

If the vector field is also solenoidal, then

$$(1.3) \qquad \nabla \cdot \mathbf{A} = \nabla \cdot (\nabla V) = \nabla^2 V = 0$$

If the vector field **A** is two-dimensional, then

$$(1.4) \qquad \mathbf{A} = iA_x + jA_y$$

where i is the unit vector in the x direction, j is the unit vector in the y direction, and A_x, A_y are the components of **A** in the x and y directions.

In this case Eq. (1.3) reduces to

$$(1.5) \qquad \nabla^2 V = \frac{\partial^2 V}{\partial x^2} + \frac{\partial^2 V}{\partial y^2} = 0$$

which is Laplace's equation in two dimensions.

In Chap. 17 we have solved Eq. (1.5) by the method of separation of variables. In this chapter the solution of (1.5) by complex-function theory will be discussed.

This method is particularly useful in determining the distribution of the following typical vector fields:

1. An electrostatic field between parallel cylindrical conductors of various shapes
2. An electric current in a uniform conducting sheet

3. The streamlines of fluid flowing in two dimensions through an unobstructed channel when the flow is irrotational

4. The flow of heat in two dimensions through a homogeneous material that has arrived at a steady state

5. The magnetic field around a straight conductor carrying current in the neighborhood of parallel ferromagnetic masses

6. The streamlines of fluid flowing in two dimensions through a homogeneous porous obstructing medium when the flow has reached a steady state

2. Conjugate Functions.   We have seen in Chap. 19 that if a function

$$(2.1) \qquad\qquad w(z) = u + jv$$

is an analytic function of the complex variable

$$(2.2) \qquad\qquad z = x + jy$$

then the real part u and the imaginary part v of $w(z)$ satisfy the Cauchy-Riemann equations

$$(2.3) \qquad\qquad \frac{\partial u}{\partial x} = \frac{\partial v}{\partial y} \qquad \frac{\partial u}{\partial y} = -\frac{\partial v}{\partial x}$$

and that as a consequence of these equations we have

$$(2.4) \qquad\qquad \frac{\partial^2 u}{\partial x^2} + \frac{\partial^2 u}{\partial y^2} = 0$$

$$(2.5) \qquad\qquad \frac{\partial^2 v}{\partial x^2} + \frac{\partial^2 v}{\partial y^2} = 0$$

so that the real and imaginary parts of $w(z)$ satisfy Laplace's differential equation in two dimensions.   The functions u and v are called *conjugate functions.*

Orthogonality Conditions.   Let us construct the two families of curves

$$(2.6) \qquad\qquad u(x,y) = c_1$$

and

$$(2.7) \qquad\qquad v(x,y) = c_2$$

If x_0, y_0 is a point of intersection of these two curves, the slopes of the tangent lines at x_0, y_0 are, respectively,

$$(2.8) \qquad\qquad \left(\frac{dy}{dx}\right)_{u=\text{const}} = -\frac{\partial u/\partial x}{\partial u/\partial y}$$

$$(2.9) \qquad\qquad \left(\frac{dy}{dx}\right)_{v=\text{const}} = -\frac{\partial v/\partial x}{\partial v/\partial y}$$

But as a consequence of the Cauchy-Riemann equations (2.3) we have

$$(2.10) \qquad \left(\frac{dy}{dx}\right)_{u=\text{const}} = \frac{-1}{(dy/dx)_{v=\text{const}}}$$

Hence the two slopes are negative reciprocals, and therefore the two curves intersect at right angles; that is, every curve of one family intersects every curve of the other family at right angles. This is expressed by saying that the families of curves corresponding to two conjugate functions form an orthogonal system.

As an example of this, consider the function

$$(2.11) \qquad w(z) = \ln z = u + jv$$

If we write z in the polar form

$$(2.12) \qquad z = re^{j\theta}$$

we have

$$(2.13) \qquad \ln re^{j\theta} = \ln r + j\theta = u + jv$$

Hence

$$(2.14) \qquad u = \ln \sqrt{x^2 + y^2}$$

and

$$(2.15) \qquad v = \theta = \tan^{-1}\frac{y}{x}$$

are conjugate functions. The curves

$$(2.16) \qquad u = \ln \sqrt{x^2 + y^2} = \text{const}$$

are a family of circles, and the curves

$$(2.17) \qquad v = \tan^{-1}\frac{y}{x} = \text{const}$$

are a family of straight lines passing through the origin and intersecting the family of circles at right angles.

3. Conformal Representation. Let

$$(3.1) \qquad w(z) = u + jv \qquad z = x + jy$$

We can represent values of z in one Argand diagram called the z plane and values of w in another called the w plane, as shown in Fig. 3.1.

Any point P in the z plane corresponds to a definite value of z and, hence, by Eq. (3.1) may give one or more values of w depending on whether $w(z)$ is or is not a single-valued function of z.

If Q is a point in the w plane that represents one of these values of w, the points P and Q are said to *correspond*.

As P describes some curve S in the z plane, the point Q in the w plane that corresponds to P will describe some curve S_0 in the w plane and the curve S_0 is said to correspond to the curve S.

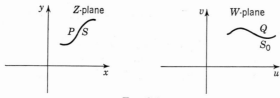

FIG. 3.1

In particular, corresponding to any infinitesimal linear path PP' in the z plane, there will correspond a small linear element QQ' in the w plane. If we let the element PP' represent dz, then QQ' will represent dw, or

$$(3.2) \qquad dw = \left(\frac{dw}{dz}\right) dz$$

if dw/dz exists and is nonzero.

In general dw/dz is complex and may be written in the polar form

$$(3.3) \qquad \frac{dw}{dz} = ae^{i\phi}$$

where

$$(3.4) \qquad a = \left|\frac{dw}{dz}\right|$$

and

$$(3.5) \qquad \phi = \arg\frac{dw}{dz}$$

We can then write

$$(3.6) \qquad dw = ae^{i\phi}\, dz$$

We thus find that the element dw may be obtained from the corresponding element dz by multiplying its length by a and turning it through an angle ϕ.

It thus follows that any element of area in the z plane is represented in the w plane by an element of area that has the same form as the original element but whose linear dimensions are a times as great and whose orientation is obtained by turning the original element through an angle θ.

Because of the fact that the forms of two corresponding elements are the same, the process of passing from one plane to the other is known as *conformal representation*.

As an example of the above general principles, let us consider the function

(3.7)
$$w = \ln z = u + jv$$

Here we have

(3.8)
$$dw = \frac{dz}{z}$$

so that

What is a?

(3.9)
$$a = \left| \frac{dw}{dz} \right| = \left| \frac{1}{z} \right| = \frac{1}{\sqrt{x^2 + y^2}}$$

(3.10)
$$\phi = - \tan^{-1} \frac{y}{x}$$

(3.11)
$$u = \ln \sqrt{x^2 + y^2} = \ln r$$

(3.12)
$$v = \tan^{-1} \frac{y}{x}$$

We thus see that a circular region in the z plane transforms conformally into a rectangular region in the w plane, as shown in Fig. 3.2. This may

Fig. 3.2

be seen from the relations

(3.13)
$$r = e^u$$

and

(3.14)
$$\tan v = \frac{y}{x}$$

We thus have the following values for the two radii,

(3.15)
$$r_1 = e^{u_1} \quad \text{and} \quad r_2 = e^{u_2}$$

and the angle θ is given by

(3.16)
$$\theta = \tan v_0$$

The quantity a, which, as we have seen, measures the linear magnification produced in a small area on passing from the z plane to the w plane, is called the *modulus of the transformation*.

Now we have

(3.17)
$$\frac{\partial w}{\partial x} = \frac{dw}{dz}\frac{\partial z}{\partial x}$$

$$\frac{dw}{dz} = \frac{\partial w / \partial x}{\partial z / \partial x}$$

But

(3.18)
$$\frac{\partial z}{\partial x} = \frac{\partial}{\partial x}(x + jy) = 1$$

Hence

(3.19)
$$\frac{dw}{dz} = \frac{\partial w}{\partial x} = \frac{\partial}{\partial x}(u + jv)$$

Therefore

(3.20)
$$\frac{dw}{dz} = \frac{\partial u}{\partial x} + j\frac{\partial v}{\partial x}$$

By the use of the Cauchy-Riemann equations this may be written in the form

(3.21)
$$\frac{dw}{dz} = \frac{\partial v}{\partial y} + j\frac{\partial v}{\partial x}$$

Hence the modulus of the transformation, a, may be written in the form

(3.22)
$$a = \left|\frac{dw}{dz}\right| = \sqrt{\left(\frac{\partial v}{\partial x}\right)^2 + \left(\frac{\partial v}{\partial y}\right)^2}$$

It is to be noted that the conformal property fails at points where a is zero or infinity.

4. Basic Principles of Electrostatics. To show the utility of the method of conjugate functions in the solution of potential problems, the method will first be used to solve certain two-dimensional electrostatic problems.

As explained in Chap. 15, Sec. 16, the basic equations of electrostatics are

(4.1)
$$\nabla \times \mathbf{E} = 0$$
(4.2)
$$\nabla \cdot \mathbf{D} = \rho$$
(4.3)
$$\mathbf{D} = K\mathbf{E}$$

where $\mathbf{E}$ = electric intensity vector, volts per m
$\mathbf{D}$ = electric displacement vector, coulombs per m²
ρ = charge density, coulombs per m³
$K = K_r K_0$ = electric inductive capacity of medium
K_r = relative dielectric constant
$K_0 = 8.854 \times 10^{-12}$ farad per m

Since the curl of the vector field $\mathbf{E}$ vanishes, it is customary to let

(4.4)
$$\mathbf{E} = -\mathrm{grad}\,\phi = -\nabla\phi$$

where ϕ is the electric potential.

Hence

(4.5) $$\mathbf{D} = K\mathbf{E} = -K\nabla\phi$$

and, substituting this into Eq. (4.2), we have

(4.6) $$\nabla \cdot \mathbf{D} = \nabla \cdot (-K\nabla\phi) = \rho$$

or

(4.7) $$\nabla^2\phi = -\frac{\rho}{K}$$

in a homogeneous medium. This is Poisson's equation. If the region under consideration is free of charges, $\rho = 0$ and Eq. (4.7) becomes Laplace's equation.

Surface Charge. Let us consider a solid conducting body as shown in Fig. 4.1.

If a charge Q is placed on the body, the electricity distributes itself so that the field inside the body is zero. Hence the surface of the body is an equipotential surface, and by Eq. (4.2) we see that all the charge is on the surface of the body. Also the electric field $\mathbf{E}$ has only a normal component to the surface of the body at the surface.

FIG. 4.1

To determine the distribution of electricity per unit area, apply Gauss's theorem to a small disk-shaped volume as shown in the figure. Since the only component of $\mathbf{E}$ is the one having the direction of the outward-drawn normal to the surface of the body, we have

(4.8) $$\int_A \int \mathbf{D} \cdot d\mathbf{s} = \int_A \int Dn\, dA = \iiint (\nabla \cdot \mathbf{D})\, dv = \iiint \rho\, dv = Q$$

where A is the area of the disk and Q is the entire charge contained within the disk-shaped volume, and A has been assumed so small that D is sensibly constant throughout A.

Now if we let

(4.9) $$\lim_{A \to 0} \frac{\int_A \int \mathbf{D} \cdot d\mathbf{s}}{A} = \lim_{A \to 0} \frac{Q}{A} = \sigma$$

where σ is the surface density, we have from (4.9)

(4.10) $$\sigma = D_N$$

where D_N is the normal component of $\mathbf{D}$ at the surface of the body. Hence σ, the surface density of charge, may be determined by computing the absolute value of the vector $\mathbf{D}$ at the surface of the conductor.

In the usual electrostatic problem we are given the geometrical configuration of the charged conducting bodies and the total charge on each body (Fig. 4.2), and we are asked to find the charge density on the several conducting bodies and the electric field in the space outside the bodies.

Let Q_r be the total charge on the rth conducting body. This charge resides entirely on the surface of the rth conductor. The entire conducting body r is at one potential, and its surface is an equipotential surface at potential ϕ_r.

We must therefore solve Laplace's equation (4.7) subject to the condition that the potential ϕ should reduce to ϕ_1, ϕ_2, ϕ_r, etc., at the surface

FIG. 4.2

of the first, second, and rth conducting body. In this chapter we concern ourselves with the solution of two-dimensional electrostatic problems.

Theoretically a two-dimensional electrostatic problem can never occur, since all conductors are finite. However, there are a great number of important cases in which the surfaces of the conducting bodies are cylindrical and can be generated by moving an infinite straight line parallel to some fixed straight line. If the lengths of the parallel cylindrical conductors are so great compared with the intervening spaces that the end effects are negligible, the problem becomes two-dimensional.

Since the real and imaginary parts of the analytic function $w(z)$ of the complex variable z satisfy Laplace's equation in two dimensions, it is natural that the use of conjugate functions should find application in the solution of two-dimensional electrostatic problems.

It is clear that if we are given a function $w(z)$ then we are assured that the real part u and the imaginary part v of $w(z)$ satisfy the two-dimensional Laplace equations

(4.11)
$$\frac{\partial^2 u}{\partial x^2} + \frac{\partial^2 u}{\partial y^2} = 0$$

and

(4.12)
$$\frac{\partial^2 v}{\partial x^2} + \frac{\partial^2 v}{\partial y^2} = 0$$

Hence either the function u or the function v may be taken as the electric potential function ϕ; if, for example, we let

(4.13)
$$\phi = u$$

then we have solved the electrostatic problem in which the family of curves

(4.14) $$u = \text{const}$$

are the equipotential surfaces. To illustrate this, consider the function

(4.15) $$w = A \ln z + c = u + jv$$

where A and c are real constants. Since

(4.16) $$\ln z = \ln r + j\theta$$

where

(4.17) $$r = \sqrt{x^2 + y^2} \qquad \tan \theta = \frac{y}{x}$$

we have

(4.18) $$u = A \ln r + c$$
(4.19) $$v = A\theta$$

If we take u for the electric potential function ϕ, we have

(4.20) $$\phi = u = A \ln r + c$$

We may use this transformation to solve the electrostatic problem of two concentric circular cylinders as shown in Fig. 4.3.

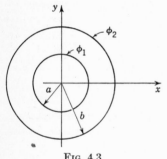

FIG. 4.3

Since the curves $\phi = \text{const}$ are circles in the z plane, let us consider the problem of determining the electric field in the region between two concentric cylinders, one of radius a at potential ϕ_1, and the other of radius b at potential ϕ_2.

We thus have from Eq. (4.20)

(4.21) $$\phi_1 = A \ln a + c$$

and

(4.22) $$\phi_2 = A \ln b + c$$

Subtracting Eq. (4.21) from (4.22), we have

(4.23) $$\phi_2 - \phi_1 = A \ln b - A \ln a = A \ln \frac{b}{a}$$

Hence

(4.24) $$A = \frac{\phi_2 - \phi_1}{\ln (b/a)}$$

From (4.21), we have

(4.25) $$c = \phi_1 - A \ln a = \phi_1 + \frac{\phi_1 - \phi_2}{\ln b - \ln a} \ln a$$
$$= \frac{\phi_2 \ln a - \phi_1 \ln b}{\ln a - \ln b}$$

Hence the potential in the region within the concentric cylindrical conductors is given by

(4.26) $$\phi = \frac{\phi_2 - \phi_1}{\ln (b/a)} \ln r - \frac{\phi_2 \ln a - \phi_1 \ln b}{\ln (b/a)} \qquad 0 < a < b$$

The electric intensity $\mathbf{E}$ is given by

(4.27) $$\mathbf{E} = -\nabla\phi = -\frac{\partial\phi}{\partial r}$$

Now, if q is the charge per unit length on the inner cylinder, we have

(4.28) $$q = 2\pi a\sigma$$

where σ is the surface density of charge on the inner cylinder.   Differentiating (4.20), we obtain

(4.29) $$\mathbf{E} = -\frac{\partial\phi}{\partial r} = -\frac{A}{r}$$

If K is the dielectric constant of the medium within the cylinder, then we have

(4.30) $$\mathbf{D} = K\mathbf{E} = -K\frac{\partial\phi}{\partial r} = -\frac{KA}{r}$$

The value of the normal component of the displacement vector at the surface of the inner cylinder gives the surface density σ, by Eq. (4.10). Hence

(4.31) $$\sigma = -\frac{KA}{a} = +\frac{q}{2\pi a}$$

Hence

(4.32) $$A = -\frac{q}{2\pi K}$$

The potential may then be expressed in the form

(4.33) $$\phi = -\frac{q}{2\pi K}\ln r + c$$

In terms of the charge per unit length q of the inner cylinder the potentials of the inner and outer cylinders are

(4.34) $$\phi_1 = -\frac{q}{2\pi K}\ln a + c$$

and

(4.35) $$\phi_2 = -\frac{q}{2\pi K}\ln b + c$$

The *capacitance* per unit length of the capacitor formed from the two cylindrical conductors is defined to be

(4.36) $$\frac{\text{Capacitance}}{\text{Length}} = \frac{q}{\phi_1 - \phi_2} = \frac{2\pi K}{\ln (b/a)} = c_0$$

This simple problem illustrates the use of the theory of functions in solving a potential problem.   In this case we have chosen the real part u of the function $w = A \ln z + c$ to be the potential function ϕ.   The curves $v = $ const are the lines of force.   They are radial lines emanating

from the center of the cylinders as shown in Fig. 4.4.

The Charge on the Surface of a Conductor. The charge on a strip of unit width between any two points P, Q on the surface of a conductor on which the potential $\phi = v$ is constant may be determined in a very simple manner.

Fig. 4.4

As a consequence of Eqs. (4.10) and (4.5) we have, for the charge density σ on a conductor, the equation

$$(4.37) \qquad \sigma = -K\left(\frac{\partial \phi}{\partial n}\right)_s = -K\left(\frac{\partial v}{\partial n}\right)_s$$

where $(\partial v/\partial n)_s$ denotes the normal derivative of v evaluated at the surface s, where v is constant.

Now, by the Cauchy-Riemann equations and Eq. (3.21), we have

$$(4.38) \qquad \frac{dw}{dz} = \frac{\partial v}{\partial y} + j\frac{\partial v}{\partial x} = \frac{\partial u}{\partial x} - j\frac{\partial u}{\partial y}$$

Hence

$$(4.39) \qquad \left|\frac{dw}{dz}\right| = \frac{\partial v}{\partial n} = -\frac{\partial u}{\partial s}$$

Fig. 4.5

where dn is an element of length *normal* to an equipotential line, $v = \phi = $ const, and ds is an element of length *parallel* to an equipotential line.   The sign is chosen so that if one faces in the direction of n the positive direction of s is to the left as shown in Fig. 4.5.

The total charge on a strip of unit width between any two points P, Q of the conductor is therefore

$$(4.40) \qquad \int_P^Q \sigma \, ds = -K\int_P^Q \left(\frac{\partial v}{\partial n}\right) ds = K\int_P^Q \frac{\partial u}{\partial s} \, ds = K(u_Q - u_P)$$

If the surfaces $v_1 = $ const and $v_2 = $ const are closed surfaces and all the charge is situated on one side of one surface and on the opposite side of the other so that all lines of force $u = $ const in the region between the surfaces v_1 and v_2 pass from one surface to the other, then the surfaces form a capacitor.   The total charge per unit width on either surface of this capacitor is

$$(4.41) \qquad q = \oint \sigma \, ds = K \oint du = K[u]$$

where $[u]$ represents the increment in going once around the $v_1 = $ const curve.   The potential difference is

(4.42) $$|v_1 - v_2| = \Delta v$$

The capacitance per unit length of the capacitor is

(4.43) $$c_0 = \frac{q}{\Delta v} = \frac{K[u]}{|v_2 - v_1|}$$

5. The Transformation $z = k \cosh w$.   A very interesting and instructive transformation is

(5.1) $$z = k \cosh w = k \cosh (u + jv)$$

where k is a real constant.

To study this transformation, we must determine the curves $u = $ const and $v = $ const.   Expanding $\cosh (u + jv)$ into its real and imaginary parts, we obtain

(5.2) $$x + jy = k(\cosh u \cos v + j \sinh u \sin v)$$

Hence

(5.3) $$\begin{aligned} x &= k \cosh u \cos v \\ y &= k \sinh u \sin v \end{aligned}$$

This may be written in the form

(5.4) $$\begin{aligned} \cos v &= \frac{x}{k \cosh u} \\ \sin v &= \frac{y}{k \sinh u} \end{aligned}$$

Therefore, on squaring these equations and adding the results, we have

(5.5) $$\frac{x^2}{k^2 \cosh^2 u} + \frac{y^2}{k^2 \sinh^2 u} = 1$$

If we let

(5.6) $$\begin{aligned} a &= k \cosh u \\ b &= k \sinh u \end{aligned}$$

Eq. (5.5) may be written in the form

(5.7) $$\frac{x^2}{a^2} + \frac{y^2}{b^2} = 1$$

FIG. 5.1

This is the equation of an ellipse with its center at the origin having a major axis of length $2a$ and a minor axis of length $2b$ as shown in Fig. 5.1.

The focal distance F is given by

(5.8) $$F = \sqrt{a^2 - b^2} = \sqrt{k^2(\cosh^2 u - \sinh^2 u)} = k$$

Hence the curves $u = $ const are a family of *confocal ellipses* all having

the focal distance k.   If

(5.9) $u = 0 \qquad a = k \qquad b = 0$

This represents a degenerate ellipse and is a straight line extending over the range $-k \leq x \leq k$.

Now

(5.10) $\lim\limits_{u \to \infty} \dfrac{b}{a} = \lim\limits_{u \to \infty} \tanh u = 1$

Hence, as $u \to \infty$, the ellipses become more and more nearly circular. Therefore all the z plane is covered if u takes the range

(5.11) $0 \leq u \leq \infty$

To obtain the curves $v = $ const, we write Eqs. (5.4) in the form

(5.12) $\cosh u = \dfrac{x}{k \cos v} \qquad \sinh u = \dfrac{y}{k \sin v}$

Hence

(5.13) $\cosh^2 u - \sinh^2 u = \dfrac{x^2}{k^2 \cos^2 v} - \dfrac{y^2}{k^2 \sin^2 v} = 1$

If we let

(5.14) $a' = k \cos v \qquad b' = k \sin v$

we have

(5.15) $\dfrac{x^2}{a'^2} - \dfrac{y^2}{b'^2} = 1$

We thus see that the curves $v = $ const represent a family of hyperbolas as shown in Fig. 5.2.

The asymptotes of the hyperbolas are given by the equation

(5.16) $\dfrac{x}{a'} = \dfrac{y}{b'}$

The focal distance F is given by

(5.17) $F = \sqrt{a'^2 + b'^2}$
$= k \sqrt{\cos^2 v + \sin^2 v} = k$

FIG. 5.2

Hence the curves $v = $ const represent a confocal family of hyperbolas having the same foci as the family of ellipses $u = $ const.

The angle θ of the asymptote is given by

(5.18) $\tan \theta = \dfrac{y}{x} = \dfrac{b'}{a'} = \tan v$

If $v = 0$, we obtain a straight line starting from the focus F and extending to infinity along the x axis.   This is the case of a degenerate hyperbola.

We thus see from the geometrical configuration of the curves $u = $ const and $v = $ const that with the proper choice of u or v to represent the potential function the transformation $z = k \cosh w$ gives the solution to the following problems:

1. The electric field around a charged elliptic conducting cylinder as shown in Fig. 5.3

Fig. 5.3

Fig. 5.4

Here we let

(5.19) $\phi = u$

The equipotential surfaces are now a family of confocal ellipses, and the lines of force are a family of confocal hyperbolas.

Consider a capacitor formed of a flat strip and an elliptic cylinder surrounding this strip as shown in Fig. 5.4.

Let the width of the flat strip be $2d$, where

(5.20) $d = \sqrt{a^2 - b^2}$

The flat strip is then given by the degenerate ellipse $u = 0$.

Let it be required to find the capacitance c_0 of this capacitor. We determine c_0 by Eq. (4.43) modified to fit this choice of potential:

(5.21) $c_0 = \dfrac{K[v]}{|u_2 - u_1|}$

In this case we have

(5.22) $u_1 = 0 \qquad \cosh u_2 = \dfrac{a}{k} = \dfrac{a}{d}$

Hence

(5.23) $u_2 = \cosh^{-1} \dfrac{a}{d}$

and

(5.24) $[v] = 2\pi$

Hence

(5.25) $c_0 = \dfrac{2\pi K}{\cosh^{-1}(a/d)}$

This is the capacitance per unit length of such a capacitor.

2. The electric field between two semi-infinite conducting plates with a slit separating them as shown in Fig. 5.5

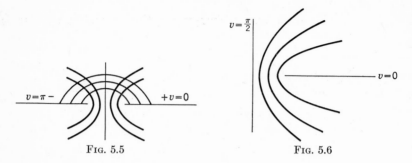

FIG. 5.5   FIG. 5.6

The two coplanar plates are degenerate hyperbolas.

3. The field between perpendicular semi-infinite plates separated by a gap as shown in Fig. 5.6

4. The field between two hyperbolic pole pieces as shown in Fig. 5.7

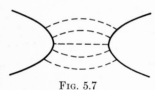

FIG. 5.7

6. General Powers of z. Another instructive transformation is the transformation

$$(6.1) \qquad w = Az^n = u + jv$$

where A is a real constant and n is a real number.

In order to obtain the curves $u = $ const and $v = $ const, it is convenient to write z^n in the polar form

$$(6.2) \qquad z^n = (re^{j\theta})^n = r^n(\cos n\theta + j \sin n\theta)$$

Hence

$$(6.3) \qquad \begin{aligned} u &= Ar^n \cos n\theta \\ v &= Ar^n \sin n\theta \end{aligned}$$

where

$$(6.4) \qquad r^2 = x^2 + y^2 \qquad \text{and} \qquad \tan \theta = \frac{y}{x}$$

If we now take v to be the potential function so that $\phi = v$, we see that

$$(6.5) \qquad v = 0 \qquad \begin{cases} \theta = 0 \\ n\theta = \pi \end{cases}$$

Hence in this case the potential v vanishes on the two sides of a wedge of angle ϕ as shown in Fig. 6.1, where

$$(6.6) \qquad n\phi = \pi$$

FIG. 6.1

Hence, if we let

(6.7)
$$n = \frac{\pi}{\phi}$$

then

(6.8)
$$v = Ar^{\pi/\phi} \sin \frac{\pi\theta}{\phi}$$

gives the potential inside a conducting wedge whose sides are the surfaces $\theta = 0$ and $\theta = \phi$.

The function

(6.9)
$$u = Ar^{\pi/\phi} \cos \frac{\pi\theta}{\phi}$$

gives the lines of force in the region inside the wedge. To determine the surface density σ on the bottom plate, we have

(6.10)
$$\sigma = -K \left| \frac{dw}{dz} \right|_{\text{on } \theta=0}$$

Now

(6.11)
$$\frac{dw}{dz} = \frac{d}{dz}(Az^n) = nAz^{n-1}$$
$$= \frac{\pi}{\phi} Az^{(\pi/\phi-1)}$$

Hence

(6.12)
$$\sigma = \frac{-K\pi}{\phi} Ar^{(\pi/\phi-1)}$$

As a special case let $\phi = \pi/2$. In this case we have the right-angle wedge shown in Fig. 6.2.

We now have

(6.13) $v = Ar^2 \sin 2\theta = Ar^2 \times 2 \sin \theta \cos \theta$
$$= 2Ar^2 \frac{y}{r}\frac{x}{r} = 2Axy$$

and

(6.14) $u = Ar^2 \cos 2\theta = Ar^2(\cos^2 \theta - \sin^2 \theta)$
$$= A(x^2 - y^2)$$

FIG. 6.2

We thus obtain two families of hyperbolas. The surface density on the lower plate is

(6.15)
$$\sigma = -2KAr$$

We thus see that the surface density is zero at the corner and increases linearly as we move away from the corner.

Another interesting case is the one for which $\phi = 2\pi$. This is the case where the wedge has been opened completely as in Fig. 6.3.

We now have

$$v = Ar^{\frac{1}{2}} \sin \frac{\theta}{2}$$
$$(6.16)$$
$$u = Ar^{\frac{1}{2}} \cos \frac{\theta}{2}$$

$\phi = 2\pi$

FIG. 6.3

To obtain the rectangular form for the curves $u = $ const and $v = $ const in this case, it is more convenient to use (6.1) directly. In this case, $n = \frac{1}{2}$, and (6.1) becomes

$$(6.17) \qquad w = Az^{\frac{1}{2}} = A\sqrt{z}$$

or

$$(6.18) \qquad z = \left(\frac{w}{A}\right)^2$$

For simplicity and with no loss of generality in studying the curves $u = $ const and $v = $ const let us take

$$(6.19) \qquad A = \sqrt{2}$$

The transformation then becomes

$$(6.20) \qquad z = \frac{w^2}{2} = \frac{(u + jv)^2}{2}$$

Hence

$$(6.21) \qquad x + jy = \frac{u^2 - v^2 + 2juv}{2}$$

or

$$(6.22) \qquad \begin{aligned} x &= \frac{u^2 - v^2}{2} \\ y &= uv \end{aligned}$$

Eliminating u between these two equations, we get

$$(6.23) \qquad y^2 = 2v^2\left(x + \frac{v^2}{2}\right)$$

These are the curves $v = $ const. It is easy to show that this is a family of parabolas with their foci at the origin as shown in Fig. 6.4.

The parabolas intersect the x axis at

$$(6.24) \qquad x = -\frac{v^2}{2}$$

FIG. 6.4

The parabola $v = 0$ degenerates into the positive side of the x axis.

Eliminating v from Eqs. (6.22), we obtain

$$(6.25) \qquad\qquad y^2 = 2u^2 \left(\frac{u^2}{2} - x \right)$$

These are the curves $u = $ const. They are a family of confocal parabolas with their foci at the origin and are orthogonal to the curves $v = $ const as shown in Fig. 6.5.

The curves $v = $ const give the equipotential lines in the region surrounding a semi-infinite charged plate, while the curves $u = $ const give the lines of force emanating from a semi-infinite charged plate.

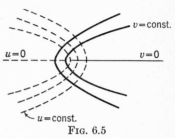

FIG. 6.5

7. The Transformation $w = A \ln \dfrac{z - a}{z + a}$. We have seen that the transformation

$$(7.1) \qquad\qquad w = - \frac{q}{2\pi K} \ln z = u + jv$$

gives the appropriate transformation to study the electric field in the region surrounding a charged circular cylinder with its center at the origin and having a charge q per unit length. In this case the real part of the transformation, u, is given by

FIG. 7.1

$$(7.2) \qquad u = - \frac{q}{2\pi K} \ln r$$

and the imaginary part is given by

$$(7.3) \qquad v = - \frac{q}{2\pi K} \theta$$

The family of curves $u = $ const and $v = $ const are given by Fig. 7.1. The lines $u = $ const are a family of concentric circles and represent the equipotentials. The lines $v = $ const are a family of straight lines and represent the lines of force. This transformation also represents the field of a line charge at the origin of charge q per unit length surrounded by a medium of dielectric constant K.

The transformation

$$(7.4) \qquad\qquad w = - \frac{q}{2\pi K} \ln (z - a)$$

gives the appropriate transformation for a line charge situated at $z = a$, as may be seen by shifting the origin of the transformation (7.1) to $z = a$.

Let us now consider the field produced by a line charge of charge $+q$ per unit length situated at $z = a$ and another line charge of $-q$ units per unit length situated at $z = -a$, as shown in Fig. 7.2.

The field produced by both line charges is equivalent to the superposition of the fields given by (7.4) and

$$(7.5) \qquad w = + \frac{q}{2\pi K} \ln (z + a)$$

Hence

$$(7.6) \quad w = - \frac{q}{2\pi K} [\ln (z - a) - \ln (z + a)] = - \frac{q}{2\pi K} \ln \frac{z - a}{z + a}$$

represents the proper transformation to determine the field and equipotentials of the two line charges of Fig. 7.2.

FIG. 7.2

Let

$$(7.7) \qquad A = - \frac{q}{2\pi K}$$

We then have

$$(7.8) \qquad u + jv = A \ln \frac{z - a}{z + a}$$

If we now let the distance from the points $z = a$ and $z = -a$ to the point z be r_1 and r_2, respectively, as shown in Fig. 7.2, we have

$$(7.9) \qquad \begin{aligned} z - a &= r_1 e^{j\theta_1} \\ z + a &= r_2 e^{j\theta_2} \end{aligned}$$

where

$$(7.10) \qquad \theta_1 = \arg (z - a) \qquad \theta_2 = \arg (z + a)$$

Hence

$$(7.11) \qquad \begin{aligned} u + jv &= A[\ln (z - a) - \ln (z + a)] \\ &= A[\ln r_1 + j\theta_1 - \ln r_2 - j\theta_2] \end{aligned}$$

Therefore

$$(7.12) \qquad u = A \ln \frac{r_1}{r_2}$$

and

$$(7.13) \qquad v = A(\theta_1 - \theta_2)$$

These are the curves $u = $ const and $v = $ const. Now from (7.12), we have

$$(7.14) \qquad \ln \frac{r_1}{r_2} = \frac{u}{A}$$

Therefore

(7.15)
$$\frac{r_1}{r_2} = e^{u/A}$$

Hence

(7.16)
$$\left(\frac{r_1}{r_2}\right)^2 = \frac{(x-a)^2 + y^2}{(x+a)^2 + y^2} = e^{2u/A} = k$$

Therefore

(7.17)
$$y^2 + \left[x - \frac{a(1+k)}{1-k}\right]^2 = \frac{4a^2k}{(1-k)^2}$$

We thus see that the curves $u = $ const are a family of circles with centers at

(7.18)
$$y = 0 \qquad x = \frac{a(1+k)}{1-k}$$

and radii

(7.19)
$$r = \frac{2a \sqrt{k}}{1-k}$$

These circles are shown in Fig. 7.3.

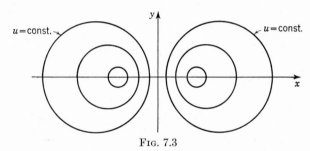

FIG. 7.3

This transformation may be used to find the capacitance of two eccentric cylinders of equal radii R, whose centers are at a distance S apart as shown in Fig. 7.4.

Since any of the circles $u = $ const of Fig. 7.3 may be replaced by a circular conductor at potential u, we must adjust the center of one of the $u = $ const circles to be at $x = S/2$. Hence by Eq. (7.18), we have

(7.20)
$$\frac{S}{2} = \frac{a(1+k)}{1-k}$$

The radius of the circle is fixed by Eq. (7.19) to be

(7.21)
$$R = \frac{2a\sqrt{k}}{1-k}$$

FIG. 7.4

Eliminating a between Eqs. (7.20) and (7.21), we have

$$(7.22) \qquad \frac{S}{R} = \frac{1 + k}{\sqrt{k}} = \frac{1 + e^{2u/A}}{e^{u/A}}$$

Therefore

$$(7.23) \qquad \frac{S}{2R} = \frac{e^{u/A} + e^{-u/A}}{2} = \cosh \frac{u}{A}$$

By Eq. (7.7), we have

$$(7.24) \qquad \cosh \left(-\frac{2\pi K u}{q} \right) = \cosh \frac{2\pi K u}{q} = \frac{S}{2R}$$

Hence

$$(7.25) \qquad \frac{2\pi K u}{q} = \cosh^{-1} \frac{S}{2R}$$

or

$$(7.26) \qquad q = \frac{2\pi K u}{\cosh^{-1} (S/2R)}$$

The capacitance per unit length formed by the conductors of Fig. 7.4 is obtained by dividing q by the total potential difference, which is obviously $2u$.   Hence

$$(7.27) \qquad C_0 = \frac{q}{2u} = \frac{K\pi}{\cosh^{-1} (S/2R)}$$

The curves $v = $ const are given by (7.13).   This may be written in the form

$$(7.28) \qquad \theta_1 - \theta_2 = \frac{v}{A}$$

Now

$$(7.29) \qquad \theta_1 = \tan^{-1} \frac{y}{x - a} \qquad \theta_2 = \tan^{-1} \frac{y}{x + a}$$

Hence we have

$$(7.30) \qquad \tan^{-1} \frac{y}{x - a} - \tan^{-1} \frac{y}{x + a} = \frac{v}{A}$$

We now use the trigonometric identity

$$(7.31) \qquad \tan^{-1} M - \tan^{-1} N = \tan^{-1} \frac{M - N}{1 + MN}$$

and let

$$(7.32) \qquad M = \frac{y}{x - a} \qquad N = \frac{y}{x + a}$$

Then Eq. (7.30) becomes

$$(7.33) \qquad \tan^{-1} \frac{2ya}{x^2 - a^2 + y^2} = \frac{v}{A}$$

and hence

(7.34)
$$\frac{2ya}{x^2 - a^2 + y^2} = \tan \frac{v}{A}$$

This is a family of circles whose centers are at

(7.35)
$$y = a \cot \frac{v}{A} \qquad x = 0$$

and having radii given by

(7.36)
$$R = a \csc \frac{v}{A}$$

These circles are orthogonal to the circles $u = $ const and represent the lines of force in the electrical application (see Fig. 7.5).

8. Determination of the Required Transformation When the Boundary Is Expressed in Parametric Form. In the last two sections we have studied transformations that enabled us to solve problems of physical interest. In general if we are given a two-dimensional potential problem arising from some physical investigation, we are required to find a trans-

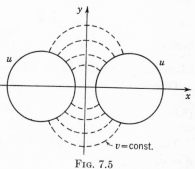

FIG. 7.5

formation $w(z) = u + jv$ of such nature that either the curves $u = $ const or the curves $v = $ const should coincide with the boundary of the region. It is sometimes possible to express the desired equipotential boundary in parametric form.

Let

(8.1)
$$F(x,y) = 0$$

be the equation of one of the desired equipotential boundaries. Let us suppose that this equation can be expressed in the parametric form

(8.2)
$$x = F_1(t) \qquad y = F_2(t)$$

where $F_1(t)$ and $F_2(t)$ are real functions of the real parameter t whose range of variation corresponds to the whole equipotential (8.1).

Then the transformation

(8.3)
$$z = F_1(kw) + jF_2(kw)$$

where k is a real constant, gives $v = 0$ over the surface (8.1). To see this, let $v = 0$ in (8.3); we then have

(8.4)
$$z = F_1(ku) + jF_2(ku) = x + jy$$

Hence

(8.5) $x = F_1(ku) \quad y = F_2(ku)$

These are exactly the parametric equations (8.2) with ku in the place of the parameter t.

This method enables one to find the proper transformations when the boundaries are confocal conics or various cycloidal curves.

For example, consider the parabola with its focus at the origin

(8.6) $y^2 = 4a(x + a)$

This may be written in the parametric form

(8.7) $(x + a) = at^2 \quad y = 2at$

Hence the transformation is $\omega \to t$

(8.8) $z = aw^2 - a + 2ajw = a(w + j)^2$

where we have placed $k = 1$ for simplicity.

Therefore

(8.9) $w = -j + \left(\dfrac{z}{a}\right)^{\frac{1}{2}}$

This transformation makes the parabola (8.6) the equipotential surface $v = 0$.

As another example, let us consider the ellipse

(8.10) $\dfrac{x^2}{a^2} + \dfrac{y^2}{b^2} = 1$

This may be expressed in the parametric form

(8.11) $x = a \cos t \quad y = b \sin t$

The required transformation is

(8.12) $z = a \cos w + jb \sin w$

where we have again placed $k = 1$, for simplicity.

If we let

(8.13) $a = c \cosh \phi \quad b = c \sinh \phi$

then

(8.14) $\tanh \phi = \dfrac{b}{a}$

and

(8.15) $c^2 = a^2 - b^2$

Then (8.12) may be written in the form

(8.16) $z = c(\cos w \cosh \phi + j \sin w \sinh \phi)$
$= c \cos (w + j\phi) = c \cos [u + j(v + \phi)]$

As another example, suppose it is required to find the field on one side of a corrugated metal sheet whose equation is that of the cycloid

(8.17) $x = a(t - \sin t)$ $y = a(1 - \cos t)$

The required transformation is

(8.18) $z = a(w - \sin u) + aj(1 - \cos w)$
$= a(w + j - je^{-jw})$

9. Schwarz's Transformation.

Schwarz[*] has shown how to obtain a transformation in which one equipotential is a linear polygon.

This is one of the most useful transformations. It transforms the interior of a polygon in the z plane into the upper half of another plane, say the z_1 plane, in such a manner that the sides of the polygon in the z plane are transformed into the real axis of the z_1 plane. Schwarz has shown that, given the required polygon, a certain differential equation may be written which when integrated gives directly the desired transformation.

FIG. 9.1

Consider the expression

(9.1) $\dfrac{dz}{dz_1} = A(z_1 - u_1)^{\phi_1}(z_1 - u_2)^{\phi_2} \cdots (z_1 - u_n)^{\phi_n}$

where A is a complex constant; $u_1, u_2, \ldots, u_n$ and $\phi_1, \phi_2, \ldots, \phi_n$ are real numbers; and

(9.2) $u_n > u_{n-1} > \cdots u_2 > u_1$

Now since the argument of a product of complex numbers is equal to the sum of the arguments of the individual factors, we have

(9.3) $\arg \dfrac{dz}{dz_1} = \arg A + \phi_1 \arg (z_1 - u_1)$
$+ \phi_2 \arg (z_1 - u_2) + \cdots + \phi_n \arg (z_1 - u_n)$

Let us now consider the z_1 plane of Fig. 9.1.

The real numbers $u_1, u_2, \ldots, u_n$ are plotted on the real axis of the

* H. A. Schwarz, *Journal für Mathematik*, vol. 70, p. 5.105, 1869.

z_1 plane. If z_1 is a real number, then the number

$$(9.4) \qquad\qquad N_r = z_1 - u_r$$

is positive if z_1 is greater than u_r and it is negative when z_1 is less than u_r. Hence

$$(9.5) \qquad\qquad \arg (z_1 - u_r) = \begin{cases} 0 & \text{if } z_1 > u_r \\ \pi & \text{if } z_1 < u_r \end{cases}$$

Let us suppose that the point z_1 traverses the real axis of the z_1 plane from left to right as shown by the arrow in Fig. 9.1.

Let

$$(9.6) \qquad\qquad \theta_r = \arg \frac{dz}{dz_1} \qquad \text{when } u_r < z_1 < u_{r+1}$$

Then, by (9.3) and (9.5), we have

$$(9.7) \qquad\qquad \theta_r = \arg A + (\phi_{r+1} + \phi_{r+2} + \cdots + \phi_n)\pi$$

and

$$(9.8) \qquad\qquad \theta_{r+1} = \arg A + (\phi_{r+2} + \phi_{r+3} + \cdots + \phi_n)\pi$$

Hence

$$(9.9) \qquad\qquad \theta_{r+1} - \theta_r = -\pi\phi_{r+1}$$

Now

$$(9.10) \qquad\qquad \arg \frac{dz}{dz_1} = \arg \frac{dx + j\,dy}{dx_1} = \tan^{-1}\frac{dy}{dx}$$

We see that this is the angle that the element dz in the z plane into which dz_1 is transformed by the transformation (9.1) makes with the real

FIG. 9.2

axis of the z plane. It is thus seen that as the point z_1 traverses the real axis of the z_1 plane the corresponding point z traverses a polygon in the z plane as shown in Fig. 9.2.

When the point z_1 passes from the left of u_{r+1} to the right of u_{r+1} in the z_1 plane, then the direction of the point z in the z plane is suddenly changed by an angle of $-\pi\phi_{r+1}$, measured in the mathematically positive sense as shown in Fig. 9.2.

If we imagine the broken line in Fig. 9.2 to form a closed polygon, then the angle α_{r+1} measured between two adjacent sides of the polygon is called an *interior angle*. We then have

$$(9.11) \qquad\qquad \alpha_{r+1} - \pi\phi_{r+1} = \pi$$

Hence

(9.12) $$\phi_{r+1} = \frac{\alpha_{r+1}}{\pi} - 1$$

Substituting this into (9.1), we have

(9.13) $$\frac{dz}{dz_1} = A(z_1 - u_1)^{\alpha_1/\pi - 1}(z_1 - u_2)^{\alpha_2/\pi - 1} \cdots (z_1 - u_n)^{\alpha_n/\pi - 1}$$

$$= A \prod_{r=1}^{r=n} (z_1 - u_r)^{\alpha_r/\pi - 1}$$

Integrating this expression with respect to z_1, we have

(9.14) $$z = A \int \prod_{r=1}^{n} (z_1 - u_r)^{\alpha_r/\pi - 1} \, dz_1 + B$$

where B is an arbitrary constant.

This transformation transforms the real axis of the z_1 plane into a polygon in the z plane. The angles α_r are the interior angles of the polygon. The modulus of the constant A determines the size of the polygon, and the argument of the constant A determines the orientation of the polygon. The location of the polygon is determined by the constant B.

10. Polygon with One Angle. As the simplest example of the Schwarz transformation (9.14), let us transform the real axis of the z_1 plane into an angle in the z plane as shown in Fig. 10.1.

FIG. 10.1

In this case the transformation reduces to

(10.1) $$z = A \int (z_1 - u_1)^{\alpha/\pi - 1} \, dz_1 + B$$

For simplicity, let

(10.2) $$u_1 = 0$$

Therefore

(10.3) $$z = A \int z_1^{\alpha/\pi - 1} \, dz_1 + B = K z_1^{\alpha/\pi} + B \qquad a \neq 0$$

where K is an arbitrary constant. If we let $B = 0$, we have

(10.4) $$z = K z_1^{\alpha/\pi}$$

This transformation gives the correspondence shown between the two planes.

Polygon with Angle Zero. If we let the interior angle of the polygon, α, be equal to zero in (10.1), we have

$$(10.5) \qquad z = A \int \frac{dz_1}{z_1} + B = A \ln z_1 + B$$

Let $B = 0$ and A be a real constant. We then obtain

$$(10.6) \qquad z = A \ln z_1$$

The correspondence between the z_1 and z_2 planes is shown in Fig. 10.2.

FIG. 10.2

To see the correspondence between the planes, let

$$(10.7) \qquad z_1 = r_1 e^{j\theta_1}$$

Then

$$(10.8) \qquad x + jy = A(\ln r_1 + j\theta_1)$$

Therefore

$$(10.9) \qquad x = A \ln r_1 \qquad y = A\theta_1$$

$\theta_1 = 0$ corresponds to the positive side of the real axis of the z_1 plane and to the entire real axis of the z plane. The origin in the z_1 plane corresponds to the point $x = -\infty$ in the z plane. The negative side of the real axis of the z_1 plane corresponds to the line $y = A\pi$ in the z plane. This transformation in the z plane is a limiting case of the transformation of Fig. 10.3.

FIG. 10.3

11. Successive Transformations. In solving two-dimensional potential problems, it is frequently convenient to use successive transformations.

Let

$$(11.1) \qquad w = F_1(z_1)$$

and

$$(11.2) \qquad z_1 = F_2(z)$$

Then, by the elimination of z_1 between (11.1) and (11.2), we obtain

(11.3) $$w = F_3(z)$$

The relation (11.2) expresses a transformation from the z plane into a z_1 plane, while (11.1) expresses a further transformation from the z_1 plane into a w plane. Therefore the final transformation (11.3) may be regarded as the result of two successive transformations.

There are two uses of successive transformations that are of great importance.

a. Conductor Influenced by a Line Charge. We have seen in Sec. 7 that the transformation

(11.4) $$w = - \frac{q}{2\pi K} \ln (z_1 - a) + \frac{q}{2\pi K} \ln (z_1 + a) = \frac{-q}{2\pi K} \ln \frac{z_1 - a}{z_1 + a}$$

gives the solution when a line charge q per unit length is placed at $z_1 = a$ and a line charge $-q$ per unit length is placed at the distance $z_1 = -a$ as shown in Fig. 11.1.

FIG. 11.1

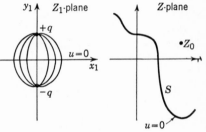

FIG. 11.2

Now let the transformation

(11.5) $$z_1 = F(z)$$

transform the real axis of the z_1 plane into the surface S and the point q into $z = z_0$ as shown in Fig. 11.2.

Then the transformation

(11.6) $$w = - \frac{q}{2\pi K} \ln \frac{F(z) - F(z_0)}{F(z) + F(z_0)}$$

gives the solution when a line charge q is placed at $z = z_0$ in the presence of the surface S that is at potential $u = 0$. The curves $u = $ const are the equipotentials, and the curves $v = $ const are the lines of force.

b. Conductors at Different Potentials. Consider the three planes of Fig. 11.3.

Let

(11.7) $$z_1 = F(z)$$

FIG. 11.3

transform the surfaces S_1 and S_2 in the z plane into the real axis of the z_1 plane in such a manner that the surface S_2 is mapped into the negative part of the real axis of the z_1 plane and the surface S_1 into the positive part of the real axis of the z_1 plane.

The transformation

$$(11.8) \qquad w = A \ln z_1 = u + jv$$

transforms the z_1 plane so that the positive part of the real axis corresponds to $v = 0$ and the negative part of the real axis corresponds to $v = A\pi$.

Hence the transformation

$$(11.9) \qquad w = A \ln F(z)$$

gives the solution for the problem in which the surface S_1 is at potential $v = 0$ and the surface S_2 is at potential $v = A\pi$. The $u = \text{const}$ curves give the lines of force.

FIG. 12.1

12. The Parallel-plate Capacitor; Flow Out of a Channel. As an illustration of the use of Schwarz's transformation and the above general principles, let us determine the proper transformation to determine the potential and field distribution of two semi-infinite conducting plates raised to different potentials as shown in Fig. 12.1.

By symmetry it is necessary only to solve the problem of a semi-infinite plane placed parallel to an infinite plane, as shown in Fig. 12.2.

FIG. 12.2

Since there are only two angles involved in the polygon in the z plane, we may write the Schwarz transformation equation (9.14) in the form

$$(12.1) \qquad \frac{dz}{dz_1} = K(z_1 - u_1)^{\alpha_1/\pi - 1}(z_1 - u_2)^{\alpha_2/\pi - 1}$$

where K is a constant. Since we are free to choose the numbers u_1 and u_2, we choose them so that the expression (12.1) is as simple as possible. The two interior angles of the polygon in the z plane are

$$(12.2) \qquad \alpha_1 = 0 \qquad \text{and} \qquad \alpha_2 = 2\pi$$

Let us take

$$(12.3) \qquad u_1 = 0 \qquad \text{and} \qquad u_2 = +1$$

Then Eq. (12.1) becomes

$$(12.4) \qquad \frac{dz}{dz_1} = Kz_1^{-1}(z_1 - 1) = \frac{K(z_1 - 1)}{z_1} = K\left(1 - \frac{1}{z_1}\right)$$

Integrating, we have

$$(12.5) \qquad z = K(z_1 - \ln z_1) + C$$

where C is an arbitrary constant. Since the sides of the polygon in the z plane are horizontal and hence have zero slope, it is necessary for the constant K to be real.

Boundary Conditions. The arbitrary constants K and C must now be determined from the correspondence between the two planes.

a. As the point z_1 moves across the origin from B to C, the point z turns through a zero angle and the imaginary part of z is increased from 0 to h.

Let

$$(12.6) \qquad z_1 = r_1 e^{j\theta_1}$$

Therefore

$$(12.7) \qquad x + jy = K(r_1 e^{j\theta_1} - \ln r_1 - j\theta_1) + C$$

Hence

$$(12.8) \qquad \begin{aligned} x &= K(r_1 \cos \theta_1 - \ln r_1) + \text{Re } C \\ y &= K(r_1 \sin \theta_1 - \theta_1) + \text{Im } C \end{aligned}$$

where Re denotes the "real part of" and Im denotes the "imaginary part of."

Now

$$(12.9) \qquad \begin{aligned} y &= 0 \qquad \theta_1 = \pi \\ y &= h \qquad \theta_1 = 0 \end{aligned}$$

Hence

(12.10)
$$0 = K(-\pi) + \text{Im } C$$
$$h = \text{Im } C$$

(12.11)
$$K = \frac{h}{\pi}$$

b. Let the point $z_1 = 1$ correspond to the point $z = x_0 + jh$. The point $z_1 = 1$ is determined by

(12.12)
$$r_1 = 1 \qquad \theta_1 = 0$$

Therefore

(12.13)
$$x_0 = \frac{h}{\pi} + \text{Re } C$$

If we choose x_0 so that

(12.14)
$$x_0 = \frac{h}{\pi}$$

then we have

(12.15)
$$\text{Re } C = 0$$

With this choice of x_0 the constant C is a pure imaginary and from Eq. (12.10) has the value

(12.16)
$$C = jh$$

The transformation (12.5) thus becomes

(12.17)
$$z = \frac{h}{\pi} (z_1 - \ln z_1) + jh$$
$$= \frac{h}{\pi} (z_1 - \ln z_1 + j\pi)$$

This transformation transforms the z_1 plane into the polygon in the z plane with the correspondence of points shown in Fig. 12.2.

Transformation to w Plane. We now transform the z_1 plane to the w plane by the transformation

(12.18)
$$w = \ln z_1 = u + jv$$

Since

(12.19)
$$z_1 = r_1 e^{j\theta_1}$$

we have

(12.20)
$$u + jv = \ln r_1 + j\theta_1$$

and

(12.21)
$$u = \ln r_1 \qquad v = \theta_1$$

The correspondence between the two planes is shown in Fig. 12.3. By (12.18) we have

$$(12.22) \qquad z_1 = e^w$$

If we now eliminate z_1 between Eqs. (12.17) and (12.22), we pass directly from the w plane to the z plane by the equation

$$(12.23) \qquad z = \frac{h}{\pi}(e^w - w + j\pi)$$

The correspondence between the two planes is shown in Fig. 12.4.

Fig. 12.3

Fig. 12.4

If we let v be the potential function, we have in the z plane a semi-infinite plane at potential zero parallel to an infinite plane at potential π. If we write (12.23) in the form

$$(12.24) \qquad x + jy = \frac{h}{\pi}[e^u(\cos v + j\sin v) - u - jv + j\pi]$$

we have

$$(12.25) \qquad \begin{aligned} x &= \frac{h}{\pi}(e^u \cos v - u) \\ y &= \frac{h}{\pi}(e^u \sin v - v + \pi) \end{aligned}$$

Let $v = 0$. Then

$$(12.26) \qquad x = \frac{h}{\pi}(e^u - u) \qquad y = h$$

For

$$(12.27) \qquad \begin{array}{ccc} u = 0 & u = \infty & u = -\infty \\ x = \dfrac{h}{\pi} & x = \infty & x = \infty \end{array}$$

Negative values of u give the region inside the capacitor, and positive values of u give the region outside the capacitor.

If u is large and positive, we have approximately

(12.28)
$$x \doteq \frac{h}{\pi} (e^u \cos v)$$
$$y \doteq \frac{h}{\pi} (e^u \sin v)$$

Hence

(12.29)
$$x^2 + y^2 \doteq \frac{h^2}{\pi^2} e^{2u} \qquad u \gg 1$$

The $u = $ const curves are a family of circles, so that the lines of force are approximately circles at a large distance from the origin as seen in Fig. 12.5.

FIG. 12.5

If u is large and negative, we have approximately

(12.30)
$$x \doteq -\frac{h}{\pi} u \qquad y \doteq \frac{h}{\pi} (\pi - v)$$

The $u = $ const and $v = $ const curves are families of straight lines. This represents the uniform field in the region inside the planes.

The Charge Density.   At a point on the equipotential $v = 0$, the charge density σ is given by the equation

(12.31)
$$\sigma = -K \left| \frac{dw}{dz} \right|_{v=0} = -\frac{K\pi}{h} \frac{1}{e^u - 1}$$

Inside the capacitor, u is large and negative, and we have approximately

(12.32)
$$\sigma \doteq -\frac{K\pi}{h}$$

At D, $u = 0$, and σ becomes infinite. On the upper part of the semi-infinite plane, u is large and positive, and we have

(12.33)
$$\sigma \doteq -\frac{K\pi}{he^u}$$

The surface density decreases as we move to the right of the point D.

This transformation also solves the hydrodynamical problem of the irrotational flow of fluid out of a long channel into a large reservoir.

13. The Effect of a Wall on a Uniform Field. As another example of the use of the Schwarz transformation, let it be required to determine the effect produced by an indefinitely thin wall or ridge on a uniform field as shown in Fig. 13.1.

FIG. 13.1

FIG. 13.2

The solution of this problem also gives the lines of flow of a fluid over an obstacle. We regard the line $PQRST$ as a polygon in the z plane and transform it into the real axis of the z_1 plane as shown in Fig. 13.2.

Let us establish the following correspondence between the two planes:

$$P \to -\infty \qquad S \to u_3$$
$$Q \to u_1 \qquad T \to +\infty$$
$$R \to u_2$$

From the figure we have

(13.1) $$\alpha_1 = \frac{\pi}{2} \qquad \alpha_2 = 2\pi \qquad \alpha_3 = \frac{\pi}{2}$$

The Schwarz expression of Sec. 9 becomes

(13.2) $$\frac{dz}{dz_1} = A(z_1 - u_1)^{\alpha_1/\pi - 1}(z_1 - u_2)^{\alpha_2/\pi - 1}(z_1 - u_3)^{\alpha_3/\pi - 1}$$
$$= A(z_1 - u_1)^{-\frac{1}{2}}(z_1 - u_2)(z_1 - u_3)^{-\frac{1}{2}}$$

For simplicity, let

(13.3) $$u_1 = -a \qquad u_2 = 0 \qquad u_3 = +a$$

Then (13.2) becomes

(13.4) $$\frac{dz}{dz_1} = \frac{Az_1}{\sqrt{z_1^2 - a^2}}$$

Integrating, we have

$$(13.5) \qquad z = A \int \frac{z_1 \, dz_1}{\sqrt{z_1^2 - a^2}} + B = A \sqrt{z_1^2 - a^2} + B$$

Boundary Conditions

a. When $z_1 = \pm a$, let $z = 0$. Therefore

$$(13.6) \qquad\qquad\qquad B = 0$$

b. If b is the height of the wall, then, when $z = jb$, let $z_1 = 0$. Therefore

$$(13.7) \qquad\qquad jb = A \sqrt{-a^2} = Aaj$$

Hence

$$(13.8) \qquad\qquad\qquad A = \frac{b}{a}$$

The transformation

$$(13.9) \qquad\qquad\qquad z = \frac{b}{a} \sqrt{z_1^2 - a^2}$$

or

$$(13.10) \qquad\qquad\qquad z_1 = \frac{a}{b} \sqrt{z^2 + b^2}$$

transforms the $y_1 = 0$ axis in the z_1 plane into the polygon $PQRST$ in the z plane.   Now let

$$(13.11) \qquad\qquad w = F_1 z = u + jv$$

This transformation transforms the lines $v = $ const in the w plane into the lines

$$(13.12) \qquad\qquad\qquad y_1 = \frac{v}{F_1}$$

in the z_1 plane.

Hence

$$(13.13) \qquad\qquad w = F_1 z = \frac{F_1 a}{b} \sqrt{z^2 + b^2}$$

in the transformation that transforms the line $v = 0$ into the polygon in the z plane.   If the field is to be uniform at large distances from the wall, we must have

$$(13.14) \qquad w = \frac{F_1 a}{b} \sqrt{z^2 + b^2} \doteq \frac{F_1 a}{b} z = Fz \qquad \text{for large } z$$

Hence

$$(13.15) \qquad\qquad\qquad F = \frac{F_1 a}{b}$$

and the transformation may be written

(13.16) $$w = F \sqrt{z^2 + b^2} = u + jv$$

where v is the potential function as shown in Fig. 13.3.   Separating (13.16) into its real and imaginary parts, we have

(13.17)
$$u^2 - v^2 = F^2(x^2 - y^2) + F^2b^2$$
$$uv = F^2xy$$

Eliminating u between these equations, we have

(13.18) $$\frac{F^4x^2y^2}{v^2} - v^2 = F^2(x^2 - y^2) + F^2b^2$$

This is the family of equipotentials, and

(13.19) $$u^2 - \frac{F^4x^2y^2}{u^2} = F^2(x^2 - y^2) + F^2b^2$$

are the lines of force.

In the hydrodynamical case $v = $ const gives lines of flow and $u = $ const gives constant-velocity potentials.

u=const.

v=const.

v=0

FIG. 13.3

14. Application to Hydrodynamics.   The theory of conjugate functions is of extreme usefulness in determining two-dimensional-flow distribution of moving fluids.   There is a very close analogy between the electrical problems discussed in the last few sections and problems in hydrodynamics.

Let **A** be the velocity vector field of an ideal nonviscous fluid.   If the flow is irrotational, then

(14.1) $$\nabla \times \mathbf{A} = 0$$

and as we have seen in Chap. 15, the velocity **A** is the gradient of a scalar, or

(14.2) $$\mathbf{A} = -\nabla\phi$$

where ϕ is the *velocity potential*.   The lines of flow are everywhere normal to the surfaces $\phi = $ const.   If the fluid is incompressible, then the equation of continuity is

$$(14.3) \qquad \nabla \cdot \mathbf{A} = 0$$

so that

$$(14.4) \qquad \nabla \cdot \mathbf{A} = \nabla(-\nabla\phi) = 0$$

or

$$(14.5) \qquad \nabla^2\phi = 0$$

so that, as in the case of the electrostatic potential, the velocity potential satisfies Laplace's equation in a region that contains no sources.

The Stream Function. Let $\Phi(x,y)$ be a function of the two independent variables x and y. Now the differential $d\Phi$ is given by

$$(14.6) \qquad d\Phi = \frac{\partial \Phi}{\partial x}\,dx + \frac{\partial \Phi}{\partial y}\,dy$$

For two-dimensional motion the equation of continuity (14.3) reduces to

$$(14.7) \qquad \frac{\partial A_x}{\partial x} + \frac{\partial A_y}{\partial y} = 0$$

If we let

$$(14.8) \qquad A_x = -\frac{\partial \Phi}{\partial y} \qquad A_y = \frac{\partial \Phi}{\partial x}$$

then (14.6) becomes

$$(14.9) \qquad d\Phi = A_y\,dx - A_x\,dy$$

The condition that this expression be a perfect differential is

$$(14.10) \qquad \frac{\partial A_y}{\partial y} = -\frac{\partial A_x}{\partial x}$$

This is exactly the equation of continuity (14.7). Hence from the velocity vector $\mathbf{A}$ we can determine a unique (to within an additive constant) function Φ, and the velocity components are given by (14.8). The function Φ is called the *stream function*. From Eq. (14.2) we have

$$(14.11) \qquad \begin{aligned} A_x &= -\frac{\partial \phi}{\partial x} = -\frac{\partial \Phi}{\partial y} \\ A_y &= -\frac{\partial \phi}{\partial y} = \frac{\partial \Phi}{\partial x} \end{aligned}$$

Hence

$$(14.12) \qquad \frac{\partial \phi}{\partial x}\frac{\partial \Phi}{\partial x} + \frac{\partial \phi}{\partial y}\frac{\partial \Phi}{\partial y} = 0$$

The two families ϕ = const and Φ = const intersect orthogonally. It is thus apparent that if we have

(14.13) $$w = u + jv = w(z)$$

a function of the complex variable z, then, if we take u for the potential, v will be the stream function, or vice versa. For example, if we consider the function

(14.14) $$w = K \ln \frac{z - a}{z + a}$$

and take u to be the potential function and v the stream function, then this transformation gives the velocity and flow pattern produced by a source and a sink of equal intensities and located at $z = a$ and $z = -a$, respectively. The analogy with the electrical case is easily seen.

15. The Joukowski Transformation. The transformation

(15.1) $$\frac{w - ka}{w + ka} = \left(\frac{z - a}{z + a}\right)^k$$

is of importance in the practical problem of mapping an airplane wing profile on a nearly circular curve. The wing profile has a sharp point at the trailing edge. The angle

(15.2) $$\phi = (2 - k)\pi$$

is the angle between the tangents to the upper and lower parts of the profile at this point. The circle that passes through the point $-a$ in the z plane so that it encloses the point $z = a$ and cuts the line joining $z = -a$ and $z = a + \delta$, where δ is small, is mapped by this transformation into a wing-shaped curve in the w plane.

In practical problems on the study of the flow of air around an airfoil, the desired transformation is one that maps the region *outside* a circle or a nearly circular curve. If we take the special case

(15.3) $$a = 1 \qquad k = 2$$

we have

(15.4) $$\frac{w - 2}{w + 2} = \left(\frac{z - 1}{z + 1}\right)^2$$

This transformation transforms a circle in the z plane passing through the point $z = -1$ and containing the point $z = 1$ into a wing-shaped curve in the w plane. This curve is known as *Joukowski's profile*.[5]

PROBLEMS

1. Given the transformation $z = a \sin w$, where a is real. What are the curves u = const and the curves v = const? What possible electrical and hydrodynamical problems may be solved by this transformation?

2. Given the transformation $z = w + e^w$. Study this transformation in the range $-\pi \leq v \leq \pi$ for all values of u. Determine the curves $u = $ const and $v = $ const for very large and very small values of u. Draw a rough sketch of the lines $u = $ const and $v = $ const. What problems may be solved by this transformation?

3. Given the transformation $z = \tanh w$. Determine the curves $u = $ const and $v = $ const, and sketch them. What practical problems are solved by this transformation?

4. Using the theory of the complex variable, show that $R^n(\cos n\theta + \sin n\theta)$ and $1/R^n(\cos n\theta + \sin n\theta)$, where n is an integer, are solutions of the two-dimensional Laplace equation, where R and θ are polar coordinates in the xy plane.

5. Two parallel infinite planes at a distance a from each other are kept at zero potential under the influence of a line charge of strength q per unit length that is located between the planes and at a distance of b from the lower plane. Find the field and potential distribution in the region between the planes.

6. A cylinder $(x/a)^{2n} + (y/b)^{2n} = 1$ carries a charge of Q units per unit length. Show that the transformation that gives the field is

$$z = a \left(\cos \frac{nw}{2Q} \right)^{1/n} + jb \left(\sin \frac{nw}{2Q} \right)^{1/n}$$

7. Determine the transformation that gives the field inside a hollow cavity of rectangular shape that contains a line charge at a distance of a from the base whose width is b.

8. Determine the surface density on an earthed conducting plane (potential zero) under the influence of a line charge of strength q at a distance of a from the plane.

9. Write down the integral from which the transformation can be obtained which represents the field near the sharp edges of a slit beveled at $45°$.

10. Using the transformation

$$w = \frac{z + \sqrt{z^2 - b^2}}{2}$$

which gives the potential and stream functions when there is a slit of width $2b$ in a thin infinite-plane conducting sheet that forms one boundary of a uniform field of unit strength, find the field when a filament carrying a charge per unit length is placed in front of the slit.

11. Write down the integral that represents the field when a slit of uniform width $2b$ in an infinite sheet of thickness d forms one boundary of a uniform field.

REFERENCES

1. Rothe, R., F. Ollendorf, and K. Pohlhausen: "Theory of Functions as Applied to Engineering Problems," Massachusetts Institute of Technology Press, Cambridge, Mass., 1938.
2. Walker, Miles: "Conjugate Functions for Engineers," Oxford University Press, New York, 1933.
3. Jeans, J. H.: "The Mathematical Theory of Electricity and Magnetism," Cambridge University Press, New York, 1925.
4. Smythe, W. R.: "Static and Dynamic Electricity," 1st ed., McGraw-Hill Book Company, Inc., New York, 1939.
5. Glauert, H.: "The Elements of Aerofoil and Airscrew Theory," The Macmillan Company, New York, 1943.

CHAPTER 21

OPERATIONAL AND TRANSFORM METHODS

1. Introduction. For a considerable time the use of symbolic or "operational" methods in mathematical operations has attracted considerable attention.[1] Leibnitz in 1695 noted that the symbol d of differentiation, now D in the symbolic method, has some of the properties of ordinary algebraic quantities. In the early part of the nineteenth century the separation of symbols of operation from their operands was studied by the French mathematicians Arbogast, Brisson, Servois, and others. From 1836 to 1860 the British school of mathematicians used the symbolic method in the differential and integral calculus, in the calculus of finite differences, and in the solution of differential and difference equations. These methods are still used in some elementary textbooks. However, these methods were frequently regarded as somewhat "shady" from the standpoint of rigorous mathematics because no explicit formulation of the conditions under which the use of these devices afforded correct results was given.

Heaviside's operational analysis of certain differential equations of importance in electrodynamics and electrical engineering carried out in the years 1887 to 1898 was the last notable advance in the symbolic method. It is well known[1] that Heaviside's methods were not orthodox and that, because of this, the Royal Society of London refused to publish some of his papers. Several mathematicians and electrical engineers, notably Bromwich, Jeffreys, Wagner, Carson, and Levy, attempted to explain Heaviside's methods and place them on a firm mathematical foundation. The activity stimulated by Heaviside's methods has been aptly summarized by the eminent British mathematician Prof. E. T. Whittaker in the following statement:[2] "Looking back on the controversy after thirty years, we should now place the operational calculus with Poincaré's discovery of automorphic functions and Ricci's discovery of the tensor calculus as the three most important mathematical advances of the last quarter of the nineteenth century. Applications, extensions, and justification of it constitute a considerable part of the mathematical activity of today."

It is now generally recognized that Heaviside's operational calculus

583

and its extensions may be based on the Laplace transform.   However, it is not very well known that Oliver Heaviside himself clearly pointed this out.[23]   It is interesting to note that the Laplace transform was known long before Heaviside used it.   Euler and Gauss both used transformations resembling the transform introduced by Laplace in 1779.[3]   Cauchy showed its relation to the Fourier transform, which is a special case, and Abel derived many of its properties.   Many investigators have in recent years contributed to bring the subject into its present form and there are now several standard texts on the subject.[4-17]

The Laplace Transform (Notation).   It is unfortunate that not all the literature of the Laplace-transform theory is written in the same notation. This state of affairs sometimes leads to confusion, and it is well to mention the important differences of the various notations in use.

a. THE p-MULTIPLIED NOTATION.   Several authors[4,5,7,8,11-13,15] have attempted to retain the operational forms of the Heaviside method and use the following notation,

$$(1.1) \qquad g(p) = p \int_0^\infty e^{-pt} h(t)\, dt \qquad \mathrm{Re}\ p > 0$$

where p is a parameter whose real part is positive.   Then, if $h(t)$ is such a function of the variable t for which the integral (1.1) exists, the function $g(p)$ is said to be the p-multiplied transform of $h(t)$.   This is the notation used in this book.   The relation (1.1) is expressed concisely in the form

$$(1.2) \qquad g(p) = Lh(t)$$

If the function $h(t)$ is zero for negative values of t and has other restrictions which are usually satisfied in the application to most physical problems (see Sec. 2), then it may be shown that Eq. (1.2) has an inverse of the following form,

$$(1.3) \qquad h(t) = \frac{1}{2\pi j} \int_{c-j\infty}^{c+j\infty} \frac{e^{pt} g(p)\, dp}{p}$$

where $j = (-1)^{\frac{1}{2}}$ and c is a positive constant.   In this case we write concisely

$$(1.4) \qquad h(t) = L^{-1} g(p)$$

and $h(t)$ is said to be the *inverse* p-multiplied Laplace transform of $g(p)$.

The p-multiplied transform notation has the following advantages:

1. The forms of the "Heaviside calculus" are retained.   These forms are of long standing and are widespread in use.

2. The transform of a constant in this notation is the same constant.

3. The Laplace transform of t^n is $n!/p^n$ in this notation.   Hence, if t and p are considered to have dimensions of t and t^{-1}, respectively, and

if $h(t)$ and its transform can be expanded in absolutely convergent series, the corresponding terms are dimensionally identical. This is very useful for purposes of checking.

b. THE UNMULTIPLIED NOTATION. Most mathematicians and several engineers use the more concise notation[6,9,10,14,16,17]

$$(1.5) \qquad g(p) = \int_0^\infty e^{-pt} h(t) \, dt$$

and

$$(1.6) \qquad h(t) = \frac{1}{2\pi j} \int_{c-j\infty}^{c+j\infty} e^{pt} g(p) \, dp$$

instead of (1.1) and (1.3). This notation has certain advantages in some applications. A few writers use the forms (1.5) and (1.6) but with the letter s instead of the letter p.[9,10,17]

Because of the various differences in notation the student is cautioned to assure himself when consulting various treatises and tables of Laplace transforms of the notation which a particular writer is using.

Uses of the Laplace Transform in Applied Mathematics. Before proceeding to a detailed exposition of the theory of the Laplace transform, it is of some interest to list some of the better-known uses of the Laplace-transform theory in applied mathematics.

1. THE SOLUTION OF ORDINARY DIFFERENTIAL EQUATIONS WITH CONSTANT COEFFICIENTS. The Laplace transform is of use in solving linear differential equations with constant coefficients. By its use the differential equation is transformed into an algebraic equation which is readily solved. The solution of the original differential equation is then reduced to the calculation of inverse transforms usually involving the ratio of two polynomials. The inverse transforms required may be obtained by consulting a table of Laplace transforms or by evaluating the inverse integral (1.3) by the calculus of residues.

The Laplace-transform method is particularly well adapted to the solution of differential equations whose boundary conditions are specified at one point. The solution of differential equations involving functions of an impulsive type may be solved by the use of the Laplace transform in a very efficient manner. Typical fields of application are the following:

a. Transient and steady-state analysis of electrical circuits[4,7−9,11,15,16]

b. Applications to dynamical problems (impact, mechanical vibrations, acoustics, etc.)[5−8,10,17]

c. Applications to structural problems (deflection of beams, columns, determination of Green's functions and influence functions)[6−10,13]

2. THE SOLUTION OF LINEAR DIFFERENTIAL EQUATIONS WITH VARIABLE COEFFICIENTS. By the use of the Laplace-transform theory a linear

differential equation whose coefficients are polynomials in the independent variable t is transformed into a differential equation whose coefficients are polynomials in the transform variable p. In many cases the transformed equation is simpler than the original, and it can be readily solved. The inverse transform of the solution of this equation gives the solution of the original equation.[17,18] Van der Pol[11,18] has shown how this may be done in the case of Bessel functions and Legendre and Laguerre polynomials.

3. THE SOLUTION OF LINEAR PARTIAL DIFFERENTIAL EQUATIONS WITH CONSTANT COEFFICIENTS. One of the most important uses of the Laplace-transform theory is its use in the solution of linear partial differential equations with constant coefficients that have two or more independent variables. The procedure employed is to take the Laplace transform with respect to one of the independent variables and thus reduce the partial differential equation to an ordinary one or one having a smaller number of independent variables. The transformed equation is then solved subject to the boundary conditions involved, and the inverse transform of this solution gives the required result. Problems involving impulsive forces and wave propagation are particularly well adapted for solution by the Laplace-transform method. In many cases it is possible to express the operational solution of the partial differential equation involved in a series of exponential terms and then interpret the solution as a succession of traveling waves. Typical physical problems that may be solved by the procedure outlined above are the following:

a. Transients and steady-state analysis of heat conduction in solids[5,6,13,16,17]

b. Vibrations of continuous mechanical systems[6-8,13,17]

c. Hydrodynamics and fluid flow[6-8,19]

d. Transient analysis of electrical transmission lines and also of cables[4,6,11,13,15,16]

e. Transient analysis of electrodynamic fields[5,7]

f. Transient analysis of acoustical systems[7,8]

g. Analysis of static deflections of continuous systems (strings, beams, plates)[6,9,17]

4. THE SOLUTION OF LINEAR DIFFERENCE AND DIFFERENCE-DIFFERENTIAL EQUATIONS. The Laplace-transform theory is very useful in effecting the solution of linear difference or mixed linear-difference–differential equations with constant coefficients. Difference equations arise in systems where the variables change by finite amounts. Typical fields of application of difference equations are the following:

a. Electrical applications of difference equations[6,9,11,13] (artificial lines, wave filters, network representation of transformer and machine windings, multistage amplifiers, surge generators, suspension insulators, cyclic switching operations)

b. Mechanical applications of difference equations[6,7,9,17]

c. Applications to economics and finance[9] (annuities, mortgages, interest, amortization, growth of populations)

d. Systems with hereditary characteristics[20] (retarded control systems, servomechanisms)

5. THE SOLUTION OF INTEGRAL EQUATIONS OF THE CONVOLUTION, OR FALTUNG, TYPE. Equations in which the unknown function occurs inside an integral or integral equations are encountered quite frequently in applied mathematics. If the integral equation happens to be of the convolution, or Faltung, type, the use of the Laplace-transformation theory transforms the equation into an algebraic equation in the transform variable and it is readily solved. Typical problems leading to this type of equation are the following:

a. Mechanical problems such as the tautochrone[14,17]

b. Economic problems (mortality of equipment, etc.)[17]

c. Electrical circuits involving variable parameters[4]

d. Problems involving heredity characteristics or aftereffect[21]

6. APPLICATION OF THE LAPLACE TRANSFORM TO THE THEORY OF PRIME NUMBERS. In a remarkable paper[22] B. van der Pol applied the methods of the Laplace-transform theory to the theory of prime numbers and demonstrated the ease and simplicity by which results obtained with considerable difficulty by using conventional methods are simply obtained by the Laplace-transform theory. It is demonstrated in this paper that the properties of many discontinuous functions belonging to the theory of numbers may be easily obtained by considering their Laplace transforms.

7. EVALUATION OF DEFINITE INTEGRALS. Certain types of definite integrals may be evaluated very easily by the use of the Laplace-transform theory. As a consequence of this fact, it is easy to establish integral relations involving Bessel functions, Legendre polynomials, and other higher transcendental functions in a simple manner by the use of the Laplace-transform theory.[11,13,14,18]

8. DERIVATION OF ASYMPTOTIC SERIES. In some applications of the Laplace-transform theory to the solution of differential equations, it frequently happens that the solution is required in the form of an asymptotic series. If it is possible to expand the transform of the solution in fractional powers of p, it is easy to obtain the asymptotic-series expansion of the solution by obtaining the inverse transform of each term. Heaviside[23] used this procedure quite extensively. Carson[4] has clarified the mathematical validity of the procedure and demonstrated the utility of the method in the solution of electrical-circuit problems.

9. DERIVATION OF POWER SERIES. If the Laplace transform of a function is known, then the power-series expansion of the function may be obtained by expanding its transform in inverse powers of p. This procedure was used extensively by Heaviside[23] and Carson[4] to compute inverse Laplace transforms.

10. DERIVATION OF FOURIER SERIES. If the Laplace transform of a periodic function is obtained, then the evaluation of the inverse integral (1.3) gives the Fourier expansion of the function.[7,8,23] In certain cases this procedure is simpler than the conventional method of obtaining Fourier-series expansions of functions.

11. SUMMATION OF POWER SERIES. It is frequently possible, when a power series is given, to sum it and obtain the function that it represents by the use of the Laplace-transform theory. This is done by taking the Laplace transform of each term of the given series and thus obtaining the series of the transform of the function represented by the original series. If the new series is a geometric or other well-known series, it may be summed and thus the Laplace transform of the function required is obtained. A calculation of the inverse transform then gives the required function. This procedure was frequently used by Heaviside[23] in order to sum series.

12. THE SUMMATION OF FOURIER SERIES. The summation of certain Fourier series involving periodic discontinuous functions may be effected by the use of the Laplace-transform theory. The method consists in taking the Laplace transform of each term of the trigonometric series, thus obtaining a series of rational functions. In many cases the series of rational functions may be summed to obtain the transform of the function represented by the original Fourier series. A computation of the inverse transform of this function then gives the sum of the Fourier series in closed form. Pipes[24] has used this method to advantage in obtaining a graphical representation of the function defined by a given Fourier series. The method is particularly well suited to cases in which the given Fourier series represents a function whose graph is composed of straight lines or a repetition of curves of simple form.

13. THE USE OF MULTIPLE LAPLACE TRANSFORMS TO SOLVE PARTIAL DIFFERENTIAL EQUATIONS. By the use of multiple Laplace transforms a partial differential equation and its associated boundary conditions can be transformed into an algebraic equation in n independent complex variables. This algebraic equation can be solved for the multiple transform of the solution of the original partial differential equation. Multiple inversion of this transform then gives the desired solution. The theory and application of multiple Laplace transforms has been the subject of recent publications by van der Pol and Bremmer,[11] Jaeger,[25] Voelker and Doetsch,[26] and Estrin and Higgins.[27]

14. THE SOLUTION OF NONLINEAR ORDINARY DIFFERENTIAL EQUATIONS. The Laplace-transform theory may be used to reduce the labor involved in solving certain nonlinear differential equations. The procedures used are of an iterative nature by which the solution of the original nonlinear differential equation is reduced to the solution of a set of simultaneous linear differential equations with constant coefficients. The Laplace-transform theory greatly reduces the labor involved in solving this set of simultaneous equations.[28-32]

2. The Fourier-Mellin Theorem. In this section the Fourier-Mellin theorem that is the foundation of the modern operational calculus will be derived. The Fourier-Mellin theorem may be derived from Fourier's integral theorem. The derivation of this theorem is heuristic in nature. For a rigorous derivation the references at the end of this chapter should be consulted.

It was shown in Chap. 3, Sec. 9, that, if $F(t)$ is a function that has a finite number of maxima and minima and ordinary discontinuities, it may be expressed by the integral

$$(2.1) \qquad F(t) = \int_{-\infty}^{\infty} ds \int_{-\infty}^{\infty} F(u) e^{2\pi js(t-u)} \, du$$

If we let

$$(2.2) \qquad 2\pi s = v$$

then (2.1) becomes

$$(2.3) \qquad F(t) = \frac{1}{2\pi} \int_{-\infty}^{+\infty} dv \int_{-\infty}^{+\infty} F(u) e^{jv(t-u)} \, du$$

For the integrals involved in (2.1) to converge uniformly, it is also necessary for the integral

$$(2.4) \qquad I = \int_{-\infty}^{\infty} |F(t)| \, dt$$

to exist.

Let us now assume that the function $F(t)$ has the property that

$$(2.5) \qquad F(t) = 0 \qquad \text{for } t < 0$$

In this case the Fourier-integral representation of the function is

$$(2.6) \qquad F(t) = \frac{1}{2\pi} \int_{-\infty}^{\infty} e^{jvt} \, dv \int_{0}^{\infty} F(u) e^{-jvu} \, du$$

where the lower limit of the second integral is zero as a consequence of the condition (2.5).

Let us now consider the function $\phi(t)$ defined by the equation

$$(2.7) \qquad\qquad \phi(t) = e^{-ct}F(t)$$

where c is a positive constant.

Substituting this into (2.6), we obtain

$$(2.8) \qquad \phi(t) = e^{-ct}F(t) = \frac{1}{2\pi} \int_{-\infty}^{+\infty} e^{ivt}\, dv \int_0^\infty F(u)e^{-uc}e^{-ivu}\, du$$

Let us now make the substitution

$$(2.9) \qquad\qquad p = c + jv$$

Then (2.8) may be written in the form

$$(2.10) \qquad e^{-ct}F(t) = \frac{1}{2\pi j} \int_{c-j\infty}^{c+j\infty} e^{(p-c)t}\, dp \int_0^\infty F(u)e^{-pu}\, du$$

On dividing both members of (2.10) by e^{-ct} we have

$$(2.11) \qquad F(t) = \frac{1}{2\pi j} \int_{c-j\infty}^{c+j\infty} e^{pt}\, dp \int_0^\infty F(u)e^{-pu}\, du$$

This modified form is more general than the Fourier integral (2.3) because, if

$$(2.12) \qquad\qquad I = \int_0^\infty |F(t)|\, dt$$

does not exist but

$$(2.13) \qquad\qquad I' = \int_0^\infty e^{-c_0 t}|F(t)|\, dt$$

exists for some $c_0 > 0$, then (2.11) is valid for some $c > c_0$.

If we now let

$$(2.14) \qquad\qquad g(p) = p \int_0^\infty F(u)e^{-pu}\, du$$

we have by (2.11)

$$(2.15) \qquad\qquad F(t) = \frac{1}{2\pi j} \int_{c-j\infty}^{c+j\infty} \frac{g(p)}{p} e^{pt}\, dp$$

Since the value of a definite integral is independent of the variable of integration, it is convenient to use the letter t instead of the letter u in the integral (2.14) and write

$$(2.16) \qquad\qquad g(p) = p \int_0^\infty e^{-pt}F(t)\, dt$$

Equations (2.15) and (2.16) are the Fourier-Mellin equations. They are the foundations of the modern operational calculus.

A more precise statement of the Fourier-Mellin theorem is the following one:

Let $F(t)$ be an arbitrary function of the real variable t that has only a finite number of maxima and minima and discontinuities and whose value is zero for negative values of t.

If

$$(2.17) \qquad g(p) = p \int_0^\infty e^{-pt} F(t)\, dt \qquad \mathrm{Re}\ p \ge c > 0$$

then

$$(2.18) \qquad F(t) = \frac{1}{2\pi j} \int_{c-j\infty}^{c+j\infty} e^{pt}\, \frac{g(p)}{p}\, dp$$

provided

$$(2.19) \qquad \int_0^\infty e^{-ct} F(t)\, dt$$

converges absolutely.*

It is convenient to use the notation

$$(2.20) \qquad g(p) = LF(t)$$

to denote the functional relation between $g(p)$ and $F(t)$ expressed in (2.17). We then say that $g(p)$ is the *direct Laplace transform of* $F(t)$. The relation (2.18) is expressed conveniently by the notation

$$(2.21) \qquad F(t) = L^{-1} g(p)$$

We then say that $F(t)$ is the *inverse Laplace transform of* $g(p)$.

3. The Fundamental Rules. In this section some very powerful and useful general theorems concerning operations on transforms will be established. These theorems are of great utility in the solution of differential equations, evaluation of integrals, and other procedures of applied mathematics.

THEOREM I. The Laplace transform of a constant is the same constant, that is,

$$(3.1) \qquad L(k) = k$$

where k is a constant. To prove this, we have from the fundamental definition of the direct Laplacian transform

$$(3.2) \qquad L(k) = p \int_0^\infty e^{-pt} k\, dt = kp \left[-\frac{e^{-pt}}{p} \right]_0^\infty = k$$

The integral vanishes at the upper limit since by hypothesis $\mathrm{Re}\ p > 0$.

THEOREM II

$$(3.3) \qquad Lk\phi(t) = kL\phi(t) \qquad \text{where } k \text{ is a constant}$$

* A rigorous discussion and derivation of this theorem will be found in E. C. Titchmarsh, "Introduction to the Theory of Fourier Integrals," Oxford University Press, New York, 1937.

This may be proved in the following manner:

$$(3.4) \quad Lk\phi(t) = p \int_0^\infty e^{-pt} k\phi(t) \, dt = kp \int_0^\infty e^{-pt} \phi(t) \, dt = kL\phi(t)$$

THEOREM III. If F is a continuous differentiable function and if F and dF/dt are L-transformable,

$$(3.5) \qquad L\frac{dF}{dt} = pLF(t) - pF(0)$$

This theorem is very useful in solving differential equations with constant coefficients. To prove it, we have

$$(3.6) \quad L\frac{dF}{dt} = p \int_0^\infty e^{-pt} \frac{dF}{dt} \, dt = pFe^{-pt} \Big|_0^\infty$$

$$+ \, p^2 \int_0^\infty e^{-pt} F \, dt = pLF - pF(0)$$

where the integration has been performed by parts.

THEOREM IV. If F is continuous and has derivatives of orders 1, 2, . . . , n which are L-transformable,

$$(3.7) \qquad L\frac{d^nF}{dt^n} = p^n LF - \sum_{k=0}^{n-1} F^{(k)}(0) p^{n-k}$$

where $\qquad F^{(k)}(0) = \dfrac{d^kF}{dt^k}$ evaluated at $t = 0$

This theorem is an extension of Theorem III. To prove this, we have

$$(3.8) \qquad L\frac{d^nF}{dt^n} = pL\frac{d^{n-1}F}{dt^{n-1}} - p\left(\frac{d^{n-1}F}{dt^{n-1}}\right)_{t=0}$$

by Theorem III. By repeated applications of Theorem III we finally obtain the result (3.7). If we let

$$(3.9) \qquad F_r = \frac{d^rF}{dt^r}$$

evaluated at $t = 0$, we have for the transforms of the first four derivatives

$$(3.10) \qquad L\frac{dF}{dt} = pLF - pF_0$$

$$(3.11) \qquad L\frac{d^2F}{dt^2} = p^2 LF - p^2 F_0 - pF_1$$

$$(3.12) \qquad L\frac{d^3F}{dt^3} = p^3 LF - p^3 F_0 - p^2 F_1 - pF_2$$

$$(3.13) \qquad L\frac{d^4F}{dt^4} = p^4 LF - p^4 F_0 - p^3 F_1 - p^2 F_2 - pF_3$$

etc.

These expressions are of use in transforming differential equations.

THEOREM V. *The Faltung Theorem.* This theorem is known in the literature as the *Faltung theorem.* In the older literature of the operational calculus it is sometimes referred to as the *superposition theorem.*

Let

$$(3.14) \qquad\qquad LF_1(t) = g_1(p)$$
$$(3.15) \qquad\qquad LF_2(t) = g_2(p)$$

Then the theorem states that

$$(3.16) \quad L \int_0^t F_1(y)F_2(t - y)\, dy = L \int_0^t F_2(y)F_1(t - y)\, dy = \frac{g_1 g_2}{p}$$

To prove this theorem, let

$$(3.17) \qquad\qquad LF_3(t) = \frac{g_1(p)g_2(p)}{p}$$

Then, by the Fourier-Mellin formula, we have

$$(3.18) \qquad F_3(t) = \frac{1}{2\pi j} \int_{c-j\infty}^{c+j\infty} \frac{g_1(p)g_2(p)}{p^2}\, e^{pt}\, dp$$

However, by hypothesis,

$$(3.19) \qquad g_2(p) = p \int_0^\infty e^{-py} F_2(y)\, dy$$

Therefore

$$(3.20) \qquad F_3(t) = \frac{1}{2\pi j} \int_0^\infty F_2(y)\, dy \int_{c-j\infty}^{c+j\infty} \frac{g_1(p)}{p}\, e^{p(t-y)}\, dp$$

if we do not question reversing the order of integration.

However, we have

$$(3.21) \qquad \frac{1}{2\pi j} \int_{c-j\infty}^{c+j\infty} \frac{g_1(p)}{p}\, e^{p(t-y)}\, dp = F_1(t - y)$$

Hence

$$(3.22) \qquad F_3(t) = \int_0^\infty F_2(y)F_1(t - y)\, dy$$

Now, by hypothesis, $F_1(t) = 0$ if t is less than 0.

$$(3.23) \qquad F_1(t - y) = 0 \qquad \text{for } y > t$$

Consequently the infinite limit of integration may be replaced by the limit t. Therefore we may write (3.22) in the form

$$(3.24) \qquad F_3(t) = \int_0^t F_2(y)F_1(t - y)\, dy$$

and, by symmetry,

(3.25) $$F_3(t) = \int_0^t F_1(y)F_2(t - y) \, dy$$

Corollary to Theorem V. By applying Theorem III to Theorem V, we have

(3.26) $$L \frac{d}{dt} \int_0^t F_2(y)F_1(t - y) \, dy = p \frac{g_1 g_2}{p} = g_1 g_2$$

THEOREM VI. If

(3.27) $$LF(t) = g(p)$$

then

(3.28) $$Le^{-at}F(t) = g(p + a) \frac{p}{p + a}$$

Proof. Let

(3.29) $$Le^{-at}F(t) = \phi(p)$$

Therefore

(3.30) $$\phi(p) = p \int_0^\infty e^{-pt}e^{-at}F(t) \, dt$$
$$= p \int_0^\infty e^{-t(p+a)}F(t) \, dt$$

But, as a consequence of (3.27), we have

(3.31) $$g(p) = p \int_0^\infty e^{-pt}F(t) \, dt$$

Hence

(3.32) $$g(p + a) = (p + a) \int_0^\infty e^{-t(p+a)}F(t) \, dt$$

Comparing this with (3.30), we have

(3.33) $$\phi(p) = g(p + a) \frac{p}{p + a} = Le^{-at}F(t)$$

THEOREM VII. If

(3.34) $$LF(t) = g(p)$$

then

(3.35) $$L^{-1}e^{-kp}g(p) = \begin{cases} 0 & t < k \\ F(t - k) & t > k \end{cases} \quad \text{provided } k > 0$$

Proof. Let

(3.36) $$L\phi(t) = e^{-kp}g(p)$$

Hence

(3.37) $$\phi(t) = \frac{1}{2\pi j} \int_{c-j\infty}^{c+j\infty} \frac{e^{pt}e^{-kp}g(p)\,dp}{p}$$

while

(3.38) $$F(t) = \frac{1}{2\pi j} \int_{c-j\infty}^{c+j\infty} \frac{e^{pt}g(p)\,dp}{p}$$

Comparing (3.37) and (3.38), we have

(3.39) $$\phi(t) = F(t - k)$$

However, $F(t) = 0$ for $t < 0$. Hence $F(t - k) = 0$ for $t < k$, since by hypothesis $k > 0$. This proves the theorem.

THEOREM VIII.   If

(3.40) $$LF(t) = g(p)$$

then

(3.41) $$L^{-1}e^{kp}g(p) = F(t + k) \qquad k > 0$$

provided that

(3.42) $$F(t) = 0 \qquad \text{for } 0 < t < k$$

Proof.   Let

(3.43) $$LF(t + k) = \phi(p)$$

Hence

(3.44) $$\phi(p) = p \int_0^\infty e^{-pt}F(t + k)\,dt$$

Now let us make the change in variable

(3.45) $$t + k = y$$

Hence

(3.46) $$\begin{aligned} \phi(p) &= pe^{pk} \int_0^\infty e^{-py}F(y)\,dy \\ &= pe^{pk} \int_0^\infty e^{-py}F(y)\,dy - pe^{pk} \int_0^k e^{-py}F(y)\,dy \\ &= e^{pk}g(p) - pe^{pk} \int_0^k e^{-py}F(y)\,dy \end{aligned}$$

Now, if $F(y) = 0$ for $0 < y < k$, then the second integral vanishes and we have

(3.47) $$LF(t + k) = e^{kp}g(p)$$

and the theorem is proved.

4. Calculation of Direct Transforms. The computation of transforms is based on the Fourier-Mellin integral theorem. If the function $F(t)$ is known and the integral

$$(4.1) \qquad g(p) = p \int_0^\infty e^{-pt} F(t) \, dt$$

can be computed, then the function $g(p)$ may be determined and the direct Laplace transform

$$(4.2) \qquad g(p) = LF(t)$$

obtained.

If, on the other hand, the function $g(p)$ is known, then to obtain the function $F(t)$ we must use the integral

$$(4.3) \qquad F(t) = \frac{1}{2\pi j} \int_{c-j\infty}^{c+j\infty} \frac{e^{pt} g(p)}{p} \, dp$$

If this complex integral can be evaluated, then the inverse transform

$$(4.4) \qquad F(t) = L^{-1} g(p)$$

may be obtained.

In Chap. 6, Sec. 6, the direct transforms of certain functions were computed by evaluating the integral (4.1) for simple types of functions $F(t)$.

Fractional Powers of p. In the applications of his operational calculus to problems of physical importance, Oliver Heaviside, in the course of his heuristic processes, encountered fractional powers of p. Since his use of the operational method was based on the interpretation of p as the derivative operator and $1/p$ as the integral operator, there was some trepidation by the followers of Heaviside in interpreting fractional powers of p.

In Chap. 12 a discussion of the gamma function based on the Euler integral

$$(4.5) \qquad \Gamma(n) = \int_0^\infty x^{n-1} e^{-x} \, dx \qquad n > 0$$

was given. This integral converges for n positive and defines the function $\Gamma(n)$.

By direct evaluation we have

$$(4.6) \qquad \Gamma(1) = 1$$

and, by an integration by parts, the recursion relation

$$(4.7) \qquad \Gamma(n + 1) = n\Gamma(n)$$

The integral and the recursion formula taken together define the gamma function for all values of n.

If we now place

(4.8)
$$x = pt$$

in (4.5), we have

(4.9)
$$\Gamma(n) = p^n \int_0^\infty e^{-pt} t^{n-1} \, dt$$

or

(4.10)
$$\frac{\Gamma(n)}{p^{n-1}} = p \int_0^\infty e^{-pt} t^{n-1} \, dt$$

Comparing this with the basic Laplace-transform integral (4.1), we have

(4.11)
$$L t^{n-1} = \frac{\Gamma(n)}{p^{n-1}} \qquad n > 0$$

If we let

(4.12)
$$n - 1 = m$$

we have

(4.13)
$$L^{-1} \frac{1}{p^m} = \frac{t^m}{\Gamma(m + 1)} \qquad m > -1$$

It will be shown in a later section that this formula holds for *any m* not a negative integer. This equation is more symmetrically written in terms of Gauss's π function

(4.14)
$$\pi(m) = \Gamma(m + 1)$$

in the form

(4.15)
$$L^{-1} p^{-m} = \frac{t^m}{\pi(m)}$$

When m is a *positive integer*, we have

(4.16)
$$\pi(m) = m!$$

and when m is a negative integer, $\pi(m)$ is not defined. We thus have

(4.17)
$$L^{-1} \frac{1}{p^m} = \frac{t^m}{m!} \qquad m \text{ a positive integer}$$

By the use of Eq. (4.13) and a table of gamma functions the transforms of fractional powers of p may be readily computed. As an example, since

(4.18)
$$\Gamma(\tfrac{1}{2}) = \sqrt{\pi}$$

we have from (4.13)

(4.19)
$$L^{-1} p^{\frac{1}{2}} = \frac{t^{-\frac{1}{2}}}{\sqrt{\pi}} = \frac{1}{\sqrt{\pi t}}$$

5. Calculation of Inverse Transforms. The problem of computing the inverse transform of a function $g(p)$ by the use of the equation

$$(5.1) \qquad F(t) = \frac{1}{2\pi j} \int_{c-j\infty}^{c+j\infty} \frac{g(p)}{p} e^{pt} \, dp$$

will now be considered.

The line integral for $F(t)$ is usually evaluated by transforming it into a closed contour and applying the calculus of residues discussed in Chap. 19. The contour usually chosen is shown in Fig. 5.1.

Let us take as the closed contour s the straight line parallel to the axis of imaginaries and at a distance c to the right of it and the large semi-circle s_0 whose center is at $(c,0)$. We then have

$$(5.2) \qquad \oint_s \frac{e^{pt}g(p)}{p} \, dp = \int_{c+jR}^{c-jR} \frac{e^{pt}g(p) \, dp}{p} + \int_{s_0} \frac{e^{pt}g(p) \, dp}{p}$$

where c is chosen great enough so that all the singularities of the integral lie to the left of the straight line along which the integral from $c - j\infty$ to $c + j\infty$ is taken.

Complex p-plane

FIG. 5.1

The evaluation of the contour integral along the contour s is greatly facilitated by the use of Jordan's lemma (Chap. 19, Sec. 15), which in this case may be stated in the following form:

Let $\phi(p)$ be an integrable function of the complex variable p such that

$$(5.3) \qquad \lim_{|p| \to \infty} |\phi(p)| = 0$$

Then

$$(5.4) \qquad \lim_{R \to \infty} \left| \int_{s_0} e^{pt}\phi(p) \, dp \right| = 0 \qquad t > 0 \qquad \mathrm{Re}\ p \le 0$$

It usually happens in practice that the function

$$(5.5) \qquad \phi(p) = \frac{g(p)}{p}$$

has such properties that Jordan's lemma is applicable. In such a case the integral around the large semicircle in (5.2) vanishes as $R \to \infty$, and we have

$$(5.6) \qquad F(t) = \frac{1}{2\pi j} \int_{c-j\infty}^{c+j\infty} \frac{g(p)}{p} e^{pt} \, dp = \lim_{R \to \infty} \frac{1}{2\pi j} \oint_s \frac{e^{pt}g(p) \, dp}{p}$$

Now, by Cauchy's residue theorem (Chap. 19, Sec. 9), we have

$$(5.7) \qquad \oint_s \frac{e^{pt}g(p) \, dp}{p} = 2\pi j \sum \mathrm{Res} \frac{e^{pt}g(p)}{p} \text{ inside } s$$

Hence by (5.6) we have

$$(5.8) \qquad F(t) = \sum \text{Res} \frac{e^{pt}g(p)}{p} \text{ inside } s$$

if R is large enough to include all singularities.

If the function $e^{pt}g(p)/p$ is not single-valued within the contour s and possesses branch points within s, it may be made single-valued by introducing suitable cuts and then applying the residue theorem.

As an example of the computation of an inverse transform, let us consider the determination of the inverse transform of

$$(5.9) \qquad g(p) = \frac{p}{p^2 + a^2} = LF(t)$$

This function clearly satisfies the condition imposed by Jordan's lemma. Hence $F(t)$ is given by (5.8) in the form

$$(5.10) \qquad F(t) = \sum \text{Res} \frac{e^{pt}}{p^2 + a^2}$$

The poles of $e^{pt}/(p^2 + a^2)$ are at

$$(5.11) \qquad p = \pm ja$$

By Chap. 19, Sec. 12, we have

$$(5.12) \qquad \text{Res}_{p=ja} \frac{e^{pt}}{p^2 + a^2} = \frac{e^{jat}}{2ja}$$

Similarly we have

$$(5.13) \qquad \text{Res}_{p=-ja} \frac{e^{pt}}{p^2 + a^2} = \frac{-e^{-jat}}{2ja}$$

Hence

$$(5.14) \qquad F(t) = \frac{1}{a} \frac{e^{jat} - e^{-jat}}{2j} = \frac{\sin at}{a}$$

As another example, consider

$$(5.15) \qquad L^{-1}g(p) = \frac{p\omega}{(p + a)^2 + \omega^2} = F(t)$$

This function also satisfies the condition of Jordan's lemma. We must compute the sum of the residues of

$$(5.16) \qquad \phi(p) = \frac{e^{pt}\omega}{(p + a)^2 + \omega^2}$$

The poles of this function are at

$$(5.17) \qquad p = -a \pm j\omega$$

The sum of the residues at these poles is

$$(5.18) \qquad \frac{e^{-at}e^{j\omega t}}{2j\omega} - \frac{e^{-at}e^{-j\omega t}}{2j\omega} = e^{-at} \sin \omega t = F(t)$$

6. The Modified Integral.   Let us consider the fundamental integral of the inverse transform

$$(6.1) \qquad F(t) = \frac{1}{2\pi j} \int_{c-j\infty}^{c+j\infty} \frac{g(p)}{p} e^{pt} \, dp$$

Now, if we perform a formal differentiation under the integral sign with respect to t, we have

$$(6.2) \qquad \frac{dF}{dt} = \frac{1}{2\pi j} \int_{c-j\infty}^{c+j\infty} \frac{pg(p)}{p} e^{pt} \, dp$$

and we see that differentiation introduces a factor of p before $g(p)$. In many cases, however, the new integral does not converge uniformly.

In such cases the process of differentiation cannot be performed in this manner, since for the operation to be valid the new integral must converge uniformly. It is possible, however, to modify the original integral in such a way that the procedure is correct. This may be done provided that $g(p)$ satisfies certain conditions. The conditions, which are usually fulfilled in practice, are the following:

1. $g(p)/p$ is analytic in the region to the right of the straight lines L_1 and L_2. $p = c + re^{j\theta}$ and $p = c + re^{-j\theta}$, where $\pi/2 < \theta \leq \pi$.

2. $g(p)/p$ tends uniformly to zero as $|p| \to \infty$ in this region (see Fig. 6.1).

It is possible, when these conditions hold, to complete the line integral by the way of a large semicircle convex to the left and with center at $(c,0)$ as before. Then, since no singularities are traversed, the path of integration may be changed into two straight lines L_1 and L_2, as shown in Fig. 6.1. This integral along L_1 and L_2 is called the *modified integral*.

FIG. 6.1

The modified integral is easily proved uniformly convergent for all positive values of t. Also, integrals of the type

$$(6.3) \qquad I = \frac{1}{2\pi j} \int_{L_1, L_2} \frac{Q(p)g(p)}{p} e^{pt} \, dp$$

where $Q(p)$ is a function that in the region under consideration increases at most as a power of p when p tends to infinity, may be proved uniformly convergent.

In Sec. 4 the relation

$$(6.4) \qquad L^{-1} \frac{1}{p^m} = \frac{t^m}{\Gamma(m+1)} \qquad m > -1$$

was derived.

We shall now remove the above restriction on m and obtain a general formula of the form

$$(6.5) \qquad L^{-1} \frac{1}{p^r} = \frac{t^r}{\Gamma(r+1)}$$

valid for all values of r.

If we begin with the restricted result (6.4), we have

$$(6.6) \qquad \frac{t^m}{\Gamma(m+1)} = \frac{1}{2\pi j} \int_{c-j}^{c+j} \frac{e^{pt}\,dp}{p^{m+1}} \qquad m > -1$$

If $m > -1$, the function

$$(6.7) \qquad \frac{g(p)}{p} = \frac{1}{p^{m+1}}$$

tends to zero uniformly as $|p| \to \infty$. Hence we are permitted to differentiate (6.6) s times with respect to t under the integral sign.

We thus obtain

$$(6.8) \qquad \frac{m(m-1)\,\cdots\,(m-s+1)t^{m-s}}{\Gamma(m+1)} = \frac{1}{2\pi j} \int_{c-j}^{c+j} \frac{e^{pt}p^s}{p^{m+1}}\,dp$$

Hence we have

$$(6.9) \qquad L^{-1} \frac{p^s}{p^m} = \frac{m(m-1)\,\cdots\,(m-s+1)}{\Gamma(m+1)} t^{m-s}$$

where

$$(6.10) \qquad m > -1$$

Now by the fundamental recursion formula of the gamma functions, we have

$$(6.11) \qquad m(m-1)\,\cdots\,(m-s+1) = \frac{\Gamma(m+1)}{\Gamma(m-s+1)}$$

Therefore we may write (6.9) in the form

$$(6.12) \qquad L^{-1} \frac{1}{p^{m-s}} = \frac{\Gamma(m+1)t^{m-s}}{\Gamma(m+1)\Gamma(m-s+1)}$$

Now, if we let

$$(6.13) \qquad m - s = r$$

we may write (6.12) in the form

$$(6.14) \qquad L^{-1} \frac{1}{p^r} = \frac{t^r}{\Gamma(r+1)}$$

for all values of r except negative integers. If r is a negative integer, let us place

$$(6.15) \qquad r = -q$$

We then have

(6.16) $L^{-1}p^q = \dfrac{1}{2\pi j} \displaystyle\int_{c-j\infty}^{c+j\infty} e^{pt}p^{q-1}\,dp = 0 \qquad \begin{cases} \text{for } t > 0 \\ \quad q = 1, 2, \ldots \end{cases}$

This result follows from the fact that the integrand in (6.16) has no poles in the finite part of the p plane.

Although (6.16) holds for all values of r when $t > 0$, the inverse transforms of *positive powers* of p are not zero at $t = 0$ but are of the nature of impulsive functions.

7. Impulsive Functions. The careful treatment of impulsive functions presents considerable difficulties and is beyond the scope of this discussion. However, many physical phenomena are of an impulsive nature. In electrical-circuit theory, for example, we frequently encounter electromotive forces that are impulsive in character, and we desire to study the behavior of the electric currents produced by the applications of electromotive forces of this type to linear circuits. In mechanics we frequently encounter problems in which a system is set in motion by the action of an impact or other impulsive force. Because of the practical importance of forces of this type, a simple treatment of them will be given.

One of the most frequently encountered functions is the Dirac function $\delta(t)$. This function is defined to be zero if $t \neq 0$ and to be infinite at $t = 0$ in such a way that

(7.1) $$\int_{-\infty}^{+\infty} \delta(t)\,dt = 1$$

This is a concise manner of expressing a function that is very large in a very small region and zero outside this region and has a unit integral. Let us consider the function $\delta(t)$ that has the following values:

(7.2) $$\delta(t) = \begin{cases} 0 & t \leq 0 \\ \dfrac{1}{\epsilon} & 0 < t < \epsilon \\ 0 & t > \epsilon \end{cases}$$

where ϵ may be made as small as we please. This function possesses the property (7.1).

We now prove the following,

(7.3) $$\int_{-\infty}^{+\infty} F(t)\delta(t - a)\,dt = F(a)$$

provided that $F(t)$ is continuous. The proof of this follows from (7.2), so that we have

(7.4) $$\int_{-\infty}^{+\infty} F(t)\delta(t - a)\,dt = \frac{1}{\epsilon}\int_{a}^{a+\epsilon} F(t)\,dt$$
$$= F(a + \theta\epsilon) \qquad \text{where } 0 < \theta < 1$$

Now, since by hypothesis $F(t)$ is continuous, we have

(7.5) $$\lim_{\epsilon \to 0} F(a + \theta\epsilon) = F(a)$$

Hence the result (7.3) follows. As an application of (7.3), let us compute the Laplacian transform of $\delta(t)$. We have

(7.6) $$L\delta(t) = p \int_0^\infty e^{-pt}\delta(t) \, dt = p$$

so that the Laplace transform of the Dirac function is p.

As an example of the use of the $\delta(t)$ function, let us consider the effect produced when a particle of mass m situated at the origin is acted upon by an impulse F_0 applied to the mass at $t = 0$. If the impulse acts in the x direction, the equation of motion is

(7.7) $$m \frac{d^2x}{dt^2} = F_0\delta(t)$$

Let

(7.8) $$Lx = y$$

Now, if the mass is at $x = 0$ at $t = 0$ and has no initial velocity, we have

(7.9) $$L \frac{d^2x}{dt^2} = p^2 y$$

Hence Eq. (7.7) is transformed into

(7.10) $$mp^2 y = F_0 p$$

Therefore

(7.11) $$y = \frac{F_0}{mp}$$

and hence

(7.12) $$x = L^{-1}y = \frac{F_0}{m} t$$

As another example, consider a series circuit consisting of an inductance L in series with a capacitance C. Initially the circuit has zero current, and the capacitor is discharged. At $t = 0$ an electromotive force of very large voltage is applied for a very short time so that it may be expressed in the form $E_0\delta(t)$. It is required to determine the subsequent current in the system.

The differential equation governing the current in the circuit is

(7.13) $$L \frac{di}{dt} + \frac{q}{C} = E_0\delta(t)$$

where

$$(7.14) \qquad i = \frac{dq}{dt}$$

Now let

$$(7.15) \qquad Li = I \qquad Lq = Q$$

Therefore (7.13) transforms into

$$(7.16) \qquad \left(Lp + \frac{1}{Cp}\right) I = E_0 p$$

Hence

$$(7.17) \qquad I = \frac{E_0}{L} \frac{p^2}{p^2 + \omega_0^2}$$

where

$$(7.18) \qquad \omega_0 = \frac{1}{\sqrt{LC}}$$

From the table of transforms we have

$$(7.19) \qquad L^{-1} \frac{p^2}{p^2 + \omega_0^2} = \cos \omega_0 t$$

Hence

$$(7.20) \qquad L^{-1} I = i = \frac{E_0}{L} \cos \omega_0 t$$

8. Heaviside's Rules. In Heaviside's application of his operational method to the solution of physical problems, he made frequent and skillful use of certain procedures in order to interpret his "resistance operators." These procedures were known as *Heaviside's rules* in the early history of the subject. At that time there appears to have been much controversy over the justification of these rules. Viewed from the Laplacian-transform point of view, the proof of these powerful rules is seen to be most simple.

a. Heaviside's Expansion Theorem. Heaviside's first rule is commonly known as *Heaviside's expansion theorem*, or the *partial-fraction rule*. In its usual form it may be stated as follows:

If $g(p)$ has the form

$$(8.1) \qquad g(p) = \frac{N(p)}{\phi(p)}$$

where $N(p)$ and $\phi(p)$ are polynomials in p and the degree of $\phi(p)$ is at least as high as the degree of $N(p)$ and, in addition, the polynomial $\phi(p)$ has n distinct zeros, $p_1, p_2, \ldots, p_n$ and $p = 0$ is *not* a zero of $\phi(p)$, we then have

$$(8.2) \qquad L^{-1} \frac{N(p)}{\phi(p)} = \frac{1}{2\pi j} \int_{c-j\infty}^{c+j\infty} \frac{N(p)e^{pt}\,dp}{p\phi(p)}$$

$$= \sum \operatorname{Res} \frac{N(p)e^{pt}}{p\phi(p)}$$

by the Cauchy residue theorem since in this case the integrand satisfies the conditions of Jordan's lemma and the contribution over the large semicircle to the left of the path of integration vanishes as $R \to \infty$.

We now compute the residues by the methods of Chap. 19, Sec. 12. Now if $p_1, p_2, p_3, \ldots, p_n$ are n *distinct* zeros of $\phi(p)$, then the points $p = 0$, $p = p_1$, $p = p_2$, $\ldots$, $p = p_n$ are simple poles of the function $N(p)e^{pt}/p\phi(p)$.

The residue at the simple pole $p = 0$ is

$$(8.3) \qquad \lim_{p \to 0} \frac{pN(p)e^{pt}}{p\phi(p)} = \frac{N(0)}{\phi(0)}$$

The residue at the simple pole $p = p_r$ is

$$(8.4) \qquad \lim_{p \to p_r} \frac{N(p)e^{pt}}{p\phi'(p)} = \frac{N(p_r)e^{p_r t}}{p_r\phi'(p_r)}$$

where

$$(8.5) \qquad \phi'(p_r) = \left(\frac{d\phi}{dp}\right)_{p=p_r}$$

It follows from (8.2) that

$$(8.6) \qquad L^{-1} \frac{N(p)}{\phi(p)} = \frac{N(0)}{\phi(0)} + \sum_{r=1}^{r=n} \frac{N(p_r)e^{p_r t}}{p_r\phi'(p_r)}$$

This result is called the Heaviside expansion theorem and is frequently used to obtain inverse transforms of the ratios of two polynomials. As a simple application of the expansion theorem, let it be required to determine the inverse transform of

$$(8.7) \qquad \frac{p^2}{p^2 + a^2} = \frac{N(p)}{\phi(p)}$$

In this case the zeros of $\phi(p)$ are

$$(8.8) \qquad p = \pm ja$$

We also have

$$(8.9) \qquad \frac{N(0)}{\phi(0)} = 0$$

and

$$(8.10) \qquad \phi'(p) = 2p$$

Hence, substituting in (8.6), we obtain

$$(8.11) \qquad L^{-1}\frac{p^2}{p^2 + a^2} = \frac{-a^2 e^{jat}}{-2a^2} + \frac{-a^2 e^{-jat}}{-2a^2}$$

$$= \frac{e^{jat} + e^{-jat}}{2} = \cos at$$

An Extension of Heaviside's Expansion Theorem. Heaviside's expansion theorem as stated above is of use in evaluating the inverse transforms of ratios of polynomials in p. The expansion theorem is sometimes used to compute the inverse transforms of certain transcendental functions in p that have simple poles and that satisfy the conditions of Jordan's lemma so that the path of integration may be closed to the left by a large semicircle. In this case the result

$$(8.12) \qquad L^{-1}g(p) = \sum \text{Res}\, \frac{g(p)e^{pt}}{p}$$

is applicable. If the poles of $g(p)$ are simple poles at $p = p_1$, $p = p_2$, . . . , $p = p_r$, . . . and $p = 0$ is not a pole, then Eq. (8.12) is very similar to the Heaviside expansion theorem (8.6).

As an example of this, consider the function

$$(8.13) \qquad g(p) = \tanh\frac{Tp}{2} = \frac{\sinh\,(Tp/2)}{\cosh\,(Tp/2)}$$

where T is real and positive. The poles of this function are at

$$(8.14) \qquad \cosh\frac{Tp}{2} = 0$$

or

$$(8.15) \qquad p_k = \frac{(2k + 1)\pi j}{T} \qquad k = 0, \pm 1, \pm 2, \ldots$$

The fact that these poles are simple poles follows from the fact that the derivative of $\cosh\,(Tp/2)$ with respect to p does not have zeros at these points. The function

$$(8.16) \qquad \frac{e^{pt}\tanh\,(Tp/2)}{p}$$

satisfies the condition of Jordan's lemma since

$$(8.17) \qquad \lim_{|p|\to\infty}\, \tanh\frac{Tp}{2} = 1$$

We thus have by (8.12)

$$(8.18) \qquad L^{-1}g(p) = \sum_{k=-\infty}^{k=+\infty} \frac{e^{p_k t}\sinh\,(p_k T/2)}{p_k(T/2)\sinh\,(p_k T/2)}$$

This expression reduces to

$$(8.19) \qquad L^{-1}g(p) = \frac{2}{T} \sum_{k=-\infty}^{k=+\infty} \frac{e^{p_k t}}{p_k}$$

Substituting (8.15) into (8.19), we finally obtain

$$(8.20) \qquad L^{-1} \tanh \frac{Tp}{2} = \frac{4}{\pi} \sum_{s=1}^{s=\infty} \frac{1}{s} \sin \frac{s\pi t}{T} \qquad s \text{ odd}$$

It is thus seen that the result (8.12) is more general than the Heaviside expansion theorem, but when applied to functions whose poles are simple and which have no singularity at the origin, then (8.12) has a close resemblance to the Heaviside expansion theorem.

b. *Heaviside's Second Rule.* Heaviside made frequent use of the following result,

$$(8.21) \qquad L^{-1} \sum_{n=0}^{\infty} \frac{a_n}{p^n} = \sum_{n=0}^{\infty} a_n \frac{t^n}{n!}$$

where the series $\sum_{n=0}^{\infty} \frac{a_n}{p^n}$ is a convergent series of negative powers of p.
This result is obtained by term-by-term substitution of

$$(8.22) \qquad L^{-1} \frac{1}{p^n} = \frac{t^n}{n!} \qquad \text{for } n \text{ a positive integer}$$

since the series converges uniformly.

c. *Heaviside's Third Rule.* This concerns the transform of the series

$$(8.23) \qquad g(p) = \sum_{n=0}^{\infty} a_n p^n + p^{\frac{1}{2}} \sum_{n=0}^{\infty} b_n p^n$$

By making use of the fact that

$$(8.24) \qquad L^{-1} \frac{1}{p^r} = \frac{t^r}{\Gamma(r+1)} \qquad r \neq \text{negative integer}$$

and the facts that

$$(8.25) \qquad \Gamma(\tfrac{1}{2}) = \sqrt{\pi}$$

and

$$(8.26) \qquad L^{-1}p^s = 0 \qquad \text{for } t > 0 \qquad s = 1, 2, 3, \ldots$$

we have directly

$$(8.27) \quad L^{-1}g(p) = a_0 + \frac{1}{\sqrt{\pi t}}\left[b_0 - \frac{b_1}{2t} + \frac{1 \times 3b_2}{(2t)^2} \right.$$
$$\left. - \frac{1 \times 3 \times 5b_3}{(2t)^3} + \cdots \right] \quad \text{for } t > 0$$

By arranging the transform of a function in the form (8.23) Heaviside was able to obtain the asymptotic expansion of certain functions valid for large values of t.

9. The Transforms of Periodic Functions. Let $F(t)$ be a periodic function with fundamental period T, that is,

$$(9.1) \qquad F(t + T) = F(t) \qquad t > 0$$

If $F(t)$ is sectionally continuous over a period $0 < t < T$, then its direct Laplace transform is given by

$$(9.2) \qquad LF(t) = p \int_0^\infty e^{-pt}F(t)\, dt$$
$$= p \sum_{n=0}^\infty \int_{nT}^{(n+1)T} e^{-pt}F(t)\, dt$$

If we now let

$$(9.3) \qquad u = t - nT$$

and realize that, as a consequence of the periodicity of the function $F(t)$, we have

$$(9.4) \qquad F(u + nT) = F(u)$$

in view of this we may write (9.2) in the form

$$(9.5) \qquad LF(t) = p \sum_{n=0}^\infty e^{-nTp} \int_0^T e^{-pu}F(u)\, du$$

We also have the well-known result

$$(9.6) \qquad \sum_{n=0}^{n=\infty} e^{-nTp} = \frac{1}{1 - e^{-Tp}}$$

Hence we may write (9.5) in the form

$$(9.7) \qquad LF(t) = \frac{p}{1 - e^{-Tp}} \int_0^T e^{-pt}F(t)\, dt$$

Let us apply this formula to obtain the transform of the "meander function" of Fig. 9.1.

FIG. 9.1

In this case we have

$$(9.8) \qquad p \int_0^T F(t)e^{-pt}\, dt = p \int_0^a e^{-pt}\, dt - p \int_a^{2a} e^{-pt}\, dt$$
$$= 1 - e^{-pa} - e^{-pa} + e^{-2pa}$$
$$= 1 - 2e^{-pa} + e^{-2pa} = (1 - e^{-pa})^2$$

Hence, substituting this into (9.7), we have

$$(9.9) \qquad LF(t) = \frac{(1 - e^{-pa})^2}{1 - e^{-2ap}} = \frac{1 - e^{-pa}}{1 + e^{-pa}}$$
$$= \frac{e^{pa/2} - e^{-pa/2}}{e^{pa/2} + e^{-pa/2}} = \frac{\sinh (pa/2)}{\cosh (pa/2)} = \tanh \frac{ap}{2}$$

Using the results of (8.20), we have

$$(9.10) \qquad F(t) = L^{-1} \tanh \frac{ap}{2} = \frac{4}{\pi} \sum_{s=1}^{s=\infty} \frac{1}{s} \sin \frac{s\pi t}{a} \qquad s \text{ odd}$$

This is the Fourier-series expansion of the meander function.

As another example, consider the function $F(t)$ defined by

$$(9.11) \qquad F(t) = \begin{cases} \sin t & 0 < t < \pi \\ 0 & \pi < t < 2\pi \end{cases}$$

This function is given graphically by Fig. 9.2.

FIG. 9.2

This function is of importance in the theory of half-wave rectification. In this case the fundamental period is 2π. To obtain the transform of this function, we have

$$(9.12) \qquad p \int_0^\pi e^{-pt} \sin t\, dt = \frac{p}{p^2 + 1} (1 + e^{-p\pi})$$

Hence, by Eq. (9.7), we obtain

(9.13) $$LF(t) = \frac{p}{p^2 + 1} \frac{1 + e^{-p\pi}}{1 - e^{-2p\pi}} = \frac{p}{(p^2 + 1)(1 - e^{-p\pi})}$$

10. Application of the Operational Calculus to the Solution of Partial Differential Equations.   We have seen in Chap. 6 the manner in which the Laplace transform may be used to obtain the solution of ordinary differential equations with constant coefficients.

The basic principle of the method is to introduce a Laplacian transformation with respect to the independent variable and in this manner obtain an algebraic equation for the transform of the dependent variable. The determination of the inverse transform, either by a calculation of the complex Bromwich integral or by a consultation of a table of transforms, then supplies the solution to the problem.

The use of the Laplace transform in the solution of linear partial differential equations with constant coefficients will now be illustrated by some examples.

a. The Dissipationless Transmission Line.   As an example of the transform method of solution of partial differential equations, let us consider the following problem: Consider the short-circuited electrical transmission line of Fig. 10.1.

FIG. 10.1

Let the line have a length of s, and let it be assumed that the conductors of the line are perfect and that the insulation between the conductors is perfect.   In this case, the series resistance R of the line is zero and the leakage conductance G is also zero.   Let L be the inductance per unit length of the line and C the capacitance per unit length.   The equations governing the distribution of potential and current along the line are (see Chap. 16, Sec. 10)

(10.1) $$-\frac{\partial e}{\partial x} = L \frac{\partial i}{\partial t}$$

(10.2) $$-\frac{\partial i}{\partial x} = C \frac{\partial e}{\partial t}$$

At $t = 0$ the switch S_0 is closed, and it is desired to determine the subsequent distribution of current and potential along the line.

In order to solve this problem by the Laplacian-transform method, let us introduce the following transforms with respect to the independent variable t,

(10.3) $$\mathscr{L}e(x,t) = E(x,p)$$
(10.4) $$\mathscr{L}i(x,t) = I(x,p)$$

where $\mathscr{L}$ denotes the Laplace transform.

Since the initial current and potential distributions of the line are assumed to be zero, we have

(10.5)
$$\mathcal{L} \frac{\partial i}{\partial t} = pI$$

(10.6)
$$\mathcal{L} \frac{\partial e}{\partial t} = pE$$

Now, since in the transformations (10.3) and (10.4) x is a parameter, it follows that

(10.7)
$$\mathcal{L} \frac{\partial e}{\partial x} = \frac{dE}{dx}$$

x is independent of t.

and

(10.8)
$$\mathcal{L} \frac{\partial i}{\partial x} = \frac{dI}{dx}$$

Therefore Eqs. (10.1) and (10.2) transform into

(10.9)
$$-\frac{dE}{dx} = LpI$$

(10.10)
$$-\frac{dI}{dx} = CpE$$

Eliminating I from these two equations, we obtain

(10.11)
$$\frac{d^2E}{dx^2} = LCp^2E$$

Eliminating E, we have

(10.12)
$$\frac{d^2I}{dx^2} = LCp^2I$$

If we let

(10.13)
$$v = \frac{1}{\sqrt{LC}}$$

Eq. (10.11) becomes

(10.14)
$$\frac{d^2E}{dx^2} = \frac{p^2}{v^2} E$$

This is an ordinary differential equation with constant coefficients, and its solution is

(10.15)
$$E = A_1 e^{-(p/v)x} + A_2 e^{+px/v}$$

where A_1 and A_2 are arbitrary constants.

In order to determine A_1 and A_2, we use the boundary conditions

(10.16)
$$\begin{array}{cc} E = E_0 & E = 0 \\ x = 0 & x = s \end{array}$$

Using these conditions, we obtain the two simultaneous linear equations

$$(10.17) \qquad \begin{aligned} E_0 &= A_1 + A_2 \\ 0 &= A_1 e^{-ps/v} + A_2 e^{ps/v} \end{aligned}$$

Hence

$$(10.18) \qquad A_1 = \frac{\begin{vmatrix} E_0 & 1 \\ 0 & e^{ps/v} \end{vmatrix}}{\begin{vmatrix} 1 & 1 \\ e^{-ps/v} & e^{ps/v} \end{vmatrix}} = \frac{E_0 e^{ps/v}}{e^{ps/v} - e^{-ps/v}}$$

and

$$(10.19) \qquad A_2 = \frac{\begin{vmatrix} 1 & E_0 \\ e^{-ps/v} & 0 \end{vmatrix}}{e^{ps/v} - e^{-ps/v}} = \frac{-E_0 e^{-ps/v}}{e^{ps/v} - e^{-ps/v}}$$

Hence, with these values of the constants A_1 and A_2, (10.15) becomes

$$(10.20) \qquad E(x,p) = \frac{E_0}{e^{ps/v} - e^{-ps/v}} \left(e^{-(p/v)(x-s)} - e^{+(p/v)(x-s)} \right)$$

WAVES ALONG AN INFINITE LINE.   Before obtaining the inverse transform of (10.20), let us consider the solution for $s \to \infty$ so that the line is of infinite length.   In this case we have

FIG. 10.2

$$(10.21) \qquad \lim_{s \to \infty} E(x,p) = E_0 e^{-px/v}$$

To calculate the inverse transform of this we make use of the following theorem: If

$$(10.22) \qquad L^{-1} g(p) = h(t)$$

then

$$L^{-1} e^{-kp} g(p) = \begin{cases} 0 & t < k \\ h(t - k) & t > k \end{cases} \qquad k > 0$$

Hence we have

$$(10.23) \qquad L^{-1} E_0 e^{-px/v} = \begin{cases} 0 & t < \dfrac{x}{v} \\[2mm] E_0 & t > \dfrac{x}{v} \end{cases}$$

This represents a potential wave of amplitude E_0 traveling with velocity v to the right end as shown in Fig. 10.2.

Now, in order to determine the inverse transform of (10.20), let us multiply the numerator and denominator of (10.20) by $e^{-ps/v}$, and we then obtain

$$(10.24) \qquad E(x,p) = \frac{E_0}{1 - e^{-2ps/v}} \left(e^{-px/v} - e^{-(p/v)(2s-x)} \right)$$

Now we have

(10.25) $\dfrac{1}{1 - e^{-2ps/v}} = 1 + e^{-2ps/v} + e^{-4ps/v} + e^{-6ps/v} + \cdots$

Hence we may write (10.21) in the form

(10.26) $E(x,p) = E_0(e^{-px/v} + e^{-(p/v)(x+2s)} + e^{-(p/v)(x+4s)} + \cdots)$
$\qquad\qquad\quad - E_0(e^{-(p/v)(2s-x)} + e^{-(p/v)(4s-x)} + e^{-(p/v)(6s-x)} + \cdots)$

We may interpret the various terms as traveling waves. The first group of terms represent waves traveling to the right with a velocity v, while the second group of terms represent waves that have been reflected at the short-circuited end and are traveling to the left with a velocity of v. The course of events is interpreted graphically in Fig. 10.3.

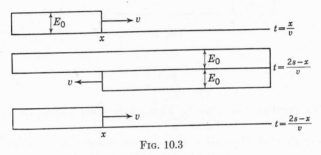

FIG. 10.3

The system of reflected waves keeps the end at $x = s$ at potential zero and the end $x = 0$ at potential E_0.

To obtain the current waves, we may use Eq. (10.9) and write it in the form

(10.27) $$I = -\frac{1}{Lp}\frac{dE}{dx}$$

Differentiating (10.26), we have

(10.28) $\dfrac{dE}{dx} = -\dfrac{pE_0}{v}(e^{-px/v} + e^{-(p/v)(x+2s)} + e^{-(p/v)(x+4s)} + \cdots)$
$\qquad\qquad\quad - \dfrac{pE_0}{v}(e^{-(p/v)(2s-x)} + e^{-(p/v)(4s-x)} + e^{-(p/v)(6s-x)} + \cdots)$

Since

(10.29) $$Lv = L\frac{1}{\sqrt{LC}} = \sqrt{\frac{L}{C}} = Z_0$$

the characteristic impedance of the line, we have from (10.27) and (10.28)

(10.30)
$$I(x,p) = \frac{E_0}{Z_0}(e^{-px/v} + e^{-(p/v)(2s-x)} + e^{-(p/v)(x+2s)} + e^{-(p/v)(4s-x)} + \cdots)$$

It is interesting to compute the current at the short-circuited end $x = s$.   Placing $x = s$ in (10.30), we have $\sum e^{-P/v(bn+1)s}$

$$\text{(10.31)} \quad I(s,p) = \frac{E_0}{Z_0} \left(e^{-ps/v} + e^{-(p/v)s} + e^{-(p/v)3s} + e^{-(p/v)3s} + \cdots\right)$$

$$= \frac{2E_0}{Z_0} \left(e^{-ps/v} + e^{-3ps/v} + e^{-3ps/v} + \cdots\right) = \mathcal{L}i(s,t)$$

The inverse transform of (10.31) is given graphically in Fig. 10.4,

FIG. 10.4

where

$$\text{(10.32)} \qquad\qquad T = \frac{s}{v}$$

so that the current continues to increase in finite jumps of magnitude $2E_0/Z_0$.

b. Linear Flow of Heat in a Semi-infinite Solid.   As another example of the use of the Laplacian transformation in the solution of partial differential equations, let us consider the determination of the flow of heat into a semi-infinite solid, $x > 0$ (Fig. 10.5).

Initially the solid is at temperature $v = 0$, and at $t = 0$ the boundary $x = 0$ is raised to a temperature v_0.   In order to determine the subsequent distribution of temperature in the solid, we must solve the heat-flow equation (Chap. 18)

FIG. 10.5

$$\text{(10.33)} \qquad\qquad \frac{\partial v}{\partial t} = h^2 \frac{\partial^2 v}{\partial x^2}$$

where h^2 is the thermometric conductivity of the solid and v the temperature, subject to the boundary conditions

$$\text{(10.34)} \qquad \begin{array}{lll} v = v_0 & x = 0 & t > 0 \\ v = 0 & x > 0 & t = 0 \end{array}$$

To do this, let us introduce the Laplacian transform

$$\text{(10.35)} \qquad\qquad Lv(x,t) = u(x,p)$$

Hence

$$(10.36) \qquad L\frac{\partial v}{\partial t} = pu$$

because of the second condition of (10.34).

We also have

$$(10.37) \qquad L\left(\frac{\partial^2 v}{\partial x^2}\right) = \frac{d^2 u}{dx^2}$$

Hence Eq. (10.33) transforms to

$$(10.38) \qquad pu = h^2 \frac{d^2 u}{dx^2}$$

or

$$(10.39) \qquad \frac{d^2 u}{dx^2} = \frac{p}{h^2} u$$

This is a linear equation with constant coefficients in the independent variable x. The general solution of (10.39) is

$$(10.40) \qquad u = Ae^{-\sqrt{p/h^2}\,x} + Be^{+\sqrt{p/h^2}\,x}$$

Since the temperature cannot be infinite for infinite values of x, we must have

$$(10.41) \qquad B = 0$$

Hence the solution reduces to

$$(10.42) \qquad u = Ae^{-\sqrt{p/h^2}\,x}$$

Now, since $v = v_0$ at $x = 0$, we must have

$$(10.43) \qquad v_0 = A$$

Therefore

$$(10.44) \qquad u = v_0 e^{-\sqrt{p/h^2}\,x} = Lv$$

To determine the inverse Laplacian transform of this expression, let

$$(10.45) \qquad a = \frac{x}{h}$$

We must therefore determine

$$(10.46) \qquad L^{-1} v_0 e^{-a\sqrt{p}} = v(x,t)$$

To do this, let us expand $e^{-a\sqrt{p}}$ into a Maclaurin series of the form

$$(10.47) \qquad e^m = 1 + \frac{m}{1!} + \frac{m^2}{2!} + \frac{m^3}{3!} + \cdots$$

Hence

$$(10.48) \quad e^{-a\sqrt{p}} = 1 - ap^{\frac{1}{2}} + \frac{a^2 p}{2!} - \frac{a^3 p^{\frac{3}{2}}}{3!} + \frac{a^4 p^2}{4!} - \frac{a^5 p^{\frac{5}{2}}}{5!} + \cdots$$

We now compute the inverse transforms of each individual term by the fundamental relation

$$(10.49) \qquad L^{-1} p^{-n} = \frac{t^n}{\Gamma(n+1)} \qquad t > 0$$

The inverse transforms of all positive powers of p are zero for $t > 0$. Hence

$$(10.50) \quad L^{-1} e^{-a\sqrt{p}} = 1 - \frac{2}{\sqrt{\pi}} \left[\frac{a}{2\sqrt{t}} - \frac{1}{3} \left(\frac{a}{2\sqrt{t}} \right)^3 \right.$$
$$\left. + \frac{1}{2! \times 5} \left(\frac{a}{2\sqrt{t}} \right)^5 - \cdots \right]$$

Now in Chap. 12, Sec. 8, we considered the function

$$(10.51) \qquad \operatorname{erf}(w) = \frac{2}{\sqrt{\pi}} \int_0^w e^{-\theta^2} d\theta$$

where erf (w) is the well-known *error function*.

If we expand $e^{-\theta^2}$ in (10.51) and integrate term by term, we obtain

$$(10.52) \quad \operatorname{erf}(w) = \frac{2}{\sqrt{\pi}} \left(w - \frac{w^3}{3 \times 1!} + \frac{w^5}{5 \times 2!} - \frac{w^7}{7 \times 3!} + \cdots \right)$$

If we now let

$$(10.53) \qquad\qquad w = \frac{a}{2\sqrt{t}}$$

we have on comparing (10.50) and (10.52)

$$(10.54) \qquad L^{-1} e^{-a\sqrt{p}} = 1 - \operatorname{erf} \left(\frac{a}{2\sqrt{t}} \right)$$

Hence, in view of (10.44), the temperature in the solid is given by

$$(10.55) \qquad v(x,t) = v_0 \left[1 - \operatorname{erf} \left(\frac{x}{2h\sqrt{t}} \right) \right]$$

This equation shows how the temperature diffuses into the solid. The time required to produce a given rise of temperature at a distance x from the surface is proportional to x^2. We notice the absence of wave phenomena in the increase in temperature.

Fig. 10.6

c. *The Oscillations of a Bar.* As a further example of the method, let us consider the following problem: A uniform bar of length s is at rest in its equilibrium position with the end $x = 0$ fixed as shown in Fig. 10.6. At $t = 0$ a constant force F_0 per unit area is applied at the free end. It is required to determine the subsequent state of motion of the bar. *in what direction*

If F_x is the stress at the point x of the bar, $u(x,t)$ the displacement, ρ the density of the bar, and E the Young's modulus, we have

$$(10.56) \qquad F_x = E \frac{\partial u}{\partial x}$$

and the equation of motion is

$$(10.57) \qquad \frac{\partial F_x}{\partial x} = \rho \frac{\partial^2 u}{\partial t^2} = E \frac{\partial^2 u}{\partial x^2}$$

Hence we have

$$(10.58) \qquad \frac{\partial^2 u}{\partial x^2} = \frac{1}{c^2} \frac{\partial^2 u}{\partial t^2}$$

where

$$(10.59) \qquad c = \sqrt{\frac{E}{\rho}}$$

Equation (10.58) determines the longitudinal displacement of the bar. The constant c is the velocity of sound in the bar.

The initial conditions of the problem are

$$(10.60) \qquad \left.\begin{array}{l} u(x,t) = 0 \\ \dfrac{\partial u}{\partial t} = 0 \end{array}\right\} \qquad t = 0 \qquad 0 < x < s$$

Starts at zero ← *Reality*
Starts at rest ← *Causality*

The boundary conditions are

$$(10.61) \qquad \begin{array}{cc} u = 0 & \dfrac{\partial u}{\partial x} = \dfrac{F_0}{E} \\ x = 0 & x = s \\ t > 0 & t > 0 \end{array}$$

fixed point at ← ↗ *Bending Force*

To solve Eq. (10.58) by the Laplace-transform method, let

$$(10.62) \qquad Lu(x,t) = v(x,p)$$

again take Laplace spectrum

Then (10.58) transforms to

$$(10.63) \qquad \frac{d^2 v}{dx^2} = \left(\frac{p}{c}\right)^2 v$$

The general solution of this equation is

$$(10.64) \qquad v = Ae^{-px/c} + Be^{+px/c}$$

$= 2k \cosh\left(\frac{px}{c} + \delta\right)$

The boundary conditions of (10.64) are

$$(10.65) \qquad \begin{array}{cc} v = 0 & \dfrac{dv}{dx} = \dfrac{F_0}{E} \\ x = 0 & x = s \end{array}$$

O.k. since one integrates in accord with causality.

Making use of the boundary conditions, we obtain

$$(10.66) \qquad v = \frac{F_0 c}{Ep} \frac{\sinh (px/c)}{\cosh (ps/c)}$$

$$= \frac{F_0 c}{Ep} \frac{e^{px/c} - e^{-px/c}}{e^{ps/c} + e^{-ps/c}}$$

$$= \frac{F_0 c}{Ep} \frac{1 - e^{-2px/c}}{1 + e^{-2ps/c}} e^{(p/c)(x-s)}$$

Now we have

$$(10.67) \qquad \frac{1}{1 + e^{-2ps/c}} = 1 - e^{-2ps/c} + e^{-4ps/c} - e^{-6ps/c} + \cdots$$

Hence we may write (10.66) in the form

$$(10.68) \qquad v = \frac{F_0 c}{Ep} (1 - e^{(-2p/c)x} - e^{-2ps/c} + e^{-2p(s+x)/c} + \cdots)$$

Let us determine the motion of the end $x = s$. Placing $x = s$ in (10.68), we have

$$(10.69) \quad v(s,p) = \frac{F_0 c}{Ep} (1 - 2e^{-2sp/c} + 2e^{-4sp/c} - 2e^{-6sp/c} + \cdots)$$

The inverse transform of (10.69) has the value

$$(10.70) \qquad
\begin{aligned}
u(s,t) &= \frac{F_0 c}{E} t & 0 < t < \frac{2s}{c} \\
u(s,t) &= \frac{F_0 c}{E} t - \frac{2F_0 c(t - 2s/c)}{E} & \frac{2s}{c} < t < \frac{4s}{c} \quad \text{etc.}
\end{aligned}$$

This is given graphically in Fig. 10.7, where

FIG. 10.7

$$(10.71) \qquad T = \frac{2s}{c}$$

It is thus seen that the end moves by jerks as shown in Fig. 10.7.

The above examples illustrate the general procedure by which the solution of linear partial differential equations may be effected by the use of the Laplacian transformation. For an extended discussion of the use of the method in this connection the reader may consult the references at the end of this chapter.

11. Evaluation of Integrals. The evaluation of certain definite integrals may be effected simply by the use of the Laplacian transformation.

In this section we shall consider certain examples that illustrate the general procedure. Many integrals may be evaluated by the use of the following theorem:

If

$$(11.1) \qquad Lh(t) = g(p)$$

then

$$(11.2) \qquad \int_0^\infty \frac{g(p)}{p} \, dp = \int_0^\infty \frac{h(t) \, dt}{t}$$

This theorem may be proved in the following manner:

By hypothesis we have

$$(11.3) \qquad g(p) = p \int_0^\infty e^{-pt} h(t) \, dt$$

Therefore

$$(11.4) \qquad \int_0^\infty \frac{g(p) \, dp}{p} = \int_0^\infty \left[\int_0^\infty e^{-pt} h(t) \, dt \right] dp$$

$$= \int_0^\infty \int_0^\infty e^{-pt} h(t) \, dp \, dt$$

provided that it is permissible to reverse the order of integration.

But we have

$$(11.5) \qquad \int_0^\infty e^{-pt} \, dp = \frac{1}{t}$$

Hence we obtain

$$(11.6) \qquad \int_0^\infty \frac{g(p)}{p} \, dp = \int_0^\infty \frac{h(t) \, dt}{t}$$

As an example of the use of this theorem, let it be required to evaluate the integral

$$(11.7) \qquad \int_0^\infty \frac{\sin at \, dt}{t} \qquad \text{where } a > 0$$

We have from the table of transforms

$$(11.8) \qquad L \sin at = \frac{ap}{p^2 + a^2}$$

Hence, by (11.6), we have

$$(11.9) \qquad \int_0^\infty \frac{\sin at \, dt}{t} = \int_0^\infty \frac{a \, dp}{p^2 + a^2} = \tan^{-1} \frac{p}{a} \Big|_0^\infty$$

$$= \frac{\pi}{2}$$

As another example, consider the integral

$$(11.10) \qquad \int_0^\infty \frac{e^{-at} - e^{-bt}}{t} \, dt$$

From the table of transforms we have

$$(11.11) \qquad Le^{-at} = \frac{p}{p+a} \qquad Le^{-bt} = \frac{p}{p+b}$$

Hence by the use of (11.6) we have

$$(11.12) \qquad \int_0^\infty \frac{(e^{-at} - e^{-bt}) \, dt}{t} = \int_0^\infty \left(\frac{dp}{p+a} - \frac{dp}{p+b} \right)$$

$$= \ln \frac{p+a}{p+b} \Big|_0^\infty = \ln \frac{b}{a}$$

Another method of evaluating definite integrals operationally depends on the introduction of a parameter in the integrand. As an example, consider the integral

$$(11.13) \qquad I = \int_0^\infty e^{-x^2} \, dx$$

As was seen in Chap. 11, Sec. 11, this integral is usually evaluated by a trick. Now let us consider the transform

$$(11.14) \qquad Le^{-tx^2} = \frac{p}{p + x^2}$$

Hence we have

$$(11.15) \qquad L \int_0^\infty e^{-tx^2} \, dx = \int_0^\infty \frac{p \, dx}{p + x^2} = \sqrt{p} \, \tan^{-1} \frac{x}{\sqrt{p}} \Big|_0^\infty$$

$$= \frac{\pi}{2} \sqrt{p}$$

Therefore

$$(11.16) \qquad \int_0^\infty e^{-tx^2} \, dx = L^{-1} \frac{\pi}{2} \sqrt{p}$$

But

$$(11.17) \qquad L^{-1} \sqrt{p} = \frac{1}{\sqrt{\pi t}}$$

Hence we have

$$(11.18) \qquad \int_0^\infty e^{-tx^2} \, dx = \frac{\pi}{2} \frac{1}{\sqrt{\pi t}} = \frac{1}{2} \sqrt{\frac{\pi}{t}}$$

Placing $t = 1$, we finally obtain

$$(11.19) \qquad \int_0^\infty e^{-x^2} \, dx = \frac{\sqrt{\pi}}{2}$$

As another example, consider the integral

(11.20) $$\int_0^\infty \frac{\cos x \, dx}{1 + x^2}$$

In this case we make use of the transform

(11.21) $$L \cos tx = \frac{p^2}{p^2 + x^2}$$

Hence we have

$$(11.22) \quad L \int_0^\infty \frac{\cos tx \, dx}{1 + x^2} = \int_0^\infty \frac{p^2 \, dx}{(p^2 + x^2)(1 + x^2)}$$

$$= \frac{p^2}{p^2 - 1} \int_0^\infty \left(\frac{1}{x^2 + 1} - \frac{1}{p^2 + x^2} \right) dx$$

$$= \frac{\pi}{2} \frac{p}{p + 1}$$

Therefore we have

(11.23) $$\int_0^\infty \frac{\cos tx \, dx}{1 + x^2} = L^{-1} \frac{\pi}{2} \frac{p}{p + 1} = \frac{\pi}{2} e^{-t}$$

If we now place $t = 1$, we finally obtain

(11.24) $$\int_0^\infty \frac{\cos x \, dx}{1 + x^2} = \frac{\pi}{2e}$$

These examples are typical and illustrate the general procedure.

A critical examination of the validity of the above procedure reveals that it is dependent on the possibility of reversing the order of integration of integrals involving infinite limits.*

12. Applications of the Laplace Transform to the Solution of Linear Integral Equations.   An integral equation is one in which the unknown function appears under the sign of integration.   The importance of integral equations in mathematical applications to physical problems lies in the fact that it is usually possible to reformulate a differential equation together with its boundary conditions as a single integral equation.   In this section certain types of integral equations that can be solved by the use of the Laplace-transform theory will be discussed.

a. Volterra's Integral Equation of the Second Kind with a Difference Kernel.   Consider the equation

(12.1) $$F(t) = G(t) - \int_0^t K(t - u)G(u) \, du$$

---

* A discussion of this will be found in H. S. Carslaw, "Fourier Series and Integrals," Dover Publications, New York, 1951.

where $F(t)$ and $K(t - u)$ are *known* functions and the function $G(t)$ is not known. This equation is known in the literature as *Volterra's integral equation of the second kind with the difference kernel* $K(t - u)$. The unknown function $G(t)$, and hence the solution of (12.1), may be readily found by the use of the Laplace-transform theory. In order to solve (12.1), introduce the following Laplace transforms:

$$(12.2) \qquad\qquad LG(t) = g(p)$$
$$(12.3) \qquad\qquad LF(t) = f(p)$$
$$(12.4) \qquad\qquad LK(t) = k(p)$$

Then, by the Faltung theorem (Theorem V), we have

$$(12.5) \qquad L \int_0^t K(t - u)G(u)\, du = \frac{g(p)k(p)}{p}$$

Hence the Laplace transform of the integral equation (12.1) is

$$(12.6) \qquad\qquad f(p) = g(p) - \frac{k(p)g(p)}{p}$$

This equation may be solved for $g(p)$ in the form

$$(12.7) \qquad\qquad g(p) = \frac{f(p)}{1 - k(p)p^{-1}}$$

The solution of (12.1) is therefore

$$(12.8) \qquad G(t) = L^{-1}g(p) = L^{-1} \frac{f(p)}{1 - k(p)/p}$$

As a simple example of this method of solution, let it be required to solve the following equation:

$$(12.9) \qquad a \sin t = G(t) - \int_0^t \sin (t - u)G(u)\, du$$

This is a special case of (12.1) with

$$(12.10) \qquad LF(t) = La \sin t = \frac{ap}{p^2 + 1} = f(p)$$

$$(12.11) \qquad LK(t) = L \sin t = \frac{p}{p^2 + 1} = k(p)$$

Therefore by (12.8) we have

$$(12.12) \qquad G(t) = L^{-1} \frac{ap}{p^2 + 1} \frac{p^2 + 1}{p^2} = L^{-1} \frac{a}{p} = at$$

b. The Liouville-Neumann Series Solution. The well-known series expansion of Liouville and von Neumann for the solution of Volterra's

Look at this next

integral equation (12.1) may be readily obtained by expanding (12.7) in the following form:

$$(12.13) \qquad g(p) = \frac{f(p)}{1 - k(p)/p} = \sum_{n=0}^{\infty} \left[\frac{k(p)}{p} \right]^n f(p) = \sum_{n=0}^{\infty} g_n(p)$$

The functions $g_n(p)$ clearly fulfill the following recurrence relation:

$$(12.14) \qquad g_n(p) = \frac{k(p)}{p} g_{n-1}(p) \qquad g_0(p) = f(p)$$

If we let

$$(12.15) \qquad L^{-1} g_n(p) = G_n(t)$$

it is evident, from (12.14) and the Faltung theorem, that

$$(12.16) \quad G_0(t) = F(t) \qquad \text{and} \qquad G_n(t) = \int_0^t K_n(t - u) F(u) \, du$$
$$n = 1, 2, 3, \ldots$$

where the functions $K_n(t)$ are given by

$$(12.17) \qquad K_n(t) = L^{-1} \frac{[k(p)]^n}{p^{n-1}} \qquad n = 1, 2, 3, \ldots$$

These functions are known as the *iterated kernels*. If the above processes converge, the solution of the integral equation (12.1) is given by

$$(12.18) \qquad G(t) = \sum_{n=0}^{\infty} G_n(t)$$

c. Volterra's Integral Equation of the First Kind with a Difference Kernel. Volterra's integral equation of the first kind with a difference kernel is a special case of (12.1) and is usually written in the following form:

$$(12.19) \qquad F(t) = \int_0^t K(t - u) G(u) \, du$$

The kernel $K(t - u)$ and the function $F(t)$ are given known functions, and it is required to determine the unknown function $G(t)$. If the Laplace transforms $f(p) = LF(t)$ and $k(p) = LK(t)$ are introduced, it is easy to show, by the same reasoning as that used in Sec. 12a, that the solution of (12.19) is given by

$$(12.20) \qquad G(t) = L^{-1} \frac{p f(p)}{k(p)}$$

In many cases of practical importance it is possible to factor the right-hand member of (12.20) and to compute the required inverse Laplace transform.   An alternative form of solution may be obtained if we write

$$(12.21) \qquad \frac{pf(p)}{k(p)} = \frac{1}{p} p^2 \frac{f(p)}{k(p)}$$

and let

$$(12.22) \qquad H(t) = L^{-1} \frac{p^2}{k(p)}$$

In terms of $H(t)$ the solution of (12.19) may be written in the following form:

$$(12.23) \qquad G(t) = \int_0^t H(t - u)F(u) \, du$$

The function $H(t)$ is called the *reciprocal kernel* of $K(t)$.

d. *Abel's Integral Equation.   The Tautochrone.*   The integral equation

$$(12.24) \qquad F(t) = \int_0^t \frac{G(u) \, du}{(t - u)^n} \qquad 0 < n < 1$$

is a special case of (12.19) and is the classical equation of Abel.   In order to obtain the solution of Abel's equation by (12.20), we have

$$(12.25) \qquad LK(t) = Lt^{-n} = p^n \Gamma(1 - n) = k(p) \qquad 0 < n < 1$$

by a table of Laplace transforms.   Hence by (12.20) the solution of (12.24) is given by

$$(12.26) \qquad G(t) = L^{-1} \frac{pf(p)}{k(p)} = L^{-1} \frac{f(p)}{p^{n-1}\Gamma(1 - n)}$$

By the use of a table of Laplace transforms we obtain the following result:

$$(12.27) \qquad L^{-1} \frac{1}{p^{n-1}\Gamma(1 - n)} = \frac{1}{\Gamma(1 - n)\Gamma(n)t^{1-n}}$$

A fundamental result of the theory of gamma functions (see Chap. 12) is that

$$(12.28) \qquad \Gamma(1 - n)\Gamma(n) = \frac{\pi}{\sin n\pi} \qquad 0 < n < 1$$

Therefore

$$(12.29) \qquad L^{-1} \frac{1}{p^{n-1}\Gamma(1 - n)} = \frac{\sin n\pi}{t^{1-n}}$$

Therefore, by an application of the Faltung theorem, we obtain

$$(12.30) \qquad L^{-1} \frac{f(p)}{p^{n-1}\Gamma(1 - n)} = \frac{\sin n\pi}{\pi} \frac{d}{dt} \int_0^t \frac{F(u) \, du}{(t - u)^{1-n}} = G(t)$$

The solution of Abel's integral equation (12.24) is therefore given by

$$(12.31) \qquad G(t) = \frac{\sin n\pi}{\pi} \frac{d}{dt} \int_0^t \frac{F(u)\, du}{(t - u)^{1-n}} \qquad 0 < n < 1$$

THE TAUTOCHRONE.   When $n = \frac{1}{2}$, Eq. (12.31) gives the solution of the classical problem of the tautochrone (the curve of equal descent).   The general form of this famous problem is to determine the path of a particle of mass m under the influence of the earth's gravitational field so that its time of fall from P (at the variable height y) to the origin at $y = 0$ shall be some given function $T(y)$ of y (see Fig. 12.1).

The time of fall of the particle from the point P to the origin 0 is given by the equation

$$(12.32) \qquad T(y) = \int_0^P \frac{ds}{v}$$

FIG. 12.1. The tautochrone.

where v is the velocity of the particle at some intermediate point of height u and ds is the line element of the required curve.   Since the particle is assumed to move without friction, the velocity v satisfies the equation of conservation of energy,

$$(12.33) \qquad \tfrac{1}{2}mv^2 = mg(y - u)$$

or

$$(12.34) \qquad v = \sqrt{2g(y - u)}$$

The line element ds of the required curve may be written in the form

$$(12.35) \qquad ds = \left(\frac{ds}{du}\right) du$$

If (12.33) and (12.35) are substituted into (12.32), the result may be written in the form

$$(12.36) \qquad T(y) = \frac{1}{\sqrt{2g}} \int_0^u \frac{(ds/du)\, du}{\sqrt{y - u}}$$

This is an Abel integral equation for the function ds/dy of the form (12.24).   By (12.31) the solution of (12.36) is seen to be

$$(12.37) \qquad \frac{ds}{dy} = \frac{\sqrt{2g}}{\pi} \frac{d}{dy} \int_0^y \frac{T(u)\, du}{\sqrt{y - u}}$$

If (12.37) is integrated with respect to y and the arc length of the required curve is measured from the origin ($y = 0$), we obtain

$$(12.38) \qquad s(y) = \frac{\sqrt{2g}}{\pi} \int_0^y \frac{T(u)\, du}{\sqrt{y - u}}$$

If the function $T(y)$ is specified, (12.38) enables the actual path to be determined.

In the problem of the tautochrone the time of falling is given to be independent of the height, so that

$$(12.39) \qquad\qquad T(y) = T_0 \qquad \text{a given constant}$$

In this case the integration of (12.38) may be performed, and the result is

$$(12.40) \qquad\qquad s(y) = \frac{2T_0}{\pi} \sqrt{2gy}$$

Therefore

$$(12.41) \qquad\qquad \frac{ds}{dy} = \frac{T_0}{\pi} \sqrt{\frac{2g}{y}} = \sqrt{1 + \left(\frac{dx}{dy}\right)^2}$$

The differential equation of the required curve is therefore

$$(12.42) \qquad\qquad 1 + \left(\frac{dx}{dy}\right)^2 = \frac{2gT_0^2}{\pi^2 y} = \frac{a}{y}$$

where

$$(12.43) \qquad\qquad a = \frac{2gT_0^2}{\pi^2}$$

Equation (12.42) may be written in the form

$$(12.44) \qquad\qquad dx = \sqrt{\frac{a - y}{y}}\, dy$$

The integration of (12.44) may be easily effected by the following trigonometric substitution:

$$(12.45) \qquad\qquad y = a \sin^2 \frac{\theta}{2}$$

With this substitution (12.43) gives

$$(12.46) \qquad\qquad dx = a \cos^2 \frac{\theta}{2}\, d\theta = \frac{a}{2}(1 + \cos\theta)\, d\theta$$

Since the curve must pass through the origin, $x = 0$ when $y = 0$. Therefore the parametric equations of the tautochrone are

$$(12.47) \quad x = \frac{a}{2}(\theta + \sin\theta) \qquad y = \frac{a}{2}(1 - \cos\theta) \qquad a = \frac{2gT_0^2}{\pi^2}$$

These are the equations of a cycloid generated by the motion of a point on a circle of radius $a/2$ as the circle rolls along the lower side of the line $y = a$.

e. Integral Equations of the First Kind Reducible to Equations with a Difference Kernel. Integral equations of the type

(12.48) $$F(t) = \int_0^t K(tu)G(u)\, du$$

and

(12.49) $$F(t) = \int_0^t K\left(\frac{t}{u}\right) G(u)\, du$$

sometimes occur in the analysis of physical problems. In these equations the kernel is a function either of the product tu or of the quotient t/u of the two variables t and u. It is possible to transform these integral equations into equations with a kernel depending on the difference $x - y$ by the substitutions $t = e^x$ and $u = e^{-y}$ in (12.48) and $t = e^x$ and $u = e^y$ in (12.49). The transformed equations are then of the type (12.19).

f. The Solution of Linear Time-varying Electrical Circuits by the Use of Integral Equations. Electrical circuits whose parameters vary with the time alone are of considerable techni-cal importance. The response of circuits of this class may sometimes be obtained by formulating the cir-cuit equations in terms of linear in-tegral equations. To illustrate the use of integral equations in electrical-circuit problems of this type, con-sider the electrical circuit of Fig. 12.2.

FIG. 12.2. Linear variable circuit.

This circuit consists of the con-stant resistance, inductance, and elastance parameters R, L, S, in series with a time-varying resistance $R_0(t)$ and an electromotive force $e(t)$. Both $R_0(t)$ and $e(t)$ are known functions of the time t, and it is desired to determine the current $i(t)$ as a function of the time. By Kirchhoff's second law the differential equation that expresses the potential balance of the circuit is

(12.50) $$\frac{L\, di}{dt} + Ri + S \int i\, dt + R_0(t)i(t) = e(t)$$

This is the linear integrodifferential equation satisfied by the current of the circuit. In order to transform (12.50) into an integral equation, introduce the following Laplace transforms:

(12.51) $$Li(t) = I(p) \qquad Le(t) = E(p)$$

By the use of these transforms (12.50) is transformed into the equation

(12.52) $$\left(Lp + R + \frac{S}{p}\right) I(p) + L[R_0(t)i(t)] = E(p)$$

where it has been assumed that the initial current and the initial charge of the circuit are both zero at $t = 0$. Let $Z(p)$, the operational impedance of the constant part of the circuit, be given by

$$(12.53) \qquad Z(p) = Lp + R + \frac{S}{p}$$

and let

$$(12.54) \qquad L[R_0(t)i(t)] = G(p)$$

With this notation (12.52) may be written in the form

$$(12.55) \qquad I(p) = \frac{E(p)}{Z(p)} - \frac{G(p)}{Z(p)}$$

Now let

$$(12.56) \qquad H(p) = \frac{p}{Z(p)} = \frac{1}{Lp^2 + Rp + S}$$

and

$$(12.57) \qquad h(t) = L^{-1}H(p) = L^{-1}\frac{1}{Lp^2 + Rp + S}$$

In terms of the transform $H(p)$, (12.55) may be written in the following form:

$$(12.58) \qquad I(p) = \frac{H(p)E(p)}{p} - \frac{H(p)G(p)}{p}$$

By the Faltung theorem the inverse transform of (12.58) may be written in the following form:

$$(12.59) \quad i(t) = \int_0^t h(t-u)e(u)\,du - \int_0^t h(t-u)R_0(u)i(u)\,du$$

This is the integral equation satisfied by the current $i(t)$ of the circuit of Fig. 12.2.

Let

$$(12.60) \qquad i_0(t) = \int_0^t h(t-u)e(u)\,du$$

This is the current that would flow in the circuit if the variable resistance $R_0(t)$ were placed equal to zero. $i_0(t)$ thus represents the current that would flow in a series circuit having the constant parameters R, L, and S under the influence of the electromotive force $e(t)$. The integral equation (12.59) may therefore be written in the form

$$(12.61) \qquad i(t) = i_0(t) - \int_0^t h(t-u)e(u)\,du$$

This integral equation is of a type that has been studied by the eminent mathematician Vito Volterra. Volterra has shown that the solution of

(12.61) may be obtained in the following form,

$$(12.62) \quad i(t) = \sum_{n=0}^{\infty} (-1)^n i_n(t) = i_0(t) - i_1(t) + i_2(t) - i_3(t) + \cdots$$

where the sequence of functions $i_k(t)$ is given by the equations

$$i_0(t) = \int_0^t h(t - u)e(u)\, du$$

$$i_1(t) = \int_0^t h(t - u)R_0(u)i_0(u)\, du$$

(12.63)

$$i_2(t) = \int_0^t h(t - u)R_0(u)i_1(u)\, du$$

$$\cdots \cdots \cdots \cdots \cdots \cdots \cdots \cdots$$

$$i_{n+1}(t) = \int_0^t h(t - u)R_0(u)i_n(u)\, du$$

It is easy to show that the series (12.62) is absolutely convergent and satisfies the integral equation (12.61). For purposes of computation it is convenient to express the sequence of functions (12.63) in terms of the following Laplace transforms:

$$i_0(t) = L^{-1}\frac{E(p)}{Z(p)}$$

$$i_1(t) = L^{-1}\frac{L[R_0(t)i_0(t)]}{Z(p)}$$

(12.64)

$$i_2(t) = L^{-1}\frac{L[R_0(t)i_1(t)]}{Z(p)}$$

$$\cdots \cdots \cdots \cdots \cdots \cdots \cdots$$

$$i_{n+1}(t) = L^{-1}\frac{L[R_0(t)i_n(t)]}{Z(p)}$$

In practice, it is usually found that the sequence $i_k(t)$ may be more simply computed by Eqs. (12.64) than by (12.63) because a table of suitable Laplace transforms greatly assists in effecting the required integrations. In the usual applications it is necessary only to compute a few terms of the series (12.62) to obtain the required accuracy for the solution of practical circuit problems.

13. Solution of Ordinary Differential Equations with Variable Coefficients. It is sometimes possible, by the introduction of a Laplacian transformation, to transform certain linear differential equations with variable coefficients to other equations that may be integrated readily. By such a procedure we are able to obtain the Laplace transforms of the solutions of the original equations. Then by determining the inverses of these transforms we find the solutions of the original equations with variable coefficients.

The procedure will be illustrated by the following example:

Let us consider the Bessel differential equation of the nth order discussed in Chap. 13:

$$(13.1) \qquad \frac{d^2z}{du^2} + \frac{1}{u}\frac{dz}{du} + \left(1 - \frac{n^2}{u^2}\right)z = 0$$

In order to simplify the coefficients of the equation, let us change the variables by the equations

$$(13.2) \qquad z = u^{-n}y \qquad \text{and} \qquad u^2 = 4t$$

These changes in variable transform the equation into the form

$$(13.3) \qquad t\frac{d^2y}{dt^2} + (1 - n)\frac{dy}{dt} + y = 0$$

To transform this equation, let

$$(13.4) \qquad Y(p) = \int_0^\infty e^{-pt}y(t)\,dt$$

that is,

$$(13.5) \qquad Ly(t) = pY(p) = w(p)$$

Now, by an integration by parts, we have

$$(13.6) \qquad \int_0^\infty e^{-pt}\frac{dy}{dt}\,dt = pY(p) - y(0)$$

$$(13.7) \qquad \int_0^\infty e^{-pt}\frac{d^2y}{dt^2}\,dt = p^2Y(p) - py(0) - y'(0)$$

Differentiating (13.7) with respect to p, we obtain

$$(13.8) \qquad \frac{d}{dp}\int_0^\infty e^{-pt}\frac{d^2y}{dt^2}\,dt = -\int_0^\infty e^{-pt}\,t\frac{d^2y}{dt^2}\,dt$$

$$= \frac{d}{dp}[p^2Y(p) - py(0) - y'(0)]$$

We thus have the result

$$(13.9) \qquad \int_0^\infty e^{-pt}t\frac{d^2y}{dt^2}\,dt = y(0) - \frac{d}{dp}(p^2Y)$$

Now since

$$(13.10) \qquad y(t) = u^nz = 2^nt^{n/2}z$$

we see that

$$(13.11) \qquad y(0) = 0$$

Hence Eq. (13.3) transforms into

$$(13.12) \qquad \frac{d}{dp}(p^2Y) + (n - 1)pY - Y = 0$$

Therefore

$$(13.13) \qquad pY + p^2Y' + npY - Y = 0$$

or

$$(13.14) \qquad p\frac{d(pY)}{dp} + \left(n - \frac{1}{p}\right)pY = 0$$

If we now let

$$(13.15) \qquad w(p) = pY$$

we may write (13.14) in the form

$$(13.16) \qquad p\frac{dw}{dp} + \left(n - \frac{1}{p}\right)w = 0$$

Hence

$$(13.17) \qquad \frac{dw}{w} = -\left(n - \frac{1}{p}\right)\frac{dp}{p}$$

or

$$(13.18) \qquad \ln w = -n\ln p - \frac{1}{p} + c$$

where c is an arbitrary constant.   Therefore,

$$(13.19) \qquad w = Kp^{-n}e^{-1/p}$$

where K is a new arbitrary constant.   Now, by (13.5), we have

$$(13.20) \qquad y(t) = L^{-1}w(p) = L^{-1}Kp^{-n}e^{-1/p}$$

or

$$(13.21) \qquad 2^n t^{n/2}(u) = L^{-1}Kp^{-n}e^{-1/p}$$

Now a solution of (13.1) that is finite at $u = 0$ is

$$(13.22) \qquad z = J_n(u) = J_n(2\sqrt{t})$$

Hence we have from (13.21)

$$(13.23) \qquad Lt^{n/2}J_n(2\sqrt{t}) = \frac{K}{2^n}p^{-n}e^{-1/p}$$

where K must be properly chosen.
Expanding the right-hand member of (13.23) in inverse powers of p, calculating the inverse transforms of the individual terms of the expansion, it can be seen by comparing with the series expansion of $t^{n/2}J_n(2\sqrt{t})$ that K must have the value

$$(13.24) \qquad K = 2^n$$

Hence we have the result

(13.25) $$Lt^{n/2}J_n(2\sqrt{t}) = p^{-n}e^{-1/p}$$

If we now place $n = 0$, we obtain

(13.26) $$LJ_0(2\sqrt{t}) = e^{-1/p}$$

If we now make use of the theorem that, if

(13.27) $$Lh(t) = g(p)$$

then

(13.28) $$Lh(st) = g\left(\frac{p}{s}\right)$$

where s is a constant whose absolute value is greater than zero, we have from (13.26)

(13.29) $$LJ_0(2\sqrt{st}) = e^{-s/p}$$

If we now let

(13.30) $$s = -j$$

we obtain

(13.31) $$J_0(2\sqrt{-jt}) = \text{ber}(2\sqrt{t}) + j\,\text{bei}(2\sqrt{t}) = L^{-1}e^{j/p}$$

Placing

(13.32) $$s = +j$$

in (13.29), we have

(13.33) $$J_0(2\sqrt{jt}) = \text{ber}(2\sqrt{t}) - j\,\text{bei}(2\sqrt{t})$$
$$= L^{-1}e^{-j/p}$$

Adding Eqs. (13.31) and (13.33), we obtain

(13.34) $$L^{-1}\cos\frac{1}{p} = \text{ber}(2\sqrt{t})$$

Subtracting (13.33) from (13.31), we have

(13.35) $$L^{-1}\sin\frac{1}{p} = \text{bei}(2\sqrt{t})$$

These two transform pairs may be used to obtain many interesting properties of these functions. The procedure followed in this example on Bessel's equation may be carried out in the case of several other linear differential equations with variable coefficients and the properties of their solutions thus studied.

14. The Summation of Fourier Series by the Laplace Transform. In the mathematical analysis of problems in electrical-circuit theory, mechanical vibrations, heat conduction, and other branches of physics and engineering one frequently arrives at solutions that are expressed in the form of infinite Fourier series. For purposes of calculation it is more convenient to have the solution of these problems in closed form. It is sometimes possible to sum and interpret certain Fourier series by the use of the Laplace-transform theory. In this section a method for doing this will be given.

The method to be described is based on the fact that certain hyperbolic functions can be expressed as infinite series of exponential functions. With the notation

$$(14.1) \qquad A_k = e^{-kap} = e^{-kap}$$

the following expansions are known,

$$(14.2) \qquad \tanh ap = 1 - 2A_2 + 2A_4 - 2A_6 + \cdots$$
$$(14.3) \qquad \coth ap = 1 + 2A_2 + 2A_4 + 2A_6 + \cdots$$
$$(14.4) \qquad \frac{1}{\sinh ap} = 2(A_1 + A_3 + A_5 + A_7 + \cdots)$$
$$(14.5) \qquad \frac{1}{\cosh ap} = 2(A_1 - A_3 + A_5 - A_7 + \cdots)$$

where a is a positive real number and p is a number whose real part is positive.

The following rational-fraction expansions of these functions are also known:[*]

$$(14.6) \qquad \tanh ap = \frac{2}{ap} \sum_{n=1}^{\infty} \frac{1}{1 + \{[(2n-1)\pi]/2ap\}^2}$$

$$(14.7) \qquad \coth ap = \frac{1}{ap} \left[1 + \sum_{n=1}^{\infty} \frac{2}{1 + (n\pi/ap)^2} \right]$$

$$(14.8) \qquad \frac{1}{\cosh ap} = \frac{1}{a^2 p^2} \sum_{n=1}^{\infty} \frac{(-1)(2n-1)\pi}{1 + (n\pi/2ap)^2}$$

$$(14.9) \qquad \frac{1}{\sinh ap} = \frac{1}{ap} \left[1 + \sum_{n=1}^{\infty} (-1)^n \frac{2}{1 + (n\pi/ap)^2} \right]$$

---

[*] E. T. Whittaker and G. N. Watson, "A Course in Modern Analysis," pp. 134–136, Cambridge University Press, New York, 1927.

It is possible to expand other combinations of hyperbolic functions in a similar manner. However, the above expansions are sufficient to illustrate the general principles of the method to be described.

Example 1. In certain investigations of physical problems the following Fourier series is obtained:

$$(14.10) \qquad F_1(t) = 4\left(\frac{\sin t}{1} + \frac{\sin 3t}{3} + \frac{\sin 5t}{5} + \cdots\right)$$

$$= 4\sum_{n=1}^{\infty} \frac{\sin (2n-1)t}{2n-1} \qquad t > 0$$

The Laplace transform of the function $F_1(t)$ represented by the series (14.10) may be obtained by taking the Laplace transform of each term of the series. If this is done, one obtains

$$(14.11) \qquad LF_1(t) = \frac{4}{p}\left[\frac{1}{1 + (1/p)^2} + \frac{1}{1 + (3/p)^2} + \frac{1}{1 + (5/p)^2} + \cdots\right]$$

We notice that if in (14.6) we place

$$(14.12) \qquad a = \frac{\pi}{2}$$

then, by comparing the expansions (14.6) and (14.11), we have

$$(14.13) \qquad LF_1(t) = 2a \tanh ap = \pi \tanh \frac{\pi p}{2}$$

The right-hand member of (14.12) may now be expanded by (14.2) in the form

$$(14.14) \qquad LF_1(t) = \pi(1 - 2e^{-\pi p} + 2e^{-2\pi p} - 2e^{-3\pi p} + \cdots)$$

This is the Laplace transform of the Fourier series (14.10). The inverse transform of (14.13) may be obtained by the use of Theorem VII of Sec. 3. By the use of this theorem it is seen that the inverse transform of the first term of (14.13) is a step function of height π formed at $t = 0$. The inverse transform of the second term is a step function of height -2π formed at $t = \pi$. The inverse transform of the third term is a step function of height $+2\pi$ formed at $t = 2$, and so on. The sum of all these step

Fig. 14.1. The function $F_1(t)$.

functions is illustrated by Fig. 14.1. The graph of this figure represents the function defined by the Fourier series (14.10).

Example 2. As a second example, let it be required to interpret the following Fourier series that occurs in certain electrical and heat-conduction problems:

$$(14.15) \qquad F_2(t) = \frac{2}{\pi}\sum_{n=1}^{\infty}\frac{1}{n}\sin\frac{n\pi t}{s}$$

If the Laplace transform of sin $(n\pi t/s)$ is taken from a table of transforms, the Laplace transform of (14.15) is seen to be

$$(14.16) \qquad LF_2(t) = \frac{1}{sp} \sum_{n=1}^{\infty} \frac{2}{1 + (n\pi/sp)^2}$$

If this series is now compared with (14.7), it is seen that we have

$$(14.17) \qquad LF_2(t) = \coth sp - \frac{1}{sp}$$

By the use of (14.3) this may be written in the following form:

$$(14.18) \qquad LF_2(t) = \left(1 - \frac{1}{sp} + 2e^{-2sp} + 2e^{-4sp} + 2e^{-6sp} + \cdots\right)$$

To obtain the inverse transform of (14.18) and hence the original function $F_2(t)$, we note that the inverse transform of the first term is a unit step function formed at $t = 0$, the inverse transform of the term $-1/sp$ is $-t/s$, the inverse transform of $+2e^{-2sp}$ is a step function of height 2 that begins at $t = 2s$, etc. The sum of the various inverse transforms of (14.18) gives the function $F_2(t)$. The result is given graphically in Fig. 14.2.

Fig. 14.2. The function $F_2(t)$.

Example 3. As another example, let it be required to obtain the graph of the function represented by the following Fourier series:

$$(14.19) \qquad F_3(t) = \sum_{n=1}^{\infty} (-1)^{n-1} \frac{\sin nt}{n}$$

If the Laplace transform of (14.19) is computed, its similarity to (14.9) will be noted and the result may be transformed by (14.4) into the following form:

$$(14.20) \qquad LF_3(t) = \frac{1}{p} - 2e^{-p} - 2e^{-3p} - 2e^{-5p} - \cdots$$

The sum of the various inverse transforms gives the function $F_3(t)$. This function is given graphically by Fig. 14.3.

Fig. 14.3. The function $F_3(t)$.

Example 4. A Row of Impulses. An interesting series which arises in the analysis of the propagation of charge along a transmission line will now be considered. This series represents a row of impulses and the function it represents is important in the analysis of the disturbances created when lightning hits a transmission line.[23] The series to be considered is the following one:

$$(14.21) \qquad F_4(x) = \frac{2}{a} \sum_{n=1}^{\infty} \sin \frac{n\pi x}{a} \sin \frac{n\pi b}{a}$$

To study this series more easily, the product of sines may be transformed into two cosines and written in the following form:

$$(14.22) \qquad F_4(x) = \frac{1}{a} \sum_{n=1}^{\infty} \cos \frac{n\pi(x-b)}{a} - \frac{1}{a} \sum_{n=1}^{\infty} \cos \frac{n\pi(x-b)}{a}$$

In order to study this series by the Laplace-transform method, substitute $t = x - b$ in the first series of (14.22). This series may be written in the form

$$(14.23) \qquad \phi(t) = \frac{1}{a} \sum_{n=1}^{\infty} \cos \frac{n\pi t}{a}$$

The Laplace transform of this series is

$$(14.24) \qquad L\phi(t) = \frac{1}{a} \sum_{n=1}^{\infty} \frac{1}{1(n\pi/ap)^2}$$

By comparing (14.24) and (14.7) it can be seen that (14.24) may be written in the form

(14.25)

$$L\phi(t) = \frac{2}{a}(ap \coth ap - 1) = 2p(1 + 2e^{-2ap} + 2e^{-4ap} + 2e^{-6ap} + \cdots) - \frac{2}{a}$$

The last result is obtained by means of the expansion (14.3). The inverse transform of (14.25) may be calculated by means of (7.6) in terms of the Dirac impulse function $\delta(t)$. The result is

$$(14.26) \quad \phi(t) = 2[\delta(t) + 2\delta(t - 2a) + 2\delta(t - 4a) + 2\delta(t - 6a) + \cdots] - \frac{2}{a}$$

$$= 2[\delta(x - b) + 2\delta(x - b - 2a) + 2\delta(x - b - 4a)$$

$$+ 2\delta(x - b - 6a) + \cdots] - \frac{2}{a}$$

In the same manner the second series of (14.22) may be computed in terms of impulse functions by the substitution $t = x + b$, and it can be shown that this series represents a row of negative impulses at $x = -b$, $x = 2a - b$, etc. The impulse form of $F_4(x)$ is therefore given by

$$(14.27) \quad F_4(x) = 2[\delta(x - b) + 2\delta(x - b - 2a) + 2\delta(x - b - 4a)$$

$$+ 2\delta(x - b - 6a) + \cdots]$$

$$- 2[\delta(x + b) + 2\delta(x + b - 2a) + 2\delta(x + b - 4a)$$

$$+ 2\delta(x + b - 6a) + \cdots]$$

The function $F_4(x)$ is therefore zero for all values of x except at the places $x = b$, $b - 2a, b - 4a, \ldots$ and $x = -b, x = -b - 2a, x = -b - 4a, \ldots$, where it has values of positive and negative impulses of the Dirac type.

General Considerations. The general Fourier series may be written in the form

$$(14.28) \qquad F(t) = A_0 + \sum_{n=1}^{\infty} A_n \cos nwt + \sum_{n=1}^{\infty} B_n \sin nwt$$

where the coefficients A_n and B_n are known functions of n. The Laplace transform of (14.28) is

$$(14.29) \quad LF(t) = A_0 + \sum_{n=1}^{\infty} \frac{A_n}{1 + (nw/p)^2} + \sum_{n=1}^{\infty} \frac{wB_n}{p[1 + (nw/p)^2]}$$

The success of the method of summation described above depends upon the possibility of effecting the summations of (14.29) by the use of (14.6) to (14.9) or by formulas derivable from them. The interpretation of the Fourier series can then be carried out by the use of (14.2) to (14.5) or combinations of these expansions. In many cases, however, the summation of the fractions (14.29) may present insurmountable difficulties, and, in such cases, this method of interpretation is *not* applicable. An interesting extension of the above method will be found in a paper by Spiegel.*

PROBLEMS

Using the complex line integral of the Fourier-Mellin transformation, show that

1. $L^{-1}1 = 1(t)$ where $1(t)$ is the Heaviside "unit" function having the values

$$1(t) = \begin{cases} 0 & t < 0 \\ \frac{1}{2} & t = 0 \\ 1 & t > 0 \end{cases}$$

2. $L^{-1} \dfrac{p}{p + a} = e^{-at} \qquad t > 0.$

3. $L^{-1} \dfrac{p^2}{p^2 + a^2} = \cos at \qquad t > 0.$

4. $L^{-1} \dfrac{p}{p^2 + a^2} = \dfrac{\sin at}{a} \qquad t > 0.$

5. $L^{-1} \dfrac{p}{(p + a)^n} = \dfrac{e^{-at}t^{n-1}}{(n - 1)!} \qquad t > 0 \qquad n$ a positive integer.

6. $L^{-1} \dfrac{p}{(p^2 + a^2)^2} = \dfrac{\sin at}{2a^3} - \dfrac{t \cos at}{2a^2} \qquad t > 0.$

7. Show that $L^{-1} \dfrac{p}{\sqrt{p^2 + a^2}} = J_0(at).$

* M. R. Spiegel, The Dirac Delta-function and the Summation of Fourier Series, *Journal of Applied Physics*, vol. 23, no. 8, pp. 906–909, August, 1952.

HINT: Expand the left-hand member into a series of inverse powers of p, compute the inverse transform of the individual terms, and show that this gives the series expansion for $J_0(at)$.

8. Show that $L^{-1} \tanh (Tp/2) = h(t)$, where $h(t)$ is the meander function given by Fig. P 8.

FIG. P 8

9. Show that $L^{-1} \sqrt{\dfrac{p}{p + 2a}} = e^{-at}J_0(jat)$.

10. Show that the solution of the differential equation $d^2y/dt^2 + a^2y = F(t)$ subject to the initial conditions

$$\left. \begin{array}{l} y = 0 \\ y' = 0 \end{array} \right\} \quad \text{at } t = 0$$

is

$$y = \frac{1}{a} \int_0^t F(u) \sin a(t - u) \, du$$

11. Solve the integral equation

$$F(t) = a \sin bt + c \int_0^t \sin b(t - u)F(u) \, du \qquad b > c > 0$$

$$Ans. \ F(t) = \frac{ab}{\sqrt{b^2 - bc}} \sin t \sqrt{b^2 - bc}.$$

12. A particle of mass m can perform small oscillations about a position of equilibrium under a restoring force mn^2 times the displacement. It is started from rest by a constant force F_0 which acts for a time T and then ceases. Show that the amplitude of the subsequent oscillation is $2F_0/mn^2 \sin (nT/2)$.

13. Three flywheels A, B, C of moments of inertia $3I$, $4I$, $3I$, respectively, are connected by equal shafts of stiffness k and negligible moment of inertia. At $t = 0$, when the system is at rest and unstrained, A is suddenly given an angular velocity w. Show that the subsequent angular velocity of c is

$$\frac{w}{10} \left(3 - 5 \cos nt + 2 \cos nt \ \sqrt{\frac{5}{2}} \right)$$

where $n^2 = k/3I$.

14. An electrical transmission line of resistance R, capacitance C, inductance L, and leakage conductance G per unit length is short-circuited at the end $x = s$, and at $t = 0$ a constant electromotive force is impressed on the line at the end $x = 0$. If the parameters of the line satisfy the relation $RC = LG$, determine the subsequent potential and current distribution along the line.

15. A uniform prismatic bar of density ρ and Young's modulus E is at rest with its end $x = s$ free to move. At $t = 0$ a constant force F_0 is applied to the rod at $x = 0$. Find the subsequent displacement of the rod.

16. A uniform prismatic bar is hung vertically, and its lower end is clamped so that its displacement is zero at all points. At $t = 0$ it is released so that it hangs from its upper point. Find the subsequent motion of the rod.

17. An electrical cable of length s is short-circuited at $x = s$. The cable has a capacitance C and resistance R per unit length. Initially the current and potential along the cable are zero. At $t = 0$ a constant electromotive force E_0 is applied to the cable at $x = 0$. Find the subsequent current and potential distribution along the cable.

18. Show that the transform of the full-wave rectification curve of a sine wave $|\sin t|$ is given by

$$L \, |\sin t| = \frac{p}{p^2 + 1} \coth \frac{\pi p}{2}$$

19. A uniform rod has its sides thermally insulated and is initially at a temperature v_0. At time zero the end $x = 0$ is cooled to temperature zero and afterward maintained at that temperature. The end $x = s$ is kept at temperature v_0. Find the variation in temperature at other points of the rod.

20. Show that $LSi(t) = \cot^{-1} p$, where $Si(t)$ is the *sine integral function* defined by

$$Si(t) = \int_0^t \frac{\sin u}{u} \, du$$

21. Show that $LEi(-t) = -\ln (p + 1)$, where $Ei(u)$ is the *exponential integral* defined by

$$Ei(u) = \int_{-\infty}^u \frac{e^x \, dx}{x}$$

Evaluate the following integrals operationally:

22. $\displaystyle \int_0^\infty \frac{\sin tx \, dx}{\sqrt{x}} = \sqrt{\frac{\pi}{2t}} \qquad t > 0.$

23. $\displaystyle \int_{-\infty}^{+\infty} \frac{x \sin tx}{a^2 + x^2} \, dx = \pi e^{-at} \qquad a > 0 \qquad t > 0.$

24. $\displaystyle \int_0^\infty \frac{e^{-tx^2}}{1 + x^2} \, dx = \frac{\pi}{2} e^t \operatorname{erf} (\sqrt{t}).$

APPENDIX: THE LAPLACE TRANSFORMATION

The modern theory of the operational calculus, a mathematical method that has proved to be such a powerful mathematical tool in the study of the transient behavior of electrical circuits, is based on the following integral, known in the mathematical literature as the *Bromwich-Wagner integral:*

$$(1) \qquad\qquad h(t) = \frac{1}{2\pi j} \int_{c-j\infty}^{c+j\infty} \frac{e^{pt} g(p) \, dp}{p}$$

The integration is supposed to be performed in the complex p plane, and the integral is assumed to converge. Following van der Pol,[11,18] we introduce the notation

$$(2) \qquad\qquad g(p) \doteqdot h(t)$$

for the relationship between two functions which satisfy Eq. (1). Under certain restrictions on the function $g(p)$, the integral (1) possesses the inversion

$$(3) \qquad\qquad \frac{g(p)}{p} = \int_0^\infty e^{-pt} h(t) \, dt$$

This integral is known in the operational literature as *Carson's integral*. Mathematicians speak of the relation (3) as a Laplacian transformation of $h(t)$ to the function $g(p)/p$. The relations (1) and (3) taken together are known in the mathematical literature as the Fourier-Mellin integral theorem.[3]

The expressions (2) and (3) are valid if either one of the following two groups of conditions *a* or *b* is satisfied:

a. 1. $g(p)/p$ is an analytic function of the complex variable p, having no points of singularity in any finite region situated to the right of the straight line Re $p = a$ parallel to the imaginary axis.

2. There exists a positive number e_0 such that

$$\lim_{\substack{p \to \infty \\ \text{Re } p > a}} |p^e g(p)| = 0 \qquad \text{for } e < e_0$$

b. 1. $g(p)/p$ is an analytic function of the complex variable p, having no points of singularity in any finite region situated to the right of the two straight lines L_1 and L_2 defined by

$$p = a + re^{\pm j\phi} \qquad j = \sqrt{-1} \qquad \pi > \phi > \frac{\pi}{2}$$

2. A positive number e_0 exists such that

$$\lim_{|p| \to \infty} \left| \frac{p^e g(p)}{p} \right| = 0 \qquad \text{for } e < e_0$$

p to the right of L_1 and L_2.

Operators satisfying either the conditions *a* or the conditions *b* are known as *restricted operators*. The solution of problems concerning dissipative electrical networks is always expressed by restricted operators, but nonrestricted operators sometimes appear as a consequence of evaluating the complete solution by splitting it into parts.

It frequently happens that the inverse of the transform $p^n g(p)$ must be found. That is, $h_n(t)$ in the expression

$$(4) \qquad h_n(t) \doteq p^n g(p)$$

where n is a positive integer, $g(p)$ is a restricted operator of class *b*, but the operator $p^n g(p)$ is a nonrestricted operator, must be determined. However, it is easy to show that, if the integral

$$(5) \qquad h(t) - \frac{1}{2\pi j} \int_{L_1 L_2} \frac{e^{pt} g(p) \, dp}{p}$$

as defined by condition *b*, converges, then the integral

$$(6) \qquad \frac{d^n h}{dt^n} = \frac{1}{2\pi j} \int_{L_1 L_2} \frac{p^n e^{pt} g(p) \, dp}{p}$$

will converge for $t \geq t_0$, where t_0 is positive but arbitrarily small.

Impulse Functions. Placing $g(p) = 1$ in (5), we obtain

$$(7) \qquad h(t) = \frac{1}{2\pi j} \int_{c-j\infty}^{c+j\infty} \frac{e^{pt} \, dp}{p}$$

The function $h(t)$, corresponding to the operator $g(p) = 1$, may be shown by the theory of residues to have the following values:

$$(8) \qquad h(t) = \begin{cases} 0 & t < 0 \\ \frac{1}{2} & t = 0 \\ 1 & t > 0 \end{cases}$$

It is thus seen that $h(t)$ is in this case equal to the unit function $1(t)$ of Heaviside, and we may place

$$(9) \qquad 1(t) \doteq 1$$

Now if we place $g(p) = p$ (which is unrestricted) in the integral (5), we obtain the following values:

$$(10) \qquad p \doteq \begin{cases} 0 & t < 0 \\ \infty & t = 0 \\ 0 & t > 0 \end{cases}$$

Following van der Pol,[11,18] we can place

$$(11) \qquad \delta(t) \doteq p$$

where $\delta(t)$ is the impulse function which has been so extensively used by Dirac in quantum mechanics. The function $\delta(t)$ has the property that

$$(12) \qquad \int_{-\infty}^{+\infty} f(t)\, \delta(t - a)\, dt = f(a)$$

where $f(t)$ is a continuous function of t, and

$$(13) \qquad \int_{-\infty}^{+\infty} \delta(t)\, dt = 1$$

We may thus treat $\delta(t)$ as an ordinary function having the properties (12) and (13). $\delta(t)$ can be formally differentiated an unlimited number of times, and we write in general

$$(14) \qquad p^n \doteq \delta^{[n-1]}(t)$$

where $\delta^{[n-1]}(t)$ is an impulse function of the nth order with the property that

$$(15) \qquad \int_{-\infty}^{+\infty} f(t)\delta^{[n]}(t - a)\, dt = f^{[n]}(a)$$

and

$$(16) \qquad \delta^{[n]}(t) = \begin{cases} 0 & t \neq 0 \\ \infty & t = 0 \end{cases}$$

TABLE 1. THE BASIC THEOREMS OF THE OPERATIONAL CALCULUS

Starting from the fundamental formulas (1) and (3), it is possible to deduce some very powerful theorems which are of the utmost importance in the transient analysis of networks. For a proof of these theorems, the reader is referred to the work of van der Pol.[11,18]

If we have two functions satisfying the relations (1) and (3), so that

$$(2) \qquad g(p) \doteq h(t)$$

then we have the following theorems:

$$g\left(\frac{p}{s}\right) \doteqdot h(st) \qquad s > 0 \tag{1}$$

$$pg(p) - ph(0) \doteqdot \frac{dh}{dt} \tag{2}$$

$$p^n g(p) - \sum_{k=0}^{k=n-1} h^{[k]}(0)p^{(n-k)} \doteqdot \frac{d^n h(t)}{dt^n} \tag{3}$$

$$\int_{-\infty}^{0} h(t)\,dt + \frac{g(p)}{p} \doteqdot \int_{-\infty}^{t} h(t)\,dt \tag{4}$$

$$\frac{p}{p+a}\,g(p+a) \doteqdot e^{-at}h(t) \tag{5}$$

$$e^{-ap}g(p) \doteqdot \begin{cases} 0 & t < a \\ h(t-a) & t > a \end{cases} \qquad a > 0 \tag{6}$$

$$e^{ap}g(p) \doteqdot h(t+a) \qquad a > 0$$
$$\text{if } h(t) = 0 \qquad 0 < t < a \tag{7}$$

$$\left(-\frac{pd}{dp}\right)^n g(p) \doteqdot \left(\frac{td}{dt}\right)^n h(t) \qquad n > 0 \tag{8}$$

$$p\left(-\frac{d}{dp}\right)^n \frac{g(p)}{p} \doteqdot t^n h(t) \qquad n > 0 \tag{9}$$

$$\int_p^\infty \frac{g(p)\,dp}{p} \doteqdot \int_0^t \frac{h(u)\,du}{u} \tag{10}$$

$$\int_0^p \frac{g(p)\,dp}{p} \doteqdot \int_t^\infty \frac{h(u)\,du}{u} \tag{11}$$

$$\int_0^\infty \frac{g(p)\,dp}{p} = \int_0^\infty \frac{h(t)\,dt}{t} \qquad \text{an ordinary equality} \tag{12}$$

$$\lim_{|p|\to\infty} g(p) = \lim_{t\to 0} h(t) \qquad \text{an ordinary equality} \tag{13}$$

a. If $g(p)$ has no points of singularity in any finite region situated to the right of the two straight lines L_1, L_2 defined by

$$p = e^{\pm j\phi} \qquad \pi > \phi > \frac{\pi}{2}$$

b. And if $g(p)$ tends uniformly toward a finite value $g(0)$ when $|p| \to 0$ on or to the right of the lines L_1 and L_2, then

$$\lim_{|p|\to 0} g(p) = \lim_{t\to\infty} h(t) \qquad \text{an ordinary equality} \tag{14}$$

$$p\int_p^\infty \int_p^\infty \cdots \int_p^\infty \frac{g(p)\,(dp)^n}{p} \doteqdot \frac{h(t)}{t^n} \tag{15}$$

If
$$g_1(p) \doteqdot h_1(t) \qquad \text{and} \qquad g_2(p) \doteqdot h_2(t)$$

then
$$\frac{g_1(p)g_2(p)}{p} \doteqdot \int_0^t h_1(u)h_2(t-u)\,du$$

$$\doteqdot \int_0^t h_2(u)h_1(t-u)\,du \tag{16}$$

If $g(p) = N(p)/D(p)$, where $N(p)$ and $D(p)$ are polynomials in p and the degree of the polynomial $D(p)$ is at least as high as the degree of the polynomial $N(p)$, then, if the polynomial $D(p)$ has the n *distinct* zeros $(p_1, p_2, \ldots, p_n)$ and $p = 0$ is not a zero of $D(p)$, it follows that

$$\frac{N(p)}{D(p)} \doteq \frac{N(0)}{D(0)} + \sum_{r=1}^{r=n} \frac{N(p_r)e^{p_r t}}{p_r D'(p_r)} \qquad \text{where } D'(p_r) = \frac{dD}{dp}\bigg|_{p=p_r} \qquad (17)$$

If $\qquad\qquad g(p) = \dfrac{N(q)}{D(q)}$

where q is a function of p, $q = q(p)$, $D(q)$ and $N(q)$ are rational polynomials of q, $N(q)$ is of a lower degree than $D(q)$, $D(q) = 0$ has n distinct roots q_r, and zero is not a root of $D(q) = 0$, then

$$\frac{N(q)}{D(q)} \doteq \frac{N(0)}{D(0)} + \sum_{r=1}^{r=n} \frac{N(q_r)}{q_r D'(q_r)} b(t,q_r)$$

where $\qquad\qquad \dfrac{q}{q - q_r} \doteq b(t,q_r) \qquad \text{and} \qquad D'(q_r) = \dfrac{dD}{dq}\bigg|_{q=q_r} \qquad (18)$

If $\qquad\qquad g(p) = \displaystyle\sum_{r=0}^{\infty} a_r p^r + p^{\frac{1}{2}} \sum_{r=0}^{\infty} b_r p^r$

where both series are convergent series in p, then

$$g(p) \doteq a_0 + \frac{1}{(\pi t)^{\frac{1}{2}}}\left[b_0 - \frac{b_1}{2t} + \frac{1 \times 3 b_2}{(2t)^2} - \frac{1 \times 3 \times 5 b_3}{(2t)^3} + \cdots \right] \qquad \text{for } t > 0 \quad (19)$$

These basic theorems are very powerful when used in connection with a table of transforms in the solution of transients in networks. Theorem 17 is the conventional Heaviside expansion formula, while Theorem 18 is a generalization of the conventional Heaviside formula. Theorem 19 is known in the operational literature as *Heaviside's third rule*.

TABLE 2

This table contains a list of transforms of great value for the solution of numerous special cases of the foregoing general theory. These transforms may be obtained by evaluating the basic integral (1) or (3). The transforms given here are those most frequently occurring in the transient solution of electrical problems, and a collection of these results in one table should be of value.

$$1 \doteq 1(t) \qquad (1)$$

where $1(t)$ is the Heaviside *unit function* having the values

$$1(t) = \begin{cases} 0 & t < 0 \\ \frac{1}{2} & t = 0 \\ 1 & t > 0 \end{cases}$$

$$p \doteq \delta(t) \qquad (2)$$

where $\delta(t)$ is the delta function of Dirac. It satisfies the relations

$$\delta(t) = \begin{cases} \infty & t = 0 \\ 0 & t \neq 0 \end{cases}$$

$$\int_{-\infty}^{\infty} \delta(t)\, dt = 1 \qquad \int_{-\infty}^{+\infty} f(t)\delta(t - a)\, dt = f(a)$$

where $f(t)$ is an integrable continuous function of the real variable t.

$$p^n \doteq \delta^{[n-1]}(t) \qquad (3)$$

where n is a positive integer and $\delta^{[n-1]}(t)$ is the Dirac impulse function of the nth order and has the properties that

$$\int_{-\infty}^{+\infty} f(t)\,\delta^{[n]}(t-a)\,dt = f^{[n]}(a)$$

and

$$\delta^{[n-1]}(t) = \begin{cases} 0 & t \neq 0 \\ \infty & t = 0 \end{cases}$$

$$p^n \doteqdot \frac{t^{-n}}{\Gamma(1-n)} \tag{4}$$

except for n a positive integer, where $\Gamma(n)$ is the gamma function of the real argument n.

$$p^{\frac{1}{2}} \doteqdot \frac{1}{\sqrt{\pi t}} \tag{5}$$

$$p^{\frac{3}{2}} \doteqdot -\sqrt{\frac{2}{\pi}}\,\frac{1}{(2t)^{\frac{3}{2}}} \tag{6}$$

$$p^{\frac{5}{2}} \doteqdot \sqrt{\frac{2}{\pi}}\,\frac{1\times 3}{(2t)^{\frac{5}{2}}} \tag{7}$$

$$p^{\frac{7}{2}} \doteqdot -\sqrt{\frac{2}{\pi}}\,\frac{1\times 3\times 5}{(2t)^{\frac{7}{2}}} \tag{8}$$

$$p^{-\frac{1}{2}} \doteqdot \sqrt{\frac{2}{\pi}}\,(2t)^{\frac{1}{2}} \tag{9}$$

$$p^{-\frac{3}{2}} \doteqdot \sqrt{\frac{2}{\pi}}\,\frac{(2t)^{\frac{3}{2}}}{1\times 3} \tag{10}$$

$$p^{-\frac{5}{2}} \doteqdot \sqrt{\frac{2}{\pi}}\,\frac{(2t)^{\frac{5}{2}}}{1\times 3\times 5} \tag{11}$$

$$p^{-\frac{7}{2}} \doteqdot \sqrt{\frac{2}{\pi}}\,\frac{(2t)^{\frac{7}{2}}}{1\times 3\times 5\times 7} \tag{12}$$

$$\frac{p^2}{p+a} \doteqdot \delta(t) - ae^{-at} \tag{13}$$

$$\frac{p}{p+a} \doteqdot e^{-at} \tag{14}$$

$$\frac{1}{p+a} \doteqdot \frac{1}{a}\,(1 - e^{-at}) \tag{15}$$

$$\frac{1}{p(p+a)} \doteqdot \frac{t}{a} - \frac{1}{a^2} + \frac{e^{-at}}{a^2} \tag{16}$$

$$\frac{p^2}{(p+a)(p+b)} \doteqdot \frac{1}{(a-b)}\,(ae^{-at} - be^{-bt}) \tag{17}$$

$$\frac{p}{(p+a)(p+b)} \doteqdot \frac{1}{(a-b)}\,(e^{-bt} - e^{-at}) \tag{18}$$

$$\frac{\omega p}{p^2 + \omega^2} \doteqdot \sin \omega t \tag{19}$$

$$\frac{p^2}{p^2 + \omega^2} \doteqdot \cos \omega t \tag{20}$$

$$\frac{\omega^2}{p^2 + \omega^2} \doteqdot 1 - \cos \omega t \tag{21}$$

$$\frac{\omega p}{p^2 - \omega^2} \doteqdot \sinh \omega t \tag{22}$$

$$\frac{p^2}{p^2 - \omega^2} \doteqdot \cosh \omega t \tag{23}$$

$$\frac{\omega p}{(p + b)^2 + \omega^2} \doteq e^{-bt} \sin \omega t \tag{24}$$

$$\frac{p(p + b)}{(p + b)^2 + \omega^2} \doteq e^{-bt} \cos \omega t \tag{25}$$

$$\frac{\omega p}{(p + b)^2 - \omega^2} \doteq e^{-bt} \sinh \omega t \tag{26}$$

$$\frac{p\omega \cos \phi \pm p^2 \sin \phi}{p^2 + \omega^2} \doteq \sin (\omega t \pm \phi) \tag{27}$$

$$\frac{p^2 \cos \phi \mp \omega p \sin \phi}{p^2 + \omega^2} \doteq \cos (\omega t \pm \phi) \tag{28}$$

$$\frac{\omega p \cos \phi \pm p(p + b) \sin \phi}{(p + b)^2 + \omega^2} \doteq e^{-bt} \sin (\omega t \pm \phi) \tag{29}$$

$$\frac{p(p + b) \cos \phi \mp \omega p \sin \phi}{(p + b)^2 + \omega^2} \doteq e^{-bt} \cos (\omega t \pm \phi) \tag{30}$$

In the following three transforms (32 to 34) let

$$\omega^2 = \omega_0^2 - a^2 \qquad \tan \phi = \frac{\omega}{a}$$

and let $(-m)$ and $(-n)$ be the two roots of

$$p^2 + 2ap + \omega_0^2 = 0 \tag{31}$$

Then
$$\frac{p^2}{p^2 + 2ap + \omega_0^2} \doteq -\frac{\omega_0}{\omega} e^{-at} \sin (\omega t - \phi) \qquad \text{if } \omega_0^2 > a^2$$

$$\doteq \frac{1}{n - m} (ne^{-nt} - me^{-mt}) \qquad \text{if } a^2 > \omega_0^2 \tag{32}$$

$$\doteq e^{-at}(1 - at) \qquad \text{if } a^2 = \omega_0^2$$

$$\frac{p}{p^2 + 2ap + \omega_0^2} \doteq \frac{e^{-at}}{\omega} \sin \omega t \qquad \text{if } \omega_0^2 > a^2$$

$$\doteq \frac{1}{n - m} (e^{-mt} - e^{-nt}) \qquad \text{if } a^2 > \omega_0^2 \tag{33}$$

$$\doteq te^{-at} \qquad \text{if } a^2 = \omega_0^2$$

$$\frac{1}{p^2 + 2ap + \omega_0^2} \doteq \frac{1}{\omega_0^2} \left[1 - \frac{\omega_0}{\omega} e^{-at} \sin (\omega t + \phi) \right] \qquad \text{if } \omega_0^2 > a^2$$

$$\doteq \frac{1}{\omega_0^2} \left[1 - \frac{\omega_0^2}{n - m} \left(\frac{e^{-mt}}{m} - \frac{e^{-nt}}{n} \right) \right] \qquad \text{if } a^2 > \omega_0^2 \tag{34}$$

$$\doteq \frac{1}{\omega_0^2} [1 - e^{-at}(1 + at)] \qquad \text{if } a^2 = \omega_0^2$$

$$\frac{p^2}{(p + a)^2} \doteq e^{-at}(1 - at) \tag{35}$$

$$\frac{p}{(p + a)^2} \doteq te^{-at} \tag{36}$$

$$\frac{1}{(p + a)^2} \doteq \frac{1}{a^2} [1 - e^{-at}(1 + at)] \tag{37}$$

$$\frac{1}{(p + a)^n} \doteq \frac{1}{\Gamma(n)} \int_0^t e^{-u} u^{n-1} \, du \tag{38}$$

where $n \geq 0$.

$$\frac{p}{(p^2 + \omega^2)(p + a)} \doteq \frac{1}{\omega \sqrt{a^2 + \omega^2}} [e^{-at} \sin \beta + \sin (\omega t - \beta)] \tag{39}$$

where
$$\beta = \tan^{-1}\frac{\omega}{a}$$

$$\frac{p^2 + 2\omega^2}{p^2 + 4\omega^2} \doteq \cos^2 \omega t \tag{40}$$

$$\frac{2n!}{(p^2 + 2^2)(p^2 + 4^2) \cdots [p^2 + (2n)^2]} \doteq \sin^{2n} t \tag{41}$$

$$\frac{(2n + 1)!p}{(p^2 + 1^2)(p^2 + 3^2) \cdots [p^2 + (2n + 1)^2]} \doteq \sin^{(2n+1)} t \tag{42}$$

$$\frac{p}{(p + a)^n} \doteq \frac{e^{-at}t^{n-1}}{(n - 1)!} \tag{43}$$

where n is a positive integer.

$$\frac{(p - a)^2}{(p + a)^2} \doteq 1 - 4at\, e^{-at} \tag{44}$$

$$\frac{p}{\sqrt{p^2 + a^2}} \doteq J_0(at) \tag{45}$$

where $J_0(y)$ is the Bessel function of zeroth order.

$$\frac{p}{\sqrt{p^2 - a^2}} \doteq J_0(iat) \tag{46}$$

where $i = \sqrt{-1}$.

$$\frac{p}{a^n \sqrt{p^2 + a^2}}(\sqrt{p^2 + a^2} - p)^n \doteq J_n(at) \tag{47}$$

where $J_n(y)$ is the Bessel function of order n.

$$e^{-a/p} \doteq J_0(2\sqrt{at})$$
$$e^{i/p} \doteq J_0(2\sqrt{-it}) \tag{48}$$
$$\doteq \text{ber}\,(2\sqrt{t}) + i\,\text{bei}\,(2\sqrt{t}) \tag{49}$$

where $i = \sqrt{-1}$.

The ber and bei functions are the Bessel real and Bessel imaginary functions of Lord Kelvin, defined by

$$J_0(in\sqrt{ix}) = \text{ber}\,(n\sqrt{x}) + i\,\text{bei}\,(n\sqrt{x})$$
$$e^{-i/p} \doteq \text{ber}\,(2\sqrt{t}) - i\,\text{bei}\,(2\sqrt{t})$$
$$\doteq J_0(2\sqrt{it}) \tag{50}$$

$$\cos\frac{1}{p} \doteq \text{ber}\,(2\sqrt{t}) \tag{51}$$

$$\sin\frac{1}{p} \doteq \text{bei}\,(2\sqrt{t}) \tag{52}$$

$$\ln\frac{1}{\sqrt{1 + p^2}} \doteq Ci(t) \tag{53}$$

where
$$Ci(y) = \int_{-\infty}^{y}\frac{\cos u}{u}\,du$$

is the integral cosine function.

$$\cot^{-1} p \doteq Si(t) \tag{54}$$

where
$$Si(y) = \int_{0}^{y}\frac{\sin u\, du}{u}$$

is the integral sine function.

$$\ln (p - 1) \doteqdot - \int_{\infty}^{-t} \frac{e^{-u} \, du}{u} \tag{55}$$

$$\sqrt{\frac{p}{p + 2a}} \doteqdot e^{-at} J_0(iat) \tag{56}$$

$$\frac{p}{\sqrt{(p + a)^2 - b^2}} \doteqdot e^{-at} J_0(ibt) \tag{57}$$

$$e^{-ap} \doteqdot \begin{cases} 0 & t < a \\ \frac{1}{2} & t = a \qquad a > 0 \\ 1 & t > a \end{cases} \tag{58}$$

$$\frac{p}{\sqrt{1 + p^2}} e^{-a\sqrt{1+p^2}} \doteqdot \begin{cases} 0 & t < a \\ J_0(\sqrt{t^2 - a^2}) & t > a \end{cases} \qquad a > 0 \tag{59}$$

$$\frac{p}{\sqrt{p + a}} \doteqdot \frac{e^{-at}}{\sqrt{\pi t}} \tag{60}$$

$$pe^{-\sqrt{ap}} \doteqdot \frac{1}{2} \sqrt{\frac{a}{\pi}} \frac{e^{-a/4t}}{t^{\frac{3}{2}}} \tag{61}$$

$$e^{-a\sqrt{p}} \doteqdot 1 - \operatorname{erf}\left(\frac{a}{2\sqrt{t}}\right) \tag{62}$$

where erf (y) is the error function defined by

$$\operatorname{erf}(y) = \frac{2}{\sqrt{\pi}} \int_0^y e^{-u^2} \, du$$

$$\frac{p^{\frac{1}{2}}}{p^{\frac{1}{2}} - a} \doteqdot e^{a^2 t}[1 + \operatorname{erf}(at^{\frac{1}{2}})] \tag{63}$$

$$\frac{p^{1/s}}{p^{1/s} - a} \doteqdot e^{ast} \sum_{n=1}^{s-1} [1 + \phi_n(t,a)] \tag{64}$$

where $$\phi_n(t,a) = \frac{1}{\Gamma(n/s + 1)} \int_0^{a^n t^{n/s}} e^{-u^{s/n}} \, du \qquad s > 0$$

$$\frac{p^3}{p^3 - a} \doteqdot \frac{1}{3} e^{a^{\frac{1}{3}}t} + \frac{2}{3} e^{-a^{\frac{1}{3}}t/2} \cos a^{\frac{1}{3}} t \frac{\sqrt{3}}{2} \tag{65}$$

$$\frac{p^4}{p^4 - a} \doteqdot \frac{1}{2} \cosh a^{\frac{1}{4}} t + \frac{1}{2} \cos a^{\frac{1}{4}} t \tag{66}$$

$$\frac{q}{q - a} \doteqdot \frac{b}{b - a^2} - \frac{a^2}{b - a^2} e^{(a^2 - b)t}$$
$$+ \frac{a\sqrt{b}}{b - a^2} \operatorname{erf}(\sqrt{bt}) - \frac{a^2}{b - a^2} e^{(a^2 - b)t} \operatorname{erf}(a\sqrt{t}) \tag{67}$$

where $$q = (p + b)^{\frac{1}{2}} \qquad \text{and} \qquad b \neq a^2$$

$$\frac{q}{q - a} \doteqdot \frac{1}{1 - a^2} \left[e^{a^2 bt(1-a^2)} + a e^{-(bt/2)} I_0 \frac{bt}{2} \right.$$
$$\left. + \frac{ab}{(1 - a^2)^2} e^{a^2 bt/(1-a^2)} \int_0^t e^{(a^2+1)bt/2(a^2-1)} I_0 \frac{bt}{2} \, dt \right] \tag{68}$$

where $$q = \left(\frac{p}{p + b}\right)^{\frac{1}{2}} \qquad a^2 \neq 1$$

and $I_0(y) = J_0(iy) = $ modified Bessel function of the first kind.

$$\frac{p^{\frac{1}{2}}}{p + a} \doteqdot \frac{1}{\sqrt{\pi t}} + ia^{\frac{1}{2}} e^{-at} \operatorname{erf}(ia^{\frac{1}{2}} t^{\frac{1}{2}}) \tag{69}$$

where $i = \sqrt{-1}$.

$$\frac{1}{p^4 - 3p^2 + 2} \doteq \frac{1}{2} + \frac{1}{2} \cosh t\sqrt{2} - \cosh t \tag{70}$$

$$\frac{\omega p^{\frac{3}{2}}}{p^2 + \omega^2} \doteq \sqrt{2\omega}\,[\sin \omega t S(\omega^{\frac{1}{2}}t^{\frac{1}{2}}\sqrt{2/\pi}) + \cos \omega t C(\omega^{\frac{1}{2}}t^{\frac{1}{2}}\sqrt{2/\pi})] \tag{71}$$

where $C(y)$ and $S(y)$ are the Fresnel integrals defined by

$$C(y) = \int_0^y \cos \frac{\pi u^2}{2}\,du$$

$$S(y) = \int_0^y \sin \frac{\pi u^2}{2}\,du$$

$$\frac{\sinh bp^{\frac{1}{2}}}{\sinh ap^{\frac{1}{2}}} \doteq \frac{b}{a} + \frac{2}{\pi}\sum_{n=1}^{\infty} \frac{(-1)^n}{n} \sin \frac{n\pi b}{a} e^{-(n^2\pi^2/a^2+c)t} \tag{72}$$

$$\frac{\sinh b(p+c)^{\frac{1}{2}}}{\sinh a(p+c)^{\frac{1}{2}}} \doteq \frac{b}{a}$$
$$+ \frac{2}{\pi}\sum_{n=1}^{\infty} \frac{(-1)^n}{n} \sin \frac{n\pi b}{a} \left(\frac{c}{c+n^2\pi/a^2} + \frac{n^2\pi^2}{a^2c+n^2\pi^2} e^{-(n^2\pi^2/a^2+c)t} \right) \tag{73}$$

$$\frac{\cosh x\sqrt{RCp}}{\cosh l\sqrt{RCp}} \doteq 1 + \frac{4}{\pi}\sum_{n=1}^{\infty} \frac{(-1)^s}{2s-1} \cos \left(\frac{2s-1}{2}\frac{\pi x}{l} \right) e^{-\frac{(2s-1)^2\pi^2 t}{4cRl^2}} \tag{74}$$

$$\frac{pC^{\frac{1}{2}}\sinh x\sqrt{RCp}}{\sqrt{R}\cosh l\sqrt{RCp}} \doteq -\frac{2}{lR}\sum_{s=1}^{\infty} (-1)^s \sin m_s x e^{-m_s^2 t/CR} \tag{75}$$

where
$$m_s = \frac{2s-1}{2}\frac{\pi}{l}$$

$$\frac{(pC)^{\frac{1}{2}}}{\sqrt{R}} \frac{\cosh x\sqrt{RCp}}{\sinh l\sqrt{RCp}} \doteq \frac{1}{Rl} + \frac{2}{Rl}\sum_{s=1}^{\infty} (-1)^s e^{-s^2\pi^2 t/CRl^2} \cos \frac{s\pi x}{l} \tag{76}$$

If
$$\alpha = \sqrt{(R+Lp)(G+pC)}$$
$$Z = R + Lp$$

then

$$\frac{\alpha \cosh \alpha x}{Z \sinh \alpha l} \doteq \sqrt{\frac{G}{R}}\frac{\cosh x\sqrt{RG}}{\sinh l\sqrt{RG}} - \frac{E}{Rl}e^{-(R/Lt)}$$
$$+ 2\sum_{s=1}^{\infty} \frac{(-1)^s l \cos(s\pi x/l)}{s^2\pi^2 + RGl^2} e^{-\rho t} \left\{ \frac{1}{\beta}\left[\frac{s^2\pi^2}{Ll^2} + \frac{1}{2}G\left(\frac{R}{L} - \frac{G}{l} \right) \right] \right.$$
$$\left. \sin \beta_s t - G\cos \beta_s t \right\} \tag{77}$$

where
$$\rho = \frac{1}{2}\left(\frac{R}{L} + \frac{G}{C} \right) m_s = \frac{s\pi}{l}$$

$$\beta_s = \sqrt{\frac{m_s^2}{LC} - \frac{1}{4}\left(\frac{R}{L} - \frac{G}{C} \right)^2}$$

$$\frac{\cosh \alpha(l-x)}{\cosh \alpha l} \doteq \frac{\cosh s(l-x)}{\cosh sl}$$

$$- \frac{\pi v^2}{l^2}e^{\rho t}\sum_{n=1,3,5}^{\infty} n\sin \frac{n\pi x}{2l}\frac{\rho \sin \beta_n t + \beta_n \cos \beta_n t}{\beta_n(\rho^2 + \beta_n)} \tag{78}$$

where

$$\beta_n = \sqrt{\frac{n^2\pi^2v^2}{4l^2} - \sigma^2} \qquad \rho = \frac{1}{2}\left(\frac{R}{L} + \frac{G}{C}\right)$$

$$\alpha = \sqrt{(R + Lp)(G + pC)} \qquad \sigma = \frac{1}{2}\left(\frac{R}{L} - \frac{G}{C}\right)$$

$$s = \sqrt{RG} \qquad v = \frac{1}{\sqrt{LC}}$$

$$\frac{\sinh \alpha(l - x)}{Z_0 \cosh \alpha l} \doteq \frac{G}{s} \frac{\sinh s(l - x)}{\cosh sl}$$

$$+ \frac{2v^2}{l} e^{-\rho t} \sum_{n=1,3,5}^{\infty} \cos \frac{n\pi x}{2l} \left[\frac{G\rho \sin \beta_n t + G\beta_n \cos \beta_n t}{\beta_n(\rho^2 + \beta_n^2)} - \frac{C \sin \beta_n t}{\beta_n} \right] \qquad (79)$$

where the constants are those defined for (78) and

$$Z_0 = \sqrt{\frac{R + Lp}{G + Cp}}$$

$$\frac{\sinh \alpha(l - x)}{\sinh \alpha l} \doteq \frac{\sinh s(l - x)}{\sinh sl}$$

$$- \frac{2v^2\pi}{l^2} e^{-\rho t} \sum_{n=1,2,3}^{\infty} \frac{n \sin (n\pi x/l)(\rho \sin \beta_n t + \beta_n \cos \beta_n t)}{\beta_n(\rho^2 + \beta_n^2)} \qquad (80)$$

where the constants are those defined in (78).

$$e^{-\alpha x} \doteq \begin{cases} 0 & t < \dfrac{x}{v} \\ e^{-\rho x/v} + \dfrac{\sigma x}{v}\displaystyle\int_{x/v}^{t} e^{-\rho u} \dfrac{I_1(\sigma \sqrt{u^2 - x^2/r^2})}{\sqrt{u^\rho - x^2/r^2}}\, du & t > \dfrac{x}{v} \end{cases} \qquad (81)$$

where

$$\alpha = \sqrt{(Lp + R)(Cp + G)} \qquad \rho = \frac{1}{2}\left(\frac{R}{L} + \frac{G}{C}\right)$$

$$\sigma = \frac{1}{2}\left(\frac{R}{L} - \frac{G}{C}\right) \qquad v = \frac{1}{\sqrt{LC}}$$

and $I_1(y)$ is the modified Bessel function of the first kind.

$$\frac{p e^{-(x/v)\sqrt{(p+\rho)^2 - \sigma^2}}}{\sqrt{(p + \rho)^2 - \sigma^2}} \doteq \begin{cases} 0 & t < \dfrac{x}{v} \\ e^{-\rho t} I_0(\sigma \sqrt{t^2 - x^2/v^2}) & t > \dfrac{x}{v} \end{cases} \qquad (82)$$

$$p e^{-\alpha x} \doteq \delta\left(t - \frac{x}{v}\right) e^{-\rho x/v} + \frac{\sigma x}{vz} e^{-\rho t} I_1(\sigma z) \qquad t > \frac{x}{v} \qquad (83)$$

where

$$\alpha = \sqrt{(Lp + R)(Cp + G)} \qquad z = \sqrt{t^2 - (x/v)^2}$$

$$v = \frac{1}{\sqrt{LC}} \qquad \rho = \frac{1}{2}\left(\frac{R}{L} + \frac{G}{C}\right)$$

$$\sigma = \frac{1}{2}\left(\frac{R}{L} - \frac{G}{C}\right)$$

$$\frac{p e^{-\alpha x}}{Z_0} \doteq \begin{cases} 0 & t < \dfrac{x}{v} \\ \dfrac{1}{k} e^{-\rho x/v}\delta\left(t - \dfrac{x}{v}\right) + \dfrac{1}{k} e^{-\rho t}\left[\dfrac{\sigma t}{z} I_1(\sigma z) - \sigma I_0(\sigma z)\right] & t > \dfrac{x}{v} \end{cases} \qquad (84)$$

where
$$\alpha = \sqrt{(Lp + R)(Cp + G)} \qquad z = \sqrt{t^2 - \left(\frac{x}{v}\right)^2}$$

$$k = \sqrt{\frac{L}{C}} \qquad\qquad \sigma = \frac{1}{2}\left(\frac{R}{L} - \frac{G}{C}\right)$$

$$v = \frac{1}{\sqrt{LC}} \qquad\qquad \rho = \frac{1}{2}\left(\frac{R}{L} - \frac{G}{C}\right)$$

$$Z_0 = \sqrt{\frac{Lp + R}{Cp + G}}$$

$$pe^{-\alpha x} \doteq \frac{y}{2t\sqrt{\pi t}}\, e^{-y^2/4t - 2\beta t} \qquad t > 0 \tag{85}$$

where
$$\alpha = \sqrt{R(Cp + G)} \qquad \beta = \frac{G}{2C} \qquad y = x\sqrt{RC}$$

$$\frac{pe^{-\alpha x}}{Z_0} \doteq \frac{u(y^2 - 2t)}{4t^2\sqrt{\pi t}}\, e^{-y^2/4t - 2\beta t} \qquad t > 0 \tag{86}$$

where
$$\alpha = \sqrt{R(Cp + G)} \qquad u = \sqrt{C/R} \qquad y = x\sqrt{RC}$$

and
$$Z_0 = \sqrt{\frac{R}{G + Cp}}$$

$$e^{-\alpha x} \doteq \frac{1}{2}\left[e^{-y\sqrt{2\beta}}\,\mathrm{erf}\left(\frac{y}{2\sqrt{t}} - \sqrt{2\beta t}\right) + e^{y\sqrt{2\beta}}\,\mathrm{erf}\left(\frac{y}{2\sqrt{t}} + \sqrt{2\beta t}\right)\right] \qquad t > 0 \tag{87}$$

where
$$\alpha = \sqrt{R(Cp + G)} \qquad \beta = \frac{G}{2C}$$

$$y = x\sqrt{RC} \qquad \mathrm{erf}\,(y) = \frac{2}{\sqrt{\pi}}\int_0^y e^{-u^2}\, du$$

$$\frac{e^{-\alpha x}}{Z_0} \doteq \frac{u}{\sqrt{\pi t}}\, e^{-y^2/4t - 2\beta t} + \frac{u\sqrt{2\beta}}{2}\left[e^{-y\sqrt{2\beta}}\,\mathrm{erf}\left(\frac{y}{2\sqrt{t}} - \sqrt{2\beta t}\right)\right.$$
$$\left. - e^{y\sqrt{2\beta}}\,\mathrm{erf}\left(\frac{y}{2\sqrt{t}} + \sqrt{2\beta t}\right)\right] \qquad t > 0 \tag{88}$$

where
$$\alpha = \sqrt{R(Cp + G)} \qquad \beta = \frac{G}{2C} \qquad u = \sqrt{\frac{C}{R}}$$

$$Z_0 = \sqrt{\frac{R}{Cp + G}} \qquad y = x\sqrt{RC}$$

$$\frac{pe^{-\alpha x}}{Z_0} \doteq \begin{cases} 0 & t < \frac{x}{v} \\ \frac{\delta}{k}\left(t - \frac{x}{v}\right)e^{\alpha x/v} + \frac{1}{k}e^{-\alpha t}\left[\frac{at}{z}I_1(az) - aI_0(az)\right] & t > \frac{x}{v} \end{cases} \tag{89}$$

where
$$\alpha = \sqrt{(Lp + R)Cp} \qquad k = \left(\frac{L}{C}\right)^{-\frac{1}{2}} \qquad z = \sqrt{t^2 - \left(\frac{x}{v}\right)^2}$$

$$Z_0 = \sqrt{\frac{Lp + R}{Cp}} \qquad v = \left(\frac{L}{C}\right)^{-\frac{1}{2}} \qquad a = \frac{R}{2L}$$

$$\frac{e^{\alpha x}}{Z_0} \doteq \begin{cases} 0 & t < \frac{x}{v} \\ \frac{1}{k}e^{-\alpha t}I_0(aZ) & t > \frac{x}{v} \end{cases} \tag{90}$$

where the constants have the same value as in (89).

$$pe^{-\alpha x} \doteq \delta\,\frac{t - x}{v}\, e^{-\rho x/v} \tag{91}$$

where
$$\alpha = \sqrt{(Lp + R)(G + Cp)} \qquad \frac{R}{L} = \frac{G}{C}$$

$$\rho = \frac{R}{2L} + \frac{G}{2C}$$

$$e^{-\alpha x} \doteqdot \begin{cases} 0 & t < \dfrac{x}{v} \\[2mm] e^{-\rho x/v} & t > \dfrac{x}{v} \end{cases} \tag{92}$$

where the constants have the values given in (91).

$$\frac{p \sqrt{p + 2a}}{\sqrt{p} + \sqrt{p + 2a}} \doteqdot \frac{\delta(t)}{2} + \frac{1}{2t} e^{-at} I_1(at) \qquad t > 0 \tag{93}$$

where
$$a = \frac{R}{2L}$$

$$\frac{\sqrt{p + 2a}}{\sqrt{p} + \sqrt{p + 2a}} \doteqdot 1 - \frac{1}{2} e^{-at}[I_0(at) + I_1(at)] \qquad t > 0 \tag{94}$$

$$\frac{pe^{-y\sqrt{p}}}{1 + \sqrt{p/a}} \doteqdot \sqrt{\frac{a}{\pi t}} e^{-y^2/4t} - ae^{y\sqrt{a}+at} \operatorname{erf}\left(\frac{y}{2\sqrt{t}} + \sqrt{at}\right) \qquad t > 0 \tag{95}$$

$$\frac{e^{-y\sqrt{p}}}{1 + \sqrt{p/a}} \doteqdot \operatorname{erf}\left(\frac{y}{2\sqrt{t}}\right) - e^{y\sqrt{a}+at} \operatorname{erf}\left(\frac{y}{2\sqrt{t}} + \sqrt{at}\right) \qquad t > 0 \tag{96}$$

$$\frac{pu\sqrt{p}\,e^{-y\sqrt{p}}}{1 + \sqrt{p/a}} \doteqdot \frac{u(y - 2t\sqrt{a})}{2t} \sqrt{\frac{a}{\pi t}} e^{-y^2/4t}$$
$$+ ua\sqrt{a}\, e^{y\sqrt{a}+at} \operatorname{erf}\left(\frac{y}{2\sqrt{t}} + \sqrt{at}\right) \qquad t > 0 \tag{97}$$

$$\frac{u\sqrt{p}\,e^{-y\sqrt{p}}}{1 + \sqrt{p/a}} \doteqdot ue^{y\sqrt{a}+at} \operatorname{erf}\left(\frac{y}{2\sqrt{t}} + \sqrt{at}\right) \qquad t > 0 \tag{98}$$

$$\frac{pu\sqrt{p}}{1 + \sqrt{p/a}} \doteqdot u\sqrt{a}\left[\delta(t) - \sqrt{\frac{a}{\pi t}} + ae^{at} \operatorname{erf}\left(\sqrt{at}\right)\right] \qquad t > 0 \tag{99}$$

$$\frac{u\sqrt{p}}{1 + \sqrt{p/a}} \doteqdot u\sqrt{a}e^{at} \operatorname{erf}\left(\sqrt{at}\right) \tag{100}$$

$$\frac{p^2 e^{-y\sqrt{p}}}{1 + \sqrt{p/a}} \doteqdot \frac{y^2 - 2yt\sqrt{a} - 2t + 4at^2}{4t^2} \sqrt{\frac{a}{\pi t}} e^{-y^2/4t}$$
$$- a^2 e^{y\sqrt{a}+at} \operatorname{erf}\left(\frac{y}{2\sqrt{t}} + \sqrt{at}\right) \qquad t > 0 \tag{101}$$

$$\frac{pe^{-y\sqrt{p}}}{1 + \sqrt{p/a}} \doteqdot \sqrt{\frac{a}{\pi t}} e^{-y^2/4t} - ae^{y\sqrt{a}+at} \operatorname{erf}\left(\frac{y}{2\sqrt{t}} - \sqrt{at}\right) \qquad t > 0 \tag{102}$$

$$\frac{p^2}{1 + \sqrt{p/a}} \doteqdot -a\delta(t) \frac{2at - 1}{2t} \sqrt{\frac{a}{\pi t}} - a^2 e^{at} \operatorname{erf}\left(\sqrt{at}\right) \qquad t > 0 \tag{103}$$

$$\frac{p}{1 + \sqrt{p/a}} \doteqdot \sqrt{\frac{a}{\pi t}} - ae^{at} \operatorname{erf}\left(\sqrt{at}\right) \qquad t > 0 \tag{104}$$

$$\frac{pw^{2n+1}[\sqrt{(p + a)^2 + w^2} + (p + a)]^{-2n}}{k\sqrt{(p + a)^2 + w^2}} \doteqdot \frac{2}{L} e^{-at} J_{2n}(wt) \tag{105}$$

where
$$k = \left(\frac{L}{C}\right)^{\frac{1}{2}} \qquad a = \frac{R}{L} = \frac{G}{C}$$

$$w = 2\left(\frac{L}{C}\right)^{-\frac{1}{2}} \qquad n \text{ a positive integer}$$

$$\frac{p^2(2a)^n}{R} \sqrt{\frac{p}{p+2a}} \left(\sqrt{p+2a} + \sqrt{p}\right)^{-2n}$$
$$\doteq \frac{a}{R} e^{-at}[I_{n-1}(at) - 2I_n(at) + I_{n+1}(at)] \qquad t > 0 \quad (106)$$

where $a = 2/RC$, n is a positive integer, and $I_n(y)$ is the modified Bessel function of the first kind and the nth order.

$$\frac{2(2a)^n}{R} \sqrt{\frac{p}{p+2a}} \left(\sqrt{p+2a} + \sqrt{p}\right)^{-2n} \doteq \frac{2}{R} e^{-at} I_n(at) \qquad t > 0 \qquad (107)$$

where the constants are the same as in (106).

$$\frac{(\sqrt{1+a} + \sqrt{a})^{-2n}}{\sqrt{(1+a)Z_1 Z_2}} \doteq \frac{1}{k} \int_0^{\omega^c t} e^{-(b/\omega c)u} J_2(u_n) \, du \qquad (108)$$

where n is a positive integer and

$$a = \frac{LC}{4}(p+b)^2 \qquad \frac{1}{Z_2} = C(p+b) \qquad k = \left(\frac{L}{C}\right)^{\frac{1}{2}}$$

$$Z_1 = L(p+b) \qquad \omega_c = \frac{2}{\sqrt{LC}}$$

$$\frac{\omega_c}{k} \frac{1}{\sqrt{p^2 + \omega_c^2}} \left(\frac{\sqrt{p^2 + \omega_c^2} - p}{\omega_c}\right)^{2n} \doteq \frac{1}{k} \int_0^{\omega^c t} J_{2n}(u) \, du \qquad (109)$$

where n is a positive integer.

$$\tanh \frac{TP}{2} \doteq h(t) \qquad (110)$$

where

$$e^{-t_1 p} - e^{-t_2 p} \doteq h(t) \qquad \begin{cases} t_1 > 0 \\ t_2 > t_1 \end{cases} \qquad (111)$$

where

$$\frac{m}{p}\left(1 - e^{-pt_1}\right) - mt_1 e^{-pt_1} \doteqdot h(t) \tag{112}$$

where m = slope:

$$\frac{1}{e^{Tp} - 1} \doteqdot h(t) \tag{113}$$

where

$$\frac{p}{m} - \frac{mT}{e^{pT} - 1} \doteqdot h(t) \tag{114}$$

where m = slope:

$$\frac{m}{p} - 2mT\left(\frac{1}{e^{Tp} - 1} - \frac{1}{e^{2Tp} - 1}\right) \doteqdot h(t) \tag{115}$$

where m = slope:

$$\frac{1}{e^{Tp} + 1} \doteqdot h(t) \tag{116}$$

where

REFERENCES

1. Davis, H. T.: "The Theory of Linear Operators," The Principia Press, Bloomington, Ind., 1936.
2. Whittaker, E. T.: Oliver Heaviside, *Bulletin of the Calcutta Mathematical Society*, vol. 20, p. 199, 1928–1929.
3. Laplace, P. S.: Sur les suites, oeuvres complètes, *Mémoires de l'académie des sciences*, vol. 10, pp. 1–89, 1779.
4. Carson, J. R.: "Electric Circuit Theory and the Operational Calculus," McGraw-Hill Book Company, Inc., New York, 1926.
5. Jeffreys, H.: "Operational Methods in Mathematical Physics," Cambridge University Press, New York, 1931.
6. Carslaw, H. S., and J. C. Jaeger: "Operational Methods in Applied Mathematics," Oxford University Press, New York, 1941.
7. McLachlan, N. W.: "Modern Operational Calculus," The Macmillan Company, New York, 1948.
8. McLachlan, N. W.: "Complex Variable Theory and Transform Calculus," Cambridge University Press, New York, 1953.
9. Gardner, M. S., and J. L. Barnes: "Transients in Linear Systems," John Wiley & Sons, Inc., New York, 1942.
10. Thomson, W. T.: "Laplace Transformation Theory and Engineering Applications," Prentice-Hall, Inc., New York, 1950.
11. van der Pol, B., and H. Bremmer: "Operational Calculus," Cambridge University Press, New York, 1950.
12. Pipes, L. A.: The Operational Calculus, *Journal of Applied Physics*, vol. 10, nos. 3–5, 1939.
13. Denis-Papin, M., and A. Kaufmann: "Cours de calcul opérationnel," Editions Albin Michel, Paris, 1950.
14. Doetsch, G.: "Theorie und Anwendung der Laplace-Transformation," Springer-Verlag OHG, Berlin, 1937.
15. Wagner, K. W.: "Operatorenrechnung," J. W. Edwards, Publisher, Inc., Ann Arbor, Mich., 1944.
16. Jaeger, J. C.: "An Introduction to the Laplace Transformation," John Wiley & Sons, Inc., New York, 1949.
17. Churchill, R. V.: "Modern Operational Mathematics in Engineering," McGraw-Hill Book Company, Inc., New York, 1944.
18. van der Pol, B., and K. F. Niessen: Symbolic Calculus, *Philosophical Magazine*, vol. 13, pp. 537–577, March, 1932.
19. Sears, W. R.: Operational Methods in the Theory of Airfoils in Non-uniform Motion, *Journal of the Franklin Institute*, vol. 230, pp. 95–111, 1940.
20. Pipes, L. A.: The Analysis of Retarded Control Systems, *Journal of Applied Physics*, vol. 19, no. 7, pp. 617–623, 1948.
21. Gross, B.: On Creep and Relaxation, *Journal of Applied Physics*, vol. 18, no. 2, pp. 212–221, 257–264, 1947.
22. van der Pol, B.: Application of the Operational or Symbolic Calculus to the Theory of Prime Numbers, *Philosophical Magazine*, ser. 7, vol. 26, pp. 921–940, 1938.
23. Heaviside, Oliver: "Electromagnetic Theory," Dover Publications, New York, 1950.
24. Pipes, L. A.: The Summation of Fourier Series by Operational Methods, *Journal of Applied Physics*, vol. 21, no. 4, pp. 298–301, 1950.

25. Jaeger, J. C.: The Solution of Boundary Value Problems by a Double Laplace Transformation, *Bulletin of the American Mathematical Society*, vol. 46, p. 687, 1940.
26. Voelker, D., and G. Doetsch: "Die zweidimensionale Laplace-Transformation," Verlag Virkhauser, Basel, 1950. [Contains an extensive table of two-dimensional Laplace transforms.]
27. Estrin, T. A., and T. J. Higgins: The Solution of Boundary Value Problems by Multiple Laplace Transformations, *Journal of the Franklin Institute*, vol. 252, no. 2, pp. 153–167, 1951.
28. Pipes, L. A.: An Operational Treatment of Nonlinear Dynamical Systems, *Journal of the Acoustical Society of America*, vol. 10, pp. 29–31, 1938.
29. Pipes, L. A.: Operational Analysis of Nonlinear Dynamical Systems, *Journal of Applied Physics*, vol. 13, no. 2, February, 1942.
30. Pipes, L. A.: The Reversion Method for Solving Nonlinear Differential Equations, *Journal of Applied Physics*, vol. 23, no. 2, pp. 202–207, 1952.
31. Pipes, L. A.: Operational Methods in Nonlinear Mechanics, *Report* 51-10, University of California, Los Angeles, 1951.
32. Pipes, L. A.: Applications of Integral Equations to the Solution of Nonlinear Electric Circuit Problems, *Communication and Electronics*, no. 8, pp. 445–450, September, 1953.
33. McLachlan, N. W., and P. Humbert: Formulaire pour le calcul symbolique, *Mémorial des sciences mathématiques*, fasc. 100, 1941.
34. Erdelyi, A. (ed.): "Tables of Integral Transforms," vol. I, McGraw-Hill Book Company, Inc., New York, 1954.

CHAPTER 22

THE ANALYSIS OF NONLINEAR OSCILLATORY SYSTEMS

1. Introduction. The mathematical analysis of many of the oscillatory phenomena that occur in nature and in technology leads to the solution of nonlinear differential equations. Such systems as a pendulum executing large oscillations, the flow of electrical current in a circuit consisting of a capacitance in series with an iron-cored inductance coil, the free oscillations of a regenerative triode oscillator, the motion of a mass restrained by a spring and undergoing dry or solid friction are typical examples of systems whose analysis leads to nonlinear differential equations.

The equations of these systems are well known in astronomy and have been studied by such investigators as Liapounoff, Linstedt, and especially H. Poincaré. A number of Russian scientists have contributed greatly to the solution of these nonlinear problems. Two of the most active Russian workers in this field are N. Kryloff and N. Bogoliuboff. In the field of nonlinear electrical oscillations van der Pol has made some notable contributions.

In this chapter some of the simpler analytical methods that have been devised to solve nonlinear oscillatory problems will be considered. The interested reader will find the references at the end of this chapter of value.

FIG. 2.1

2. Oscillator Damped by Solid Friction. Perhaps the simplest nonlinear vibrating system is the oscillator of Fig. 2.1.

This system consists of a mass m connected to rigid supports by means of springs of total effective spring constant k. The mass is supposed to slide on a rough surface and hence experience a constant frictional force F, which is directed in a direction opposite to the velocity. Let the motion start in such a manner that

$$(2.1) \qquad \left. \begin{array}{l} x = a \\ \dot{x} = 0 \end{array} \right\} \quad \text{at } t = 0$$

That is, the mass is pulled out a distance a from its equilibrium position and released at $t = 0$. The equation of motion is, by Newton's law,

(2.2) $$m\ddot{x} + kx = \pm F$$

If we let

(2.3) $$\omega^2 = \frac{k}{m} \qquad A = \frac{F}{m}$$

then

(2.4) $$\ddot{x} + \omega^2 x = +A \qquad 0 < t < \frac{\pi}{\omega}$$

when the force is acting in the positive x direction. It is expressly understood that this is true provided that the initial position $x = a$ is such that

(2.5) $$\omega^2 a > A$$

so that the spring force is greater than the frictional force. This means that the initial displacement lies outside the so-called "dead region"

(2.6) $$x = \pm \frac{A}{\omega^2}$$

If motion is possible and the first swing to the left is of such magnitude that it is still outside the dead region, then

(2.7) $$\ddot{x} + \omega^2 x = -A \qquad \frac{\pi}{\omega} < t < \frac{2\pi}{\omega}$$

We can thus write the equation of motion in the form

(2.8) $\quad \ddot{x} + \omega^2 x = h(t)$

$$T = \frac{\pi}{\omega}$$

Fig. 2.2

where $h(t)$ is a discontinuous function of the meander type whose graph is given by Fig. 2.2.

This is provided that $\dot{x} \neq 0$, that is, that the motion continues, and that successive swings are of such amplitude that they lie outside the dead region.

Equation (2.8) may be solved by the Laplacian-transform, or operational, method. To do this, let

(2.9) $$Lx(t) = y(p)$$
$$Lh(t) = g(p) = A(1 - 2e^{-Tp} + 2e^{-2Tp} - 2e^{-3Tp} + \cdots)$$

Now, as a consequence of the initial conditions (2.1), we have

(2.10) $$L\ddot{x} = p^2 y - p^2 a$$

Hence Eq. (2.8) transforms to

(2.11) $\quad (p^2 + \omega^2)y = p^2 a + A(1 - 2e^{-Tp} + 2e^{-2Tp} - 2e^{-3Tp} + \cdots)$

Therefore we have

(2.12) $y = \dfrac{p^2 a}{p^2 + \omega^2} + \dfrac{A}{p^2 + \omega^2}(1 - 2e^{-Tp} + 2e^{-2Tp} - 2e^{-3Tp} + \cdots)$

Now, from the table of transforms, we have

(2.13)
$$L^{-1}\frac{p^2}{p^2 + \omega^2} = \cos \omega t$$
$$L^{-1}\frac{1}{p^2 + \omega^2} = \frac{1 - \cos \omega t}{\omega^2}$$

Hence we have, on calculating the inverse transforms of (2.12),

(2.14) $x = a \cos \omega t + \dfrac{A}{\omega^2}(1 - \cos \omega t) \qquad 0 < t < T$

(2.15) $x = a \cos \omega t + \dfrac{A}{\omega^2}(1 - \cos \omega t) - \dfrac{2A}{\omega^2}[1 - \cos \omega(t - T)]$

$$\text{for } T < t < 2T$$

The solution for greater values of t may be written down in a similar manner. It is noted that at

(2.16) $t = T \qquad x = -a + \dfrac{2A}{\omega^2}$

(2.17) $t = 2T \qquad x = a - \dfrac{4A}{\omega^2} \qquad$ etc.

That is, each successive swing is $2A/\omega^2$ shorter than the preceding one. The solution should be continued until one of the swings lies inside the dead region $x = \pm A/\omega^2$. In such a case the motion stops.

3. The Free Oscillations of a Pendulum. As another simple example of a nonlinear dynamical system, let us discuss the motion of the simple pendulum of Fig. 3.1.

Figure 3.1 represents a particle of mass m suspended from a fixed point O by a massless inextensible rod of length s, free to oscillate in the plane of the paper under the influence of gravity. If the pendulum is displaced

FIG. 3.1

by an angle θ from its position of equilibrium as shown in the figure, then the potential energy of the system V is the work done against gravity to lift the mass of the pendulum a distance h, given by

(3.1) $h = s(1 - \cos \theta)$

Hence the potential energy is

(3.2) $V = mgs(1 - \cos \theta)$

The kinetic energy of motion of the pendulum is given by

$$(3.3) \qquad T = \tfrac{1}{2}mv^2$$

where v is the linear velocity of the pendulum.   In terms of the angle θ we have

$$(3.4) \qquad v = s\frac{d\theta}{dt} = s\dot{\theta}$$

Hence

$$(3.5) \qquad T = \tfrac{1}{2}ms^2\dot{\theta}^2$$

Now, since there is no loss of energy from the system, we must have

$$(3.6) \qquad T + V = C$$

where C is a constant representing the total energy.   Hence, substituting (3.2) and (3.5) into (3.6), we have

$$(3.7) \qquad mgs(1 - \cos\theta) + \tfrac{1}{2}ms^2\dot{\theta}^2 = C$$

To determine the constant C, let us assume that $\theta = \theta_0$ is the maximum amplitude of swing so that

$$(3.8) \qquad \dot{\theta} = 0 \qquad \text{when } \theta = \theta_0$$

Substituting this condition into (3.7), we have

$$(3.9) \qquad C = mgs(1 - \cos\theta_0)$$

Hence we have

$$(3.10) \qquad g(1 - \cos\theta) + \frac{s}{2}\dot{\theta}^2 = g(1 - \cos\theta_0)$$

or

$$(3.11) \qquad \dot{\theta}^2 = \frac{2g}{s}(\cos\theta - \cos\theta_0)$$

To obtain the equation of motion, we differentiate (3.11) with respect to time and obtain

$$(3.12) \qquad 2\dot{\theta}\ddot{\theta} = -\frac{2g}{s}\sin\theta\,\dot{\theta}$$

or

$$(3.13) \qquad \frac{d^2\theta}{dt^2} + \frac{g}{s}\sin\theta = 0$$

This is the equation of motion, and Eq. (3.11) is its first integral.

Equation (3.13) is a nonlinear differential equation because of the presence of the trigonometric function $\sin\theta$.   In the theory of *small* oscillations of a pendulum we expand $\sin\theta$ into a Maclaurin series of the form

$$(3.14) \qquad \sin\theta = \theta - \frac{\theta^3}{3!} + \frac{\theta^5}{5!} - \frac{\theta^7}{7!} + \cdots$$

If θ is always small, the approximation

(3.15) $$\sin \theta \doteq \theta$$

is a very good one, and in this case (3.13) becomes

(3.16) $$\frac{d^2\theta}{dt^2} + \frac{g}{s}\theta = 0$$

This is a linear equation with constant coefficients whose general solution is of the form

(3.17) $$\theta = A \sin (\omega t + \phi)$$

where

(3.18) $$\omega = \sqrt{\frac{g}{s}}$$

and A and ϕ are arbitrary constants that depend on the initial conditions of the motion.   The period of the motion P_0 is given by

(3.19) $$P_0 = \frac{2\pi}{\omega} = 2\pi \sqrt{\frac{g}{s}}$$

We thus see that the period is independent of the amplitude of oscillation in this case.   By measuring s and P_0 the acceleration g due to gravity may be determined by (3.19) to a high degree of accuracy.

To determine the period of oscillation for large amplitudes, we return to Eq. (3.11) and write it in the form

(3.20) $$\frac{d\theta}{dt} = \sqrt{\frac{2g}{s}} \sqrt{\cos \theta - \cos \theta_0}$$

or

(3.21) $$dt = \sqrt{\frac{s}{2g}} \frac{d\theta}{\sqrt{\cos \theta - \cos \theta_0}}$$

Now the period P_{θ_0} is twice the time taken by the pendulum to swing from $\theta = -\theta_0$ to $\theta = \theta_0$.   Therefore

(3.22) $$P_{\theta_0} = 2 \sqrt{\frac{s}{2g}} \int_{-\theta_0}^{\theta_0} \frac{d\theta}{\sqrt{\cos \theta - \cos \theta_0}}$$

If we use the trigonometric identities

(3.23) $$\cos \theta = 1 - 2 \sin^2 \frac{\theta}{2} \qquad \cos \theta_0 = 1 - 2 \sin^2 \frac{\theta_0}{2}$$

then we may write (3.22) in the form

(3.24) $$P_{\theta_0} = \sqrt{\frac{s}{g}} \int_{-\theta_0}^{+\theta_0} \frac{d\theta}{\sqrt{\sin^2 (\theta_0/2) - \sin^2 (\theta/2)}}$$

Let us now introduce the two new variables k and ϕ by the equations

$$(3.25) \qquad k = \sin \frac{\theta_0}{2}$$

and

$$(3.26) \qquad \sin \frac{\theta}{2} = k \sin \phi$$

Hence

$$(3.27) \qquad d\theta = \frac{2k \cos \phi \, d\phi}{\cos (\theta/2)} = \frac{2k \cos \phi \, d\phi}{\sqrt{1 - k^2 \sin^2 \phi}}$$

In terms of these two new variables the integral of (3.24) becomes

$$(3.28) \qquad P_{\theta_0} = 4 \sqrt{\frac{s}{g}} \int_0^{\pi/2} \frac{d\phi}{\sqrt{1 - k^2 \sin^2 \phi}}$$

Now the integral

$$(3.29) \qquad K(k) = \int_0^{\pi/2} \frac{d\phi}{\sqrt{1 - k^2 \sin^2 \phi}}$$

is called the complete elliptic integral of the first kind and is tabulated.[*]
We therefore may write

$$(3.30) \qquad P_{\theta_0} = 4 \sqrt{\frac{s}{g}} K(k)$$

Equation (3.25) determines k in terms of the maximum angle of swing θ_0. From the tables of the function $K(k)$ and Eq. (3.30), we may determine the period P_{θ_0}. We thus find that, for $\theta_0 = 60°$, we have

$$(3.31) \qquad P_{60°} = 1.07 P_0$$

and, for $\theta_0 = 2°$, we have

$$(3.32) \qquad P_{2°} = 1.000076 P_0$$

where P_0 is given by (3.19).

We thus see that the period of a pendulum depends on its amplitude of oscillation.

4. Restoring Force a General Function of the Displacement.

Let us consider the motion of a particle of mass m. Let the mass be subjected to a restoring force $F(x)$ of an elastic nature tending to restore the mass m to the position of equilibrium $x = 0$.

The equation of motion of this system is, by Newton's law,

$$(4.1) \qquad m \frac{d^2x}{dt^2} + F(x) = 0$$

---

[*] See, for example, B. O. Peirce, "A Short Table of Integrals," p. 121, Ginn & Company, Boston, 1929.

If we let

(4.2)
$$v = \frac{dx}{dt}$$

be the velocity, then we have

(4.3)
$$\frac{d^2x}{dt^2} = \frac{dv}{dt} = \frac{dv}{dx}\frac{dx}{dt} = v\frac{dv}{dx}$$

Hence Eq. (4.1) may be written in the form

(4.4)
$$mv\,dv + F(x)\,dx = 0$$

Now the potential energy of the system is, at any instant,

(4.5)
$$V(x) = \int_0^x F(u)\,du$$

The kinetic energy is

(4.6)
$$T = \tfrac{1}{2}mv^2$$

Let us suppose that the motion is started in such a way that the mass is pulled out a certain distance $x = a$ and then released. We then have

(4.7)
$$x = a$$
$$\dot{x} = v = 0$$

In this case the *total energy* E imparted to the system is

(4.8)
$$E = \int_0^a F(u)\,du = V(a)$$

Now, integrating Eq. (4.4), we obtain

(4.9)
$$\frac{mv^2}{2} + \int_0^x F(u)\,du = C$$

where C is a constant of integration. To determine C, we use the conditions (4.7), and we have

(4.10)
$$\int_0^a F(u)\,du = C = E$$

Equation (4.9) may therefore be written in the form

(4.11)
$$\frac{mv^2}{2} = E - V(x)$$

or

(4.12)
$$v^2 = \frac{2(E - V)}{m} = \left(\frac{dx}{dt}\right)^2$$

Hence

(4.13)
$$\frac{dx}{dt} = \sqrt{\frac{2}{m}}\sqrt{E - V}$$

or

$$(4.14) \qquad t = \sqrt{\frac{m}{2}} \int \frac{dx}{\sqrt{E - V(x)}} + t_0$$

where t_0 is an arbitrary constant.   If we measure t so that

$$(4.15) \qquad t = 0 \qquad \text{at } x = 0$$

then we have from Eq. (4.14)

$$(4.16) \qquad t = \sqrt{\frac{m}{2}} \int_0^x \frac{du}{\sqrt{E - V(u)}} = N(x)$$

If it is possible to integrate this expression, we obtain

$$(4.17) \qquad t = N(x)$$

or, inversely,

$$(4.18) \qquad x = F(t)$$

In some cases it is possible to integrate the expression (4.16) explicitly. Usually the integration leads to elliptic integrals, and Eq. (4.18) leads to elliptic functions.

The period of the motion is given by the equation

$$(4.19) \qquad P = 4\sqrt{\frac{m}{2}} \int_0^a \frac{du}{\sqrt{E - V(u)}}$$

A special case of this general theory is the motion of a pendulum with large amplitude discussed in Sec. 3.   In the case of the pendulum the kinetic energy is

$$(4.20) \qquad T = \tfrac{1}{2} m s^2 \dot{\theta}^2$$

The potential energy is

$$(4.21) \qquad V(\theta) = mgs(1 - \cos\theta)$$

The total energy is

$$(4.22) \qquad E = mgs(1 - \cos\theta_0)$$

Substituting these expressions into (4.16), we have

$$(4.23) \qquad t = s\sqrt{\frac{m}{2}} \int_0^\theta \frac{du}{\sqrt{mgs(\cos u - \cos\theta_0)}}$$

or

$$(4.24) \qquad t = \sqrt{\frac{s}{2g}} \int_0^\theta \frac{du}{\sqrt{\cos u - \cos\theta_0}}$$

The period of the pendulum P is given by

(4.25)
$$P = 4 \sqrt{\frac{s}{2g}} \int_0^{\theta_0} \frac{du}{\sqrt{\cos u - \cos \theta_0}}$$

Equation (4.19) enables one to calculate the natural frequency of a conservative oscillatory system whose restoring force is nonlinear. If the integration cannot be performed, numerical or graphical integration may be resorted to in order to obtain the period P.

5. An Operational Analysis of Nonlinear Dynamical Systems. A powerful method of determining the free oscillations of certain nonlinear systems will be given in this section. The method presented here is an operational adaptation of the one developed by Linstedt and Liapounoff.*

The method may be illustrated by a consideration of a mechanical oscillating system consisting of a mass attached to a spring. The equation of the free vibration of such a system is

(5.1)
$$\frac{m \, d^2x}{dt^2} + F(x) = 0$$

where $m \, d^2x/dt^2$ is the inertia force of the mass, $F(x)$ is the spring force, and x is measured from the position of equilibrium of the mass when the spring is not stressed. Let us consider the symmetrical case where

(5.2)
$$F(x) = kx + bx^3$$

Hence (5.1) becomes

(5.3)
$$\frac{m \, d^2x}{dt^2} + kx + bx^3 = 0$$

or

(5.4)
$$\frac{d^2x}{dt^2} + \omega^2 x + \alpha x^3 = 0$$

where

(5.5)
$$\omega = \left(\frac{k}{m}\right)^{\frac{1}{2}}$$

(5.6)
$$\alpha = \frac{b}{m}$$

Equation (5.4) occurs in the theory of nonlinear vibrating systems and certain types of nonlinear electrical systems and serves to illustrate the general method of analysis. Let us consider the solution of Eq. (5.4) subject to the initial conditions

(5.7)
$$\left. \begin{array}{l} x = a \\ \dot{x} = 0 \end{array} \right\} \quad \text{at } t = 0$$

* See A. M. Kryloff, *Bulletin of the Russian Academy of Sciences*, no. 1, p. 1, 1933.

That is, the mass is displaced a distance a and allowed to oscillate freely. We are interested in studying the subsequent behavior of the motion.

Let us now multiply Eq. (5.4) by $pe^{-pt}\, dt$ and integrate from 0 to ∞. We thus obtain

$$(5.8) \qquad p \int_0^\infty e^{-pt}\left(\frac{d^2x}{dt^2} + \omega^2 x + \alpha x^3\right) dt = 0$$

Let us use the notation of Chap. 21 and write

$$(5.9) \qquad Lx(t) = y(p)$$

Now, by an integration by parts, it may easily be shown that

$$(5.10) \qquad \frac{L\, d^2x}{dt^2} = -p\dot{x}_0 - p^2 x_0 + p^2 y$$

where $\dot{x}_0$ and x_0 are the initial velocity and displacement of the particle at $t = 0$.

In view of the initial conditions (5.7) and the transform (5.10), Eq. (5.8) may be written in the form

$$(5.11) \qquad (p^2 + \omega^2)y = p^2 a - \alpha Lx^3$$

Now let

$$(5.12) \qquad x = x_0 + \alpha x_1 + \alpha^2 x_2 + \alpha^3 x_3 + \cdots$$
$$(5.13) \qquad \omega^2 = \omega_0^2 + c_1\alpha + c_2\alpha^2 + c_3\alpha^3 + \cdots$$
$$(5.14) \qquad y = y_0 + \alpha y_1 + \alpha^2 y_2 + \alpha^3 y_3 + \cdots$$
$$(5.15) \qquad y_i(p) = Lx_i(t)$$

In these expressions the quantities $x_r(t)$ are functions of time to be determined, and ω_0 is the frequency, which will be determined later. The c_i quantities are constants which are chosen to eliminate resonance conditions in a manner that will become clear as we proceed. The functions $y_r(p)$ are the Laplace transforms of the functions $x_r(t)$.

In most nonlinear dynamical systems the quantity α is small compared with ω^2, and the series (5.12) may be shown to converge. In the following discussion let us limit our calculations by omitting all the terms containing α to a power higher than the third. Substituting the above expressions into (5.11), we obtain

$$(5.16) \quad \begin{aligned} p^2(y_0 &+ \alpha y_1 + \alpha^2 y_2 + \alpha^3 y_3) \\ &+ (\omega_0^2 + c_1\alpha + c_2\alpha^2 + c_3\alpha^3)(y_0 + \alpha y_1 + \alpha^2 y_2 + \alpha^3 y_3) \\ &= p^2 a - L(x_0 + \alpha x_1 + \alpha^2 x_2 + \alpha^3 x_3)^3 \end{aligned}$$

If we now neglect all terms containing α to powers higher than the third, we obtain

$$(5.17) \quad (p^2y_0 + \omega_0^2 y_0) + \alpha(p^2y_1 + \omega_0^2 y_1 + c_1y_0 + Lx_0^3)$$
$$+ \alpha^2(p^2y_2 + \omega_0^2 y_2 + c_2y_0 + c_1y_1 + L3x_0^2x_1)$$
$$+ \alpha^3[p^2y_3 + \omega_0^2 y_3 + c_3y_0 + c_2y_1 + c_1y_2 + L(3x_0^2x_2 + 3x_0x_1^2)] = p^2a$$

This equation must hold for any value of the quantity α. This means that each factor for each of the three powers of α must be zero. Hence Eq. (5.17) splits up into the following system of equations:

$$(5.18) \quad p^2y_0 + \omega_0^2 y_0 = p^2a$$
$$(5.19) \quad p^2y_1 + \omega_0^2 y_1 = -c_1y_0 - Lx_0^3$$
$$(5.20) \quad p^2y_2 + \omega_0^2 y_2 = -c_2y_0 - c_1y_1 - L3x_0^3x_1$$
$$(5.21) \quad p^2y_3 + \omega_0^2 y_3 = -c_3y_0 - c_2y_1 - c_1y_2 - L(3x_0^2x_2 + 3x_0x_1^2)$$

Using the notation

$$(5.22) \qquad\qquad T(\phi) = \frac{1}{p^2 + \phi^2}$$

Eq. (5.18) may be written in the form

$$(5.23) \qquad\qquad y_0 = p^2aT(\omega_0) = Lx_0$$

From the table of transforms (see page 676), we have

$$(5.24) \qquad\qquad L^{-1}p^2aT(\omega_0) = a \cos \omega_0 t = x_0$$

This represents the first approximation to the solution of Eq. (5.4) subject to the initial conditions (5.7). The transform of the second approximation as given by (5.19) may be written in the form

$$(5.25) \qquad\qquad y_1 = -c_1y_0T(\omega_0) - T(\omega_0)Lx_0^3$$

From the table of transforms we have

$$(5.26) \qquad Lx_0^3 = La^3 \cos^3 \omega_0 t = \frac{a^3}{4}[3p^2T(\omega_0) + p^2T(3\omega_0)]$$

Substituting (5.23) and (5.26) into (5.25), we obtain

$$(5.27) \qquad y_1 = -p^2T^2(\omega_0)\left(c_1a + \frac{3a^3}{4}\right) - \frac{a^3}{4}p^2T(\omega_0)T(3\omega_0)$$

Now, from the table of transforms, it is seen that

$$(5.28) \qquad\qquad L^{-1}p^2T^2(\omega_0) = \frac{t}{2\omega_0}\sin \omega_0 t$$

Hence the first term of the right-hand member of (5.27) corresponds to a condition of resonance. We may eliminate this condition of resonance by placing the coefficient of this term equal to zero.   Then

$$(5.29) \qquad c_1 a + \frac{3a^3}{4} = 0$$

or

$$(5.30) \qquad c_1 = -\frac{3a^2}{4}$$

This determines the constant c_1.   With the resonance condition eliminated, (5.27) reduces to

$$(5.31) \qquad y_1 = -\frac{a^3}{4} p^2 T(\omega_0) T(3\omega_0)$$

Making use of the table of transforms, we obtain the second approximation

$$(5.32) \quad x_1 = L^{-1} y_1 = L^{-1}\left[-\frac{a^3}{4} p^2 T(\omega_0) T(3\omega_0) \right]$$
$$= \frac{a^3}{32\omega_0^2} (\cos 3\omega_0 t - \cos \omega_0 t)$$

If we limit our calculations to the second approximation, we obtain from (5.12), (5.24), and (5.32)

$$(5.33) \qquad x = a \cos \omega_0 t + \frac{\alpha a^3}{32\omega_0^2} (\cos 3\omega_0 t - \cos \omega_0 t)$$

The angular frequency is obtained by substituting the value of c_1 given by (5.30) into (5.13).   This gives

$$(5.34) \qquad \omega_0^2 = \omega^2 + \tfrac{3}{4}a^2\alpha$$

From this we see that the presence of the term x^3 in the equation introduces a higher harmonic term $\cos 3\omega_0 t$ and the fundamental frequency is not constant but depends on the amplitude a and increases with a provided that the quantity α is positive.

The third approximation is obtained by substituting the above values of y_0, y_1, x_0, and x_1 into (5.20).   This gives

$$(5.35) \quad y_2 = -c_2 p^2 a T^2(\omega_0) + \frac{c_1 a^3}{4} T(\omega_0) p^2 T(\omega_0) T(3\omega_0) - T(\omega_0) L(3x_0^2 x_1)$$

We must now compute

$$(5.36) \qquad L(3x_0^2 x_1) = L\left(\frac{3a^5}{32\omega_0^2} \cos^2 \omega_0 t \cos 3\omega_0 t - \cos^3 \omega_0 t \right)$$

By using the table of transforms we easily obtain

$$(5.37) \quad L(3x_0^2 x_1) = \frac{3a^5 p^2}{(4 \times 32)\omega_0^2} [T(5\omega_0) + T(3\omega_0) + T(3\omega_0) - 2T(\omega_0)]$$

Substituting this value of $L(3x_0^2 x_1)$ and making use of the identity

$$(5.38) \qquad T(a)T(b) = \frac{1}{b^2 - a^2}[T(a) - T(b)]$$

we write (5.35) in the form

$$(5.39) \quad y_2 = p^2 T^2(\omega_0)\left(-c_2 a + \frac{c_1 a^3}{32\omega_0^2} + \frac{3a^5}{64\omega_0^2}\right)$$
$$+ p^2 T(\omega_0) T(3\omega_0)\left[-\frac{c_1 a^3}{32\omega_0^2} - \frac{3a^5}{(4 \times 32)\omega_0^2}\right] - p^2 T(\omega_0) T(5\omega_0)\frac{3a^5}{(4 \times 32)\omega_0^2}$$

To eliminate the condition of resonance, we equate the coefficient of the $p^2 T^2(\omega_0)$ term to zero, substituting the value of c_1 into the coefficient. We thus obtain

$$(5.40) \qquad c_2 = \frac{3a^4}{128\omega_0^2}$$

On substituting the value of c_1 into the second member of (5.39), we see that this term vanishes and we have

$$(5.41) \qquad y_2 = -\frac{3a^5}{128\omega_0^2}p^2 T(\omega_0) T(5\omega_0)$$

Using the table of transforms to obtain the inverse transform of y_2, we have the third approximation

$$(5.42) \qquad x_2 = \frac{a^5}{1,024\omega_0^4}(\cos 5\omega_0 t - \cos \omega_0 t)$$

From (5.12) we thus have the third approximation

$$(5.43) \quad x = a \cos \omega_0 t + \frac{\alpha a^3}{32\omega_0^2}(\cos 3\omega_0 t - \cos \omega_0 t)$$
$$+ \frac{\alpha^2 a^5}{1,024\omega_0^4}(\cos 5\omega_0 t - \cos \omega_0 t)$$

where now the fundamental frequency is given by (5.13) as

$$(5.44) \qquad \omega_0^2 = \omega^2 + \tfrac{3}{4}a^2\alpha - \frac{3a^4\alpha^2}{128\omega_0^2}$$

The fourth approximation is obtained in the same manner from (5.21). We compute

$$(5.45) \quad L(3x_0^2 x_2 + 3x_0 x_1^2) = \frac{3a^7 p^2}{(4 \times 1,024)\omega_0^4}[2T(7\omega_0) + T(5\omega_0) - 3T(3\omega_0)]$$

by using the table of transforms. Substituting the values of the quantities y_0, y_1, and y_2 as given above into Eq. (5.21) and making use of the relation (5.45), we obtain

$$(5.46) \quad y_3 = -c_3 p^2 a T^2(\omega_0) - \frac{c_2 T(\omega_0) a^3 p^2}{32\omega_0^2} [T(3\omega_0) - T(\omega_0)]$$

$$- \frac{c_1 T(\omega_0) a^5 p^2}{1{,}024\omega_0^4} [T(5\omega_0) - T(\omega_0)]$$

$$- \frac{3a^7 p^2 T(\omega_0)}{(4 \times 1{,}024)\omega_0^4} [2T(7\omega_0) + T(5\omega_0) - 3T(3\omega_0)]$$

The condition for no resonance leads to

$$(5.47) \qquad c_3 a = \frac{c_2 a^3}{32\omega_0^2} + \frac{c_1 a^5}{1{,}024\omega_0^4}$$

Substituting the values of c_1 and c_2 given by (5.30) and (5.40) into (5.47), we obtain

$$(5.48) \qquad c_3 = 0$$

Suppressing the resonance terms, Eq. (5.46) reduces to

$$(5.49) \quad y_3 = p^2 T(\omega_0) T(3\omega_0) \frac{3a^7}{2{,}048\omega_0^4} + p^2 T(\omega_0) T(7\omega_0) \left(- \frac{6a^7}{4{,}096\omega_0^4}\right)$$

Computing the inverse transform by the use of the table of transforms, we obtain

$$(5.50) \qquad x_3 = \frac{a^7}{32{,}768\omega_0^6} (5 \cos \omega_0 t - 3 \cos 3\omega_0 t + \cos 7\omega_0 t)$$

Substituting x_0, x_1, x_2, x_3 into (5.12), we obtain the fourth approximation

$$(5.51) \quad x = a \cos \omega_0 t + \frac{\alpha a^3}{32\omega_0^2} (\cos 3\omega_0 t - \cos \omega_0 t)$$

$$+ \frac{\alpha^2 a^5}{1{,}024\omega_0^4} (\cos 5\omega_0 t - \cos \omega_0 t)$$

$$+ \frac{\alpha^3 a^7}{32{,}768\omega_0^6} (5 \cos \omega_0 t - 3 \cos 3\omega_0 t + \cos 7\omega_0 t)$$

To this approximation the fundamental frequency ω_0 is given by (5.13) and is

$$(5.52) \qquad \omega_0^2 = \omega^2 + \tfrac{3}{4}\alpha a^2 - \tfrac{3}{128}\alpha^2 \frac{a^4}{\omega_0^2}$$

Now, in all the calculations, terms to higher power than the third have been omitted. We may simplify Eq. (5.52) by substituting on the right-hand side the value of ω_0^2 given by (5.34). We thus obtain

$$(5.53) \qquad \omega_0^2 = \omega^2 + \tfrac{3}{4}\alpha a^2 - \tfrac{3}{128}\alpha^2 \left(\frac{a^4}{\omega_0^2 + \tfrac{3}{4}\alpha a^2}\right)$$

Expanding the term in parentheses in powers of α and retaining powers of α only up to the third, we have

$$(5.54) \qquad \omega_0^2 = \omega^2 + \tfrac{3}{4}\alpha a^2 - \frac{3\alpha^2}{128}\frac{a^4}{\omega^2} + \frac{9\alpha^3 a^6}{512\omega^4}$$

Further approximations may be carried out by the same general procedure.

a. The Vibrations of a Pendulum. The above analysis may be applied to the study of a theoretical pendulum. The equation of motion of such a pendulum is

$$(5.55) \qquad \ddot{\theta} + \frac{g}{l}\sin\theta = 0$$

where l is the length of the pendulum and g is the gravitational constant. If we develop $\sin\theta$ in a power series in θ and retain only the first two terms of the series, we obtain

$$(5.56) \qquad \ddot{\theta} + \frac{g}{l}\theta - \frac{g}{6l}\theta^3 = 0$$

If we stipulate the initial condition that, at $t = 0$, $\theta = \theta_0$, we may make use of the preceding analysis by letting

$$(5.57) \qquad \theta_0 = a$$

$$(5.58) \qquad \omega^2 = \frac{g}{l}$$

$$(5.59) \qquad \alpha = -\frac{g}{6l}$$

Using the first approximation for the angular frequency as given by (5.34), we have

$$(5.60) \qquad \omega_0^2 = \frac{g}{l} - \frac{g\theta_0^2}{8l}$$

To this approximation the period of the oscillations is given by

$$(5.61) \qquad T = \frac{2\pi}{\omega_0} = \frac{2\pi}{[(g/l)(1 - \theta_0^2/8)]^{\frac{1}{2}}}$$

For small amplitude θ_0 the radical may be expanded in powers of θ_0, and we may write

$$(5.62) \qquad T = 2\pi \left(\frac{l}{g}\right)^{\frac{1}{2}}\left(1 + \frac{\theta_0^2}{16}\right)$$

This formula gives excellent results for small amplitudes of oscillation.

b. Nonlinear Electrical Circuit. As another example of the method, let us consider the free oscillations of an electrical circuit consisting of an inductance and a capacitor in series. The equation of such a circuit may be written in the form

$$(5.63) \qquad \frac{d\phi}{dt} + \frac{Q}{C} = 0$$

where ϕ is the total flux linking the circuit, Q is the charge on the capacitor, and C is the capacitance of the system. For simplicity we assume that the circuit is devoid of resistance. If the inductance of the system consists of a coil of wire wound on an iron core, we have in general

$$(5.64) \qquad i = F(\phi)$$

where i is the current flowing in the circuit. The functional dependence between the current in the circuit and the flux ϕ depends on the functional variation of the flux density B of the material of the inductance coil with the magnetizing force, which is proportional to the current i. This function is many-valued in general. However, it may be taken to be single-valued at large magnetizing forces for Nickalloy, Permalloy, and low-loss steels.

Several analytical expressions have been suggested to express approximately the relation between the magnetizing current i and the total flux ϕ in a ferromagnetic material. Some of the expressions are

$$(5.65) \qquad i = \sum_{n=1}^{m} a_n \phi^n$$

$$(5.66) \qquad i = A \sinh \phi$$

$$(5.67) \qquad i = A_0 + \sum_{n=1}^{\infty} A_n \cos n\phi + \sum_{n=1}^{\infty} B_n \sin n\phi$$

and other forms may be derived. In ordinary circuit theory the linear relation

$$(5.68) \qquad i = \frac{1}{L} \phi$$

is assumed. The coefficient L is then the inductance of the system. In our analysis we shall assume that the relation between i and ϕ is given by

$$(5.69) \qquad i = \frac{1}{L} \phi + \frac{1}{b} \phi^3$$

where the coefficient $1/b$ is a measure of the nonlinearity of the system. This expression may be regarded as the first two terms of the power series of the relation (5.66) and by a proper choice of the coefficients may be made to approximate the actual i-ϕ curve of a material quite accurately. If we differentiate Eq. (5.63), we obtain

(5.70)
$$\frac{d^2\phi}{dt^2} + \frac{i}{C} = 0$$

in view of the relation

(5.71)
$$i = \frac{dQ}{dt}$$

Substituting the value of i given by (5.69) into (5.70) yields

(5.72)
$$\frac{d^2\phi}{dt^2} + \frac{1}{LC}\phi + \frac{1}{Cb}\phi^3 = 0$$

If we now let

(5.73)
$$\omega^2 = \frac{1}{LC}$$

(5.74)
$$\alpha = \frac{1}{bC}$$

(5.75)
$$\phi = x$$

then Eq. (5.72) is identical with Eq. (5.4). Let us now consider the case in which at $t = 0$ there is no current flowing in the system and the capacitor has an initial charge of Q_0. In view of Eqs. (5.63) and (5.69) we therefore have the following initial conditions of the independent variable x:

(5.76)
$$\left. \begin{array}{l} x = 0 \\ \dfrac{dx}{dt} = -\dfrac{Q_0}{C} = v_0 \end{array} \right\} \quad \text{at } t = 0$$

In this case, therefore, we have to solve Eq. (5.4) subject to the initial conditions (5.76). As before, we let y be the transform of x. The transformed equation is in this case

(5.77)
$$(p^2 + \omega^2)y = pv_0 - Lx^3$$

To treat this case, we again establish the sequence (5.16) to (5.21), and by equating like powers of α we obtain the set of equations

(5.78) $p^2y_0 + \omega_0^2 y_0 = pv_0$

(5.79) $p^2y_1 + \omega_0^2 y_1 = -c_1y_0 - Lx_0^3$

(5.80) $p^2y_2 + \omega_0^2 y_2 = -c_2y_0 - c_1y_1 - L(3x_0^2 x_1)$

(5.81) $p^2y_3 + \omega_0^2 y_3 = -c_3y_0 - c_2y_1 - c_1y_2 - L(3x_0^2 x_2 + 3x_0 x_1^2)$

This set of equations is the same as the set (5.18) to (5.21) with the exception of the first one because of the different boundary conditions. The first approximation is obtained from (5.78) by writing

(5.82)
$$y_0 = pv_0 T(\omega_0) = Lx_0$$

From the table of transforms this gives the first approximation

$$(5.83) \qquad x_0 = \frac{v_0}{\omega_0} \sin \omega_0 t$$

We now write (5.79) in the form

$$(5.84) \qquad y_1 = T(\omega_0)(-c_1 y_0 - L x_0^3)$$

From the table of transforms we have

$$(5.85) \qquad L x_0 = \frac{3v_0^3}{4\omega_0^2} [pT(\omega_0) - pT(3\omega_0)]$$

Substituting (5.82) and (5.85) into (5.84), we obtain

$$(5.86) \qquad y_1 = pT^2(\omega_0)\left(-c_1 v_0 - \frac{3v_0^3}{4\omega_0^2}\right) + \frac{3v_0^3}{4\omega_0^2}$$
$$pT(\omega_0)T(3\omega_0) = L x_1$$

The term $pT^2(\omega_0)$ leads to resonance, as may be seen from the table of transforms; hence its coefficient must be set equal to zero. This yields

$$(5.87) \qquad c_1 = -\frac{3v_0^2}{4\omega_0^2}$$

By means of the table of transforms we then obtain

$$(5.88) \qquad x_1 = L^{-1} y_1 = \frac{3v_0^3}{32\omega_0^5} (\sin \omega_0 t - \sin 3\omega_0 t)$$

To this approximation we obtain the angular frequency ω_0 from (5.13) as

$$(5.89) \qquad \omega_0^2 = \omega^2 + \frac{3v_0^2 \alpha}{4\omega^2}$$

The second approximation is therefore

$$(5.90) \qquad x = \frac{v_0 \sin \omega_0 t}{\omega_0} + \frac{3v_0^3 \alpha}{32\omega_0^5}\left(\sin \omega_0 t - \frac{\sin 3\omega_0 t}{3}\right)$$

The variation of the charge on the capacitor may be obtained from (5.63) in the form

$$(5.91) \qquad Q = -C \frac{dx}{dt} = Q_0 \cos \omega_0 t + \frac{3Q_0^3}{32\omega_0^4 bc^3} (\cos \omega_0 t - \cos 3\omega_0 t)$$

In view of (5.89) the natural frequency of the system may be written in the form

$$(5.92) \qquad f = \frac{1}{2\pi}\left(\frac{1}{LC} + \frac{3}{4}\frac{Q_0^2 L^2}{bC}\right)^{\frac{1}{2}}$$

to the second approximation. We see that the frequency varies with the initial charge on the capacitor Q_0.

c. *Oscillator Nonlinearly Damped.* As another application of the method in the study of free oscillations, let us apply it to the study of a freely vibrating system whose damping force is proportional to the square of the velocity. The equation of motion of this system is given by

$$(5.93) \qquad \ddot{x} + \omega^2 x \pm \alpha \dot{x}^2 = 0$$

The minus sign must be taken when the velocity is in the direction of the negative x axis and the plus sign when the velocity is in the direction of the positive x axis. Let us assume the initial conditions

$$(5.94) \qquad \left. \begin{array}{c} x = a \\ \dot{x} = 0 \end{array} \right\} \quad \text{at } t = 0$$

We thus have to consider the equation

$$(5.95) \qquad \ddot{x} + \omega^2 x - \alpha \dot{x}^2 = 0$$

for the first half of the oscillation. As before, we set up the sequence (5.12) to (5.15), and if we limit our calculations to the terms containing α^2, we obtain the following set of equations:

$$(5.96) \qquad p^2 y_0 + \omega_0^2 y_0 = p^2 a$$
$$(5.97) \qquad p^2 y_1 + \omega_0^2 y_1 = -c_1 y_0 + L\dot{x}_0^2$$
$$(5.98) \qquad p^2 y_2 + \omega_0^2 y_2 = -c_1 y_1 - c_2 y_0 + L(2\dot{x}_0 \dot{x}_1)$$

From (5.96) we obtain

$$(5.99) \qquad y_0 = p^2 a T(\omega_0) = La \cos \omega_0 t = L x_0$$

Substituting this into (5.96), we get

$$(5.100) \quad y_1 = -c_1 p^2 a T^2(\omega_0) + \frac{\omega_0^2 a^2}{2}[T(\omega_0) - p^2 T(\omega_0) T(2\omega_0)]$$

In order to eliminate resonance, we must choose

$$(5.101) \qquad c_1 = 0$$

Hence

$$(5.102) \qquad y_1 = \frac{\omega_0^2 a^2}{2}\left[T(\omega_0) - \frac{p^2}{3\omega_0^2} T(\omega_0) + \frac{p^2}{3\omega_0^2} T(2\omega_0)\right]$$

By means of the table of transforms we obtain

$$(5.103) \qquad x_1 = L^{-1} y_1 = \frac{a^2}{2} - \tfrac{2}{3}a^2 \cos \omega_0 t + \frac{a^2}{6} \cos 2\omega_0 t$$

Substituting the various transforms involved into (5.98) gives

$$(5.104) \quad y_2 = p^2 T^2(\omega_0)\left(-c_2 a + \frac{2a^3\omega_0^2}{6}\right) - \frac{2a^3\omega_0^2 p^2}{6} T(\omega_0) T(3\omega_0)$$
$$+ \frac{4a^3\omega_0^2}{6} p^2 T(\omega_0) T(2\omega_0) - \frac{4a^3\omega_0^2}{6} T(\omega_0)$$

The condition that there be no resonance in this case gives

$$(5.105) \qquad\qquad c_2 = \frac{a^2\omega_0^2}{3}$$

From the table of transforms we obtain

$$(5.106) \quad x_2 = L^{-1}y_2 = -\tfrac{2}{3}a^3 + \frac{a^3}{72}\left(61\cos\omega_0 t - 16\cos 2\omega_0 t + 3\cos 3\omega_0 t\right)$$

Substituting the above values of x_0, x_1, and x_2 into (5.12), we obtain

$$(5.107) \quad x = a\cos\omega_0 t + \frac{\alpha a^2}{6}\left(3 - 4\cos\omega_0 t + \cos 2\omega_0 t\right)$$
$$- \frac{\alpha^2 a^3}{72}\left(48 - 61\cos\omega_0 t + 16\cos 2\omega_0 t - 3\cos 3\omega_0 t\right)$$

Substituting the above values of c_1 and c_2 into (5.13) gives

$$(5.108) \qquad\qquad \omega^2 = \omega_0^2 + \frac{\omega_0^2 a^2 \alpha^2}{3}$$

or

$$(5.109) \qquad\qquad \omega_0 = \frac{\omega}{(1 + \tfrac{1}{3}a^2\alpha^2)^{\frac{1}{2}}}$$

If we let $T_1/2$ be the time required for the oscillation to reach its maximum negative displacement to the left, we have

$$(5.110) \qquad \frac{T_1}{2} = \frac{\pi}{\omega_0} = \frac{\pi(1 + 1a^2\alpha^2)^{\frac{1}{2}}}{\omega} \doteq \frac{\pi}{\omega}\left(1 + \tfrac{1}{6}a^2\alpha^2\right)$$

To determine the maximum negative displacement $+a_1$, we place $\omega_0 t = \pi$ in (5.107), and we obtain

$$(5.111) \qquad\qquad +a_1 = -a + \tfrac{4}{3}\alpha a^2 - \tfrac{16}{9}\alpha^2 a^3$$

Now, to determine the motion for the next half cycle, we must solve the equation

$$(5.112) \qquad\qquad \ddot{x} + \omega^2 x + \alpha\dot{x}^2 = 0$$

subject to the initial conditions

$$(5.113) \qquad\qquad \left.\begin{array}{l} x = -a_1 \\ \dot{x} = a \end{array}\right\} \quad \text{at } t = 0$$

However, if we make the change in variable

(5.114) $$x = -y$$

we see that we must then solve the equation

(5.115) $$y + \omega^2 y - \alpha \dot{y}^2 = 0$$

subject to the conditions

(5.116) $$\left. \begin{array}{l} y = a_1 \\ \dot{y} = 0 \end{array} \right\} \quad \text{at } t = 0$$

However, this is the same equation whose solution we have just obtained. The only difference is that we have a_1 instead of a in the initial conditions. We thus obtain

(5.117) $$\frac{T_2}{2} \doteq \frac{\pi}{\omega}\left(1 + \tfrac{1}{6}a_1^2\alpha^2\right)$$

for the time required for the second half cycle and

(5.118) $$a_2 = -a_1 + \tfrac{4}{3}\alpha a_1^2 - \tfrac{16}{9}\alpha^2 a_1^3$$

for the displacement of the system at the end of the second half cycle. It is thus evident that the oscillation has a gradually decreasing amplitude. Its amplitude after the $(n + 1)$st half cycle is given by

(5.119) $$a_{n+1} = -a_n + \tfrac{4}{3}\alpha a_n^2 - \tfrac{16}{9}\alpha^2 a_n^3$$

TABLE OF TRANSFORMS

Let $T(\omega) = \dfrac{1}{p^2 + \omega^2}$.

1. $L \sin \omega t = \omega p T(\omega)$
2. $L \sin^2 \omega t = \tfrac{1}{2}[1 - p^2 T(2\omega)]$
3. $L \sin^3 \omega t = \tfrac{1}{4}[3p\omega T(\omega) - 3\omega p T(3\omega)]$
4. $L \cos \omega t = p^2 T(\omega)$
5. $L \cos^2 \omega t = \tfrac{1}{2}[1 + p^2 T(2\omega)]$
6. $L \cos^3 \omega t = \tfrac{1}{4}[3p^2 T(\omega) + p^2 T(3\omega)]$
7. $L \sin At \cos Bt = \tfrac{1}{2}[(A + B)p T(A + B) + (A - B)p T(A - B)]$
8. $L \cos At \cos Bt = \dfrac{p^2}{2}[T(A + B) + T(A - B)]$
9. $L \sin At \sin Bt = \dfrac{p^2}{2}[T(A - B) - T(A + B)]$
10. $L \sin At \sin Bt \sin ct = \dfrac{p}{4}[(A + B - c)T(A + B - c)$
$$+ (B + c - A)T(B + c - A) + (c + A - B)T(c + A - B)$$
$$- (A + B + c)T(A + B + c)]$$
11. $L \sin At \cos Bt \cos ct = \dfrac{p}{4}[(A + B - c)T(A + B - c)$
$$- (B + c - A)T(B + c - A) + (c + A - B)T(c + A - B)$$
$$+ (A + B + c)T(A + B + c)]$$

12. $L \sin At \sin Bt \cos ct = \dfrac{p^2}{4} [T(B + c - A) - T(A + B - c)$

$$+ T(c + A - B) - T(A + B + c)]$$

13. $L \cos At \cos Bt \cos ct = \dfrac{p^2}{4} [T(A + B - c) + T(B + c - A)$

$$+ T(c + A - B) + T(A + B + c)]$$

14. $L^{-1}p^2 T(a) T(b) = \dfrac{\cos at - \cos bt}{b^2 - a^2}$

15. $L^{-1}p^2 T^2(\omega) = \dfrac{t \sin \omega t}{2\omega}$

16. $L^{-1}p T^2(\omega) = \dfrac{\sin \omega t}{2\omega^3} - \dfrac{t \cos \omega t}{2\omega^2}$

17. $L^{-1}T(\omega) = \dfrac{1 - \cos \omega t}{\omega^2}$

18. $T(a) T(b) = \dfrac{1}{b^2 - a^2} [T(a) - T(b)]$

6. Forced Vibrations of Nonlinear Systems.

In the last section the *free vibrations* of oscillating systems with nonlinear restoring forces were considered. In this section the *forced* oscillations of systems with nonlinear restoring forces will be considered.

As a typical example of such a system, let us consider the mechanical case of an oscillator of mass m acted upon by a nonlinear elastic restoring force $F(x)$ and by a periodic external force $F_0 \cos \omega t$.

The equation of motion of such a system is

$$(6.1) \qquad m \frac{d^2x}{dt^2} + F(x) = F_0 \cos \omega t$$

Let us first discuss the case in which the restoring force is symmetric, that is, has equal magnitude at corresponding points on both sides of the position of equilibrium or position of rest. In this case only *odd* powers may occur in the law of force. Otherwise we have an unsymmetrical law of force and hence an unsymmetric vibration. This is expressed mathematically by the condition

$$(6.2) \qquad F(-x) = F(x)$$

Since the methods of analysis and the qualitative results do not depend greatly upon the special form of $F(x)$, we shall choose the following form for the restoring force $F(x)$,

$$(6.3) \qquad F(x) = kx - \delta x^3$$

where $k > 0$.

If $\delta > 0$, it is said that the restoring force corresponds to a *soft* spring, while if $\delta < 0$, the restoring force is said to correspond to a *hard* spring. In the case that $\delta > 0$ the restoring force decreases with the amplitude of oscillation as in the case of a pendulum. In this case the *natural frequency* decreases with increasing amplitude.

Inserting (6.3) into (6.1), we have the equation of motion

$$(6.4) \qquad m\frac{d^2x}{dt^2} + kx - \delta x^3 = F_0 \cos \omega t$$

This equation is known in the literature as *Duffing's equation*.[7]

Experiments performed on dynamical systems whose equations of motion are of the form (6.4) show that as the time t increases the motion of the system becomes periodic after some transient motions have died out. The period of the resulting oscillations is found to have a fundamental frequency of $\omega/2\pi$ and may therefore be represented by a Fourier series in multiples of ω.

The amplitude of the steady state (as $t \to \infty$) may be calculated by the following approximate method:

As a first approximation let us assume

$$(6.5) \qquad x_1 = a \cos \omega t$$

where the amplitude a is to be determined. If we substitute this expression for x in (6.4) and make use of the trigonometric identity

$$(6.6) \qquad \cos^3 \omega t = \tfrac{1}{4} \cos 3\omega t + \tfrac{3}{4} \cos \omega t$$

we obtain the equation

$$(6.7) \qquad -ma\omega^2 + ka - \tfrac{3}{4}\delta a^3 - \frac{\delta}{4}a^3 \cos 3\omega t = F_0 \cos \omega t$$

If the fundamental vibration is to satisfy Eq. (6.4), we must have

$$(6.8) \qquad \frac{3}{4}\frac{\delta}{m}a^3 + (\omega^2 - \omega_0^2)a + \frac{F_0}{m} = 0$$

where

$$(6.9) \qquad \omega_0 = \sqrt{\frac{k}{m}}$$

This is the natural angular frequency of the system in the absence of the nonlinear term.

Equation (6.8) determines the amplitude of the oscillation. If we divide Eq. (6.8) by ω_0^2, we obtain

$$(6.10) \qquad \frac{3\delta a^3}{4m\omega_0^2} = \left(1 - \frac{\omega^2}{\omega_0^2}\right)a - \frac{F_0}{\omega_0^2 m}$$

The roots of this cubic equation in a may be obtained graphically by constructing a y-a coordinate system as shown in Fig. 6.1.

This figure represents the cubical parabola

$$(6.11) \qquad y = \frac{3\delta a^3}{4m\omega_0^2}$$

and the straight line

$$(6.12) \qquad y = \left(1 - \frac{\omega^2}{\omega_0^2}\right) a - \frac{F_0}{\omega_0^2 m}$$

FIG. 6.1

The possible values of a are the abscissa of the points of intersection of these curves.

If ω is large, the slope of the straight line is negative and there is only one point of intersection, P_0. There is also only one point of intersection for $\omega = \omega_0$. If now ω decreases, the straight line rotates until it intersects the cubical parabola at three points, P_1, P_2, and P_3. The abscissa of these points corresponds to three possible amplitudes. The amplitude-versus-frequency curve has the form shown in Fig. 6.2.

A more precise analysis* shows that if we approach from the low-frequency side, the amplitude corresponding to the lower branch is the

FIG. 6.2

stable one. As ω increases, we arrive at the limiting point, G. As a continues to increase beyond this point, only the upper branch yields a real point of intersection in Fig. 6.1. It is then seen that with a continuous increase of ω, the amplitude a will suddenly jump from the lower branch to the upper one at G.

These discontinuities or jumps in amplitude are frequently observed in nonlinear vibration processes both electrical and mechanical.†

The Higher Approximations. It will now be shown how the next approximations of the motion are obtained. If Eq. (6.4) is solved for d^2x/dt^2 and if the first approximation (6.5) is substituted in the right-hand member for x, we obtain

$$(6.13) \qquad \frac{d^2x}{dt^2} = \frac{F_0}{m}\cos\omega t - \frac{ka}{m}\cos\omega t + \frac{3}{4}\frac{\delta a^3}{m}\cos\omega t + \frac{\delta a^3}{4m}\cos 3\omega t$$

---

* E. V. Appleton, On the Anomalous Behaviour of a Galvanometer, *Philosophical Magazine*, ser. 6, vol. 47, p. 609, 1924.

† See O. Martienssen, Ueber neue Resonanzer-scheinungen in Wechselstromkreisen, *Physikalische Zeitung*, vol. 11, p. 448, 1910.

Making use of (6.8), this reduces to

$$(6.14) \qquad \frac{d^2x}{dt^2} = -\omega^2 a \cos \omega t + \frac{\delta a^3}{4m} \cos 3\omega t$$

Integration gives

$$(6.15) \quad x_2 = a \cos \omega t - \frac{\delta a^3}{36m\omega^2} \cos 3\omega t = a \cos \omega t - \frac{\delta a^3 \omega_0^2}{36k\omega^2} \cos 3\omega t$$

This second approximation may then be substituted into (6.4) to obtain the third approximation. In this manner any number of terms of the Fourier-series solution may be obtained. The investigation of the convergence of the process shows that the series obtained converges if δ is small.

The Case of an Unsymmetric Restoring Force. If we add a quadratic term to the elastic restoring force so that

$$(6.16) \qquad F(x) = kx + \delta x^2$$

then the vibration becomes unsymmetric since changing the sign of x does not change that of the quadratic term, and hence the restoring force has different values at two points that are symmetric with respect to the origin. The equation of motion is now

$$(6.17) \qquad m \frac{d^2x}{dt^2} + kx + \delta x^2 = F_0 \cos \omega t$$

In this case we assume

$$(6.18) \qquad x_1 = a \cos \omega t + b$$

as the first approximation. The constant b is introduced to allow for the lack of symmetry. We insert this approximation into (6.17) and determine a and b in such a way that the constant term and the fundamental vibration satisfy the differential equation.

Using the trigonometric identity

$$(6.19) \qquad \cos^2 \omega t = \frac{1 + \cos 2\omega t}{2}$$

we obtain the two equations

$$(6.20) \qquad b^2 + \frac{k}{\delta} b + \frac{a^2}{2} = 0$$

and

$$(6.21) \qquad a(\omega^2 - \omega_0^2) - \frac{2\delta ab}{m} + \frac{F_0}{m} = 0$$

If δ is small, we have from (6.20)

$$(6.22) \qquad b = -\frac{\delta a^2}{2k}$$

If we now substitute this into (6.21), we have

$$(6.23) \qquad \frac{\delta^2}{km} a^3 + a(\omega^2 - \omega_0^2) + \frac{F_0}{m} = 0$$

This is a cubic equation for the amplitude a. It may be solved graphically, and it is found that under certain conditions it has three roots so that the "jump" phenomenon occurs here as in the case of the symmetrical vibrations. The higher approximations are obtained in the same manner as in the symmetrical case.

Subharmonic Response. Periodic solutions of the Duffing equation (6.4) have been considered. These solutions have a fundamental period $P = 2\pi/\omega$ equal to the period of the external exciting force. Experiments show that permanent oscillations with a frequency of $\frac{1}{2}$, $\frac{1}{3}$, $\ldots$, $1/n$ of that of the applied force can occur in nonlinear systems. This phenomenon is called *subharmonic resonance.*

It is known that in linear systems having damping the permanent oscillations of the system have a frequency exactly equal to that of the exciting force, and hence subharmonic resonance is impossible in linear systems. In nonlinear systems, however, even with damping present, the phenomenon of subharmonic resonance is exhibited.

The usual explanation offered of the phenomenon of subharmonic resonance is that the oscillations of a nonlinear system contain higher harmonics in profusion. It is therefore possible that an external force with a frequency the same as one of the higher harmonics may be able to sustain and excite harmonics of lower frequency. This of course requires certain conditions to be true of the system. The mathematical discussion of the problem of subharmonic resonance is a matter of some difficulty. An interesting discussion of the question will be found in the works of Kármán and Stoker given in the references at the end of this chapter.

As an example of a typical investigation of the possibility of subharmonic response, consider the following nonlinear differential equation:

$$(6.24) \qquad \frac{d^2x}{dt^2} + w_0^2 x + bx^3 = \frac{F_0}{m} \cos wt$$

Assume that a possible periodic solution of this equation has the following form:

$$(6.25) \qquad x = A_0 \cos \frac{wt}{3}$$

If this assumed form of the solution is substituted into (6.24), the result may be written in the following form:

$$(6.26) \qquad \left(w_0^2 A_0 - \frac{w^2}{9} A_0 + \tfrac{3}{4} b A_0^3 \right) \cos \frac{wt}{3} + \frac{b}{4} A_0^3 \cos wt = \frac{F_0}{m} \cos wt$$

For (6.25) to satisfy (6.24) we must therefore have

$$(6.27) \qquad w_0^2 A_0 - w^2 \frac{A_0}{9} + 3b \frac{A_0^3}{4} = 0$$

and

$$(6.28) \qquad \frac{b}{4} A_0^3 = \frac{F_0}{m}$$

Hence an oscillation of the type (6.25) with an amplitude of

$$(6.29) \qquad A_0 = \left(\frac{4F_0}{mb} \right)^{\frac{1}{3}}$$

is possible provided the angular frequency of the forcing function satisfies the equation

$$(6.30) \qquad w^2 = 9w_0^2 + \tfrac{27}{4}b \left(\frac{4F_0}{mb} \right)^{\frac{2}{3}}$$

The *stability* of this solution requires a separate investigation.[14]

7. Forced Oscillations with Damping. In many practical problems, particularly in the field of electrical-circuit theory, approximate solutions of nonlinear differential equations must be determined in which the forcing function contains a constant plus a harmonic term and the circuit contains damping. The following equation is typical of this class of differential equations:

$$(7.1) \qquad L\frac{di}{dt} + Ri + S_0 q + aq^3 = E_0 + E_m \sin (wt + \theta)$$

This equation governs the oscillations of an electrical circuit consisting of an inductance L and a resistance R, both of which are linear, in series with a nonlinear capacitor. S_0 is the constant *initial elastance* of this capacitor, and a is a constant which is the measure of the departure of the capacitor from linearity. In practical circuits a is a small positive number. The functions i and q are the current of the circuit and the charge separation on the plates of the capacitor, respectively. The functions are related by the differential equation

$$(7.2) \qquad i = \frac{dq}{dt}$$

In order to obtain an approximate steady-state solution by Duffing's method, a periodic solution of the following form is assumed for (7.1),

$$(7.3) \qquad i = I_m \sin wt$$

$$(7.4) \qquad q = Q_0 - \frac{I_m}{w} \cos wt$$

where Q_0 is the constant charge accumulation on the plates of the capacitor and I_m is the maximum amplitude of the alternating current of the circuit.   Substitute these expressions into (7.1), and let

$$(7.5) \quad F(t) = \left(L\frac{di}{dt} + Ri + S_0 q + aq^3\right) i = I_m \sin wt$$

$$q = Q_0 - \frac{I_m}{w}\cos wt$$

$$= \left(S_0 Q_0 + aQ_0^3 + \frac{3aQ_0 I_m^2}{2w^2}\right) + RI_m \sin wt$$

$$+ \left(wLI_m - S_0\frac{I_m}{w} - \frac{3aI_m^3}{4w^3} - 3aQ_0^2\frac{I_m}{w}\right)\cos wt$$

$$+ \frac{3Q_0 aI_m^2}{2w^2}\cos 2wt - \frac{aI_m^3}{4w^3}\cos 3wt$$

With this notation Eq. (7.1) becomes

$$(7.6) \qquad F(t) = E_0 + E_m \cos\theta\sin wt + E_m\sin\theta\cos wt$$

The undetermined coefficients I_m and Q_0 and the phase angle θ may be adjusted to make (7.3) and (7.4) an approximate solution of (7.1) by equating the constant term and the coefficients of $\sin wt$ and $\cos wt$ to the right-hand member of (7.6).   This procedure leads to the following three equations:

$$(7.7) \qquad S_0 Q_0 + aQ_0\left(Q_0^2 + \frac{3I_m^2}{2w^2}\right) = E_0$$

$$(7.8) \qquad\qquad\qquad RI_m = E_m\cos\theta$$

$$(7.9) \qquad I_m\left(wL - \frac{S_0}{w}\right) - 3a\frac{I_m}{w}\left(Q_0^2 + \frac{I_m^2}{4w^2}\right) = E_m\sin\theta$$

The above equations are three simultaneous equations for the determination of the unknowns I_m, Q_0, and the phase angle θ.   If numerical values for the parameters involved are available, a solution of these equations may be effected by a graphical procedure similar to that outlined in Sec. 6.   In practical applications, however, considerable simplification may be introduced because the parameter a is a very small number.   Since a is small, the second term of (7.7) may be neglected and the following approximate value for Q_0 obtained,

$$(7.10) \qquad\qquad Q_0 = \frac{E_0}{S_0} = C_0 E_0$$

where $C_0 = 1/S_0$ is the *initial capacitance* of the nonlinear capacitor.   If the direct potential E_0 is large in comparison with the maximum value of the harmonic potential so that $E_0 \gg E_m$, then, for the frequencies ordinarily used in practice, we have

$$(7.11) \qquad\qquad Q_0^2 \gg \frac{I_m^2}{4w^2}$$

If the term $I_m^2/4$ is neglected in (7.9), this equation may be written in the form

$$(7.12) \qquad I_m \left[wL - \frac{1}{w}(S_0 + 3aC_0^2E_0^2) \right] = E_m \sin \theta$$

Hence, if (7.8) and (7.12) are squared and the results added, we obtain

$$(7.13) \qquad I_m^2 \left\{ R^2 + \left[wL - \frac{1}{w}(S_0 + 3aC_0^2E_0^2) \right]^2 \right\} = E_m^2$$

and the amplitude of the alternating current of the system is given by

$$(7.14) \qquad I_m = \frac{E_m}{\sqrt{R^2 + [wL - (1/w)(S_0 + 3aC_0^2E_0^2)]^2}}$$

It is thus apparent that the effect of the direct potential is to increase the *effective elastance* of the system by an amount $3aC_0^2E_0^2$. The tangent of the phase angle θ may be determined by the division of (7.12) by (7.8). This procedure yields

$$(7.15) \qquad \tan \theta = \frac{wL - (1/w)(S_0 + 3aC_0^2E_0^2)}{R}$$

The principal harmonics of the current i may be obtained by writing (7.1) in the form

$$(7.16) \qquad Ri = E_0 + E_m \sin(wt + \theta) - \left(L\frac{di}{dt} + S_0q + aq^3 \right)$$

and substituting (7.3) and (7.4) into the right-hand member of (7.16). If this is done and Eqs. (7.7), (7.8), and (7.9) used to simplify the resulting expression, the result yields the following value for the current i:

$$(7.17) \qquad i = I_m \sin wt + \frac{aI_m^3}{4w^3R} \cos 3wt - \frac{3aQ_0I_m^2}{2w^2R} \cos 2wt$$

Higher-order harmonics may be obtained by substituting (7.17) into the right-hand member of (7.16) and repeating the procedure. It may be noted that, if $a = 0$, the system becomes a linear one and the denominator of (7.14) reduces to the ordinary impedance of a linear series circuit.

8. Solution of Nonlinear Differential Equations by Integral Equations.

A method for solving nonlinear differential equations based on the theory of nonlinear integral equations will now be described. The general features of the method are clearly demonstrated by applying it to a series electrical circuit containing a nonlinear element. Such a circuit is depicted in Fig. 8.1.

This circuit consists of a linear component whose operational impedance is $Z(D)$, where $D = d/dt$, the time derivative operator, in series with a nonlinear component. It will be assumed that the potential drop across the nonlinear component is a function $F(i)$ of the current that flows through it. The differential equation that expresses the potential balance of the circuit may be written in the following symbolic form,

$$(8.1) \qquad Z(D)i(t) + F[i(t)] = e(t)$$

where $e(t)$ is the applied potential and $i(t)$ is the circuit current. In order to formulate Eq. (8.1) as an integral equation, let the p-multiplied Laplace transform be introduced:

$$(8.2) \qquad \mathcal{L}i(t) = p \int_0^\infty e^{-pt} i(t)\, dt = I(p)$$
$$(8.3) \qquad \mathcal{L}e(t) = E(p)$$
$$(8.4) \qquad \mathcal{L}F[i(t)] = G(p)$$

Let it be assumed that initially the circuit is at rest so that, at $t = 0$, $i(0) = 0$ and $q(0) = 0$. That is, the initial current i and the charge

FIG. 8.1. General series nonlinear circuit.

separation q of the circuit are both zero at $t = 0$. With these initial conditions the Laplace transform of Eq. (8.1) is given by

$$(8.5) \qquad Z(p)I(p) + G(p) = E(p)$$

or

$$(8.6) \qquad I(p) = \frac{E(p)}{Z(p)} - \frac{G(p)}{Z(p)}$$

For simplicity, introduce the notation

$$(8.7) \qquad H(p) = \frac{p}{Z(p)}$$

With this notation (8.6) may be written in the following form:

$$(8.8) \qquad I(p) = \frac{E(p)H(p)}{p} - \frac{G(p)H(p)}{p}$$

Let the inverse transform of $H(p)$ be $h(t)$, that is,

$$(8.9) \qquad L^{-1}H(p) = L^{-1}\frac{p}{Z(p)} = h(t)$$

The current of the circuit $i(t)$ may be obtained by taking the inverse Laplace transform of Eq. (8.8) in the form

$$(8.10) \qquad i(t) = L^{-1} \frac{E(p)H(p)}{p} - L^{-1} \frac{G(p)H(p)}{p}$$

If the Faltung, or superposition, theorem (see Chap. 21, Sec. 3) is applied to the right-hand member of Eq. (8.10), the following result is obtained:

$$(8.11) \qquad i(t) = \int_0^t h(t - u)e(u)\, du - \int_0^t h(t - u)F[i(u)]\, du$$

This is a nonlinear integral equation of the type studied by T. Lalesco.*

If $F(i) = 0$, so that the nonlinear component of the circuit is not present, then Eq. (8.11) reduces to

$$(8.12) \qquad i_0(t) = \int_0^t h(t - u)e(u)\, du$$

This is the current that would flow in the circuit of Fig. 8.1 in the absence of the nonlinear component. Thus it is seen that Eq. (8.11) may be written in the form

$$(8.12a) \qquad i(t) = i_0(t) - \int_0^t h(t - u)F[i(u)]\, du$$

Lalesco has shown that the limit of the infinite sequence of functions

$$
\begin{aligned}
i_0(t) &= \int_0^t h(t - u)e(u)\, du \\
i_1(t) &= i_0(t) - \int_0^t h(t - u)F[i_0(u)]\, du \\
i_2(t) &= i_0(t) - \int_0^t h(t - u)F[i_1(u)]\, du \\
&\quad \cdots\cdots\cdots\cdots\cdots\cdots\cdots\cdots \\
i_{n+1}(t) &= i_0(t) - \int_0^t h(t - u)F[i_n(u)]\, du
\end{aligned}
$$

(8.13)

is the solution of the integral equation (8.11). That is,

$$(8.14) \qquad i(t) = \lim_{n \to \infty} i_n(t)$$

is the desired solution.

The investigation of the convergence of the sequence (8.13) is given in the treatise of Lalesco. The results of this investigation indicate that the sequence converges rapidly in applications of this method of solution to special cases arising from physical problems.

---

* See T. Lalesco, "Introduction à la théorie des équations intégrales, Gauthier-Villars & Cie, Paris, 1912.

Solution of the Integral Equation by an Operational Procedure. A convenient operational procedure that has been found useful in the calculation of the sequence of functions $i_n(t)$ of (8.13) is based on the inverse Laplace transform of (8.6), which may be written in the form

$$(8.15) \qquad i(t) = L^{-1}I(p) = L^{-1}\frac{E(p)}{Z(p)} - L^{-1}\frac{LF[i(t)]}{Z(p)}$$

The current $i_0(t)$ is given by

$$(8.16) \qquad i_0(t) = L^{-1}\frac{E(p)}{Z(p)}$$

Hence (8.15) may be written in the form

$$(8.17) \qquad i(t) = i_0(t) - L^{-1}\frac{LF[i(t)]}{Z(p)}$$

The sequence of functions $i_1(t)$, $i_2(t)$, . . . , $i_n(t)$ of (8.13) may be conveniently expressed by the following equations:

$$(8.18) \qquad \begin{aligned} i_1(t) &= i_0(t) - L^{-1}\frac{LF[i_0(t)]}{Z(p)} \\ i_2(t) &= i_0(t) - L^{-1}\frac{LF[i_1(t)]}{Z(p)} \\ & \cdots\cdots\cdots\cdots\cdots \\ i_{n+1}(t) &= i_0(t) - L^{-1}\frac{LF[i_n(t)]}{Z(p)} \end{aligned}$$

In practice, it is usually found that the sequence $i_1(t)$, $i_2(t)$, . . . may be more simply computed by (8.18) than by (8.13) because a table of suitable Laplace transforms greatly assists in effecting the required integrations.[16]

As a simple example of the method, let it be required to solve the following nonlinear differential equation:

$$(8.19) \qquad L\frac{di}{dt} + Ri - k\frac{d}{dt}i^3 = E$$

This equation occurs in the study of the transient analysis of a nonlinear inductor with constant excitation. In this special case we have

$$(8.20) \qquad Z(D) = LD + R \qquad F(i) = k\frac{d}{dt}i^3 \qquad D = \frac{d}{dt}$$

Hence

$$(8.21) \quad H(p) = \frac{p}{Z(p)} = \frac{p}{Lp + R} \qquad h(t) = L^{-1}H(p) = \frac{e^{-bt}}{L} \qquad b = \frac{R}{L}$$

The integral equation satisfied by the current in the circuit is in this case

$$(8.22) \qquad i(t) = i_0(t) - \frac{k}{L} \int_0^t e^{b(u-t)} Di^3(u)\, du$$

where

$$(8.23) \qquad i_0(t) = \frac{L^{-1}E}{Lp + R} = \frac{E(1 - e^{-bt})}{R}$$

The operational form of the current (8.17) is

$$(8.24) \qquad i(t) = \frac{E}{R}(1 - e^{-bt}) - kL^{-1} \frac{L(Di^3)}{Lp + R}$$

The second approximation for the current is given by

$$(8.25) \qquad i_1(t) = \frac{E}{R}(1 - e^{-bt}) - kL^{-1} \frac{L(Di_0^3)}{Lp + R}$$

Carrying out the indicated operations with the aid of a table of Laplace transforms, the following result is obtained:

$$(8.26) \quad i_1(t) = \frac{E}{R}(1 - e^{-bt}) - \frac{kE^3}{LR^3}(3bte^{-bt} - \tfrac{9}{2}e^{-bt} + 6e^{-2bt} - \tfrac{3}{2}e^{-3bt})$$

The higher approximations may be obtained by computing more functions of the sequence (8.18). If the coefficient of the nonlinear term is small, the sequence converges rapidly and the second or third approximations usually give the accuracy required.

9. The Method of Kryloff and Bogoliuboff. The mathematical analysis of many important technical problems leads to differential equations of the following general form,

$$(9.1) \qquad \ddot{x} + \mu f(x,\dot{x}) + w^2 x = 0$$

where the parameter μ is a small constant and $f(x,\dot{x})$ is a given function of x and its derivative. Equations of this type are called quasi-linear differential equations. The Russian scientists Kryloff and Bogoliuboff have devised a method for the approximate solution of equations of this type.[6] This method is similar in principle to the familiar *method of variation of parameters*, introduced by Lagrange in 1774.* The Kryloff-Bogoliuboff method is based on the fact that, if $\mu = 0$ in (9.1), this equation becomes the equation of simple harmonic motion,

$$(9.2) \qquad \ddot{x} + w^2 x = 0$$

whose solution is

$$(9.3) \qquad x = a \sin(wt + \phi)$$

* See E. L. Ince, "Ordinary Differential Equations," pp. 122–123, Longmans, Green & Co., Inc., New York, 1927.

where a and ϕ are arbitrary constants. The derivative of (9.3) is

(9.4) $$\dot{x} = wa \cos (wt + \phi)$$

Kryloff and Bogoliuboff attempt to find a solution of (9.1) that preserves the form (9.3) and has a derivative of the form (9.4) but in which a and ϕ are now functions of the time $a(t)$ and $\phi(t)$, so that the solution of (9.1) now has the form

(9.5) $$x(t) = a(t) \sin [wt + \phi(t)]$$

If (9.5) is differentiated, the following result is obtained:

(9.6) $$\dot{x}(t) = aw \cos (wt + \phi) + \dot{a} \sin (wt + \phi) + a\dot{\phi} \cos (wt + \phi)$$

For $\dot{x}$ to retain the form (9.4), the sum of the last two terms of (9.6) must be equal to zero, so that

(9.7) $$\dot{a} \sin (wt + \phi) + a\dot{\phi} \cos (wt + \phi) = 0$$

This ensures that the derivative of x will have the form

(9.8) $$\dot{x} = wa(t) \cos [wt + \phi(t)]$$

If (9.8) is differentiated, the result is

(9.9) $$\ddot{x} = -w^2 a \sin (wt + \phi) + w\dot{a} \cos (wt + \phi) - wa\dot{\phi} \sin (wt + \phi)$$

Introduce the notation $\theta = wt + \phi$ and substitute (9.9) into (9.1). The result of this operation gives

(9.10) $$w\dot{a} \cos \theta - wa\dot{\phi} \sin \theta = -\mu f(a \sin \theta, wa \cos \theta)$$

Equations (9.7) and (9.10) may be written in the following form:

(9.11) $$\frac{da}{dt} \sin \theta + a \frac{d\phi}{dt} \cos \theta = 0$$

(9.12) $$\frac{da}{dt} \cos \theta - a \frac{d\phi}{dt} \sin \theta = \frac{-\mu f}{w} (a \sin \theta, wa \cos \theta)$$

These two equations may be solved for da/dt and $d\phi/dt$ simultaneously, with the following results:

(9.13) $$\frac{da}{dt} = \frac{-\mu f}{w} (a \sin \theta, wa \cos \theta) \cos \theta$$

(9.14) $$\frac{d\phi}{dt} = \frac{\mu f}{wa} (a \sin \theta, wa \cos \theta) \sin \theta$$

These equations give the variations of the amplitude a and the phase ϕ with the time t. So far in the analysis no approximations have been made, and therefore (9.13) and (9.14) are *exact* equations.

The Kryloff and Bogoliuboff Approximation. Since da/dt and $d\phi/dt$ are proportional to the small quantity μ, it follows that these derivatives are small and that therefore $a(t)$ and $\phi(t)$ are slowly varying functions of the time t. Therefore, in the time $T = 2\pi/w$, $\theta = wt + \phi$ will increase approximately by 2π, while a and ϕ have not changed appreciably. In order to compute da/dt and $d\phi/dt$, Kryloff and Bogoliuboff replace the right-hand members of (9.13) and (9.14), as a first approximation, by their *average values* over a range of 2π in θ. The amplitude a is *regarded as a constant* in taking the average. This procedure leads to the following equations:

$$(9.15) \qquad \frac{da}{dt} = -\frac{\mu}{2\pi w} \int_0^{2\pi} f(a \sin \theta, aw \cos \theta) \cos \theta \, d\theta$$

$$(9.16) \qquad \frac{d\phi}{dt} = \frac{\mu}{2\pi wa} \int_0^{2\pi} f(a \sin \theta, aw \cos \theta) \sin \theta \, d\theta$$

The exact equations (9.13) and (9.14) are thus replaced by the approximate ones (9.15) and (9.16). The approximations involved in these equations are physically reasonable. A justification of these approximations and methods of higher approximations will be found in the book by Kryloff and Bogoliuboff. The general manner in which various terms in the function $f(x,\dot{x})$ affect the amplitude $a(t)$ and the phase $\phi(t)$ of the oscillation may be deduced from (9.15) and (9.16). If $f(x,\dot{x})$ contains only powers of x, such as x^2, x^3, . . . , the amplitude a is not affected because the integral in (9.15) vanishes. These terms affect the function $\phi(t)$, since the integral in (9.16) does not vanish. If, on the other hand, $f(x,\dot{x})$ contains terms of the form $\dot{x}$, $\dot{x}^2$, $\dot{x}^3$, etc., these terms affect the amplitude a but not the phase function $\phi(t)$.

10. Applications of the Method of Kryloff and Bogoliuboff. In this section several applications of the Kryloff-Bogoliuboff procedure to effect the approximate solutions of typical quasi-linear differential equations of technical importance will be given.

a. The Anharmonic Oscillator. Let the differential equation of the anharmonic oscillator of Sec. 5 be written in the following form,

$$(10.1) \qquad \frac{d^2x}{dt^2} + w^2x + \mu x^3 = 0$$

where μ is a small parameter. This equation is of the quasi-linear form (9.1) with

$$(10.2) \qquad \mu f(x,\dot{x}) = \mu x^3$$

Hence (9 15) and (9.16) in this case are given by

$$(10.3) \qquad \frac{da}{dt} = -\frac{\mu}{2\pi w} \int_0^{2\pi} a^3 \sin^3 \theta \cos \theta \, d\theta = 0$$

and

$$(10.4) \qquad \frac{d\phi}{dt} = \frac{\mu}{2\pi wa} \int_0^{2\pi} a^3 \sin^4 \theta \, d\theta = \frac{3a^2\mu}{8w}$$

Therefore, since $da/dt = 0$, the amplitude does not change with time. The phase function $\phi(t)$ can be determined by integrating (10.4) and thus obtaining

$$(10.5) \qquad \phi = 3\mu \frac{a^2 t}{8w} + \phi_0 \qquad \phi_0 = \text{an arbitrary constant}$$

Hence the solution (9.5) is, in this case,

$$(10.6) \qquad x = a \sin\left[wt\left(1 + 3\frac{\mu a^2}{8w^2}\right) + \phi_0 \right]$$

The period of the oscillations T is given by

$$(10.7) \quad T = \frac{2\pi}{w}\left(1 + 3\frac{\mu a^2}{8w^2}\right)^{-1} \doteq \frac{2\pi}{w}\left(1 - 3\frac{\mu a^2}{8w^2}\right) \qquad \text{for } \mu \ll 1$$

Therefore, if μ is *positive*, the period *decreases* with increasing amplitude, and if μ is *negative*, the period *increases* with increasing amplitude.

 b. *The Quasi-linear van der Pol Equation.* The differential equation

$$(10.8) \qquad \frac{d^2x}{dt^2} - \mu(1 - x^2)\frac{dx}{dt} + x = 0 \qquad 0 < \mu \ll 1$$

is a very important equation in the theory of vacuum-tube oscillators and is known in the literature as *van der Pol's equation.** This equation is of the form (9.1) with

$$(10.9) \qquad \mu f(x, \dot{x}) = \mu(x^2 - 1)\frac{dx}{dt} \qquad w^2 = 1$$

In this case (9.15) and (9.16) reduce to

$$(10.10) \quad \frac{da}{dt} = \frac{\mu a}{2\pi} \int_0^{2\pi} (1 - a^2 \sin^2 \theta)\cos^2 \theta \, d\theta = \frac{\mu a}{2}\left(1 - \frac{a^2}{4}\right)$$

and

$$(10.11) \qquad \frac{d\phi}{dt} = \frac{\mu}{2\pi} \int_0^{2\pi} (a^2 \sin^2 \theta - 1)\cos \theta \sin \theta \, d\theta = 0$$

From (10.10) it can be seen that, after the amplitude has reached a steady state so that $da/dt = 0$, then $a = 2$. In order to determine the growth of the amplitude a, we may write (10.10) in the form

$$(10.12) \qquad \frac{da}{a(1 - a^2/4)} = \frac{\mu \, dt}{2}$$

---

* See B. van der Pol, Nonlinear Theory of Electric Oscillations, *Proceedings of the Institute of Radio Engineers,* vol. 22, p. 1051, 1934.

If this differential equation is integrated with the stipulation that $a = a_0$ when $t = 0$, then, after some algebraic reductions, the result may be written in the following form:

$$(10.13) \qquad a = \frac{a_0 e^{\mu t/2}}{\sqrt{1 + (a_0^2/4)(e^{\mu t} - 1)}} \qquad [a - u]$$

This solution indicates that, if $a_0 = 0$, then $a = 0$ and no oscillation will develop. However, if $a_0 > 0$, no matter how small, the amplitude of the oscillation will develop so that

$$(10.14) \qquad \lim_{t \to \infty} a(t) = 2$$

If $a_0 > 2$, then the amplitude will *decay* so that (10.14) is satisfied. Since by (10.11) $d\phi/dt = 0$, we have

$$(10.15) \qquad \phi = \phi_0$$

and the solution (9.5) becomes

$$(10.16) \qquad x(t) = \frac{a_0 e^{\mu t/2} \sin(t + \phi_0)}{\sqrt{1 + (a_0^2/4)(e^{\mu t} - 1)}}$$

When the parameter μ in the van der Pol equation is large, $\mu \gg 1$, the solutions of the equation are known as *relaxation oscillations*. These oscillations are discussed in Sec. 13.

c. *Negatively Damped Oscillator.* In a fundamental paper Lord Rayleigh* considered the motion of an electrically driven tuning fork by studying the following equation,

$$(10.17) \qquad \frac{d^2x}{dt^2} - 2k\frac{dx}{dt} + c\dot{x}^3 + w^2 x = 0$$

where k and c are small positive constants. The term $-2k\dot{x}$ represents an effective negative resistance which is equivalent to a driving force. In this case, we have

$$(10.18) \qquad \mu f(x, \dot{x}) = -2k\dot{x} + c\dot{x}^3$$

Equations (9.15) and (9.16) now reduce to

$$(10.19) \qquad \frac{da}{dt} = \frac{2k}{2\pi w}\int_0^{2\pi} aw\cos^2\theta\, d\theta - \frac{c}{2\pi w}\int_0^{2\pi} a^3 w^3 \cos^4\theta\, d\theta$$
$$= a(k - \tfrac{3}{8}cw^2 a^2)$$

---

* See Lord Raleigh, On Maintained Vibrations, *Philosophical Magazine*, vol. 15, p. 229, 1883.

10.20) $\dfrac{d\phi}{dt} = -\dfrac{2k}{2\pi wa} \displaystyle\int_0^{2\pi} aw \cos\theta \sin\theta \, d\theta$

$$+ \dfrac{c}{2\pi wa} \int_0^{2\pi} a^3 w^3 \cos^3\theta \sin\theta \, d\theta$$

$$= 0$$

As a consequence of (10.19), it may be seen that, when a steady state has been reached so that $da/dt = 0$, we must have

10.21) $$k - \tfrac{3}{8}cw^2 a^2 = 0$$

or

10.22) $$a = \dfrac{2}{w}\left(\dfrac{2k}{3c}\right)^{\frac{1}{2}} = a_s$$

The equation for the amplitude (10.19) may be written in the following form:

(10.23) $$\dfrac{da}{ak(1 - g^2 a^2)} = dt \qquad \text{where } g^2 = \dfrac{3cw^2}{8k}$$

If this differential equation is solved subject to the condition that $a = a_0$ at $t = 0$, then, after some algebraic reductions, the result may be written in the form

(10.24) $$a(t) = \dfrac{a_0 e^{kt}}{\sqrt{1 + g^2 a_0^2 (e^{2kt} - 1)}}$$

From this it may be seen that, if $a_0 = 0$, there is no motion. However, if the motion is started so that $a_0 \neq 0$, the amplitude attains a final steady-state value of a_s given by (10.22). Since $d\phi/dt = 0$ by (10.20), we have $\phi = \phi_0$, where ϕ_0 is arbitrary. The motion is therefore given by

(10.25) $$x(t) = \dfrac{a_0 e^{kt} \sin(wt + \phi_0)}{\sqrt{1 + g^2 a_0^2 (e^{2kt} - 1)}}$$

Additional examples of applications of this method will be found in the book by Kryloff and Bogoliuboff.

11. Topological Methods: Autonomous Systems. If the nonlinear differential equation under consideration is of the second order and does not contain the independent variable t *explicitly*, much information concerning the properties of the solution may be obtained by a geometrical procedure. Dynamical systems whose equations of motion do not contain the time explicitly are called *autonomous* systems. The equations of motions of second-order autonomous systems usually have the following form:

(11.1) $$\ddot{x} + \phi(\dot{x}) + f(x) = 0$$

If the velocity $y = \dot{x}$ of the system is introduced as another dependen variable, the differential equation (11.1) may be reduced to the followin; first-order system of equations:

(11.2)
$$\frac{dy}{dt} = -[\phi(y) + f(x)]$$

(11.3)
$$\frac{dx}{dt} = y$$

This is a special case of the more general system

(11.4)
$$\frac{dy}{dt} = Q(x,y)$$

(11.5)
$$\frac{dx}{dt} = P(x,y)$$

where $Q(x,y)$ and $P(x,y)$ are functions of x and y. In order to study Eq. (11.1) topologically, the quantities x and y can be considered as cartesian coordinates in a certain (x,y) plane called the *phase plane*. If (11.2) is divided by (11.3), the following equation is obtained:

(11.6)
$$\frac{dy}{dx} = -\frac{[\phi(y) + f(x)]}{y}$$

This differential equation specifies a definite curve in the phase plane. This curve is called the *phase trajectory*, or the *trajectory*, of the differential equation (11.1). The equation

(11.7)
$$\frac{dy}{dx} = \frac{Q(x,y)}{P(x,y)}$$

specifies the phase trajectory of the system (11.4). A point (x_0,y_0) of the phase plane for which

(11.8)
$$P(x_0,y_0) = Q(x_0,y_0) = 0$$

is called a *singular point*. The points of the phase plane that *do not* have the property (11.8) are called *ordinary points*. It is convenient to regard the derivatives (11.4) and (11.5) as the y and x components of the velocity of a point in the phase plane. This point is called the *representative* point of the system, and its component velocities are given by

(11.9)
$$v_x = \frac{dx}{dt} = P(x,y) \qquad v_y = \frac{dy}{dt} = Q(x,y)$$

At a singular point we have $v_x = 0$ and $v_y = 0$, so that such a point may be regarded as a position of equilibrium with zero velocity. For purposes of illustration, it is convenient to obtain the phase trajectory of the differential equation of a linear harmonic oscillator having inertia m and elastic spring constant k. The differential equation of such an oscillator is

$$(11.10) \qquad m\frac{d^2x}{dt^2} + kx = 0 \qquad \frac{dx}{dt} = y$$

In this case Eq. (11.6) takes the following form:

$$(11.11) \qquad \frac{dy}{dx} = -\frac{kx}{my} \qquad \text{or} \qquad my\,dy + kx\,dx = 0$$

If this equation is integrated, the result is

$$(11.12) \qquad \frac{my^2}{2} + \frac{kx^2}{2} = K$$

The arbitrary constant K can be determined by requiring that $x = x_0$ at $y = y_0$. This fixes the total energy E of the oscillator, and K is given by

$$(11.13) \qquad K = \frac{my_0^2}{2} + \frac{kx_0^2}{2} = E$$

Hence (11.12) may be written in the form

$$(11.14) \qquad my^2 + kx^2 = 2E$$

or

$$(11.15) \qquad \frac{x^2}{2E/k} + \frac{y^2}{2E/m} = 1$$

This equation has the form

$$(11.16) \qquad \frac{x^2}{a^2} + \frac{y^2}{b^2} = 1$$

the well-known equation for an ellipse with its center at the origin and a semimajor axis $a = (2E/k)^{\frac{1}{2}}$ and a semiminor axis $b = (2E/m)^{\frac{1}{2}}$, as shown in Fig. 11.1.

FIG. 11.1. Phase trajectory of a linear oscillator.

The phase trajectory of the differential equation (11.10) is a definite ellipse for a definite amount of total energy E. For different values of total energy (11.11) fixes an entire family of ellipses. The size of the ellipses depends on the total energy E of the system; large values of E determine large ellipses. The equation $y = \dot{x}$ indicates that the representative point P traverses the phase trajectory in a *clockwise* direction. If $x = x_0$, $y = y_0$ at $t = 0$, the time integral of the differential equation (11.10) is

$$(11.17) \qquad \left. \begin{array}{l} x = \dfrac{y_0}{w} \sin wt + x_0 \cos wt \\[2mm] y = y_0 \cos wt - wx_0 \sin wt \end{array} \right\} \quad w = \left(\dfrac{k}{m}\right)^{\frac{1}{2}}$$

These are the parametric equations of the ellipse (11.15). It can be seen from the periodicity of the solution (11.17) that the representative point completes one revolution of the ellipse in time

$$T = 2\pi \left(\frac{m}{k}\right)^{\frac{1}{2}} = \frac{2\pi}{w}$$

The time required for the representative point to perform one revolution may be obtained also by writing $dx/dt = y$ or $dt = dx/y$ and integrating this expression in the form

$$(11.18) \qquad T = \oint \frac{dx}{y} = 4 \int_0^a \frac{dx}{\sqrt{(2E/m - w^2x)\,dx}} = \frac{2\pi}{w}$$

The significance of the circular arrow in (11.18) is that the line integral must be taken about a closed path. The center of the ellipse, $x = 0$, $y = 0$, is a singular point of Eq. (11.10). The possible phase trajectories are ellipses that enclose this point. A singular point of this type is called a *vortex point*. It is noted that all the phase trajectories enclose the vortex point and none approaches it. The vortex point is a position of stable equilibrium of the system.

Aperiodic Motion. The equation of a mass being repulsed from the origin by a force proportional to its distance from the origin is

$$(11.19) \qquad m \frac{d^2x}{dt^2} = cx \quad \text{or} \quad \frac{d^2x}{dt^2} = a^2x \quad a = \left(\frac{c}{m}\right)^{\frac{1}{2}}$$

The equation for the phase trajectories is in this case

$$(11.20) \qquad \frac{dy}{dx} = a^2 \frac{x}{y}$$

If this equation is integrated, the result is

$$(11.21) \qquad y^2 - a^2x^2 = h \qquad h = \text{an arbitrary constant}$$

For various values of the constant h, (11.21) is the equation for a family of *hyperbolas*. If it is required that $x = x_0$ and $y = y_0$ at $t = 0$, the solution of the differential equation (11.19) takes the following form:

$$(11.22) \qquad \begin{array}{l} x = x_0 \cosh at + \dfrac{y_0}{a} \sinh at \\[2mm] y = ax_0 \sinh at + y_0 \cosh at \end{array}$$

These are the parametric equations of the hyperbolic phase trajectories (11.21), shown in Fig. 11.2.

The family of hyperbolas (11.21) has two asymptotes $y = \pm ax$. The origin O is a singular point of a special type called a *saddle point*. In this case there are two special trajectories that pass through the saddle point. The motion of the representative point along the trajectories that approach the saddle point is asymptotic with the time t. The trajectories in the neighborhood of a saddle point represent the possible motions that occur in the neighborhood of a point of *unstable equilibrium*.

FIG. 11.2. Phase trajectory of aperiodic motion.

The Motion of a Damped Oscillator. The differential equation of a linear oscillator with damping is

$$(11.23) \qquad \frac{d^2x}{dt^2} + 2h\frac{dx}{dt} + w_0^2 x = 0 \qquad y = \dot{x}$$

The equation for the phase trajectories of this oscillator is

$$(11.24) \qquad \frac{dy}{dx} = -\frac{2hy + w_0^2 x}{y}$$

If $h^2 < w_0^2$, the oscillator performs damped oscillations. Let

$$(11.25) \qquad w = (w_0^2 - h^2)^{\frac{1}{2}}$$

The general solution of (11.23) is

$$(11.26) \qquad \begin{aligned} x &= Ke^{-ht}\cos(wt + \theta) \\ y &= \dot{x} = -Ke^{-ht}[h\cos(wt + \theta) + w\sin(wt + \theta)] \end{aligned}$$

where K and θ are arbitrary constants. These equations are the parametric equations of a family of spirals one of which is depicted in Fig. 11.3.

FIG. 11.3. Phase trajectory of a damped oscillator.

The origin O is a singular point of a type called a *focal point*. The representative point spirals around the phase plane and approaches the focal point at the origin in an asymptotic manner. The focal point is a point of *stable* equilibrium. Since as the representative point approaches the origin it spirals an infinite number of times about it, it is clear that it does not approach O with a *definite direction*.

The Motion of an Overdamped Oscillator. If the frictional term of the damped oscillator is large, the parameter h of (11.23) satisfies the inequality $h^2 > w_0^2$ and the motion is no longer oscillatory. Let

(11.27) $$g = (h^2 - w_0^2)^{\frac{1}{2}}$$

In this case the general solution of (11.23) may be expressed in the form

(11.28)
$$x = Ae^{-ht} \cosh (bt + \theta)$$
$$y = \dot{x} = Ae^{-ht}[b \sinh (bt + \theta) - h \cosh (bt + \theta)]$$

where A and θ are arbitrary constants. These are the parametric equations of the phase trajectories. A typical trajectory is depicted in Fig. 11.4.

Nodal point O

FIG. 11.4. Phase trajectory of an overdamped system.

The origin, $x = 0$, $y = 0$, is a singular point called a *nodal point*. The phase trajectories are now such that the representative point moves toward the nodal point with a *definite* direction. The four common types of singular points are summarized in the following table:

BASIC TYPES OF SINGULAR POINTS

Name	Type of motion	Stability	Approach
Vortex point............	Oscillatory	Stable	None
Saddle point............	Aperiodic	Unstable	Only along asymptotes
Focal point.............	Damped oscillatory	Stable	With no definite direction
Nodal point.............	Aperiodic	Stable	With a definite direction

12. Nonlinear Conservative Systems. The motions of nonlinear conservative systems that have one degree of freedom may be effectively studied by topological methods. As an example of the application of this method to nonlinear systems of this type, consider the motion of a mass m that is attracted toward a fixed point, the origin, by a nonlinear restoring force $F(x)$. The equation of motion of such a mass is

(12.1) $$m \frac{d^2x}{dt^2} = -F(x)$$

This equation is equivalent to the first-order differential equations

(12.2) $$\frac{dy}{dt} = -\frac{F(x)}{m}$$

(12.3) $$\frac{dx}{dt} = y$$

If (12.2) is divided by (12.3), we obtain the following equation for the phase trajectory of the motion of the nonlinear oscillator:

$$(12.4) \qquad \frac{dy}{dx} = -\frac{F(x)}{my}$$

If the variables are separated and the resulting equation is integrated, the result may be written in the form

$$(12.5) \qquad \frac{m}{2} y^2 + \int_{x_0}^{x} F(x)\, dx = C$$

The arbitrary constant may be evaluated by requiring that, at $t = 0$, $x = x_0$ and $y = y_0$. If this is done, (12.5) becomes

$$(12.6) \qquad \frac{m}{2} y^2 + \int_{x_0}^{x} F(x)\, dx = \frac{m}{2} y_0^2$$

The quantity $(m/2)y^2$ is the *kinetic* energy of the system, and

$$(12.7) \qquad V(x) = \int_0^x F(x)\, dx$$

is the *potential* energy of the system. In terms of $V(x)$, (12.6) may be written in the form

$$(12.8) \qquad \frac{m}{2} y^2 + V(x) = \frac{m}{2} y_0^2 + \int_0^{x_0} F(x)\, dx = E$$

where E is the *total energy* of the system. Hence (12.8) may be solved for the velocity y in the form

$$(12.9) \qquad y = \sqrt{\frac{2}{m}[E - V(x)]}$$

This equation can be given an interesting topological interpretation. In order to fix the ideas involved, let

$$(12.10) \qquad F(x) = k \sin x$$

where k is a positive constant, to take a special case. The potential energy is in this case given by

$$(12.11) \qquad V(x) = \int_0^x k \sin (x)\, dx = k(1 - \cos x) = 2k \sin^2 \frac{x}{2}$$

In order to study the topology of the motion, it is convenient to plot the potential energy $V(x)$ against x. Directly below this diagram the phase-plane trajectory is plotted as shown in Fig. 12.1.

The upper part of Fig. 12.1 is a plot of $V(x) = 2k \sin^2(x/2)$ against x. The three horizontal lines on this diagram represent three distinct values of *total energy* E_1, E_s, and E_2. The lower diagram is a plot of three different phase trajectories corresponding to the three values of the total energy given above. The phase trajectories are obtained by plotting $y = \sqrt{(2/m)[E - V(x)]}$ for the three given values of the total energy E. It may be noted that if $k/m = g/s$ then Fig. 12.1 represents the phase

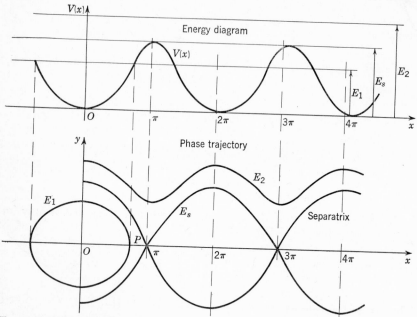

FIG. 12.1. Phase trajectories of

$$\frac{dy}{dx} = \frac{-k \sin x}{my}$$

trajectories of the equation of the simple pendulum discussed in Sec. 3. The physical significance of the phase trajectories of Fig. 12.1 can be clearly visualized by regarding it as the phase-plane plot of the simple pendulum. The phase trajectory for E_1 represents the oscillations of a pendulum having less energy than is necessary for it to go "over the top." The phase trajectory corresponding to E_s is the one in which the system has just enough total energy to take it to the top at $x = 2\pi$. This phase trajectory is called the *separatrix* because it separates the motions of one type from those of an entirely different type. The point P is a *saddle point;* this is a point at which the potential energy $V(x)$ is a *maximum* and is a point of *unstable equilibrium*. This point corresponds to the inverted position of the pendulum and has entirely different properties then the point O, which is a *vortex point* and corresponds to a position of *stable equilibrium*, the bottom position of the pendulum.

If the pendulum is given a total energy E_2 which exceeds the critical energy E_s to take it "over the top," then the phase trajectory is a curve that continues with x and the motion is no longer periodic.   In this case the pendulum continues to revolve about its point of support with *maximum* angular velocity at $x = 0$, 2π, 4π, etc., and *minimum* angular velocity at $x = \pi$, 3π, 5π, etc., when the pendulum passes the top position. If the motion is periodic so that the phase trajectory is a closed path, the period T of the oscillations may be obtained by the equation

$$(12.12) \qquad T = \oint \frac{dx}{y} = \frac{m}{2} \oint \frac{dx}{\sqrt{E - V(x)}}$$

where the line integral (12.12) must be taken around the closed trajectory.

The simple discussion given above illustrates the power of the topological aspects of the phase trajectories to give general qualitative information on the behavior of autonomous systems.   If the system being studied contains damping of a negative or positive type, the phase trajectories may be rather complicated but a great deal of information may be obtained by their construction.

13. Relaxation Oscillations.   A great many periodic oscillatory processes in nature take place in such a manner that external energy is supplied to the system over part of a period and dissipated within the system in another part of the period. The name *relaxation oscillations* has been given to periodic processes of this type.   As a simple example of a relaxation oscillation, consider the electrical circuit depicted in Fig. 13.1.

FIG. 13.1. Diode oscillator.

This circuit consists of a battery of potential E connected in series with a resistor R and a capacitor C.   A diode tube D is connected across the capacitor.   This tube has the property that, when the potential across its plates exceeds a value E_0, it suddenly becomes conducting and discharges the capacitor completely.   After this has happened, the capacitor begins to charge again and the procedure repeats itself.

The charge on the capacitor, q, satisfies the differential equation

$$(13.1) \qquad R\frac{dq}{dt} + \frac{q}{C} = E$$

If we assume $q = 0$ at $t = 0$, the solution of this equation is

$$(13.2) \qquad q = CE(1 - e^{-t/RC})$$

The potential $e(t)$ across the plates of the capacitor is

(13.3) $$e(t) = \frac{q}{C} = E(1 - e^{-t/RC})$$

If we let T be the time required for the potential $e(t)$ to attain the breakdown potential of the diode, we have

(13.4) $$E_0 = E(1 - e^{-t/RC})$$

or

(13.5) $$T = RC \ln \frac{E}{E - E_0}$$

At this value of time the capacitor is discharged, and the process repeats itself with a period of T. The graph of the periodic variation of the charge on the capacitor q is given by Fig. 13.2.

FIG. 13.2. Relaxation oscillations of diode oscillator.

It is thus seen that the period T of the oscillations of the diode oscillator of Fig. 13.1 is not determined by inertia and elastance parameters but by some form of *relaxation time*. There are many types of relaxation times, such as the time necessary for a current to build up in a system containing self-inductance, a diffusion time, heating-up time, etc. It is typical in the case of relaxation oscillations for *aperiodic* phenomena to repeat themselves periodically. This automatic periodic reoccurrence of the aperiodic phenomena is closely related to the presence of some form of energy source, such as the battery of the diode oscillator. Another interesting example of a relaxation oscillation is the phenomenon involved in the action of the aeolian harp. In this case the oscillation of the system is by the formation of air eddies that develop alternately on one side and the other of the harp string. As each eddy is formed, it diffuses away and allows another eddy to be formed. The time period of the oscillation of the harp string is determined by a diffusion or relaxation time and does not depend on the natural period of the string when it is performing sinusoidal oscillations. In a fundamental paper van der Pol* has enumerated many other instances of relaxation oscillations such

* See B. van der Pol, Relaxation Oscillations, *Philosophical Magazine*, vol. 2, p. 928, 1926.

as a pneumatic hammer, the scratching noise of a knife on a plate, the waving of a flag in the wind, the humming noise of a water tap, the squeaking of a door, the oscillations of a steam engine with a flywheel that is too small, the multivibrator, the periodic sparks of a Whimshurst machine, the periodic reoccurrence of epidemics and economic crises, the fluctuation of populations of animal species, the motion of sleeping flowers, the periodic reoccurrence of showers behind a depression, the shivering from cold, and the beating of the heart.

By suitable changes in variables van der Pol has shown that the mathematical analyses of many relaxation phenomena lead to a study of the following differential equation:

$$(13.6) \qquad \frac{d^2x}{dt^2} - \mu(1 - x^2)\frac{dx}{dt} + x = 0$$

This equation has been the subject of considerable investigation and is known as *van der Pol's equation*. The approximate solution of this equation has been studied by the method of Kryloff and Bogoliuboff in Sec. 10. It was there shown that, for *small* values of the parameter μ, the solution is a sustained *sinusoidal* oscillation. These sinusoidal oscillations exist for $0 < \mu \ll 1$, and in this case (13.6) is a quasi-linear differential equation.

It is of interest to consider the nature of the solution of (13.6) for *large* values of μ so that $\mu \gg 1$. The physical significance of (13.6) is facilitated if it is regarded as the equation of motion of an oscillator of unit mass and unit spring constant and variable damping. If μ is large, the initial damping is large and *negative;* this makes the system *highly aperiodic.* This aperiodic system with large negative resistance tends to run away from zero without any oscillations whatever. However, as soon as the momentary value of x^2 becomes larger than unity, the negative character of the resistance ceases to exist and the resistance becomes positive. This makes the amplitude x decrease aperiodically. It is thus seen that for large values of μ the system has the tendency initially to jump away from $x = 0$ to a positive value of x, decreasing afterward gradually, and suddenly to jump to a negative value of x, etc. The variation of x with time is thus a relaxation oscillation. This qualitative discussion will now be examined topologically.

14. Phase Trajectories of the van der Pol Equation. The parametric equations of the phase trajectories of the van der Pol equation (13.6) are

$$(14.1) \qquad \frac{dy}{dt} = \mu(1 - x^2)y - x$$

$$(14.2) \qquad \frac{dx}{dt} = y$$

If (14.1) is divided by (14.2), the equation of the phase trajectory is

obtained. This equation has the form

(14.3)
$$\frac{dy}{dx} = \mu(1 - x^2) - \frac{x}{y}$$

In his paper Relaxation Oscillations, quoted above, van der Pol plotted the phase-trajectory curves for three different values of the parameter μ ($\mu = 0.1$, $\mu = 1.0$, $\mu = 10.0$). The phase trajectories corresponding to these values of μ are reproduced in Figs. 14.1, 14.2, and 14.3.

FIG. 14.1. Phase trajectory of

$$\frac{dy}{dx} = \mu(1 - x^2) - \frac{x}{y} \qquad \mu = 0.1$$

It can be seen by examining the figures of the phase trajectories that, no matter where the motion begins, the trajectories converge to closed curves. These closed curves represent periodic motions with constant amplitude. For small values of μ, for example, $\mu = 0.1$, the closed curve is only slightly different from a circle. However, as μ is increased, the closed curves differ quite radically from circles and thus represent periodic motions that are distinctly nonharmonic. Figure 14.3 is the phase trajectory of a relaxation oscillation ($\mu = 10$), and in this case the motion is made up of sudden transitions between deflections of opposite sign.

FIG. 14.2. Phase trajectory of

$$\frac{dy}{dx} = \mu(1 - x^2) - \frac{x}{y} \qquad \mu = 1.0$$

FIG. 14.3. Phase trajectory of

$$\frac{dy}{dx} = \mu(1 - x^2) - \frac{x}{y}$$
$$\mu = 10.0$$

The amplitudes of the oscillations corresponding to the various values of μ are given in Fig. 14.4.   In this figure the manner in which the oscillations build up for $\mu = 0.1$, 1.0, and 10.0 is given.

The final values of the oscillations for $\mu = 0.1$, 1.0, and 10.0 are also clearly illustrated by these graphs.   The graph of the oscillation for $\mu = 10.0$ is a typical relaxation oscillation; it differs radically from the sinusoidal oscillation for $\mu = 0.1$.

FIG. 14.4. The building up of self-excited oscillations

$$\frac{d^2x}{dt^2} - \mu(1 - x^2)\frac{dx}{dt} + x = 0$$

15. The Period of Relaxation Oscillations. An approximate expression for the period of relaxation oscillations may be obtained by a graphical procedure. For this purpose it is more convenient to consider the following differential equation:

(15.1) $$\frac{d^2x}{dt^2} + \mu\left(\frac{\dot{x}^3}{3} - \dot{x}\right) + x = 0$$

This equation is known in the literature as the *Rayleigh equation*. It may be shown that, if (15.1) is differentiated with respect to t and the substitution $u = dx/dt$ is made, the result is

(15.2) $$\frac{d^2u}{dt^2} + \mu(u^2 - 1)\frac{du}{dt} + u = 0$$

Hence (15.1) is seen to be equivalent to the van der Pol equation (15.2), and will have oscillations of the same period.

The parametric equations of the phase trajectories of the Rayleigh equation are

(15.3) $$\frac{dy}{dt} = \mu\left(y - \frac{y^3}{3}\right) - x$$

(15.4) $$\frac{dx}{dt} = y$$

The equation of the phase trajectories is obtained by dividing (15.3) by (15.4). It is

$$(15.5) \qquad \frac{dy}{dx} = \frac{\mu(y - y^3/3) - x}{y}$$

It is convenient to introduce the variable $z = x/\mu$ and write (15.5) in the form

$$(15.6) \qquad \frac{dy}{dz} = \frac{\mu^2(y - y^3/3 - z)}{y}$$

and to consider the form taken by the periodic phase trajectory in the yz plane given by (15.6). If the parameter μ is *large*, it is seen from (15.6) that the slope $dy/dz = \pm M$, where M is a large number unless

$$(15.7) \qquad z = y - \frac{y^3}{3}$$

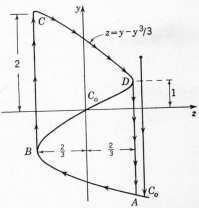

and in this case $dy/dz = 0$ and the phase trajectory is horizontal. The nature of the phase trajectories of (15.6) for large values of μ ($\mu \gg 1$) may be explained by an examination of Fig. 15.1.

In this diagram the curve C_0 is a graph of $z = y - y^3/3$. Let it be supposed that the representative point of a phase trajectory begins to move from P. Since (15.6) gives a large negative value for dy/dz, the

Fig. 15.1. Phase trajectories of
$$\frac{dy}{dz} = \frac{\mu^2 (y - y^3/3 - z)}{y} \qquad \mu \gg 1$$

phase trajectory will be nearly vertical and the point P will move down in a vertical direction until it reaches C_0. On C_0 the dy/dz is zero, but since the field direction at all points other than those on C_0 is nearly vertical, the point P will follow the curve C_0 until B is reached. At B the representative point will move vertically upward until C_0 is reached at C. After reaching C the representative point will follow C_0 until the point D is reached, and it will then move downward and meet C_0 again at A.

By this type of reasoning, one can see that, for large values of μ, it does not matter where the motion starts and that eventually the representative point moves along the closed trajectory $ABCDA$ and the motion is periodic. To compute the period, the formula

$$(15.8) \qquad T = \oint \frac{dx}{y} = \mu \oint \frac{dz}{y}$$

may be used. In order to evaluate this line integral, it may be noticed that the vertical-straight-line portions of the cycle $ABCDA$ make no contribution to T. Because of symmetry, (15.8) may be evaluated by integrating from C to D and taking twice the value of this integral to obtain T. From C to D we have $z = y - y^3/3$ or $dz = 1 - y^2$. Hence

$$(15.9) \quad T = \mu \oint \frac{dz}{y} = 2\mu \int_C^D \frac{dz}{y}$$

$$= 2\mu \int_{y=2}^{y=1} \left(\frac{1}{y} - y \right) dy = 2\mu \left(\ln y - \frac{y^2}{2} \right) \Big|_2^1$$

$$= 2\mu \left(\frac{y^2}{2} - \ln y \right) \Big|_1^2 = \mu(3 - 2 \ln 2) = 1.612\mu$$

This is the approximate formula for the period of the relaxation oscillations for *very large* values of μ given by van der Pol. For very small values of μ we have seen that the period is independent of μ and given by 2π. The value $T = 1.612\mu$ is based on the assumption that μ is very large, and it gives a good estimate of the length of the period for moderately large values of μ. However, even for the case $\mu = 10$, Eq. (15.9) gives results that are about 20 per cent too low. A better approximation to the period has been given by Shohat,[*] whose result is

$$(15.10) \qquad\qquad T = \frac{2\pi}{S(\mu)}$$

where $S(\mu) = \dfrac{1}{1 + \mu} + \dfrac{\mu}{(1 + \mu)^2} + \dfrac{15\mu^2}{16(1 + \mu)^3} + \dfrac{13\mu^3}{16(1 + \mu)^4} + \cdots$

It is interesting to note that for very large values of μ (15.9) gives $\lim\limits_{\mu \to \infty} (2\pi\mu/T) = 3.89 \cdots$, while (15.10) gives 3.75 for the same expression.

16. Relaxation Oscillations of a Motor-Generator Combination. A very interesting and spectacular relaxation oscillator occurs in electrical engineering. This oscillator consists of a separately excited direct-current motor operating with no load, whose current is supplied by a direct-current generator that has a series field as shown in Fig. 16.1.

If the generator of this combination is driven at constant speed by a prime mover and the circuit parameters are adjusted properly, it is found that the rotation of the motor will reverse periodically in such a manner that its angular velocity of rotation w will execute *relaxation oscillations*. In order to explain the action of this oscillator, consider the potential E_θ of the generator. Since the machine is driven at *constant* speed by

---

[*] J. Shohat, On van der Pol's and Related Nonlinear Differential Equations, *Journal of Applied Physics*, vol. 15, no. 7, pp. 568–574, July, 1944.

the prime mover, E_g is proportional to the strength of the magnetic field of the generator. Because the generator has a *series* field, E_g is given approximately by

$$(16.1) \qquad E_g = C_1 i - C_2 i^3$$

where C_1 and C_2 are positive constants. The cubic term in (16.1) represents the influence of the saturation of the iron of the generator field. The generated potential also satisfies the following equation:

$$(16.2) \qquad E_g = L \frac{di}{dt} + Ri + C_3 w$$

The first term of (16.2) represents the inductive potential drop in the circuit of Fig. 16.1. i is the generator current, and L is the effective

Constant
speed
prime mover

Constant speed
d-c series generator

Separately excited
d-c motor (no load)

FIG. 16.1. Motor-generator oscillator.

inductance of the field coils of the generator. Ri is the resistive drop of the circuit, and the term $C_3 w$ represents the counterelectromotive force of the separately excited direct-current motor. w is the angular velocity of the motor, and C_3 is a positive constant. The power supplied to the motor is

$$(16.3) \qquad P_m = iC_3 w$$

or the product of the current and the counterelectromotive force. If I is the moment of inertia of the rotating parts of the motor, its kinetic energy of rotation is $Iw^2/2$. Since it is assumed that the motor is running with no load, the power being furnished to it is expended in changing its kinetic energy, so that

$$(16.4) \qquad P_m = C_3 wi = \frac{d}{dt}\left(\frac{Iw^2}{2}\right) = Iw \frac{dw}{dt}$$

or

$$(16.5) \qquad \frac{dw}{dt} = \frac{C_3 i}{I}$$

Equating (16.1) and (16.2), we obtain

$$(16.6) \qquad E_g = L \frac{di}{dt} + Ri + C_3 w = C_1 i - C_2 i^3$$

If (16.6) is differentiated with respect to t and dw/dt eliminated by (16.5), the result is

$$(16.7) \qquad L\frac{d^2i}{dt^2} - (C_1 - R - 3C_2i^2)\frac{di}{dt} + \frac{C_3^2i}{I} = 0$$

Let the following parameters be introduced:

$$(16.8) \qquad w_n = C_3(LI)^{-\frac{1}{2}}$$

and

$$(16.9) \qquad \mu = \frac{(C_1 - R)(I/L)^{\frac{1}{2}}}{C_3}$$

Then, if the following changes in variables are made in (16.7),

$$(16.10) \qquad x = i\left(\frac{3C_2}{C_1 - R}\right)^{\frac{1}{2}}$$

and

$$(16.11) \qquad \tau = w_n t$$

this equation is transformed into the van der Pol equation

$$(16.12) \qquad \frac{d^2x}{d\tau^2} - \mu(1 - x^2)\frac{dx}{d\tau} + x = 0$$

In the usual installation the value of μ given by (16.9) is much larger than unity, and the value (15.9) may be used to estimate the period of the oscillation. If this is done, the period of the oscillation governed by (16.7) is seen to be given by

$$(16.13) \qquad T = \frac{1.612(C_1 - R)I}{C_3^2}$$

so that the period of the reversal of the current, and hence the period of the angular velocity $w(t)$, is proportional to the inertia I of the motor and *not* to the *square root* of the inertia, as would be the case if the oscillations were harmonic.

PROBLEMS

1. Given the second-order linear differential equation,

$$\frac{d^2x}{dt^2} + F^2(x)x = 0$$

where $F(x)$ is a slowly varying positive function of x. Show that the substitution $x = e^{i\phi(x)}$ leads to the following nonlinear differential equation of the Ricatti type:

$$j\frac{d^2\phi}{dx^2} - \phi^2 + F^2 = 0 \qquad j = (-1)^{\frac{1}{2}}$$

Obtain an approximate solution of the Ricatti equation, and show that

$$x = [F(x)]^{-\frac{1}{4}}[A \cos \phi(x) + B \sin \phi(x)]$$

where $\phi(x) = \int F(x) \, dx$ and A and B are arbitrary constants, is the approximate solution of the original equation (Wentzel-Kramers-Brillouin approximation).

2. A body of mass m falls through a medium that opposes its fall with a force proportional to the square of its velocity so that its equation of motion is

$$m \frac{d^2x}{dt^2} = mg - Kv^2 \qquad v = \dot{x}$$

where x is the distance of fall and v is the velocity. If, at $t = 0$, $x = 0$ and $v = 0$, find the velocity of the body and the distance it has fallen at a time t. Plot the phase trajectory of the motion.

3. Solve Bernoulli's equation

$$\frac{dx}{dt} + P(t)x = Q(t)x^n$$

subject to the initial condition $x = x_0$ at $t = 0$.

4. Given the differential equation

$$\frac{d^2x}{dt^2} + w_0^2 x + hx^2 = A \cos w_1 t + B \cos w_2 t$$

where w_0, h, A, B, w_1, and w_2 are constants. Devise a method of successive approximations for the solution of this equation. Let the initial conditions be $x = x_0$ and $\dot{x} = 0$ at $t = 0$. (This equation* is the basis of Helmholtz's *theory of combinations of tones*.)

5. A particle oscillates in a straight line under the action of a central force tending to a fixed point O on the straight line and varying as the distance from O. If the motion takes place in a medium that resists the motion with a force proportional to the square of the velocity of the particle, find the relation between the amplitudes of any two successive arcs on each side of O. Plot the phase trajectory of the motion.

6. The nonlinear resistive material thyrite has a voltage-current characteristic of the form $V = Bi^b$, where V is the potential difference applied across the thyrite resistor, i the current, B a constant that depends on the length and cross section of the resistor. The parameter b has the value 0.28. An electrical circuit is composed of a linear inductor L and a thyrite resistor in series with a harmonic electromotive force. The equation of the circuit is

$$L \frac{di}{dt} + Bi^b = E_m \sin wt \qquad b = 0.28$$

Obtain an approximate expression for the steady-state periodic current of this circuit.

7. Show that the solution of the differential equation

$$\frac{d^2x}{dt^2} + ke^x = 0$$

* See L. A. Pipes, An Operational Treatment of Nonlinear Dynamical Systems, *Journal of the Acoustical Society of America*, vol. 10, pp. 29–31, July, 1938.

with the initial conditions $dx/dt = 0$, $x = x_0$, at $t = 0$, is

$$x = x_0 - 2\ln(\cosh at) \qquad \text{where } a = \left(\frac{ke^{x_0}}{2}\right)^{\frac{1}{2}}$$

This is the equation of motion of a particle undergoing a restoring force which increases exponentially with the displacement.

8. Show that $x = 2b^{-\frac{1}{2}}\sin wt$ is the *exact* solution of the differential equation

$$\frac{d^2x}{dt^2} - 2aw(1 - bx^2)\frac{dx}{dt} + w^2x = -\frac{4aw^2}{\sqrt{b}}\sin 3wt$$

This is a special case of a phenomenon called *frequency demultiplication* by van der Pol.*

9. Show that, if the motor of the motor-generator oscillator of Fig. 16.1 is replaced by a large capacitor and the rest of the system is left unchanged, the current will execute relaxation oscillations.

10. Discuss the oscillations of the height $h(t)$ of the level of water in the tank of Fig. P 10. Does $h(t)$ execute relaxation oscillations? Plot the phase trajectory of $h(t)$.

FIG. P 10

11. Given the differential equation

$$\frac{d^2x}{dt^2} + c\frac{dx}{dt} + w_0^2x - hx^3 = F\sin wt \qquad h \ll 1$$

Determine a solution of this equation of the form

$$x = A(t)\sin wt + B(t)\cos wt$$

where $A(t)$ and $B(t)$ are slowly varying functions of t. Assume that $dA/dt \ll wA$, $dB/dt \ll wB$, and $d^2A/dt^2 = d^2B/dt^2 = 0$.

12. Solve the *linear* equation

$$\frac{d^2x}{dt^2} + \mu\frac{dx}{dt} + w^2x = 0$$

for small values of μ by the method of Kryloff and Bogoliuboff.

13. Show that the differential equation

$$\frac{d^2x}{dt^2} + k^2\sin x = 0$$

has the approximate solution $x = x_0\sin wt$, where the angular frequency w is given by $w = k[2J_1(x_0)/x_0]^{\frac{1}{2}}$. $J_1(x_0)$ is the Bessel function of the first kind and first order. If $k = (g/L)^{\frac{1}{2}}$, the above equation governs the motion of a simple pendulum of length L.

* B. van der Pol, Frequency Demultiplication, *Nature*, vol. 120, p. 363, 1927.

14. The forced oscillations of a simple pendulum are governed by the equation

$$\frac{d^2\theta}{dt^2} + k^2 \sin \theta = F \sin wt \qquad k = \left(\frac{g}{L}\right)^{\frac{1}{2}}$$

Show that the first approximation for the periodic motion is given by $\theta = A \sin wt$, where the amplitude A satisfies the equation $A(1 - w^2/k^2) - F/k^2 = A - 2J_1(A)$, where $J_1(A)$ is the Bessel function of the first kind and first order.

15. A particle of mass m moves along the x axis under the action of a restraining force $F(x) = 1/x^2 - 1/x$. Show that, if the motion of the mass is started with a small amount of energy E_0, the motion will be oscillatory. If, however, the motion is started with a large amount of energy E, show that the motion is *not* periodic and extends to infinity. Determine the critical energy that forms the dividing line between the two cases. Draw the phase trajectories for the oscillatory and non-oscillatory cases.

16. A pendulum (Froude's pendulum) is suspended from a dry horizontal shaft, of circular cross section, by a ring. It is well known that, if the shaft rotates with a suitable constant angular velocity w_0, the pendulum oscillates with a gradually increasing amplitude which reaches a final ultimate value. Write the differential equation of motion of this pendulum, and use it to explain the above phenomenon. (HINT: Assume the frictional force at the suspension to be a function of $w_0 - \theta$, the difference between the angular velocity of the shaft and the pendulum.)

17. Devise a graphical method for the solution of the equation

$$m \frac{d^2x}{dt^2} + F(x) = 0$$

subject to the initial conditions $x = a$ and $\dot{x} = 0$ at $t = 0$.*

18. The differential equation of an oscillator whose motion is retarded by viscous and Coulomb friction and is being driven by a harmonic force is

$$m \frac{d^2x}{dt^2} + c \frac{dx}{dt} + kx + F sgn(\dot{x}) = F_0 \sin (wt + \theta)$$

where
$$sgn(\dot{x}) = \begin{cases} +1 & \text{if } \dot{x} \geq 0 \\ -1 & \text{if } \dot{x} < 0 \end{cases}$$

The term $F sgn(\dot{x})$ represents the effect of dry friction. Obtain an approximate expression for the periodic-steady-state solution of this equation.†

REFERENCES

Books and Reports

1. McLachlan, N. W.: "Ordinary Nonlinear Differential Equations in Engineering and Physical Sciences," 2d ed., Oxford University Press, New York, 1956. (This book contains an excellent discussion of the better-known analytical procedures and an extensive bibliography of 211 titles covering the international literature to 1950.)

* See Lord Kelvin, On Graphic Solutions of Dynamical Problems, *Philosophical Magazine*, vol. 34, pp. 332–348, 1892.

† See J. P. Den Hartog, Forced Vibrations with Combined Coulomb and Viscous Friction, *Transactions of the American Society of Mechanical Engineers*, vol. 53, pp. 107–115, 1931.

→2. Stoker, J. J.: "Nonlinear Vibrations," Interscience Publishers, Inc., New York, 1950. (Contains a clear exposition of the topological methods for solving autonomous systems and a fairly complete discussion of stability.)
3. Andronow, A. A., and C. E. Chaikin: "Theory of Oscillations," Princeton University Press, Princeton, N.J., 1949. (Contains a clear and interesting exposition of the topological properties of many autonomous systems.)
4. Minorsky, N.: "Introduction to Nonlinear Mechanics," J. W. Edwards, Publisher, Inc., Ann Arbor, Mich., 1947. (An extensive survey of the international literature to 1947; a clear discussion of topological methods, analytical methods, nonlinear resonance, and relaxation oscillations.)
5. von Kármán, T.: The Engineer Grapples with Nonlinear Problems, *Bulletin of the American Mathematical Society*, vol. 46, no. 8, pp. 615–683, 1940. (An excellent exposition of self-excited nonlinear oscillations, subharmonic resonance, large-deflection theory, elasticity with finite deformations, fluid jets, waves with finite amplitudes, viscous fluids, and compressible fluids; contains excellent bibliographies on these fields.)
6. Kryloff, N., and N. Bogoliuboff: "Introduction to Nonlinear Mechanics," Princeton University Press, Princeton, N.J., 1943. (A clear and careful exposition of the Kryloff-Bogoliuboff method, with interesting applications to electrical circuits and dynamics.)
7. Duffing, G.: "Erzwungene Schwingungen bei veranderlicher Eigenfrequenz und ihre technische Bedeutung," Vieweg-Verlag, Brunswick, Germany, 1918. (A pioneer study of nonlinear vibration problems; discusses methods of approximation and questions of stability with technical applications.)
8. Lefshetz, S.: "Contributions to the Theory of Nonlinear Oscillations," vol. II, Princeton University Press, Princeton, N.J., 1952. (Discussions of several topics of nonlinear differential equations by several mathematicians from the rigorous point of view.)
9. Pipes, L. A.: "Operational Methods in Nonlinear Mechanics," Department of Engineering, University of California, Los Angeles, 1951. (Contains some useful methods for the solution of certain classes of nonlinear technical problems; operational methods are introduced to reduce the algebraic labor of the solution.)

The bibliographies in the above books and reports are quite extensive and cover the most important papers to 1950. The following technical papers are representative of recent publications in the field of nonlinear problems:

Scientific Papers

10. Sim, A. C.: A Generalization of Reversion Formulae with Their Application to Nonlinear Differential Equations, *Philosophical Magazine*, ser. 7, vol. 42, pp. 237–240, March, 1951. (Discusses an ingenious method for the approximate solution of nonlinear differential equations similar to the reversion of a power series.)
11. Cartwright, M. L.: Forced Oscillations in Nonlinear Systems, *Journal of Research of the National Bureau of Standards*, vol. 45, no. 6, December, 1950. (A rigorous discussion of the van der Pol equation with a forcing term.)
12. Hayashi, C.: Forced Oscillations with Nonlinear Restoring Force, *Journal of Applied Physics*, vol. 24, no. 2, pp. 198–207, 1953. (An excellent discussion of forced oscillations of nonlinear systems; the equation is transformed so that topological methods can be used.)
13. Hayashi, C.: Stability Investigation of the Nonlinear Periodic Oscillations, *Journal of Applied Physics*, vol. 24, no. 3, pp. 238–246. 1953. (The stability of

nonlinear periodic oscillations is discussed by solving the variational equation for small deviations from the periodic state.)

14. Hayashi, C.: Subharmonic Oscillations in Nonlinear Systems, *Journal of Applied Physics*, vol. 24, no. 5, pp. 521–529, 1953. (The possibility of subharmonic solutions and their stability is studied for systems having a nonlinear restoring force and driven by a harmonic forcing function.)

15. Pipes, L. A.: A Mathematical Analysis of a Series Circuit Containing a Nonlinear Capacitor, *Communication and Electronics*, July, 1953, pp. 238–244. (An extension of Duffing's method and its application to a technically important problem.)

16. Pipes, L. A.: Applications of Integral Equations to the Solution of Nonlinear Electric Circuit Problems, *Communication and Electronics*, September, 1953, pp. 445–450. (The formulation of some nonlinear differential equations in terms of integral equations and their solution by iterative procedures.)

17. Thomsen, J. S.: Graphical Analysis of Nonlinear Circuits Using Impedance Concepts, *Journal of Applied Physics*, vol. 24, no. 11, pp. 1379–1382, 1953. (An interesting extension of linear-impedance concepts to the calculation of the amplitudes of nonlinear oscillations.)

18. Jacobsen, L. S.: On a General Method of Solving Second Order Ordinary Differential Equations by Phase-plane Displacements, *Journal of Applied Mechanics*, vol. 19, no. 4, pp. 533–553, December, 1952. (This paper presents a powerful graphical procedure for the solution of complicated equations; the method is illustrated by several important examples.)

19. Klotter, K.: Nonlinear Vibration Problems Treated by the Averaging Method of W. Ritz, *Proceedings of the First National Congress of Applied Mechanics*, pp. 125–131, American Society of Mechanical Engineers, 1952.

20. Clauser, F. H.: The Behavior of Nonlinear Systems, *Journal of the Aeronautical Sciences*, vol. 23, no. 5, pp. 411–434, May, 1956. (An excellent expository paper. It presents a diversified group of nonlinear phenomena in terms of fundamental and well-understood concepts. Contains a comprehensive bibliography of recent papers.)

INDEX